PERSPECTIVES IN
REPRODUCTION
AND SEXUAL BEHAVIOR

PERSPECTIVES IN REPRODUCTION AND SEXUAL BEHAVIOR

edited by

Milton Diamond

School of Medicine
University of Hawaii
Honolulu, Hawaii

Indiana University Press
Bloomington & London · 1968

This book is respectfully dedicated, by all its contributors, to the memory of Professor William C. Young, who himself dedicated so much to the understanding of reproduction and sexual behavior.

Preface

In the broad area of reproduction and sexual behavior, the organization of another symposium or preparation of a new book in the present period of scientific proliferation might hardly be cause for prolonged positive reflection. The onlooking investigator questions: What's new here and is it worthwhile? For the solicited participants in such an undertaking the venture may even pose a definite problem. They actively ask: Why another symposium or book; what new could be said or needs restatement? The organizer or editor, in turn, must justify his promotional aims. In the present instance the questions seem easily answered and justification easily found.

Primarily this book is the developmental outgrowth of an effort for perpetuating and recognizing the achievements of a dedicated scholar and respected scientist well known for his studies in reproduction and sexual behavior: William C. Young.

Originally, this recognition was to consist of a program organized and presented in his honor. Over fifty investigators initially volunteered to take part in such an undertaking. From these, sixteen distinguished scientists were invited to participate in a symposium and discussion on selected topics within the field of reproduction and sexual behavior to be held in collaboration with the 1966 San Francisco meeting of the American Association of Anatomists. Before the symposium could be held, Dr. Young died. The program was held in memoriam and a dinner, with Mrs. Young in attendance, followed.

The caliber of the presentations and the manifold challenging problems discussed prompted consideration that, as a lasting memorial to Dr. Young, a permanent record be made of the proceedings. With this impetus all participants to the original program were asked to prepare their presentations for publication. I'm sorry to say that several were not able to do this. To round out the coverage of the field and include some of the scientists originally precluded from participation by program time limits, several others were also invited to submit contributions. Their papers, for the sake of cohesiveness of the volume, have been placed following the discussion papers and preceding the dinner eulogies.

The inductive method of science calls for a wealth of data being available before conclusions are drawn. I have, nevertheless, requested each contributor to present, in addition to an area of pertinent research data, discussion and projections that may indeed be speculative. Good data and review could thereby be supplemented with incisive questioning, exposure to unsolved problems, and cogent speculation. Not all authors, however, have taken this course and several formats are to be seen. Although this has resulted in a collection of various types of papers, there nevertheless remains a communality in that each manuscript represents coverage of an active area of research presented from the perspective of a leading proponent in its development. The resulting book, I trust, provides a mixture of basic material as well as an invigorating intellectual experience. The chapters reveal not only what is known but much of what we need to know. The sophisticated investigator as well as the new graduate student should find areas galore for deep discussion as well as experimental inspiration and well-spent perspiration. For a memorial volume to do as much should indeed honor any man, for it provides a living source of ideas and challenges that is not soon to be exhausted.

To increase the utility of the contribution and facilitate search and retrieval, I have attempted to index the volume's material from various viewpoints. Attention is called to several categories that the reader might not spontaneously consider: Clinical problems; Organizing action; Sensory deprivation; Sex problem therapy; Sex research; Sex research, future problems; Species comparisons; and various "Neonatal" and "Sexual" categories. For any significant omission, I apologize.

Throughout the preparation of this volume the encouragement of the contributors, well wishers, and the publisher was of immeasurable assistance and comfort to me. Special thanks, however, are due to my wife Kit, who despite her own problems always sought ways of solving mine.

MILTON DIAMOND

Contents

Contributors

Dr. Lester R. Aronson, Department of Animal Behavior, American Museum of Natural History, New York, New York

Dr. Frank A. Beach, Department of Psychology, University of California, Berkeley, California

Dr. David W. Bishop, Department of Animal Sciences, Cornell University, Ithaca, New York

Dr. P. N. Brody, Department of Psychology, Purdue University, Lafayette, Indiana

Dr. Frank H. Bronson, The Jackson Laboratory, Bar Harbor, Maine

Dr. H. H. Cole, Department of Animal Husbandry, College of Agriculture, University of California, Davis, California

Dr. Madeline L. Cooper, Department of Animal Behavior, American Museum of Natural History, New York, New York

Dr. Edward W. Dempsey, Department of Anatomy, College of Physicians and Surgeons, Columbia University, New York, New York

Dr. Victor H. Denenberg, Department of Psychology, Purdue University, Lafayette, Indiana

Dr. Milton Diamond, Department of Anatomy, School of Medicine, University of Hawaii, Honolulu, Hawaii

Dr. Ralph I. Dorfman, Syntex Research Corporation, Stanford Industrial Park, Palo Alto, California

Dr. John W. Everett, Department of Anatomy, School of Medicine, Duke University, Durham, North Carolina

Dr. Paul H. Gebhard, Institute for Sex Research, Indiana University, Bloomington, Indiana

Dr. Robert W. Goy, Department of Reproductive Physiology, Oregon Regional Primate Research Center, Beaverton, Oregon

Dr. E. S. E. Hafez, Department of Animal Science, Washington State University, Pullman, Washington

Mrs. Virginia E. Johnson, The Reproductive Biology Research Foundation, St. Louis, Missouri

Dr. P. Landis Keyes, Endocrinology Research Laboratory, School of Dental Medicine, Harvard University, Boston, Massachusetts

Dr. Robert D. Lisk, Department of Biology, Princeton University, Princeton, New Jersey

Dr. William H. Masters, The Reproductive Biology Research Foundation, St. Louis, Missouri

Dr. Harland W. Mossman, Department of Anatomy, School of Medicine, University of Wisconsin, Madison, Wisconsin

Dr. Andrew V. Nalbandov, Department of Animal Science, University of Illinois, Urbana, Illinois

Dr. G. D. Niswender, Department of Animal Science, University of Illinois, Urbana, Illinois

Dr. Robert W. Noyes, Department of Anatomy, School of Medicine, University of Hawaii, Honolulu, Hawaii

Dr. Charles H. Phoenix, Oregon Regional Primate Research Center, Beaverton, Oregon

Dr. Gregory Pincus, Worcester Foundation for Experimental Biology, Shrewsbury, Massachusetts*

Dr. John A. Resko, Department of Reproductive Physiology, Oregon Regional Primate Center, Beaverton, Oregon

Dr. S. R. M. Reynolds, Department of Anatomy, School of Medicine, University of Illinois, Chicago, Illinois

Dr. Paul G. Roofe, Department of Comparative Biochemistry and Physiology, University of Kansas, Lawrence, Kansas

Dr. W. H. Rooks, Syntex Research Corporation, Stanford Industrial Park, Palo Alto, California

Dr. Charles H. Sawyer, Department of Anatomy, UCLA School of Medicine, University of California, Los Angeles, California

Dr. Berta Scharrer, Department of Anatomy, Albert Einstein College of Medicine, Yeshiva University, New York, New York

Dr. J. Shimazaki, Department of Pharmacology, School of Medicine, The Johns Hopkins University, Baltimore, Maryland

Dr. Claude A. Villee, Department of Biological Chemistry, School of Medicine, Harvard University, Cambridge, Massachusetts

Dr. Richard E. Whalen, Department of Psychobiology, University of California, Irvine, California

Dr. H. G. Williams-Ashman, Department of Pharmacology, School of Medicine, The Johns Hopkins University, Baltimore, Maryland

Dr. James G. Wilson, Department of Anatomy, School of Medicine, University of Florida, Gainesville, Florida

Dr. M. X. Zarrow, Department of Psychology, Purdue University, Lafayette, Indiana

* Deceased.

Symposium

REPRODUCTION AND SEXUAL BEHAVIOR (M. Diamond ed.), 3–4, © Indiana University Press

1

Symposium Introduction

Milton Diamond

Although it is not completely unusual to deviate from the standard schedule here at the Anatomists meetings, I think that tonight does form somewhat of an exception. In 1967, Dr. William C. Young would have completed 40 years of active research in the field of reproduction and sexual behavior. This productive career was not limited to research papers and writings of various sorts, but perhaps more significantly provided and produced ideas which have found a wide range of areas for amplification and ramification. Along with this, there was a production of students and colleagues who would carry out, implement, and associate with these ideas.

Originally this program was planned as an honorary program. I think this in itself is significant. Whereas too often an individual is not recognized while he is alive but only after passing, I think one can say that here was someone recognized in his own right for his stature while still alive. Chance was such that Dr. Young could not make this performance, and yet I understand from Mrs. Young that knowledge of this impending symposium was something which helped sustain him in his last days. I think it was heartening to him to know of the overwhelming response of his colleagues to help and some way to show appreciation.

In honor, then, of his contributions and the esteem in which his colleagues held him, we've tried to organize this program as best

we could. The caliber of the volunteers and the work each represents, in themselves reflect the range and magnitude of the area
that we have all set out to understand; that, of course, is reproduction and sexual behavior.

The symposium reflects this range and basically is divided into
two portions. The first speakers will cover material primarily related
to reproduction and the second group of speakers will stress sexual
behavior. Following the symposium presentations, per se, a discussion
panel will pick up questions or items of particular interest relative to
the field of reproduction and sexual behavior and will present perspectives on how some of their work or Dr. Young's work contributed to
the field.

All the participants have met the criteria of keeping with Dr.
Young's standards of high goals and high attainment. It is grati-
fying, not only personally, but I think to Dr. and Mrs. Young and
to those he represented, that so many were willing to participate. To
all of them we owe thanks.

2

Comparative Aspects of Maintenance and Function of Corpora Lutea

A. V. Nalbandov, P. L. Keyes, and
G. D. Niswender

Comparative studies on the mechanism of formation and maintenance of corpora lutea have revealed that different mechanisms exist in different species. As research emphasis has shifted from the rat to other laboratory and domestic animals, it became apparent that prolactin is luteotropic only in rats, mice, and ferrets (Rothchild, 1966). This realization initiated a still continuing search for the factor or factors involved in corpus luteum formation and function in species other than rats and mice. These efforts have met with some success; however, the answers which have been obtained are still incomplete.

It seems evident that hypophyseal hormones may exert steroidogenic efforts on corpora lutea without necessarily having pronounced luteotropic activity. Care must therefore be taken to distinguish between luteotropic and steroidogenic effects. Luteinizing hormone (LH) has been shown to possess luteotropic activity in the heifer (Hansel, 1966) and rabbit (Kilpatrick et al., 1964). Follicle-stimu-

lating hormone (FSH) together with prolactin constitutes the luteotropic complex in the hamster (Greenwald, 1967), but in other
species the factors responsible for maintenance of the corpus luteum
remain unknown. A single release of LH at the time of ovulation
appears to be sufficient to cause the corpora lutea of pigs to form
and to be maintained for normal duration of the estrous cycle
(Brinkley et al., 1964; du Mesnil du Buisson and Leglise, 1963).
A similar situation appears to hold for the corpus luteum of the
cycle in guinea pigs (Aldred et al., 1961). Thus the corpora lutea in
these species do not appear to need pituitary support for the duration of the luteal phase other than an initial discharge of the ovulation inducing hormone.

There have been conflicting reports concerning the dependency
of the corpus luteum of the sheep on a continued luteotropic stimulation. It was stated by Denamur and Mauleon (1963) that the formation of the corpus luteum of the sheep proceeds normally if the
sheep is hypophysectomized immediately after ovulation. These workers later revised their hypothesis to state that a pituitary luteotropin
is needed during the last half of the cycle for normal corpus luteum
function (Denamur et al., 1966). However, recent work of Kaltenbach
et al. (1966b) indicates pituitary support is needed throughout
the estrous cycle for normal corpus luteum formation, maintenance,
and function in the ewe. Corpus luteum weight and progesterone
content were the criteria used to assess corpus luteum function.
Table 1 shows the number of animals in which corpora lutea either
failed to develop after hypophysectomy on the day of ovulation, or
regressed following hypophysectomy on day 5 of the estrous cycle.

Table 1

Effect of Partial and Complete Hypophysectomy on the
Corpus Luteum of the Ewe

Day of hypophy-sectomy	Day CL removed	No. of animals	No. of animals completely hypophysectomized	No. of animals partially hypophysectomized	
1	8	28	7 (7) [a]	21 (8) [a]	(13) [b]
5	12	17	5 (5) [a]	12 (6) [a]	(6) [b]

[a] Number of animals in which CL either did not develop or completely
regressed.
[b] Number of animals in which CL were functional.

Complete regression or lack of formation was noted in every ewe provided hypophysectomy was complete, as demonstrated by histological examination of the sella turcica. However, variable results were obtained in those animals which were incompletely hypophysectomized even though only small quantities of hypophysial tissue remained. Corpus luteum function was absent in 14 of these animals, while in 19 animals with a comparable amount of pituitary tissue remaining, the corpora lutea appeared to develop and function at near-normal levels. These data indicate that in sheep the pituitary gland must be present if the corpus luteum of the cycle is to form and function.

These experiments established that in the sheep hypophysial hormones are essential for formation and function of the corpus luteum, but which of these hormones are involved remains to be determined.

Several workers, using in vitro incubation, have shown that LH significantly increases progesterone synthesis by luteal tissue of the cow, human, and rat (Romanoff, 1966; Armstrong, 1966; Marsh and Savard, 1966). Cook (1966) and Kaltenbach et al. (1966a) have recently shown that LH also has a stimulatory effect on progesterone synthesis by incubated pig and sheep luteal tissue. Table 2 shows

Table 2

Progresterone Concentrations of Sheep Luteal Tissue (μg/g)
after Incubation with Ovine Pituitary Hormones

Hormone concentration, μg/ml	0.4	0.4	5.0
No. of flasks	3	5–6	6
Treatment			
None	81 ± 13 [a]	258 ± 11	227 ± 18
LH	138 ± 13 [b]	328 ± 11 [c]	300 ± 18 [a]
FSH	100 ± 13	270 ± 12	270 ± 18
Prolactin	98 ± 13	226 ± 12 [c]	228 ± 18

[a] Mean ± pooled S.E.
[b] $p = 0.05$.
[c] $p = 0.001$.

that only LH caused a significant increase in progesterone concentration of incubated ovine CL and that neither FSH nor prolactin had that effect.

Similar results were obtained when porcine CL were incubated with porcine LH, FSH, or prolactin (Cook, 1966). These data strongly suggest that LH may affect the steroidogenic mechanism of CL but offer no evidence for a luteotropic action of this gonadotropin.

There is evidence that hormones other than gonadotropins are capable of influencing corpus luteum function. Estrogen appears to be both luteotropic and steroidogenic in rabbits. Robson (1939) has shown that 2 μg per day of estradiol benzoate were required to maintain the CL and pregnancy in hypophysectomized rabbits. Keyes and Nalbandov (1966) have also studied the influence of estrogen on morphologic maintenance and steroidogenesis of CL of rabbits. By X-irradiation the great majority of follicles were destroyed, leaving corpora lutea and interstitial tissue which were indistinguishable in gross or histological appearance from these organelles in the normal unirradiated ovaries.

In the first experiment, rabbit does were bred to fertile bucks and on day 10 of pregnancy one ovary was X-irradiated at a dose which from previous experience was known to destroy follicles but not luteal or interstitial tissue. Ten days later, after the disappearance of all follicles from the irradiated ovary, the normal ovary was removed to test the ability of the irradiated ovary to maintain pregnancy. It was previously established that a single normal (non-irradiated) ovary was able to maintain pregnancy to term. In contrast, the irradiated ovary containing CL and interstitial tissue was unable to maintain pregnancy after removal of the normal ovary, and abortion occurred within 60 hours after hemicastration (Table 3). If 2 to 4 μg per day of 17β-estradiol were given daily after removal of the normal ovary, abortion was prevented and pregnancies were maintained until autopsy 4 to 7 days after the removal of the normal ovary. The daily administration of large quantities of LH (NIH-LH-S7 or S10) both in saline (400 μg per day) and in oil (550 μg per day) or of ovine anterior pituitary powder (30 or 80 mg per day) failed to prevent the abortions in six of six animals. To study the mode of action of estrogen, ovarian venous blood and CL were obtained from does treated with gonadotropin shortly after completion of abortion, and from does which had received either no treatment or 3 μg of estradiol per day following removal of the normal ovary. The blood and ovaries were obtained for analysis from does in the latter two groups, 24 hours after removal of the normal ovary and before any abortions were observed. The CL and ovarian plasma from does without any hormone treatment, or from does given daily

Table 3

Maintenance of Pregnancy by an X-Irradiated Ovary Containing Corpora Lutea
with or without Hormone Treatment [a]

Treatment	No. of animals	Day of pregnancy ovary removed or sham-operated and treatment started	Results
Normal ovary removed	9	20–25	Abortion 27–60 hours after hemicastration
Normal ovary removed; 17β-estradiol	7	20 or 21	No abortion up to 4–7 days after hemicastration
Normal ovary removed; NIH-LH-S7 or NIH-LH-S10	3	20 or 21	Abortion 36–45 hours after hemicastration
Normal ovary removed; ovine pituitary powder	3	20 or 21	Abortion 24–48 hours after hemicastration
Normal ovary sham-removed	3	20 or 21	No abortions up to autopsy 4 days after sham operation
X-irradiated ovary removed	3	20 or 21	Embryos carried to term

[a] For doses used, see the text.

gonadotropin injections contained no measurable quantities of progesterone, but significant quantities of that hormone were found in
plasma and CL from all animals treated with 17β-estradiol (Table 4).
Pooled samples of interstitial tissue contained no measurable quantities (<2 μg) of progesterone. Thus, in the presence of either endogenous or exogenous estrogen, the corpora lutea were able to secrete
progesterone in amounts sufficient to maintain pregnancy. The question whether estrogen is steroidogenic, luteotropic, or both in rabbits
remains to be investigated. Some of the results suggest that estrogen
may have both effects. Thus the weights of CL from X-irradiated and
normal ovaries were not significantly different, provided both normal
and irradiated ovaries remained in situ or, in the absence of the
normal ovary, provided exogenous estradiol was administered (Table
5). In the absence of estrogen the weights of CL were not maintained.

This brief summary of recent data cautions against attempts to
propose all-embracing models for mechanisms controlling corpus

Table 4

Progesterone Concentrations in Corpora Lutea, Interstitial Tissue, or Ovarian Venous Plasma of Rabbits with Only an X-Irradiated Ovary with or without Hormone Treatment [a]

	Treatment								
	None			LH or whole pituitary powder			17 β-Estradiol		
Source	No. of samples analyzed		Progesterone (μg/100 mg or /100 ml)	No. of samples analyzed		Progesterone (μg/100 mg or /100 ml)	No. of samples analyzed		Progesterone (μg/100 mg or /100 ml)
Corpora lutea	4		NM [b]	3		NM	4		10.0 ± 1.2 (± S.E.)
Interstitial tissue	3		NM	4		NM	4		NM
Plasma	8		NM	5		NM	9		46.0 ± 7.4

[a] For doses used, see the text.
[b] Not measurable (<2 μg of progesterone in 2 ml of final eluate).

luteum function. It is becoming increasingly more apparent that the processes involved in corpus luteum formation, maintenance, and function differ from species to species. The fact that prolactin is responsible for maintenance of the corpora lutea in rats and mice, while apparently having no effect on the life span of the corpora lutea of other species, points to differences between these laboratory rodents and other mammals. The dependence of the corpus luteum on pituitary support throughout the cycle in the ewe, the independence from hypophyseal activity in the pig, and partial dependence in the guinea pig are just some of the differences discovered thus far. Thus it seems that no unifying concept on the endocrine mechanism of formation and function of corpora lutea can be formulated and that it will be necessary to study this problem in each species of interest rather than to assume that information obtained in one species may apply to another.

Table 5

Effects of Various Treatments on the Weight of Corpora Lutea
in Normal or X-Irradiated Ovaries

Treatment	Type of ovary	No. of animals	Time of removal of ovary	Average corpus luteum weights, mg
None	X-rayed	9	22–28 hr after removal of normal ovary	14.3 ± 0.6 (± S.E.)
Estrogen	X-rayed	6	22–28 hr after removal of normal ovary	18.3 ± 0.8
None	X-rayed	3	6–8 hr after abortion	11.8 ± 1.1
LH	X-rayed	3	6–8 hr after abortion	11.0 ± 1.0
None	X-rayed	10	Days 20–23 of pregnancy	19.4 ± 1.2
None	Normal	31	Days 20–23 of pregnancy	19.1 ± 0.6

References

Aldred, J. P., P. H. Sammelwitz, and A. V. Nalbandov. 1961. Mechanisms of formation of corpora lutea in guinea-pigs. *J. Reprod. Fertility,* **2:** 391–399.

Armstrong, D. T. 1966. Comparative studies of the action of luteinizing hormone upon ovarian steroidogenesis. *J. Reprod. Fertility Suppl.,* **1:** 101–112.

Brinkley, H. J., H. W. Norton, and A. V. Nalbandov. 1964. Role of a hypophysial luteotrophic substance in the function of porcine corpora lutea. *Endocrinology,* **74:** 9–13.

Cook, B. 1966. A comparative study of the control of progesterone synthesis in vitro in the corpus luteum. Ph.D. thesis, University of Illinois, Urbana.

Denamur, R., and P. Mauleon. 1963. Effets de l'hypophysectomic sur la morphologie et l'histologie de corps jaune chez les brebis. *Compt. Rend.,* **257:** 264–268.

Denamur, R., J. Martinet, and R. V. Short. 1966. Secretion de la progesterone par les corps jaunes de la brebis apres hypophysectomie, section de la tige pituitaire et hysterectomie. *Acta Endocrinol.,* **52:** 72–90.

du Mesnil du Buisson, F., and P. C. Leglise. 1963. Effet de l'hypophysectomie sur les corps jaunes de la truie. Resultats preliminaires. *Compt. Rend.,* **257:** 261–263.

Greenwald, G. S. 1967. Luteotropic complex of the hamster. *Endocrinology,* **80:** 118–130.

Hansel, W. 1966. Luteotropic and luteolytic mechanisms in bovine corpora lutea. *J. Reprod. Fertility Suppl.,* **1:** 33–48.

Kaltenbach, C. C., B. Cook, G. D. Niswender, and A. V. Nalbandov. 1966a. Progesterone synthesis by ovine luteal tissue in vitro. *J. Animal Sci.,* **25**: 926.

Kaltenbach, C. C., G. D. Niswender, J. W. Graber, and A. V. Nalbandov. 1966b. Corpus luteum function in the hypophysectomized ewe. 48th Proc. Endocrin. Soc. Abstr. 112, p. 82.

Keyes, P. L., and A. V. Nalbandov. 1966. *Endocrinology,* **80**: 938–946.

Kilpatrick, R., D. T. Armstrong, and R. O. Greep 1964. Maintenance of the corpus luteum by gonadotrophins in the hypophysectomized rabbit. *Endocrinology,* **74**: 453–461.

Marsh, J. M., and K. Savard, 1966. Studies on the mode of action of luteinizing hormone on steroidogenesis in the corpus luteum in vitro. *J. Reprod. Fertility Suppl.,* **1**: 113–126.

Robson, J. M. 1939. Maintenance of pregnancy in the hypophysectomized rabbit by the administration of oestrin. *J. Physiol. (London),* **95**: 83–91.

Romanoff, E. B. 1966. Steroidogenesis in the perfused bovine ovary. *J. Reprod. Fertility Suppl.,* **1**: 89–99.

Rothchild, I. 1966. The nature of the luteotropic process. *J. Reprod. Fertility Suppl.,* **1**: 49–61.

REPRODUCTION AND SEXUAL BEHAVIOR (M. Diamond ed.), 13–23, © Indiana University Press

3

The Brain and Feedback Control of Pituitary-Gonad Function

Charles H. Sawyer

First, I should like to express my gratitude for the privilege of participating in this program which is honoring the memory of a great scientist. Dr. Young's interest in the effects of hormones on brain and behavior are closely related to the subject about which I should like to speak, and he was always most helpful and encouraging in the annual discussions that I had with him at the Anatomy meetings.

Under natural conditions the synthesis and release of the pituitary gonadotropins, FSH and LH, are controlled by the feedback action of the target-organ gonadal steroids. Superimposed upon, or included within the feedback circuit, is nervous control of adenohypophyseal function exerted by the brain and implemented by hypothalamic releasing factors transported in the hypophyseal portal system. In general each of the trophic hormones has its own releasing factor. For the present discussion we shall concentrate on luteinizing hormone and the luteinizing-hormone releasing factor LHRF and the feedback action of estrogen on this system in the two species which have been most thoroughly studied. These are the rabbit, representing the reflex ovulators which ordinarily require a coital stimulus to trigger the release of an ovulating quantum of gonadotropin, and the rat, representing the more common spontaneously ovulating species.

The feedback action of sex steroids on pituitary gonadotropic function has been recognized for some 35 years, since the classic papers of Moore and Price (1932) and Meyer et al. (1932). However, even in those days, the German endocrinologists Höhlweg and Junkmann (1932) suggested that a hypothalamic sex center was involved in the feedback circuit because they were unable to induce characteristic cytological changes in the pituitary (the production of "castration" cells) if they castrated a rat while the pituitary was separated from the hypothalamus by transplantation.

About ten years ago, the Hungarian anatomists, Flerkó and Szentagothai (1957) reported that implanting estrogen, in the form of ovarian tissue, in the anterior hypothalamus inhibited pituitary gonadotropic function, whereas similar implants in the pituitary itself gave negative results. A few years later, the Princeton biologist Robert Lisk found that he could implant solid estradiol in stainless-steel tubes in the rat hypothalamus. He found that stereotaxic implants of estrogen or testosterone in the basal hypothalamus around the arcuate nucleus were effective in causing ovarian and testicular atrophy (Lisk, 1960), whereas more anteriorly placed estrogen implants restored reproductive behavior in ovariectomized female rats (Lisk, 1962). In other words, there were separate receptor sites for the two types of implants. At about the same time Dr. Davidson in our laboratory was implanting estradiol benzoate in the rabbit brain and finding that implants in the posterior median eminence-basal tuberal region were effective in inducing ovarian atrophy, whereas implants in other parts of the brain or in the pituitary itself were not effective (Davidson and Sawyer, 1961). The basal tuberal implant site was not the same region as that in which Dr. Smelik in our laboratory found that implants of solid cortisol blocked the stress-induced release of adrenal steroids (Smelik and Sawyer, 1962), so there was also evidence for separate receptor loci for the different steroids.

The site in which estrogen was effective in inducing ovarian atrophy (Fig. 1) was the same as that in which we had earlier found that electrical stimulation would induce ovulation in the rabbit and lesions would block copulation-induced ovulation and eventually lead to ovarian atrophy (Sawyer, 1959a, 1959b). This was different from the locus, which, in the rabbit, lies somewhat posterior and in which the lesions do not cause ovarian atrophy but do produce permanent

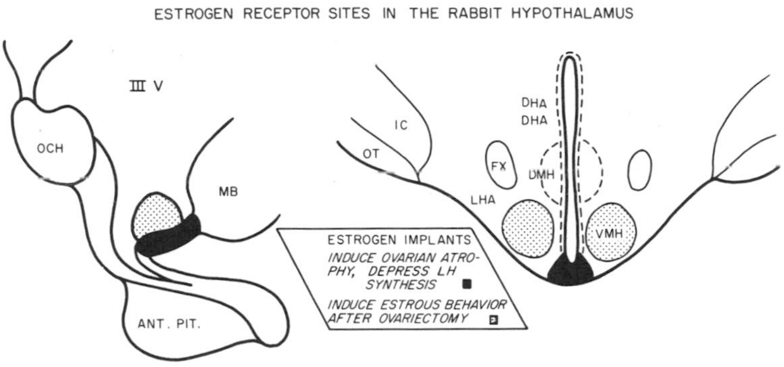

ESTROGEN RECEPTOR SITES IN THE RABBIT HYPOTHALAMUS

Fig. 1 Hypothalamic areas controlling sex behavior and pituitary gonadotropic function in the female rabbit, summarized from the estrogen implant data of Davidson, Kanematsu, Palka, and Sawyer.

anestrus. Even though supplied with extra estrogen, rabbits with lesions in the mammillary bodies would not mate.

To return to the estrogen implant data, Kanematsu and Sawyer (1963a) found that estrogen in the pituitary did exert a direct effect on hypophyseal cells, in that it caused the release of prolactin and the activation of the mammary glands, but did not cause ovarian atrophy or uterine atrophy. On the other hand, the implants in the basal hypothalamus, right in the midline, while not affecting the mammary glands, did cause ovarian atrophy and uterine atrophy. This is the area, then, which appears to be important in gonadotropic control. It must be contrasted with the regions in which Dr. Palka has recently found that implants of diluted estrogen will maintain estrous behavior in the ovariectomized rabbit (Palka and Sawyer, 1966). The latter lie in the ventromedial and premammillary region laterally, whereas implants in the midline are ineffective (Fig. 1). It would appear that the posterior lesions interfered with sex behavior by damaging afferent or efferent connections with the hypothalamus rather than by destroying estrogen receptors. These are the sort of data in which I am sure Dr. Young would have been most interested.

With respect to the pituitary and basal hypothalamic implants of estrogen affecting gonadotropic function, Dr. Kanematsu measured pituitary luteinizing and lactogenic hormones after implanting estrogen into the basal hypothalamus and other parts of the brain and the pituitary in the rabbit (Kanematsu and Sawyer, 1963b). He found that intrapituitary implants were essentially inactive in lowering the LH content, whereas basal hypothalamic ones were effective

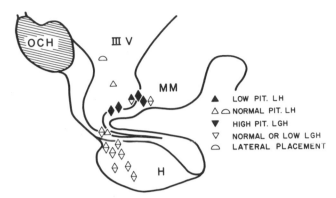

Fig. 2   Locations of estrogen implants in the hypothalamus and hypophysis and effects on pituitary LH and prolactin (LGH) content. [From Kanematsu and Sawyer (1963b); courtesy of *American Journal of Physiology.*]

(Fig. 2). Intrapituitary estrogen did cause a lowering of the level of prolactin, while basal hypothalamic implants were consistent with a higher level of the hormone. These implants were also effective in blocking the rise in serum LH following ovariectomy; two months after ovariectomy the rabbit showed a measurable amount of serum luteinizing hormone by the ovarian ascorbic acid depletion assay but intrahypothalamic implants counteracted this effect (Kanematsu and Sawyer, 1964). They also prevented the formation of hypertrophied gonadotropic cells, the rabbit equivalent of castration cells (Kanematsu and Sawyer, 1963c). Two months after ovariectomy the gonadotropic cells, the aldehyde fuchsin negative basophils, represented about 5 percent of anterior pituitary cells in Dr. Kanematsu's counts, whereas basal hypothalamic implants of estrogen all but obliterated these cells. Implants in other parts of the hypothalamus were partially effective, depending on how close they were to the median eminence, but the implants in the anterior pituitary did not produce results significantly different from the controls in this regard. With estrogen in the pituitary there were still many hypertrophied gonadotropic cells in the pituitary. The colored plate in *Endocrinology* (Kanematsu and Sawyer, 1963c) illustrating these cells caused us considerable grief because it was published with the labels reversed, and in this form it supported the opposing concept of the paper following it, that of Bogdanove (1963).

Bagdanove's work in the rat proposed that estrogen implanted in the basal hypothalamus acts directly on the pituitary cells and that the median eminence is the best possible spot to apply the estrogen for direct action because it can be carried down the stalk by the portal system. Whereas we have cited evidence against this interpretation in the rabbit (Kanematsu and Sawyer, 1963c), we must admit that it is very hard to refute this argument in the rat, especially when our own laboratory has discovered data that seem to support it. Palka et al. (1966) implanted radioactive estrogen in this region in the rat and after 4 or 5 days found significant amounts of radio-activity in the pituitary. They also studied the effect of unilateral implants of estrogen on pituitary hypertrophy ipsilaterally, and the output of luteinizing hormone into the serum by measuring the serum LH (Palka et al. 1966). They found that unilateral intra-pituitary implants did cause ipsilateral hypertrophy by the 4th and 5th days and considerably more so by the 18th day. These implants did not, however, stimulate the release of luteinizing hormone to the extent that it could be measured in the blood, whereas similar uni-lateral implants in the hypothalamus did stimulate LH release (Fig. 3). We were led to conclude from these results that, whereas there was a direct growth effect of estrogen on pituitary cells, the phenom-enon of stimulation of LH release was one which required inter-mediation by the hypothalamus.

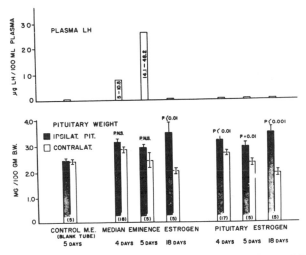

Fig. 3 Comparison of the effects on pituitary weight and plasma LH of tritiated estradiol implanted in the median eminence and pituitary of the female rat. Ipsilateral and contralateral pituitary indicate the halves of the anterior pituitary on the same and opposite sides, respectively, as the implanted estrogen. Note that, while pituitary implants induced greater unilateral hypertrophy, they had no effect on the release of LH. [From Palka et al. (1966); courtesy of *Endocrinology*.]

The findings of Sawyer and Kawakami (1961) suggested that antifertility steroids such as norethynodrel and norethindrone, composed of molecules similar to sex hormones, might be blocking ovulation by an action on the brain. With Kanematsu (Kanematsu and Sawyer, 1965) we tested the effects of implanting solid norethindrone into the rabbit hypothalamus and hypophysis on ovulation and pituitary LH content. We found that intrahypophyseal implants of norethindrone did not block copulation-induced ovulation, whereas, without interfering with LH synthesis, intrahypothalamic implants were effective in blocking its release for 5 to 7 weeks. These results indicated that the ovulation-blocking action of the steroid occurred at the hypothalamic level.

In the intact female rabbit coitus triggers the secretion of luteinizing-hormone releasing factor (LHRF), which stimulates LH release from the pituitary, and this results in ovulation about 10 hours later. Additionally, coitus or LH immediately stimulates the release of progestin from the ovary (Hilliard et al. 1963). By collecting ovarian blood and measuring the progestin, one has an indicator of the timing of LH release from the pituitary (Hilliard et al., 1964). This system has been used to test the site of action of norethindrone in a completely different manner from that described above. We reasoned that if norethindrone were acting exclusively on the brain the injection of LHRF directly into the pituitary should still activate the release of LH, inducing progestin secretion and ovulation. Hilliard et al. (1966) extracted freshly frozen rabbit hypothalami for LHRF and slowly infused this hypothalamic extract through implanted cannulae directly into the pituitaries of test rabbits. In the untreated recipient the extract stimulated progestin release and ovulation (Fig. 4), but in the norethindrone-treated animals there was no evidence that LH was released. The situation was partially reversed with estrogen but not enough LH was released to induce ovulation. Exogenous LH was still effective in the norethindrone-treated rabbit, indicating that the ovary was not the site of blocking action. It was concluded that norethindrone exerted at least part of its blocking action at the pituitary level.

In addition to the positive and negative feedback actions of gonadal steroids on hypothalamo-pituitary function, there are indications of an internal "short-loop" feedback action of LH on the hypothalamus. This was suggested to us some years ago by electroencephalographic (EEG) work with Dr. Kawakami, in which we found postcoital changes in the EEG pattern of the rabbit that occurred after reflexogenous stimulation of the pituitary must have been at

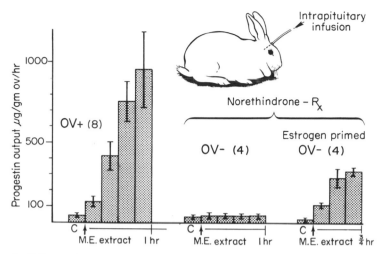

Fig. 4 Effects of norethindrone pretreatment on ovarian progestin output and ovulation in response to intrapituitary infusion of hypothalamic extract containing LHRF. Complete blockade of gonadotropin release by norethindrone is partially overcome by exogenous estrogen. [From Hilliard et al. (1966); courtesy of *Endocrinology*.]

least partially completed (Kawakami and Sawyer, 1959). We concluded that this might possibly not be a correlate of stimulating release of the hormone but might represent feedback action of the hormone on the nervous system. We were able, with large intraperitoneal doses of LH, to evoke this peculiar pattern, which involves both slow wave and paradoxical sleep sequences, but we were not able to induce the pattern with large doses of FSH, TSH, ACTH, or growth hormone. These findings have led us recently to more carefully controlled experiments in rats (Ramirez et al., 1967), in which we have been studying the effects of very small amounts of LH injected intravenously on not only the EEG activity from the cortex but also the firing rates of hypothalamic neurons as registered by "unit" activity with microelectrodes. In the upper tracing of Fig. 5 can be seen the effect of vaginal stimulation in the rat during late diestrus or early proestrus. A sleep-like EEG response is induced by cervical prodding and, simultaneously, the unit firing is inhibited for some 20 minutes; it appears again as the animal becomes alert following this sleep period. In other words, changes in neuronal unit firing follow the overall pattern of sleep-wakefulness in the animal's behavior. With LH, on the other hand, we have been able, in many units, to see rather specific effects on hypothalamic cells, independent of any

STIMULATION OF VAGINAL CERVIX – HYPOTHALAMIC UNIT

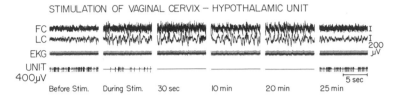

LUTEINIZING HORMONE 5µg in 0.5ml i.v.–HYPOTHALAMIC UNIT

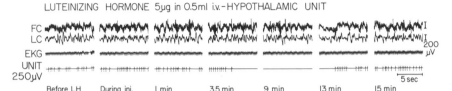

Fig. 5 Effects of vaginal stimulation and luteinizing hormone (LH) on the cortical EEG and unit firing of neurons in the ventromedial hypothalamus of the rat under light urethane anesthesia. The changes induced by vaginal stimulation during proestrus appear to be related to a generalized sleeplike response ("EEG after-reaction"), whereas the LH effect appears to be exerted more specifically on the hypothalamic neuron. [From unpublished work of Ramirez, Komisaruk, Whitmoyer, and Sawyer; see Ramirez et al. (1967).]

effects on the rest of the brain (Fig. 5, lower tracing). In other words, without inducing any particular changes in the EEG, LH alters the pattern of unit firing in the hypothalamus. For several minutes the unit is quiescent following LH injection and its recovery is independent of EEG changes. Figure 6 shows the location of the hypothalamic neurons in which the unit firing pattern was altered by injections of LH (Ramirez et al., 1967).

Further evidence of an LH feedback action on the nervous system is provided by experiments in which LH has been directly applied to the hypothalamus. Corbin and Cohen (1966) and David et al. (1966) have reported that LH implanted in the basal hypothalamus will lower the pituitary and serum LH content, and there have also been suggestions that the same treatments will lower the median eminence's content of luteinizing hormone's releasing factor (David et al., 1966).

To summarize: Different areas of the hypothalamus are directly sensitive to the feedback action of gonadal steroids, one concerned with reproductive behavior and the other with control of pituitary-gonad function. In the latter capacity the steroids may also act directly on hypophysial cells, and there is evidence that the antifertility

RAT HYPOTHALAMUS

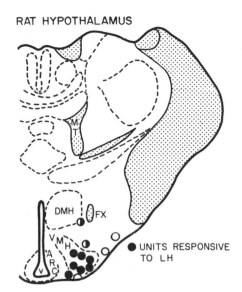

Fig. 6 Location of hypothalamic units influenced by intravenous injections of LH as revealed by the Prussian blue reaction at histology. Open-circle sites were unresponsive to LH, and sites of half-open circles responded in a nonspecific manner. Solid-circle sites were relatively specific in their responses to LH. [From Ramirez et al. (1967); courtesy of *American Journal of Physiology*.]

progestogens exert their inhibitory influence on both the hypothalamus and the pituitary gland. The trophic hormones of the hypophysis may themselves act on the hypothalamus in a "short-loop" internal feedback circuit independent of their influence on their classic target organs.

Acknowledgments

The recent research from the author's laboratory cited in this review was supported by grants from the National Institutes of Health (NB-01162) and the Ford Foundation.

References

Bogdanove, E. M. 1963. Direct gonad-pituitary feedback: an analysis of effects of intracranial estrogenic depots on gonadotrophin secretion. *Endocrinology,* 73: 696–712.

Corbin, A., and A. I. Cohen. 1966. Effect of median eminence implants of LH on pituitary LH of female rats. *Endocrinology,* 78: 41–46.

David, M. A., F. Fraschini, and L. Martini, 1966. Control of LH secretion: role of a "short" feedback mechanism. *Endocrinology,* 78: 55–60.

Davidson, J. M., and C. H. Sawyer. 1961. Effects of localized intracerebral implantation of oestrogen on reproductive function in the female rabbit. *Acta Endocrinol.*, **37**: 385–393.

Flerkó, B., and J. Szentagothai. 1957. Oestrogen sensitive nervous structures in the hypothalamus. *Acta Endocrinol.*, **26**: 121–127.

Hilliard, J., D. Archibald, and C. H. Sawyer. 1963. Gonadotropic activation of preovulatory synthesis and release of progestin in the rabbit. *Endocrinology*, **72**: 59–66.

Hilliard, J., J. N. Hayward, and C. H. Sawyer. 1964. Postcoital patterns of secretion of pituitary gonadotropin and ovarian progestin in the rabbit. *Endocrinology*, **75**: 957–963.

Hilliard, J., H. B. Croxatto, J. N. Hayward, and C. H. Sawyer. 1966. Norethindrone blockade of LH release to intrapituitary infusion of hypothalamic extract. *Endocrinology*, **79**: 411–419.

Höhlweg, W., and K. Junkmann. 1932. Die hormonal-nervöse Regulierung der Funktion des Hypophysenvorderlappens. *Klin. Wochschr.*, **11**: 321–323.

Kanematsu, S., and C. H. Sawyer. 1963a. Effects of intrahypothalamic and intrahypophysial estrogen implants on pituitary prolactin and lactation in the rabbit. *Endocrinology*, **72**: 243–252.

Kanematsu, S., and C. H. Sawyer. 1963b. Effects of hypothalamic estrogen implants on pituitary LH and prolactin in rabbits. *Am. J. Physiol.*, **205**: 1073–1076.

Kanematsu, S., and C. H. Sawyer. 1963c. Effects of hypothalamic and hypophysial estrogen implants on pituitary gonadotrophic cells in ovariectomized rabbits. *Endocrinology*, **73**: 687–695.

Kanematsu, S., and C. H. Sawyer. 1964. Effects of hypothalamic and hypophysial estrogen implants on pituitary and plasma LH in ovariectomized rabbits. *Endocrinology*, **75**: 579–585.

Kanematsu, S., and C. H. Sawyer. 1965. Blockade of ovulation in rabbits by hypothalamic implants of norethindrone. *Endocrinology*, **76**: 691–699.

Kawakami, M., and C. H. Sawyer. 1959. Induction of behavioral and electroencephalographic changes in the rabbit by hormone administration or brain stimulation. *Endocrinology*, **65**: 631–643.

Lisk, R. D. 1960. Estrogen-sensitive centers in the hypothalamus of the rat. *J. Exptl. Zool.*, **145**: 197–207.

Lisk, R. D. 1962. Diencephalic placement of estradiol and sexual receptivity in the female rat. *Am. J. Physiol.*, **203**: 493–496.

Meyer, R. K., S. L. Leonard, F. L. Hisaw, and S. J. Martin. 1932. The influence of oestrin on the gonad-stimulating complex of the anterior pituitary of castrated male and female rats. *Endocrinology*, **16**: 655–665.

Moore, C. R., and D. Price. 1932. Gonad hormone functions, and the reciprocal influence between gonads and hypophysis with its bearing on the problem of sex hormone antagonism. *Am. J. Anat.*, **50**: 13–71.

Palka, Y. S., and C. H. Sawyer. 1966. The effects of hypothalamic implants of ovarian steroids on oestrous behaviour in rabbits. *J. Physiol. (London)*, **185**: 251–269.

Palka, Y. S., V. D. Ramirez, and C. H. Sawyer. 1966. Distribution and biological effects of tritiated estradiol implanted in the hypothalamo-hypophysial region of female rats. *Endocrinology*, **78**: 487–499.

Ramirez, V. D., B. R. Komisaruk, D. I. Whitmoyer, and C. H. Sawyer. 1967.

Effects of hormones and vaginal stimulation on the EEG and hypothalamic units in rats. *Am. J. Physiol.*, **212:** 1376–1384.

Sawyer, C. H. 1959a. Nervous control of ovulation. In *Recent Progress in the Endocrinology of Reproduction* (C. W. Lloyd, ed.). Academic Press, New York, Chap. 1, pp. 1–20.

Sawyer, C. H. 1959b. Effects of brain lesions on estrous behavior and reflexo-genous ovulation in the rabbit. *J. Exptl. Zool.*, **142:** 227–246.

Sawyer, C. H., and M. Kawakami. 1961. Interactions between the central nervous system and hormones influencing ovulation. In *Control of Ovulation* (C. A. Villee, ed.), Pergamon Press, New York, pp. 79–100.

Smelik, P., and C. H. Sawyer. 1962. Effects of implantation of cortisol into the brain stem or pituitary gland on the adrenal response to stress in the rabbit. *Acta Endocrinol.*, **41:** 561–570.

REPRODUCTION AND SEXUAL BEHAVIOR (M. Diamond ed.), 25–31, © Indiana University Press

4

"Delayed Pseudopregnancy" in the Rat, a Tool for the Study of Central Neural Mechanisms in Reproduction

John W. Everett

The principal hypophyseal luteotropin in the rat and mouse appears to be prolactin. It follows (1) that the progravid (i.e., the pseudopregnant) state expresses primarily an increased secretion of prolactin and (2) that information about mechanisms inciting or inhibiting pseudopregnancy is, at once, information about control of prolactin synthesis and release. An abundance of peripheral information exists about pseudopregnancy in these rodents, especially in the rat. Many methods of producing it are known. It is well recognized that the rat is most susceptible during estrus to artificial stimulation of the cervix and to even much less specific stimuli. The dependence of the deciduoma reaction on critical timing of uterine traumatization has been well documented. The central mechanisms controlling prolactin, however, are not well understood.

The hypothalamus is known to inhibit prolactin secretion (Everett, 1956), apparently by a neurohumor not yet well characterized,

25

but now already bearing the designation PIF. While it is recognized that progesterone exerts a positive feedback action on prolactin secretion in rats (Rothchild, 1960), it is a mere assumption that this action involves the central nervous system. While it has long been taken for granted that artificial stimulation of the hypothalamus would induce pseudopregnancy and Harris (1936) produced it about 30 years ago by passing an electric current through the head, only recently was it shown that one can do this selectively with stimulus parameters and electrode locations not conducive to ovulation (Everett and Quinn, 1966). In the course of that study we encountered once more the phenomenon of delayed pseudopregnancy, observed in other contexts years ago. Since one can now differentially activate the neural apparatus controlling at least this aspect of prolactin secretion, we have a means of more direct experimental approach to this apparatus.

The first record of delayed pseudopregnancy is a brief report by Greep and Hisaw (1938). When cycling rats were subjected to electrical stimulation of the cervix on the first or second days of diestrus, in many cases pseudopregnancy was initiated, not immediately, but after the ensuing estrus. The delayed response was seen in 4 of the 13 rats stimulated on the first day of diestrus and in 7 of the 13 rats stimulated on the second day.

In retrospect, it is clear that a comparable response, delayed for a longer interval, was encountered by Everett (1939) in rats that copulated during persistent estrus. The infertile matings were followed by short periods of diestrus and subsequent cycle estrus, after which there were long pseudopregnancy-like periods. Long delays of the same order were again seen (Everett, 1952, 1964) when rats copulated during cycles in which ovulation was blocked by pentobarbital or phenobarbital. About 50 percent of the rats injected with one of these agents shortly before the critical period for LH release on the afternoon of proestrus accepted coitus during the following night, as shown by the presence of sperm in the vaginal smear on the following morning. Without further treatment such animals ovulated during the second night and became immediately pseudopregnant. However, a second treatment with barbiturate on the second afternoon usually prevented ovulation of the current set of follicles. A short diestrus of ordinary length intervened before a new cycle and the ovulation of newly grown follicles. Thereupon a pseudopregnancy of normal duration began. Parenthetically, it may be noted that in a few cases (approximately 20 percent, 14 of 72) the mating stimulus apparently induced ovulation in spite of the blocking agent; corpora lutea thus induced established pregnancies, although the more usual result was the delayed pseudopregnancy.

Zeilmaker (1965) has demonstrated delayed pseudopregnancy in a new and interesting way, making use of the fact that a homografted ovary in an otherwise normal host rapidly acquires functional status after the normal ovaries are removed. Ovaries of 3-week-old rats were transplanted to the kidney capsules of adult females. Later on, the females were placed with males during the night of expected ovulation. Those that copulated were spayed on either the day of estrus or the first to fourth day of the ensuing diestrus. In all cases vaginal estrus returned 4 to 5 days after the operation. If ovariectomy had been performed as late as the second day of the intervening diestrus, pseudopregnancy appeared after the animal passed through this new estrus; the functional status of newly formed corpora lutea in the graft was demonstrable by the decidual reaction to uterine trauma. The only exceptions were five rats in which the experimental cycle lasted more than 6 days, counting the day after copulation and ovulation as zero time; these rats continued to cycle. When ovariectomy was postponed until day 3 or 4 of diestrus, the ensuing estrus was not followed by pseudopregnancy in any case. Zeilmaker also obtained delayed pseudopregnancy in two other ways: (1) in engrafted rats like those just mentioned, not allowed to copulate, but given an injection of reserpine on the day after ovulation when the normal ovaries were removed; and (2) in normal pseudopregnant rats in which function of the initial set of corpora was interrupted by ergocornine injection on day 4. The foreshortened initial pseudopregnant cycle of 7 to 8 days duration was followed by a second pseudopregnancy of normal length in 11 of 30 rats. In other experiments, the stimulus from suckling by sharp contrast with the copulatory stimulus proved to be inadequate to bring about delayed pseudopregnancy responses after removal of the in situ ovaries postpartum and removal of the litter at various times after delivery.

Zeilmaker concluded that copulation invokes a period of prolactin secretion lasting about 8 days independently of the presence or absence of corpora lutea. This estimate takes into account a requirement for positive feedback action of progesterone for at least 2 days to produce a self-sustaining pseudopregnancy. By the same token, it would seem from the observations of Greep and Hisaw (1938) that the effect of cervical stimulation might be retained almost as long as that of copulation, i.e., for at least 5 or 6 days.

However, in a small number of trials with cervical stimulation in pentobarbital-blocked rats I was unable to demonstrate long delays like those after copulation (unpublished). The stimulus used was first tested in four 5-day cyclic rats during the afternoon of the third day of diestrus. The electrode consisted of two nichrome wires sealed in the closed end of a glass tube at a spacing of 2 mm. Two 30-second trains of pulses at 25 per second at standard voltage were delivered to the cervix at an interval of 1 minute. All four rats became proestrous as expected on the day after the stimulus, then were in full vaginal estrus the next day, after which they became pseudopregnant. The same stimulus was administered to five pentobarbital-blocked rats in the following manner. Each received the blocking dose of pentobarbital just before the critical period on the afternoon of proestrus (4-day cycle). The cervical stimulus was applied on the following morning at 7:45 to 8:15. That afternoon pentobarbital was again administered in two injections, one just before the critical period and the other about 1½ hours later, precisely as in the experiments in which copulation regularly induced the delayed pseudopregnancy. Pseudopregnancy failed to appear in any of the five rats. A possible explanation is that the stimulus was too brief; by contrast, the copulatory stimuli in both my own study and that of Zeilmaker were undoubtedly multiple, inasmuch as male and female were caged together throughout the night.

Our new approach to the general problem emerged in some work with brain stimulation in pentobarbital-blocked rats, reported in part by Everett and Quinn (1966). It goes back to the observation by Critchlow (1958) that pentobarbital-blocked rats can be induced to ovulate in spite of the blocking agent by stimulation of the hypothalamus. It is also based on our subsequent findings that stimulation of the preoptic brain by an electrochemical method is predictably effective for ovulation (Everett and Radford, 1961), by contrast with similar stimulation localized in the basal tuber. Such preoptic stimulations, however, did not usually lead to pseudopregnancy whenever an experiment was continued; approximately 80 percent of the animals continued to cycle without interruption. It thus seemed feasible to use animals prepared and stimulated for ovulation in this way as subjects in searching for areas of the brain that might be more specifically concerned with pseudopregnancy. Proestrous 4-day cyclic rats were blocked by pentobarbital shortly before 2:00 P.M. During the resulting sedation each rat was stimulated successively in two ways: (1) by a stimulative focal lesion in the medial preoptic area produced by passing 10 μamp dc for 60 seconds through a concentric stainless-steel electrode, and (2) by electrical stimulation immediately thereafter, the exploring tool being either the same electrode or one of platinum similarly constructed, delivering trains of matched biphasic pulse pairs, 200 μamp peak to peak. A null instrument in series with the preparation during the second stimulation ensured that there was no net current flow. Histologic sections of the brains disclosed no evidence of brain damage other than that ascribed to the mechanical effect of the electrode itself. Each member of the pulse pair was 1 msec in duration; frequency was 100 pairs per second. They were delivered in 30-second trains at 30-second intervals for 10 minutes. It should be emphasized that all stimulations were unilateral. In control experiments the second electrode was simply inserted into the basal tuberal region, left for 10 minutes and withdrawn.

Only one of the 10 control rats became pseudopregnant. By contrast, pseudopregnancy was regularly observed when the exploring electrode delivered the 10-minute stimulus to sites ranging from the anterior hypothalamic area and paraventricular nucleus caudally into the premamillary complex and dorsally into the dorsomedial nucleus. Representative pseudopregnancies were proved by the deciduoma reaction to uterine trauma and the remainder by the finding of a heavily mucified vaginal smear at the first estrus.

The type of stimulus employed does not cause ovulation when applied in these areas, yet it easily induces pseudopregnancy, a fact that made possible the following extension of the experiment. These animals, like the previous ones, were blocked with pentobarbital during the critical period on the day of proestrus. They differed, however, in that no ovulation-inducing stimulus was introduced. They were simply stimulated electrically through a unilateral platinum concentric bipolar electrode at one or another hypothalamic site approximately 0.5 mm from the midline. Again, the electrode was inserted, but no current was passed. In all others the stimulus consisted of the matched biphasic pulse pairs described before. With a single exception (one of the six rats stimulated in or near the ventromedial nucleus), the stimulus failed to induce ovulation and yet resulted in a delayed pseudopregnancy that began after the spontaneous luteinization that was postponed to the second night by the pentobarbital blockade. In these characteristic cases the vagina remained cornified for an extra day, becoming leukocytic thereafter. Uterine traumatization on the fourth day after cornification yielded large deciduomata. In the exceptional case the stimulus seems to have caused both ovulation and pseudopregnancy, inasmuch as vaginal cornification was not prolonged, leukocytic vaginal smears appeared at the normal time and uterine traumatization on the fourth day after cornification produced large deciduomata.

The results in this latter experiment thus indicate that an electrical stimulus not appropriate for inducing ovulation, by virtue of the electrode location, electrical characteristics, and electrical parameters, can set in motion events that lead to activation of corpora lutea at some later time. To be sure, the delayed response shown in this last experiment is rather minimal, comparable to that obtained by Greep and Hisaw (1938) from cervical stimulation on the second day of diestrus. However, the method appears feasible for attempts to reproduce the long delays produced by copulation. These attempts are in progress. Although the results to date have been less uniform than with copulatory stimuli, several rats have shown the long delay after stimulation of the dorsomedial nucleus was extended to 60 minutes.

At this juncture we may ask what the delayed response means, what the information now at hand implies. It has long seemed unlikely to me that induction of a prolonged period of secretion by an acute event such as coitus, cervical stimulation, or the brain stimuli just described can result from a brief triggering stimulus to the gland itself (Everett, 1952). Rather it would seem that a new pattern of central nervous activity must be instituted by the brief stimulus. This implies establishment of a new chemistry within the hypothalamus such as that the stimulus is "remembered" for several days. Zeilmaker (1965) and Everett (1964) agree that the simplest explanation of the delayed pseudopregnancy is that prolactin secretion is at once accelerated at the time of the special stimulus whether or not competent corpora lutea are present to respond. If they are not present the beginning of pseudopregnancy must await their later formation. Once they appear, the prolactin secretion carries through into the ensuing 2 or 3 days. This promotes secretion of progesterone in amount sufficient to act by positive feedback in further prolonging the elevated level of prolactin output. The resulting pseudopregnancy is then of normal duration. Alternative hypotheses must also be given serious consideration. For example, it is conceivable that although the stimulus is "remembered" in the central nervous system, prolactin secretion can be increased only in the hormonal environment of the next estrus. It is well known that estrogen favors prolactin secretion and by itself can induce pseudopregnancy if administered in appropriate dosage and at appropriate time. A crucial test of this alternative will require direct demonstration of whether or not prolactin secretion is truly increased throughout the interval between the special stimulus and the ensuing estrus that heralds the delayed onset of the pseudo-pregnancy response. If either of those two choices proves correct, the question will remain: In what manner is the information from the special stimulus stored within the central nervous system? What is the "new chemistry" which the stimulus invokes, and what are its correlates in neuronal and neurosecretory activity?

Acknowledgment

Research in the author's laboratory was supported in part by the National Science Foundation.

References

Critchlow, B. V. 1958. Ovulation induced by hypothalamic stimulation in the anesthetized rat. *Am. J. Physiol.,* **195:** 171–174.

Everett, J. W. 1939. Spontaneous persistent estrus in a strain of albino rats. *Endocrinology,* **25:** 123–127.

Everett, J. W. 1952. Presumptive hypothalamic control of spontaneous ovulation. *Ciba Found. Colloq. Endocrinol.,* **4:** 167–177.

Everett, J. W. 1956. Functional corpora lutea maintained for months by autografts of rat hypophyses. *Endocrinology,* **58:** 786–796.

Everett, J. W. 1964. Central neural control of reproductive functions of the adenohypophysis. *Physiol. Rev.,* **44:** 373–431.

Everett, J. W., and D. L. Quinn. 1966. Differential hypothalamic mechanisms inciting ovulation and pseudopregnancy in the rat. *Endocrinology,* **78:** 141–150.

Everett, J. W., and H. M. Radford. 1961. Irritative deposits from stainless steel electrodes in the preoptic rat brain causing release of pituitary gonadotropin. *Proc. Soc. Exptl. Biol. Med.,* **108:** 604–609.

Greep, R. O., and F. L. Hisaw. 1938. Pseudopregnancies from electrical stimulation of the cervix in the diestrum. *Proc. Soc. Exptl. Biol. Med.,* **39:** 359–360.

Harris, G. W. 1936. The induction of pseudopregnancy in the rat by electrical stimulation through the head. *J. Physiol. (London),* **88:** 361–367.

Rothchild, I. 1960. The corpus luteum-pituitary relationship: the association between the cause of luteotrophin secretion and the cause of follicular quiescence during lactation; the basis for a tentative theory of the corpus luteum-pituitary relationship in the rat. *Endocrinology,* **67:** 9–41.

Zeilmaker, G. H. 1965. Normal nad delayed pseudopregnancy in the rat. *Acta Endocrinol.,* **49:** 558–566.

REPRODUCTION AND SEXUAL BEHAVIOR (M. Diamond ed.), 33–49, © Indiana University Press

5

Psychosexual Differentiation as a Function of Androgenic Stimulation

Charles H. Phoenix, Robert W. Goy, and John A. Resko

Among mammals the sex of an individual is generally said to be dependent upon contribution of either an X or Y chromosome by the male. However, the mechanism whereby these chromosomes determine the sex of the individual has until recently received little attention. In practice, the sex of an individual is commonly decided upon by the appearance of the external genitalia without reference to the chromosomal status (see Chapter 25).

To each sex is ascribed a characteristic pattern of reproductive behavior which varies from one species to another. In addition, other behavioral characteristics are commonly attributed to members of a given sex. For example, the bitch is commonly thought to be more gentle than the dog, and the bull to be dangerously aggressive when compared to the cow. These behavioral characteristics, or in many cases what amounts only to expectations, are assumed to follow from the appearance of the external genitalia. In man, an elaborate set of behaviors and attitudes are labeled as masculine and another

33

constellation of behaviors are considered feminine. The behavior expected of an individual within a given society is determined by assignment to the class male or female.

Very little is known about what determines masculinity or femininity. Because research on problems of sexuality in the human is virtually impossible, researchers have looked to mammals lower on the phylogenetic scale for answers to some of the basic questions. For example, what are the biological mechanisms by which sexual and sex related behaviors are determined?

From research on adult laboratory animals and from clinical observations it has long been believed that hormones do not establish patterns of behavior but only serve to bring to expression previously established behavior patterns. The consensus of opinion is that gonadal hormones themselves are not masculine or feminine; they only permit the masculine or feminine pattern of behavior that exists within the individual to be brought to expression. The question arises as to whether or not the hormones, especially the gonadal hormones, play any role at all in establishing the basic sexuality of the individual.

We approached this question by first studying sexual behavior, that is, behavior instrumental to reproduction of the species, and initially directed our attention to the guinea pig. Much was known about the reproductive behavior of this species (Young, 1961), and it seemed to be a model eminently suited to the investigation.

Our first series of studies on the guinea pig led us to conclude that the gonadal hormones did indeed play a role in establishing basic patterns of reproductive behavior. We learned that when pregnant female guinea pigs are injected with testosterone propionate, the genetic female offspring from such pregnancies are masculinized (Phoenix et al., 1959). The masculinization included not only morphological characteristics which had previously been demonstrated (Dantchakoff, 1938) but, more significantly, physiological and psychosexual masculinization as well. Such experimentally produced pseudohermaphrodites possess ovaries, although there is evidence of ovarian disfunction (Tedford and Young, 1960). The external vaginal orifice is completely obliterated, and a well-developed penis is formed. The genital tract shows variable abnormalities. The O_2 consumption rate resembles that of the male rather than that of the female (Goy et al., 1962). The spayed, adult pseudohermaphrodite when injected with estrogen and progesterone fails to display estrous behavior characteristic of the normal spayed female similarly injected with estrogen and progesterone. Not only is responsiveness to the female hormones suppressed but there is a heightened sensitivity to testosterone propionate as evidenced by the increase in mounting frequency. Furthermore, the effect of the prenatal treatment is permanent. Thus, although it is possible to increase the frequency of mounting behavior in a normal female by treating the animals with testosterone propionate in adulthood, the effect is transient and mounting frequency returns to pretreatment levels when treatment is discontinued (Phoenix et al., 1959). Informal observation of the behavior of the female pseudohermaphrodite reveals a level of aggression not unlike that observed in male guinea pigs.

In producing masculinization of the genetic female both the stage of fetal development and the hormonal dosage are critical. Treatment confined to very early or late stages in fetal development are ineffective with the dosages that have been used (Goy et al., 1964). Maximum masculinization in the guinea pig was obtained when treatment with 5 mg of testosterone propionate was started at day 30 of gestation and continued daily for 6 days, followed by 1 mg per day to day 55. Other times and dosages produced variable degrees of modification. In general, the animals displaying the highest degree of psychosexual modification were also the most modified morphologically. These findings from our early research on the guinea pig led us to conclude that the gonadal hormones, especially testosterone, had a dual function. During the period of differentiation the gonadal hormones, we hypothesized, had an organizing action on the central neural tissues that controlled the display of sexual behavior. This function we contrasted to the action of the same hormones in the adult, where the hormones functioned to bring to expression patterns of behavior that had been previously established during development (Young, 1961). We viewed the action of the gonadal hormones on the central neural tissues in the developing fetus as analogous to their action on genital tract tissue, including those tissues constituting the external genitalia.

In further study of the role that testosterone plays in organizing the neural tissues that underly reproductive behavior, genetic male rats were castrated on the day of birth and at various times to maturity (Grady et al., 1965). When rats were castrated on the day of birth and injected as adults with estrogen and progesterone, they responded much as did genetic females. Males that were castrated after the first 10 days of life failed to give typical female responses when injected in adulthood with the ovarian hormones. The results supported our hypothesis that it is the presence of the testicular hormone during the period of differentiation that masculinizes the individual whether that individual is genetically male or female.

From our work with the rat it become obvious that it was not prenatal treatment per se that was critical but treatment during the period of psychosexual differentiation. Generally one might expect that in long gestation animals such as the guinea pig, monkey, and man, the critical stage of development would occur during the prenatal period, whereas, in short gestation animals such as the mouse, rat, and hamster, the critical period for psychosexual differentiation might occur during the late fetal and early postnatal period. If one compares the ages at which psychosexual differentiation is found to occur in the rat, guinea pig, and monkey on the basis of post-fertilization age, the differences among these species become relatively small. More work is needed, especially in the monkey, to establish the critical time limits of psychosexual differentiation, and virtually nothing is known about man.

Attempts to feminize the genetic male guinea pig by injecting estrogen into pregnant females failed. Very small doses had no effect on the offspring and larger doses without exception caused abortion. Administering estrogen prenatally or to the neonatal rat did not have feminizing effects on the genetic male, and estrogens have been found to interfere with the normal development of estrous behavior in the genetic female (Whalen and Nadler, 1963; Whalen, 1964; Phoenix and Grady, 1964; Feder and Whalen, 1965; Feder, 1967). The results of these experiments with estrogen led us to modify our hypothesis. It became clear to us that it was not the presence of estrogen or androgen during psychosexual differentiation that organized patterns of sexual behavior but rather that androgens, or some particular androgens, were the hormones responsible for determining the organization of the neural tissues that mediated sexual behavior. In the absence of the appropriate androgenic stimulation during development, female patterns of behavior are laid down in both genetic male and female. The presence of androgen in the proper amounts during critical periods masculinizes the individual whether genetic male or female.

The mere presence of androgen does not produce an all or none effect either on genital morphology or behavior. Varying degrees of differentiation in treated rats and guinea pigs have been observed both in morphology and behavior. The exact amount of androgen, its distribution over time during critical stages necessary to produce maximum effects in male and female, has yet to be determined. The absence of testicular androgen resulting from castration of the newborn rat produces a male highly responsive behaviorally to the ovarian hormones, yet the genital morphology is not modified to the degree that the animal possesses a patent vagina. At present many of the details of the process need to be worked out. However, in broad outline, the hypothesis is widely supported that the pattern of sexual behavior, or the potentiality for the later display of specific behavior, is established during the period of differentiation by the action of androgen.

Largely as a result of aggressive behavior observed among pseudohermaphroditic guinea pigs we suggested in our first definitive paper on the organizing action of testosterone (Phoenix et al., 1959) that the ". . . masculinity or femininity of an animal's behavior beyond that which is purely sexual has developed in response to certain hormonal substances within the embryo and fetus." Considerable evidence gathered on the rodent has confirmed our suggestion. Cyclic running activity (Harris, 1964; Kennedy, 1964) and open-field behavior (Gray et al., 1965; Swanson, 1966, 1967) have been shown to be dependent upon the presence or absence of androgen during the period of psychosexual differentiation.

Until recently the evidence that testosterone produced an organizing action on sexual behavior was based on experiments in which genetic females were either treated with testosterone or in which males (in the case of the rat) were castrated during the critical period. Two supporting lines of evidence have developed using different approaches to the problem.

Recent work in our laboratory using gas chromatography demonstrates that testosterone is present in peripheral plasma obtained from rats on the day of birth (Resko et al., 1968). The amount of hormone declines with age until it reaches a minimal value in the plasma of rats between 20 and 30 days of age. Our hypothesis derived from experiments on the day-1 castrated rat assumed the presence of testosterone of testicular origin which at this stage of development set the psychosexual orientation of the male rat and blocked later responsiveness to the female hormones. The trace amount of androstenedione found in our recent chemical assays in the neonate suggests that testosterone rather than this less potent androgen is in fact the chemical substance responsible for psychosexual differentiation.

The view that testosterone rather than androstenedione is the critical masculinizing agent is supported by results from a recent physiological study carried out in our laboratory. It was found that male rats castrated on the day of birth and injected every other day to 19 days of age with 0.25 mg of androstenedione displayed lordosis of good quality when tested as adults following injection of estradiol and progesterone. Males castrated on the day of birth and given only vehicle showed an average lordosis quotient of 0.90 (i.e., lordosis occurred on 90 percent of the occasions that each subject was mounted by a normal male partner). Males castrated on the day of birth and treated with androstenedione had a lordosis quotient of 0.78, and males not castrated until 20 days of age showed an average lordosis quotient of 0.12. Thus exogenous androstenedione, even in relatively large amounts, does not have the ability to suppress the development of lordosis behavior to the same extent as the secretory products of the intact testis.

Castration of the male rat on the day of birth does not permit the development of an individual that is identical in all behavioral respects with the normal genetic female. Although male rats castrated the day of birth will display female behavior when injected as adults with estrogen and progesterone, they will, when injected with testosterone propionate, show a higher frequency of mounting behavior than the genetic female given the same amount of testosterone during adulthood. The display of the intromission and ejaculatory pattern of behavior by the day-1 castrate is, however, clearly deficient compared with that of males castrated at later ages (Grady et al., 1965; Beach and Holz, 1946). The question remains as to why mounting frequency should be higher in the genetic male than in the genetic female if, as we suggest, the male pattern is determined by the presence of testosterone during psychosexual differentiation. We suggest the possibility that some differentiation has occurred prior to birth even in the short gestation rat and that prenatal castration would be required to produce males whose mounting frequency would not differ from that of the genetic female. It has been shown that administration of testosterone prenatally to genetic female rats contributes to the masculinization (Gerall and Ward, 1966). It is therefore possible that in the male rat, as in the guinea pig, psychosexual differentiation is initiated prior to birth but, unlike the guinea pig, extends into the early neonatal stage of development.

A chemical agent which would block the action of testosterone would provide a technique for evaluating the prenatal contribution of testosterone to psychosexual differentiation. It has been shown that in the rat the antiandrogen, cyproterone acetate, when injected prenatally, prevents differentiation of normal male external genitalia and permits the differentiation of female sexual behavior (Neumann and Elger, 1965, 1966). Working in our laboratory, Mr. David Goldfoot, using cyproterone acetate, has produced extensive feminization of the external genitalia in the genetic male guinea pig. The animals do not display the normal male intromission and ejaculatory patterns, but neither do they display the typical female lordosis when castrated and treated with estrogen and progesterone. It is possible that other more effective antiandrogens will prove useful in producing a prenatal chemical castration. The compound must of course be specific to androgen, presumably testosterone, and block the organizing actions of androgen not only on genital tract tissues but on central neural structures as well.

The success achieved with work on the rodent led us to pursue the work on a species which in a number of respects was more similar to man (Young et al., 1964). We chose to work with the rhesus monkey in which sexually dimorphic social behavior in the infant had been demonstrated (Rosenblum, 1961; Harlow, 1965). If, as we had postulated, behaviors other than those instrumental to reproduction were determined by the action of testosterone during differentiation, the rhesus, because of its rich behavioral repertoire, would prove an ideal model for study.

We set about producing female pseudohermaphroditic rhesus monkeys by injecting pregnant females with testosterone propionate.* The procedure followed essentially that reported by Wells and van Wagenen (1954) in which they produced animals described as showing marked morphological masculinization. Pregnant rhesus were given daily intramuscular injections of 20 mg of testosterone propionate beginning on day 40 and extending through day 69 of pregnancy. The average gestation period in the monkey is approximately 168 days. Using this treatment we obtained two female pseudohermaphrodites. Both animals possessed well-developed scrota and well-formed but small penes. The external urethral orifice was located at the tip of the penis as in the normal male. Testes could not be palpated as they can be in the genetic male, buccal smears were 34 to 37 percent sex-chromatin positive, and it was assumed that the animals possessed ovaries and Müllerian derivatives such as described by Wells and van Wagenen for the pseudohermaphroditic monkey and as we had observed in the pseudohermaphroditic guinea pig. We have had the opportunity to study the internal genital morphology of several treated fetuses that were aborted and in a few female pseudohermaphrodites that died shortly after birth. We confirmed the presence of an ovary in these pseudohermaphroditic animals but have not studied the internal morphology on any of the living pseudohermaphrodites whose behavior is reported here.

All the evidence from work on the guinea pig and rat in which

* Testosterone propionate (Perandren) was supplied by courtesy of Ciba, Inc., Summit, N.J.

we varied dosage and time of treatment suggested that for each species there is an optimal regimen for maximum behavioral and morphological modification. The opportunity to explore various treatments on the monkey has been sorely limited because of the few animals available coupled with the relatively high abortion rates we have encountered. It should be recalled that approximately half of the offspring from treated mothers are genetic males thus further reducing the pseudohermaphroditic females available for study. Evidence thus far assembled suggests that the original treatment was less than optimal both for morphological and behavioral modification. We also know from our limited experience that the animal with greatest penis development is not necessarily the animal showing the greatest behavioral modification. We assume that as the number of animals we study increases there then will be a correlation between the extent of morphological and behavioral modification. This was

Table 1

Amount and Temporal Distribution of Prenatal Injections
of Testosterone Propionate in Rhesus Monkeys

No. of off-spring	Genetic sex	Gesta-tional age Rx started	Gesta-tional age Rx ended	Amount and no. of injections of TP into mother			Total mg
				Mg × days	Mg × days	Mg × days	
828	♀	40	69	20 × 30			600
829	♀	40	69	20 × 30			600
1239	♀	38	66	25 × 25 [a]			625
1656	♀	40	111	10 × 50 →	5 × 22		610
836	♀	40	89	25 × 10 →	15 × 20 →	10 × 20	750
1616	♀	39	88	25 × 10 →	15 × 20 →	10 × 20	750
1619	♀	39	88	25 × 10 →	15 × 20 →	10 × 20	750
1640	♀	39	88	25 × 10 →	15 × 20 →	10 × 20	750
1558	♂	42	92	25 × 10 →	15 × 20 →	10 × 20	750
1561	♂	39	45	25 × 7			175
1618	♂	43	92	25 × 10 →	15 × 20 →	10 × 20	750
1644	♂	44	113	10 × 50 →	5 × 20		600
1645	♂	39	129	25 × 10 →	10 × 19 [b] →	5 × 22 [b]	550
1648	♂	39	119	25 × 3 →	5 × 78		465
1653	♂	43	134	25 × 10 →	10 × 17 →	5 × 24	540
1966	♂	40	109	15 × 10 →	10 × 40 →	5 × 20	650

[a] Injected 6 days per week.
[b] Injected on alternate days.

the situation that prevailed in our research on the guinea pig and there is no evidence for believing that the relationship will not hold for the rhesus.

The various treatment parameters employed for each surviving treated animal are indicated in Table 1. It is obvious from the table that few dosages and time periods are represented among the pseudo-hermaphrodites. It may be noted in the table that the mother of pseudohermaphrodite 1239 was treated with testosterone 6 days per week. This procedure followed exactly one of the treatments described by Wells and van Wagenen (1954). The abortion rate in animals so treated was as high as in animals treated 7 days per week and thus the 7-day-per-week treatment schedule was followed in all other animals. Animal 1656, who received hormone through day 111 of fetal life, possesses the most extensively modified external genitalia. However, its initial dosage level was low and the total amount received was also relatively low. We are now preparing a series of treatment schedules which will extend later into pregnancy. The rationale for adopting the more protracted treatment procedure is based upon evidence obtained in our laboratory. Using the gas chromatographic technique, testosterone has been shown to be present in the plasma of the male rhesus fetus late in gestation and even on the day of birth. In small samples of plasma that have been analyzed at intervals during the first 30 days of life no detectable amounts of testosterone were found, whereas comparable-sized samples of plasma from adult male rhesus did reveal the presence of testosterone. By continuing testosterone treatment during late pregnancy we hope to produce conditions which resemble more closely the hormonal environment of the genetic male, thus maximizing degree of modification of the genetic female. In a proportionate sense, the situation for the rhesus may not be greatly different from that which exists for the guinea pig. In that species, the best psychological modifications of the genetic female were obtained with treatments extending to day 55 or 65 of the 68-day gestational period. The organizing action of testosterone is therefore very likely completed at or shortly after birth in the rhesus.

The first two pseudohermaphrodites studied by us and the two untreated females with whom they were studied were taken from their mothers at birth and fed at appropriate intervals by nursery technicians. The animals were housed in individual cages that contained a terry-cloth surrogate mother such as described by Harlow (1961). The four animals constituting the study group were placed together for approximately 30 minutes each day to avoid isolation effects. The animals were taken from their mothers at birth, because we were particularly concerned that whatever sexually dimorphic behavior patterns might be observed would not be the result of differential treatment of the sexes by the mother. The behavior displayed by these two pseudohermaphrodites has been reported previously (Young et al., 1964).

All other animals, experimental and control, have been permitted to remain with the mother for the first 3 months of life. At that time the infant is taken from the mother, placed in a separate cage, and weaned to solid food. Peer groups are formed consisting of four to six animals each. The animals continue to be housed individually, but each weekday the members of a group are brought together in a 6 ft. by 10 ft. experimental room for observation. Each subject in a group of peers is observed for 5 consecutive minutes. The behavior of each subject is recorded on an inventory check list for the 5 minutes during which it is observed. To eliminate a possible time effect, the order of observation within a group is rotated daily. Each group is observed at approximately the same time each day. During the first year of life the subjects are studied for 100 days in the same social setting and for 50 days during the second and each subsequent year. During the interval between yearly tests just described, the animals are tested for social and sexual behavior in pairs. All pair combinations possible within a given peer group are studied.

Our findings have confirmed those reported by Rosenblum (1961) and Harlow (1965) with respect to sexual dimorphism in play behavior of young rhesus. We have compared the frequency of occurrence of threat, play initiation, rough and tumble play, and chasing play for 20 normal males and 17 females during the first year of life (Table 2). The mean performance level for males in each successive block of 10 daily trials over the 100 days of observation is clearly above that of the female. Males also show a greater frequency of mounting behavior than do females (Table 3). This higher level of performance is maintained by males during the second year of life as well as for all the behavior items mentioned above.

Our purpose in studying the rhesus monkey was not simply to confirm the observation that differences in sexual behavior and other behaviors not directly associated with reproduction existed between male and female but to determine whether or not these differences could be accounted for by the organizing action of testosterone. Our observations of female pseudohermaphrodites over the past few years substantiates our initial hypothesis. Not only is sexual behavior, such

Table 2

Frequency of Social Behavior during the First Year of Life
by Male and Female Rhesus Monkeys

			Frequency per block of 10 trials		
		Threat	Play initiation	Rough and tumble play	Chasing play
Males	Mean	24.2	37.5	30.5	8.2
($N = 20$)	Median	18.3	29.5	27.6	7.7
	Semi-inter-quartile range	7.9 → 35.8	22.2 → 46.3	16.7 → 40.5	4.4 → 11.8
Females	Mean	6.1	9.2	8.9	1.3
($N = 17$)	Median	4.2	8.8	6.6	0.8
	Semi-inter-quartile range	1.9 → 10.0	3.4 → 15.1	2.5 → 13.2	0.1 → 2.4

as mounting, increased in the female pseudohermaphrodite compared with that of untreated female rhesus, but their play behavior also resembles that of the genetic male rather than that of the genetic female (Table 4 and Fig. 1).

The augmentation of mounting behavior of the pseudohermaphroditic compared with the normal female seems to be a specific effect of androgenic stimulation during the prenatal period of development. When large amounts of testosterone propionate are injected into each member of three pairs of adult female rhesus monkeys mounting activity is not increased (Phoenix et al., 1967). Recently we have extended these tests of adult females by adding a fourth pair to the experiment. Our procedure, briefly, was to test compatible pairs of females by bringing them together in a neutral observation cage for 10 minutes each weekday. Following 1 or 2 weeks of such tests, the subordinate member of each pair was injected for two weeks with 5 mg of testosterone propionate daily followed by two additional weeks with 10 mg daily of the same hormone. One week later, exactly the same sequence of injections was administered to the more dominant member of the pair, and the daily observations were continued. Our analysis of the results obtained from these observations show that dominant females mounted their partners about 0.8 times per test without androgen treatment. When they were injected with

Table 3

Total Number of Mounts Displayed in 100 Daily Observations
during the First Year of Life

Normal males		Normal females	
Animal no.	Total frequency of mounting	Animal no.	Total frequency of mounting
839	19	830	0
1242	117	831	0
1243	169	1252	1
1617	44	1551	1
1620	11	1642	0
1625	4	1649	0
1636	0	1654	0
1657	5	1769	0
1658	12	1838	0
1662	1	2362	1
1954	18	2369	0
1958	28	2539	0
1960	40	2551	0
2354	4	2569	0
2356	12	2575	0
2358	2	2577	0
2359	15	2580	0
2552	8		
2555	3	Median	0
2557	25		
Median	12.0		

testosterone, the average frequency for these same females increased
to 1.2 mounts per test, but the increase was not statistically significant.
The subordinate females mounted less than once in every 10 tests
prior to treatment with testosterone, and no increase was observed
during treatment. The results suggest that testosterone does not augment mounting behavior in the adult female primate regardless of
her dominance status in the testing situation, and the lack of effect
in the adult clearly contrasts with the marked effect of prenatally
administered androgen on the mounting behavior of the developing
infant female pseudohermaphrodite.

We find no differences in the kind or frequency of social or
sexual behavior displayed by normal males and males whose mothers

Table 4

Total Number of Mounts Displayed in Pseudohermaphroditic Females
in 100 Daily Observations during the First Year of Life

Animal no.	Total frequency of mounting
828	20
829	7
836 [a]	4
1239	9
1616	9
1619	22
1640	33
1656	0
Median	9.0

[a] Data obtained between 10½ and 16 months of age rather than 3½ to 9 months as in all other cases.

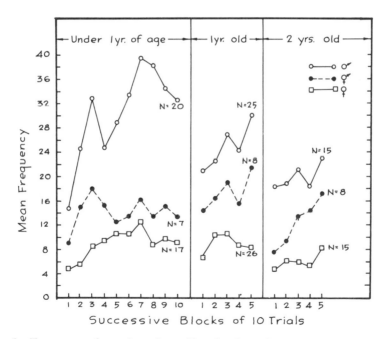

Fig. 1 Frequency of rough and tumble play by infant and juvenile monkeys studied from 3 months of age to approximately 2½ years of age.

were injected with testosterone propionate during pregnancy. We have not discounted the possibility, however, that differences may eventually appear.

From our work with the female pseudohermaphroditic monkey we feel reasonably certain that not only are patterns of sexual behavior determined by the presence of testosterone during development, but that other behaviors not directly associated with reproduction are also influenced by the action of androgens during the period of psychosexual differentiation.

We do not know the limits of this organizing action. It may, in fact, extend to behaviors we had not initially anticipated as being influenced by hormone action. We have suspected the frequency of display of aggression and fighting in general to be related to the presence of testosterone during psychosexual development and this indirectly to dominance. We have barely started to tease out the complex social interactions that account for dominance in a group. In other areas, too, we have just begun. For example, we are investigating the role of prenatal testosterone on what may be loosely termed parental behavior. In fact, our approach to the broad problem of the organizing action of prenatal testosterone has led us to look more closely and carefully at sex differences and similarities as they exist in the untreated population.

The simple cataloguing of sex differences is not being pursued as an end in itself. The aim rather is to investigate the array of behaviors which come under hormonal influence during the period of psychosexual differentiation. What has been found thus far in our investigations broadens our initial hypothesis such that we now suggest that testosterone not only organizes the tissues that mediate patterns of sexual behavior but many other sex-related behaviors. In this regard it is important to emphasize that the organizing actions of testosterone are not manifested on certain types or classes of behaviors independently of the species. For example, aggressiveness cannot be said to be enhanced by early treatment with androgen. In species like the monkey and the guinea pig a relationship between early androgen and aggressiveness may in fact exist, but in species like the hamster, in which the female is normally more aggressive than the male, early androgen may reduce the level and frequency of aggressive displays. Correspondingly, urinary postures which are sex-related in dogs (Martins and Valle, 1948; Berg, 1944) and other Canidae may be influenced in a male direction by early androgen, but urinary postures in general cannot be said to be susceptible to the same kind of influence. In short, androgens can be shown to act organizationally only upon those behaviors which exist as dimorphisms in the species. Those behavioral characteristics which the sexes display with equal frequency (such as huddling, grooming, withdrawing, and fear-grimacing—to mention only a few in the rhesus monkey) are not influenced in any detectable manner by the early administration of androgens.

The term "organizing action of testosterone" is used in the sense of setting a bias on a system such that differential sensitivity and responsiveness are built into the mechanism. Being ignorant of the specific body parts that constitute the control mechanisms we have referred simply to the tissues that mediate, in this instance, sexual behavior. From what is known about the role of the hypothalamus in the control of sexual behavior it is an easy step to assume that testosterone acts to organize tissues of the hypothalamus. Learning that an ovary implanted in a male rat castrated on the day of birth would ovulate and produce corpora lutea, Harris (1964) has suggested (in view of the evidence of hypothalamic control of the pituitary) that castration on the day of birth in the rat prevents masculinization of the hypothalamus, and the work of Barraclough and Gorski (1962) supports such a view. Our findings of modified play behavior in the female pseudohermaphroditic rhesus monkey suggests that other areas of the central nervous system in addition to the hypothalamus are also modified by the prenatal treatment with testosterone. It is premature to conjecture just how widespread modification of central neural tissues might be, but the neural modifications obviously have relatively extensive effects on behavior.

The phenomena with which we are dealing are broad and their implications probably not yet fully appreciated. As more investigators from more disciplines become involved with the problem, Its total scope and limits will become delineated.

In describing the research that has been done we have for the most part referred to the organizing action of *testosterone*. This was done primarily to simplify presentation. We have not established that it is testosterone per se and none of its metabolites that produces the many effects we have observed. We do not know, nor do we claim, that in the intact genetic male it is testosterone alone to the exclusion of other fetal morphogenic substances that masculinizes the nervous system controlling patterns of behavior. Those investigators familiar with hormone action are especially aware of the complex interrelationships that exist and of the need for caution in assuming that the injected material itself is producing the effect observed. This limitation does not detract from the generality of the findings, but rather suggests the need for additional research to spell out the complete and specific hormonal condition that accounts for the observed behavioral modifications.

Acknowledgment

Publication No. 320 of the Oregon Regional Primate Research Center supported in part by Grant MH-08634 of the National Institutes of Health, and in part by Grant FR-00163.

References

Barraclough, C. A., and R. A. Gorski. 1962. Studies on mating behaviour in the androgen-sterilized female rat in relation to the hypothalamic regulation of sexual behaviour. *J. Endocrinol.*, **25**: 175–182.

Beach, F. A., and A. M. Holz. 1946. Mating behavior in male rats castrated at various ages and injected with androgen. *J. Exptl. Zool.*, **101**: 91–142.

Berg, I. A. 1944. Development of behavior: The micturition pattern in the dog. *J. Exptl. Psychol.*, 34:343–368.

Dantchakoff, V. 1938. Rôle des hormones dans la manifestation des instincts sexueles. *Compt. Rend.*, **206**: 945–947.

Feder, H. H. 1967. Specificity of testosterone and estradiol in the differentiating neonatal rat. *Anat. Rec.*, **157**: 79–86.

Feder, H. H., and R. E. Whalen. 1965. Feminine behavior in neonatally castrated and estrogen-treated male rats. *Science,* **147**: 306–307.

Gerall, A. A., and I. L. Ward. 1966. Effects of prenatal exogenous androgen on the sexual behavior of the female albino rat. *J. Comp. Physiol. Psychol.*, **62**: 370–375.

Goy, R. W., W. E. Bridson, and W. C. Young. 1964. Period of maximal susceptibility of the prenatal female guinea pig to masculinizing actions of testosterone propionate. *J. Comp. Physiol. Psychol.*, **57**: 166–174.

Goy, R. W., J. C. Mitchell, and W. C. Young. 1962. Effect of testosterone propionate on O_2 consumption of female and female pseudohermaphroditic guinea pigs. *Am. Zoologist,* **2**: 525 (Abstr.).

Grady, K. L., C. H. Phoenix, and W. C. Young. 1965. Role of the developing rat testis in differentiation of the neural tissues mediating mating behavior. *J. Comp. Physiol. Psychol.*, **59**: 176–182.

Gray, J. A., S. Levine, and P. L. Broadhurst. 1965. Gonadal hormone injections in infancy and adult emotional behavior. *Animal Behavior,* **13**: 33–43.

Harlow, H. F. 1961. The development of affectional patterns in infant monkeys. In *Determinants of Infant Behaviour* (B. M. Foss, ed.). Wiley, New York, pp. 75–97.

Harlow, H. F. 1965. Sexual behavior in the rhesus monkey. In *Sex and Behavior* (F. A. Beach, ed.). Wiley, New York, pp. 234–265.

Harris, G. W. 1964. Sex hormones, brain development and brain function. *Endocrinology,* **75**: 627–647.

Kennedy, G. C. 1964. Mating behaviour and spontaneous activity in androgen-sterilized female rats. *J. Physiol. (London),* **172**: 393–399.

Martins, T., and J. R. Valle. 1948. Hormonal regulation of the micturition behavior of the dog. *J. Comp. Physiol. Psychol.*, **41**: 301–311.

Neumann, F., and W. Elger. 1965. Physiological and psychical intersexuality of male rats by early treatment with an anti-androgenic agent (1,2α-methylene-6-chloro-△⁶-hydroxyprogesterone-acetate). *Acta Endocrinol. Suppl.*, **100**: 174 (Abstr.).

Neumann, F., and W. Elger. 1966. Permanent changes in gonadal function and sexual behavior as a result of early feminization of male rats by treatment with an anti-androgenic steroid. *Endocrinology*, **50**: 209–225.

Phoenix, C. H., and K. L. Grady. 1964. Inhibitory effects of estradiol benzoate administered prenatally on the sexual behavior of female rats. *Anat. Rec.*, **148**: 395 (Abstr.).

Phoenix, C. H., R. W. Goy, A. A. Gerall, and W. C. Young. 1959. Organizing action of prenatally administered testosterone propionate on the tissues mediating mating behavior in the female guinea pig. *Endocrinology*, **65**: 369–382.

Phoenix, C. H., R. W. Goy, and W. C. Young. 1967. Sexual behavior: General aspects. In *Neuroendocrinology*, Vol. II (L. Martini and W. F. Ganong, eds.). Academic Press, New York, pp. 163–196.

Resko, J. A., H. H. Feder, and R. W. Goy. 1968. Androgen concentrations in plasma and testis of developing rats. *J. Endocrinol.*, **40**: 485–491.

Rosenblum, L. 1961. The development of social behavior in the rhesus monkey. Unpublished doctoral dissertation, Univ. of Wisconsin Libraries, Madison.

Swanson, H. H. 1966. Modification of sex differences in open field and emergence behaviour of hamsters by neonatal injections of testosterone propionate. *J. Endocrinol.*, **34**: vi–vii.

Swanson, H. H. 1967. Alteration of sex-typical behaviour of hamsters in open field and emergence by neo-natal administration of androgen or oestrogen. *Animal Behavior*, **15**: 209–216.

Tedford, M. D., and W. C. Young. 1960. Ovarian structure in guinea-pigs made hermaphroditic by the administration of androgen prenatally. *Anat. Rec.*, **136**: 325 (Abstr.).

Wells, L. J., and G. van Wagenen. 1954. Androgen-induced female pseudohermaphroditism in the monkey (*Macaca mulatta*): Anatomy of the reproductive organs. *Carnegie Inst. Wash. Publ. 235; Contribut. Embryol.*, **35**: 95–106.

Whalen, R. E. 1964. Hormone-induced changes in the organization of sexual behavior in the male rat. *J. Comp. Physiol. Psychol.*, **57**: 175–182.

Whalen, R. E., and R. D. Nadler. 1963. Suppression of the development of female mating behavior by estrogen administered in infancy. *Science*, **141**: 272–275.

Young, W. C. 1961. The hormones and mating behavior. In *Sex and Internal Secretions* (W. C. Young, ed.). Williams & Wilkins, Baltimore, 3rd ed., pp. 1173–1239.

Young, W. C., R. W. Goy, and C. H. Phoenix. 1964. Hormones and sexual behavior. *Science*, **143**: 212–218.

REPRODUCTION AND SEXUAL BEHAVIOR (M. Diamond ed.), 51–82, © Indiana University Press

6

Desensitization of the Glans Penis and Sexual Behavior in Cats

Lester R. Aronson and Madeline L. Cooper

Investigations of the neurological basis of mating behavior in mammals developed historically along two major lines of inquiry. One line dealt with central neural mechanisms and the other with peripheral systems. Both lines became active during the latter part of the last century through the pioneering effects of several famous investigators, such as Goltz (1892), Schrader (1892), Steinach (see 1940), and von Bechterew (1911).

The rapid growth of endocrinology during the early 1900s was a major impetus to studies of both central and peripheral processes. It became abundantly clear that external sexual characters, both primary and secondary, were under direct control of gonadal hormones. Since altering the level of these hormones affected many structures and processes, it seemed likely that male and female hormones could exert at least part of their effects on sexual behavior by their action on peripheral receptors. This argument has been suggested in several investigations but is still inadequately established. It seemed equally probable that specific groups of sensory receptors would play a special role in sexual behavior, but this, too, has not been well established and evidence to the contrary has been suggested (Stone, 1922, 1923; Beach, 1942a).

The rise of endocrinology also led to the belief that hormones exerted their influence on mating behavior by acting directly on some part of the brain (Beach, 1942b). This popular idea remained speculative for many years until Kent and Liberman (1949) provided experimental evidence by injecting progesterone directly into the lateral ventricle. A locus of hormone action in the hypothalamus has now been established in females (Harris et al., 1958; Harris and Michael, 1964) and in males (Davidson, 1966). A second locus is also claimed for the spinal cord of the female cat (Maes, 1939, 1940) and male rat (Hart, 1967). These dramatic findings do not exclude the possibility of pertinent action of gonadal hormone on the peripheral receptors. In Davidson's experiment, castrated rats were still mounting females regularly at the time that testosterone was implanted into the hypothalamus, so that precastrational effects of male hormone on peripheral receptors were still possible. In his experiment and in those by Harris and Michael on female cats, the hormone-stimulated hypothalamus may not function entirely by direct action on the motor systems mediating sexual behavior. The possibility should not be overlooked that through the autonomic nervous system the hypothalamus exerts an effect on peripheral receptors which then feed back to the brain or spinal mechanisms. The central autonomic control of receptors, especially touch receptors, is emphasized by Livingston (1959, p. 742).

Early studies of the effects of sensory deprivations on sexual behavior have been reviewed by Beach (1942c). Male and/or female rabbits, rats, cats, and male guinea pigs still mated following the surgical elimination of olfaction, vision, or audition. Similarly, desensitization of the snout, lips, vibrissae, ventral body wall, scrotum, uterus, vagina, or male genitalia did not abolish sexual behavior. Brooks (1937) found no deficits in mating behavior of male rabbits when the olfactory bulbs alone were removed, but when this operation was combined with extensive destruction of the neocortex, mating ceased. Brooks suggested that sexual arousal in male rabbits must be dependent on several sensory mechanisms. This study paved the way for an important experiment by Beach (1942b) in which he destroyed the olfactory bulbs, enucleated the eyes, or desensitized the snout by transection of the sensory branches of the trigeminal nerve. Sexually experienced male rats subjected to any one of these operations continued to mate readily. There was a marked decline in sexual performance by those given any two of the operations while the one rat deprived of all three modalities ceased all sexual activity. In sexually inexperienced males, the effects were more pronounced in that sexual arousal declined markedly following deprivation of any one sense. This finding has been confirmed recently by Orbach and Kling (1966), who performed olfactory and visual desensitizations of infantile rats.

Beach (1947a, 1947b) concluded on the basis of his studies and a comprehensive review of the literature that the sensory input for the neural mechanisms controlling sexual arousal is nonspecific in respect to modality and location, and is additive. Accordingly, any major sensory deprivation should cause a proportional decrease in sexual arousal, and, conversely, any increase in sexual stimuli in the environment, such as the presence of a highly receptive female, should increase arousal. The threshold for sexual performance is regulated by such factors as previous social and sexual experience, androgen level, and neural activity, especially of the neocortex. Finally, according to Beach, alterations in sensory input which affect sexual arousal do not cause qualitative changes in mating behavior.

A few years later Beach and Levinson (1950) correlated the decline in sexual behavior in male rats after castration with a corresponding regression of the spiny denticles or papillae located on the glans penis. The authors suggested that during intromission the spines are deflected by the walls of the vagina and in doing so they activate touch corpuscles located directly beneath the base of the papillae. In castrated rats with denticles absent, the touch receptors are not so readily activated, thus contributing to lowered sensory input and a decline in sexual arousal.

In discussing the decline in sexual behavior of castrated male cats, Rosenblatt and Aronson (1958) suggested that hormonally changed sensory receptors could be partially responsible for the observed behavioral changes. The glans penis of the cat is also covered with horny spines which are considerably larger and less numerous than in the rat. Aronson and Cooper (1967) found in cats a similar correlation as in rats between the decline in sexual behavior and the regression of the spines after castration, but in this species the situation is more complicated. The rate at which the spines regress is rather consistent, but the rate at which sexual behavior declines is highly variable among cats. As a result, some castrated males with large spines no longer showed sex behavior and conversely some long-standing castrates without spines were still mating regularly.

In females of many mammalian species, as in human females,

androgens increase the level of sexual excitability (reviewed by Young, 1961; Diamond, 1965). Androgens also cause enlargement of the clitoris in many mammals (reviewed by Dorfman and Shipley, 1956), and in women (Shorr et al., 1938; Foss, 1951). These findings have led a number of clinical investigators (reviewed by Carter et al., 1947; Money, 1961; Whalen, 1966) to conclude that the sexually arousing effects of androgens are produced entirely or in part by increasing end organ sensitivity of the clitoris. These conclusions must be tempered, however, by recent findings of Palka and Sawyer (1966) that in ovariectomized female rabbits, androgens have the same locus of action as estrogens in the ventromedial-premammillary hypothalamus when stimulating estrous behavior. In this case, as in the experiments with estrogens, androgen implanted into the hypothalamus did not diffuse into the systemic circulation in sufficient quantities to stimulate uterine growth or masculinize the external genitalia. The importance of clitoral stimulation is also questioned by Diakow (1967), who found no changes in mating behavior of domestic cats up to 20 weeks after bilateral section of the pudendal nerve. This operation partially desensitizes the anogenital region and completely desensitizes the clitoris.

The few experimental studies that have been performed on the sensory role of the genitalia have all involved drastic surgical procedures which included much more than genital desensitizations. Following removal of the vagina and uterus, Ball (1934) reported that female rats still mated. Bard (1935) observed sex behavior in female cats following abdominal sympathectomy, after removal of the oviducts, uterus, and much of the vagina, and after removal of the sacral segments of the spinal cord. Following ablation of the spinal cord from Lumbar 5 through Sacral 3, male cats still had erections and mounted receptive females (Root and Bard, 1937). With these major sensory and motor losses, however, the males never achieved intromission. In a later paper, Root and Bard (1947) found no changes in sexual aggressiveness after removal of the spinal cord between L5 or 6 and S3 even when this deprivation was coupled with abdominal sympathectomy or with transection of the cord between L1 and L4 (which interferes with erection). They concluded on the basis of these operations that afferent impulses from the pelvic viscera, the external genitalia, and from a wide area of skin surrounding the external genitalia are not necessary for the initiation or maintenance of sexual activity. Abdominal sympathectomy, however, abolishes ejaculation.

The present experiment was designed to test the immediate and long-term effects of a relatively small, discrete sensory impairment limited to cutaneous receptors of the glans penis. This sensory deprivation was achieved through a minor surgical procedure—bilateral section of the nerve dorsalis penis—which did not interfere with erection or other motor processes. A preliminary report has been published (Aronson and Cooper, 1966) and we are now presenting a final report of this experiment in which the subjects were observed regularly for a period of 1 to 4 years.

Methods

The main study is based on 19 adult domestic short-hair male cats of unknown ancestry. Ten cats had been obtained as adults and probably had sexual experiences prior to the experiment. The other nine were raised from age of weaning in laboratory cages under controlled conditions. Their only sexual experiences were obtained during the sex tests of the experiment. Fourteen of these males were assigned to the experimental group, four were used as unoperated controls, and one as a sham-operated control. Nine additional adult males were used in auxiliary physiological experiments. Temperature in the colony rooms was kept relatively constant throughout each year, but day-length followed natural seasonal variations. Animals over 6 months old were always kept in individual cages.

Sex Tests and Scores

Methods of observation and sex tests were similar to those described by Rosenblatt and Aronson (1958). Females used as test animals were spayed and hysterectomized and then brought into heat by weekly injections of 0.15 mg of estradiol benzoate in 0.15 ml of sesame oil. With this procedure estrous females were available for 3 to 4 days per week. All males were given a 20-minute test in a specific test room once a week except for occasional gaps resulting from chance circumstances. Usually the males were tested with the same female but this was not always possible, since females required occasional rests from the estrogen treatment to avoid excessive debilitation.

The major items of male sexual behavior observed and recorded were:

1. *Approach*—male walks or runs to female, sometimes followed by anogenital sniffing.

2. *Neck grip*—male grips with his teeth the loose skin on the back of female's neck.

3. *Mount*—male straddles the back of female, usually holding the neck grip.

4. *Stepping*—while mounted, male makes a series of step-like movements with hind limbs.

5. *Thrusting*—while mounted, male performs a series of thrust-like movements of pelvic region (Fig. 1).

6. *Intromission*—brief insertion of penis into vagina, during which time ejaculation occurs; marked by cessation of thrusting and a loud copulatory cry of female.

7. *Withdrawal and dismount*—penis withdrawn from vagina; male dismounts or is thrown off by strenuous action of the female.

To provide an estimate of the highest level of sexual activity achieved during a given test, an index figure (sex score) modified from Rosenblatt and Aronson (1958) was used. Two major shortcomings of this technique should be noted. First, the derived scores are ordinal. A score of eight, for example, is larger than a score of four, but is not necessarily twice as large. This limits the kinds of statistical analyses that can be used. Second, the system does not

Fig. 1   Male HA before operation in a typical mounting and thrusting position.

handle completely the complicated and largely unknown relation between frequency, duration, and modality of the various behavior patterns. A single mount lasting over 5 minutes, for example, gives a test a higher score than one having many mounts of less than 1 minute duration. Despite these difficulties, the sex score provides a crude way of describing the level of sexual activity in terms of a single figure.

The scoring system used is as follows:

No interest in the female	0 points
Attention to the female (e.g., definite approach to the female, anogenital sniffing)	1 point
One or more neck grips	2 points
One short mount (< 1 minute)	3 points
More than one short mount or one medium mount (1 to 5 minutes)	4 points
More than one medium mount	5 points
One or more long mounts (> 5 minutes)	6 points
Stepping movements	add 1 to achieved score
Pelvic thrusting	add 1 to achieved score
One intromission	9 points
Each additional intromission	add 1 to achieved score

The score represents the highest level of sexual behavior shown by a subject during a given session. A male, for example, having two intromissions during a test would receive 9 + 1, or 10, points. A male not achieving intromission but having one 6-minute mount accompanied by stepping and thrusting, would receive 6 + 1 + 1, or 8, points.

Surgical Procedure

The operations were performed under nembutal anesthesia injected intraperitoneally. The normally retracted penis was everted and the skin of the sheath incised along the middorsal line. Upon spreading the superficial and deep fascia, the two dorsal nerves and accompanying dorsal arteries were exposed. Sections about 3 mm in length were removed from the main nerve bundle and major branches (Fig. 2). An equivalent portion of the arteries was removed, after which the fascia was separated laterally as far as the ventral surface of the penis in a search for fine nerve branches. Healing was always rapid and uneventful, and the males were ready for testing the following week.

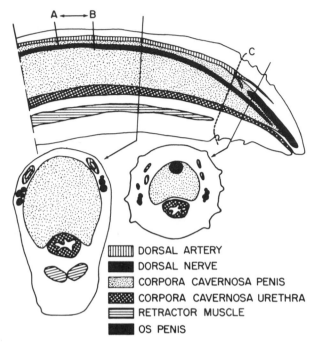

Fig. 2 Schematic drawing of shaft and glans of penis. A↔B indicates section of nerve removed. C indicates line of attachment of prepuce. (From Aronson and Cooper, 1966.)

Results

Immediate Effects of Operation

During the first 5 postoperative weeks, sexual arousal remained high, as indicated by the readiness with which males approached and mounted females. None, however, achieved intromission, and this brought the sex scores down to a maximum of 8 (Table 1). Copulatory activity of intact males generally involves a brief mount terminating in intromission, which is followed by a long period of inactivity (5 to 10 minutes or longer). This is often followed by a second and sometimes a third and fourth brief mount, intromission, and inactive period. Mounts not terminating in intromissions are generally brief and are not frequent. After operation, when intromissions no longer occurred, mounting behavior increased precipitously. Most of the males spent the greater part of each test period mounting the female, some performing many brief mounts and others

Table 1

Immediate Effects of the Sensory Deprivation

Animal	Total no. of tests [a]	Preoperative median of last 5 tests			Postoperative, median of first 5 tests		
		Total mount time, sec [b]	No. of intromissions	Sex score	Total mount time, sec [b]	No. of intromissions	Sex score
Obtained as kittens							
BG	15	0	2	10	1200	0	8
CG	47	602	1	9	1200	0	8
MV	6	0	3	11	360	0	6
PH	6	0	2	10	1120	0	8
RO	43	0	2	10	1200	0	8
RS	39	34	2	10	574	0	8
ST	5	0	2	10	405	0	8
Median	15	0	2	10	1120	0	8
Obtained as adults							
HA	86	0	2	10	634	0	8
LI	12	27	2	10	1154	0	8
OD	9	1	3	11	971	0	8
PG	24	0	2	10	764	0	8
SY	9	0	2	10	1148	0	8
TM	24	0	2	10	879	0	8
WD	11	0	2	10	870	0	8
Median	12	0	2	10	879	0	8
Sham operate							
SG	22	4	2	10	294	2	10

[a] Approximately one per week starting with first test in which mounting occurred.
[b] Mounts not terminating in intromission.

performing one or two very long mounts. A similar increase in mounting behavior occurs in some castrated males that are still sexually aroused but can no longer achieve intromission because of incomplete erection (Rosenblatt and Aronson, 1958).

Failure to achieve intromission in the present experiment was not due to inadequate erection (see p. 67). Rather, it correlated completely with improper orientation of the male on the back of the female during the mount. At most times the pelvic region of the male was so far forward and highly elevated that the penis seldom came near the genital area of the female.

Sham Operation

As noted above, operative procedure included removal of the paired dorsal arteries of the penis which run adjacent to the nerves (Fig. 2). These arteries constitute only a minor blood supply to the penis, the major supply coming from the deep and urethral branches of the penile artery. Nevertheless, to be sure that removal of the dorsal blood vessels or other surgical procedures did not interfere with penile function, a sham operation was performed on male SG in which the dorsal arteries were removed, leaving the dorsal nerves intact. Intromission occurred during each of the first five postoperative tests (Table 1), and no decrements in behavior were observed. The only notable difference in postoperative behavior was an increase in total mounting time for mounts not terminating in intromissions.

Postoperative Recovery of Function

Intromissions reappeared in two males, HA and RO, 6 and 18 weeks, respectively, after operation, and mating in subsequent tests was close to the preoperative level. Two other males, PH and OD, had occasional intromissions spread over a period of several years. The remaining 10 subjects never intromitted again during observation periods as late as 40 months after operation. Evidence presented below in the section on histology points to a high correlation between restitution of function and extensive regeneration of the dorsal nerves.

Long-Term Effects of Operation

The persisting disorientation while mounting, failure to achieve intromission, and unusually long mounts led us to ask whether these changes in behavior would eventually have a further detrimental effect on sexual activity. With this in mind we continued to test most of the subjects for several years (Table 2) and discovered three further changes in sexual behavior.

Cylical Activity

Regardless of the month of the year that the operation was performed, the level of sexual arousal as measured by sex score, total

Table 2

Long-Term Postoperative Effects of Sensory Deprivation [a]

Animal [a]	No. of tests [b]	No. of intro-missions	Date of operation, week of year	Start of low periods, week of year	Threshold of glans, log .1 mg [c]
Obtained as kittens					
BG	52	0	39	33	
CG	149	0	10	31, 37, 23	2.43
MV	140	0	15	35, 20, 26	2.78
PH	133	11	13	34, 37	3.23
RS	148	0	41	23, 24	
ST	127	0	39	43, 41, 40	
Obtained as adults					
LI	84	0	13	39, 12, 39	
OD	162	11	27	3, 38, 37, 29	2.78
PG	85	0	9	32, 26, 39	
SY	14	0	24	—	
TM	80	0	27	40	
WD	174	0	29	36, 38, 33, 38	2.43
Controls					
TO	143	215	......		
FL	147	174	......		
MO	58	64	......		
SH	107	58	......		

[a] Males RO and HA that showed complete recovery of sex behavior are omitted.
[b] Approximately one test per week.
[c] From smooth area distal to spines.

mount time, and initial latency (time from beginning of test to first mount) dropped markedly in the fall of the year, around weeks 35 to 40 and remained at a very low level until the end of the year, when high levels of responding again appeared. These low periods appeared each year at approximately the same time. They are illustrated in Fig. 3, which gives by week of year the median sex scores, initial mount latencies, and total mount times for all 12 animals for the full time that the subjects were observed. Four cycles are clearly evident. As a further example, individual scores of a single animal, WD, are presented in Fig. 4. These graphs show, by the three measures used, a rather sudden decline in sexual arousal in the fall of four successive years, and rapid recuperation at the beginning of the new year.

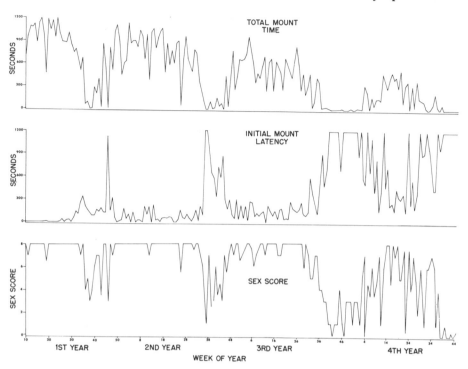

Fig. 3   Median sex scores (bottom), initial mount latencies (middle), and total mount times (top) for all 12 animals for all postoperative tests.

Qualitative Changes in Behavior

As noted above, section of the dorsal nerve of the penis caused sufficient disorientation in all the subjects to prevent intromission. Other changes were observed, most common of which was falling on the side during a mount. While still holding a neck grip, these males often thrust vigorously in the side position while the penis was often several centimeters or more from the female (Fig. 5). Sometimes the male would get up after a few seconds, lie down again, and continue this up and down behavior for most of the test. Lying on a side during a mount occurred in only 3 of 19 subjects before operation (Table 3). After operation it was observed in 11 out of 15 subjects. There is some indication that this unusual behavior may be related to physical exhaustion resulting from prolonged mounting behavior characteristic of the operates. On numerous occasions, however, males fell on their side during the first minute of the first mount of a test. Exhaustion is clearly not the only explanation.

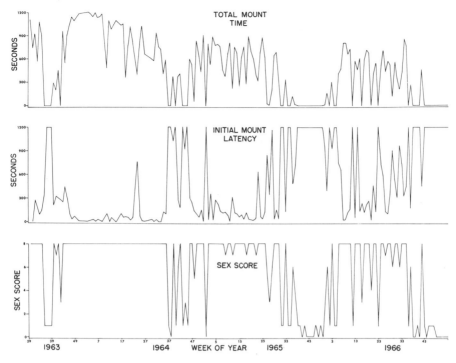

Fig. 4 Median sex scores (bottom), initial mount latencies (middle), and total mount times (top) for all postoperative observations of male WD.

In four of five males in which lying on the side was pronounced (CG, PH, LI, and TM) the frequency of occurrence of this behavior gradually increased over many months of testing (Table 3), suggesting to us a developing habit. For male TM, during the first 20 tests, the first bout of lying on side did not occur until 4 to 5 minutes of a long mount, and may have been related, as we have said, to exhaustion. In further tests this latent period became considerably smaller. In test 74, for example, lying on side took place only 25 sec after the first mount began. What may have started as a behavioral response to exhaustion seemingly developed into a habit relating to the test situation.

In male PG, a high level of on-side behavior occurred during the entire postoperative testing period, but this male sometimes fell on his side preoperatively. Turning to male CG, the explanation for the decrease in frequency of on-side behavior in later tests is not evident, nor is it easy to understand why some males seldom showed this behavior.

Fig. 5   Atypical mounting behavior of male RO. While lying on his side the male is thrusting vigorously. The erect penis can be seen.

Another type of pronounced qualitative change in behavior was observed in three males. In the early postoperative tests, MV acted in a frenzied manner following the initial mount. He moved back and forth incessantly from one side of the female to the other. At some moments he was at right angles to the female and in a few tests he went completely around, circling the female repeatedly while still holding the neck grip. At times he mounted and thrust while facing the rear of the female (head to tail) with the penis thrusting at the female's head. In other tests he lay on his side during a mount similar to male TM. This frenzied behavior was also reflected in a large number of short mounts per session. As testing continued, MV became less excitable. Circling, lying on the side, and head to tail mounts gradually decreased. The number of short mounts declined from an average of 7.5 per test for the first block of 20 tests to 3.9 in tests 101–120 (only positive tests—those with at least 1 mount— were counted). Males RO and OD showed similar qualitative changes in mating behavior. These included lying on side, circling, cross mounting, and head to tail mounting. When intromissions started again in RO these abnormal behavior patterns disappeared.

Percent of Tests with Mounts in Which Male Lay on His Side at Least Once During a Mount[a]

Subjects	Preoperative[b]		Postoperative tests,[b] percent on side						
	No. of tests	% on side	1–20	21–40	41–60	61–80	81–100	101–120	121–140
Obtained as kittens									
BG	15	0	5	17[c]					
CG	37	0	10	35	60	30	10[c]		
MV	6	0	15	10	0	0[c]			
PH	5	0	15	10	70	85	80	85[c]	
RO	25	0	30[c]						
RS	20	0	0	0	0	10	0[c]		
ST	5	0	0	0	0	0	0	0[c]	
Median		0	10	10	0	10	5	42	
Obtained as adults									
HA	35	0	0[c]						
LI	12	0	10	35	45	50	75[c]		
OD	9	11	10	5	0	0[c]			
PG	23	30	85	60	75	88[c]			
SY	7	0	0[c]						
TM	24	0	80	95	85	100[c]			
WD	11	0	0	0	5	0	0	0	0[c]
Median		0	10	35	45	50	37	0	0
Controls									
FL	122	0							
TO	121	0							
SH	80	0							
MO	48	0							
Sham									
SG	20	25	6[c]						

[a] Mounts which did or did not terminate in intromission.
[b] Only tests in which mounts occurred are counted.
[c] Based on less than 20 tests.

General Decline in Sexual Behavior

In addition to regularly occurring periods of minimal sexual activity in the fall of each year, the general level of sexual behavior declined and became less consistent in succeeding years. Following each low period, the behavior did not quite reach the level of the previous high, and scattered throughout the third and fourth postoperative high periods were numerous tests with surprisingly low scores. These phenomena are illustrated best in the graphs for total mount time (Figs. 3 and 4) and are also seen in those for latency and sex scores. Six of the seven males whose tests were continued for 2½ to 4 years showed this decline, which was also definite in one male that had been tested for only 1 year. This male, BG, stopped all sexual behavior after the thirty-second test. In addition, a qualitative decrease in sexual excitability was clearly evident in males LI and PG, characterized by a notable decrease in the forcefulness of pelvic thrusting. This was first noticed in PG six weeks after operation, and by 4 months, thrusting was reduced to occasional twitches of the thigh muscles. This change was readily seen in motion pictures taken at 3 and 22 months postoperatively. After about 4 months of testing, thrusting in LI became erratic in that strong thrusts appeared in some sessions and in others they could hardly be seen.

Preoperatively all the males held the neck grip for the full duration of the mount. After operation, several of the males occasionally released the neck grip during a mount and then retook it after a few seconds or minutes. This behavior was sometimes repeated many times during a test. Related to the less persistent neck grips, there occurred a notable increase in neck licking by some operated males.

Comparison of Subjects Obtained as Adults or Kittens. Examination of the data shows no obvious differences between the two groups in either preoperative, immediate postoperative (Table 1) or long-term (Table 2) effects of the operation on sexual behavior. Although lying on side was observed more frequently among cats obtained as adults (Table 3), the differences were not staitstically significant (Mann-Whitney "U" test). An increase in lying on side behavior might be expected among cats obtained as adults, since they were considerably older during the course of the experiment and possibly more subject to exhaustion.

Unoperated Controls. While it is well established that male cats mate throughout the year (Rosenblatt and Schneirla, 1962), two investigators (Leyhausen, 1956; Michael, 1961) reported that male cats are less active sexually in the fall. Root and Bard (1947) found less sexual activity in the summer months. In the present experiment, the sexual behavior of four unoperated males was followed for 75 to 156 tests. Three, TO, FL, and MO were consistent in their copulatory activity. The fourth male, SH, who apparently had a low level of sexual arousal, seemed particularly sensitive to the degree of receptivity of the test female and mated very irregularly. In the fall or early winter of each year, TO, FL, and MO each had one or two tests in which they reacted minimally to the female (Fig. 6). During the fall and early winter of 1965, the sexual activity of SH was higher and more regular than usual. During the same period in 1966 it was considerably lower than usual. While our control animals did show some evidence of cycles, with one possible exception these were minimal when compared to the pronounced cycles of the sensory-deprived subjects.

Effects of Operation on Erection. Since the dorsal nerves of the penis carry some sympathetic nerve fibres, an important question raised in this study is whether our surgical procedures not only anesthetsized the penis but also interfered to some extent with erection. This has been answered in three ways.

Neuroanatomical and Neurophysiological Relations

Examination of the literature shows that erection is controlled by the pelvic nerve (n. erigens) from the ventral roots of S_1, S_2, and S_3, of which S_2 seems most important in cats for the erectile function (Langley and Anderson, 1895). The pelvic nerve also controls bladder function and other visceral processes. This nerve, which is primarily parasympathetic, runs to the pelvic plexus, which in turn sends branches deep into the penis as the nerve cavernosus penis. Our surgical intervention, which did not penetrate the strong tunica albuginea of the corpora cavernosa, could not touch this nerve or its branches. Rami of the cavernous plexus, however, do communicate with the dorsal nerve (Kuntz, 1953).

The pelvic plexus also receives sympathetic fibers from the inferior mesenteric ganglion and hypogastic plexus (Kuntz, 1953). These are primarily vasoconstrictors related to detumescence, but they do contain vasodilator fibers that on stimulation will elicit at least partial erection, but only when the pelvic nerve has been cut (Root and Bard, 1947; Bessou and Laporte, 1963).

The dorsal nerve of the penis is a branch of the pudendal nerve

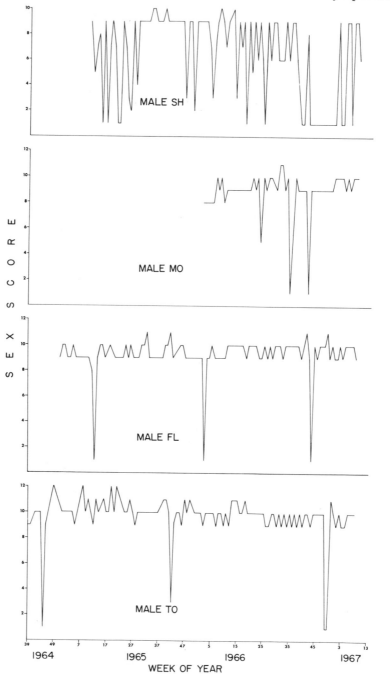

Fig. 6 Sex scores for the four control males for all tests.

which arises from the dorsal roots of S_1, S_2, and S_3. It is mostly sensory, but it does contain some sympathetic fibers which are presumably vasoconstrictors. After cutting the pudendal nerve Semans and Langworthy (1939) still obtained full erection upon stimulation of the sacral roots in the cat.

Observations of Erection

During normal copulatory behavior it is not possible to see the erect penis without manipulating the male. However, many of the experimental animals lay on their side during a mount, and in this position erection could sometimes be seen. These observations were facilitated in some males by shaving the hair in the genital region. In the more tractable animals the observer could raise a hind limb momentarily during a mount and palpate the penis. Erection was observed one or more times in 10 of the 14 operates and in all instances seemed complete.

Experimental Induction of Erection (Performed by K. K. Cooper)

Erection was induced in 5 additional males by electrical stimulation of the ventral roots of S_2, which gives rise to the pelvic nerve (Cooper et al., 1964). Using chloralose anesthesia, lumbosacral laminectomies were performed. The ventral roots of S_2 of both sides were tied centrally and were mounted on bipolar platinum wire electrodes. Square-wave stimulation at an impulse frequency of 20 per second and 0.4-msec duration regularly produced protrusion and erection within 1 minute. The degree of protrusion and erection was determined by palpation. The nerve dorsalis penis was then sectioned bilaterally and the ventral roots of S_2 were again stimulated by pulses having the same parameters. Protrusion and erection were obtained as rapidly and to the same degree as before nerve section. In each case the extent of the nerve section was verified by histological examination of the shaft and glans.

Topical Anesthetics

Experiment I. A 5 percent lidocaine ointment (xylocaine, Astra) was applied to the penis of the intact male FL. In three tests disorientation in mounting lasted 26 to 30 minutes, after which intromission occurred. During the period of disorientation, full erection was observed. In three control tests using blank ointment, intromission

occurred in 5 to 8 minutes. In two additional tests a 2 percent tetracaine hydrochloride solution (Cetocaine, Cetylite Industries) was
sprayed on the penis. Disoriented mounting and failure to achieve
intromission persisted for 37 minutes when the observations were
terminated.

Experiment II. Four intact males from another experiment were
used. All had been tested regularly once a week for several months
and all had had one or more intromission per test. The penises were
sprayed with a 2 percent solution of tetracaine hydrochloride and
immediately thereafter each male was placed with a receptive female
in the standard test situation. All showed the typical disorientation
of desensitized males, and none achieved intromission during the
20 minutes of the test. The first mount of male CA lasted 7 minutes,
55 seconds and a full erection was seen when he dismounted. The
first mount for male CB lasted 5 minutes, 25 seconds. This was followed by eight short mounts and one of medium length. This male
fell on his side during the sixth mount and thrusting was seen in
this position. Male CC had just one 12-minute mount and lay on his
side once. Male GM had a 4-minutes, 40-second mount and turned
on his side after 2 minutes, 25 seconds of this mount. Six repetitions
of this lying on side behavior occurred in this and two subsequent
medium-length mounts.

It is clear from these two experiments that all the immediate
consequences of surgical desensitization of the glans can be duplicated
by the application of topical anesthetics. Since the anesthesia wears off
in an hour or so, this technique cannot be used readily in the study
of long-term effects.

Bonadonna (1956) treated the penises of bulls with a 10 to 20
percent solution of novocaine and reported that "In spite of peripheral insensitivity, the sexual drive and eagerness to copulate remained unchanged. Although the bull makes several attempts, ejaculation never occurs either in the living female or into the artificial
vagina." Adler and Bermant (1966) applied the topical anesthetic,
lidocaine, to the penis of rats and reported loss of erection and intromission but no loss in sexual arousal. In a similar experiment using
a tetracaine anesthetic, Carlsson and Larsson (1964) found no loss
of erection in rats but a decline in arousal as the test proceeded. In
the human male, Bieber (personal communication) reports that application of cocaine or nupercaine to the glans penis delays orgasm for
periods of 1 hour or longer, during which time the penis remains
erect. Nupercaine is recommended by some urologists for treatment of
premature ejaculation.

Terminal Neurophysiological Experiments (performed by K. K. Cooper)

Under nembutal anesthesia terminal operations were performed on nine of the desensitized animals 6 to 42 months after operation. The dorsal nerve of the penis was exposed deeply just distal to its origin from the pudendal nerve. Using unipolar or bipolar silver electrodes, action potentials were obtained on a cathode ray oscilliscope following stimulation of the glans with nylon monofilaments (Semmes–Weinstein aesthesiometer, Semmes et al., 1960). Seven of the nine animals responded to contact of the tip of the filament against the glans (of sufficient pressure to bend the filament) with a strong burst of action potentials. The filaments were calibrated on an analytical balance and thresholds are given in units equal to the log of one tenth the force in milligrams required to bend them to approximately the same degree as during stimulation. Thresholds were obtained on five animals using graded filaments in ascending and descending sequences as commonly used in threshold determinations. These varied between 2.43 and 3.23 (Table 2). In four additional intact animals thresholds varied from 2.43 to 2.89. Two additional operated animals did not respond to stimulation by the filaments, but these were the first two used in the experiment and it is possible that failure to respond was due to inadequate techniques.

In two subjects, PH and WD, a topical anesthetic, 2 percent solution of tetracaine hydrochloride, was applied to the glans. This procedure raised the minimally effective filaments to 4.09 and 3.85, respectively. At these levels artifacts were produced by movement of the penis by the stiff filament. These stiff filaments may also have activated deep pressure receptors.

After action potentials had been obtained in two additional intact animals by using the normal range of filaments, the dorsal nerves of the penis were sectioned in the same way as in the main experiment. In both cases action potentials could no longer be obtained with the normal range of filaments.

Histological Evidence

Testes and Epididymides. The cyclical variations in reproductive behavior were clearly paralleled by changes in the size of the interstitial cells of the testes, and in the height of the pseudostratified epithelium of the ductus epididymis. Testes of 16 males, 8 intact and 8 nerve-cut, obtained during every month of the year except June were sectioned and stained with hematoxylin and eosin. Interstitial cells were clearly smaller during September and October (Fig. 7, A and

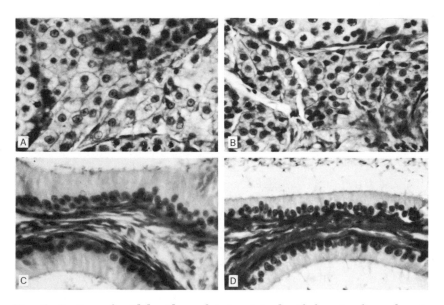

Fig. 7 Sections of epididymides and testes stained with hematoxylin and eosin. A, Interstitial cells of testes in May. ×300. B, Interstitial cells of testes in September. Note reduced size. ×300. C, Epididymis in May. ×300. D, Epididymis in September. Note reduced height of pseudostratified columnar epithelium. ×300.

B). During these months the rim of cytoplasm surrounding the nucleus was narrower and did not have the foamy appearance seen during the rest of the year.

The size of the columnar cells of the pseudostratified epithelium of the ductus epididymis varied in a similar manner (Fig. 7, C and D). Average cell height measured in five different locations for each specimen are presented in Fig. 8. Again we see a decided low period in September and October and a high period from March to July. Although the number of animals is limited, no difference is evident between the intact and nerve-cut groups. We conclude from these data that androgen secretion by the testes is lower in the fall and that this accounts for the seasonal cycles in sexual activity.

Penises. At the termination of the experiment the penises of all 14 experimental subjects were sectioned serially and stained with Bodian silver proteinate–gold chloride technique. In the two males,

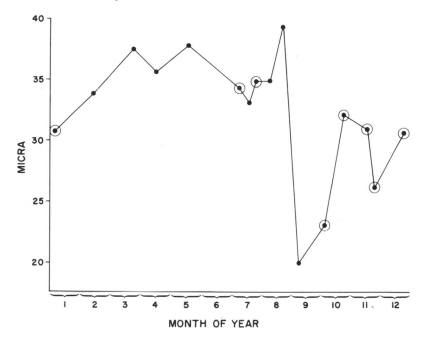

Fig. 8 Seasonal variations in height of columnar cells of ductus epididymis. Dots represent intact males; circles surrounding dots are specimens from nerve-cut animals taken at termination of the experiment.

HA and RO, in which regular intromissions had returned, some uninterrupted bundles of nerve fibers were present bilaterally in the dorsal fascia. In four males, SY, TM, PG, and CG, there were only a few scattered fibers in the lateral fascia. These may represent anastomoses with the nerve cavernosus or else they were fine twigs of the dorsal nerves that were missed at the time of surgery. The remaining eight animals showed partial regeneration of the dorsal nerves through the scar tissue on one or both sides. Two of these males with partially regenerated nerves, PII and OD, had occasional intromissions (Table 1), but the other six never intromitted.

Discussion

Extent of Denervation of Glans

Although we removed a 3-mm segment of each nerve and the stumps shrank back still further, some regeneration occurred in 11 of the 14 subjects, as demonstrated by the histological and neurophysiological evidence. Regeneration was undoubtedly aided by the location of the nerves between two flat connective tissue sheets, superficially the fascia penis and deeply the tough tunica albuginea. In two males, HA and RO, where histological evidence showed that nerve section was incomplete, regeneration was presumably sufficient to provide full restitution of function. In two others, PH and OD, regeneration apparently provided partial restitution of function. These animals achieved intromission occasionally but only during the season of maximal sexual activity when androgen levels were high. This interesting observation suggests to us that the rise in androgen level in the winter must enable the partially destroyed sensory mechanism of the glans to provide sufficient information (either peripherally or centrally) for adequate orientation and intromission. Similarly, the drop in androgen level in the fall must prevent transmission of this information. In the remaining seven males there was good evidence for incomplete desensitization, but the amount of sensory tissue remaining was apparently insufficient to provide proper orientation.

In the neurophysiological experiment, action potentials were still obtained from the nerve-cut subjects when the glans was lightly stimulated with fine nylon filaments. In additional intact males, when the dorsal nerves were first cut during the terminal experiment or when the glans had been anesthetized with tetracaine no action potentials could be elicited. These findings lend further support to our conclusion that in most subjects in the main experiment some regeneration had occurred.

Effects of Denervation

Section of the nerve dorsalis penis produced three major changes: (1) disorientation of the male while mounting the female and other qualitative changes in behavior, (2) gradual, nonseasonal decline in sexual excitability, and (3) augmentation of the normally slight seasonal cycle of sexual excitability.

Disorientation. Qualitative changes in sex behavior following sensory deprivation would not be predicted from Beach's theory as outlined in the introduction. Desensitization of the penis, however, represents a special situation where the sensory information is utilized directly in a critical motor response which provides precise orientation for intromission. The only other evidence of this function that we could find in the literature is a Swedish veterinary report by Rubarth (1946) describing the failure of a bull to achieve intromission following pathological degeneration of the pudendal nerve. In the rhesus monkey, on the other hand, bilateral section of the nerve dorsalis penis did not prevent mounting, erection, or intromission, but the male's pelvic thrusts were grossly uncoordinated. Ejaculation did not occur in three out of four males, and sexual activity declined to low levels during a series of observations (Herbert, 1967).

In addition to loss of orientation, other qualitative changes in sexual behavior were observed. The frenzied circling behavior which was so characteristic of several of the desentitized individuals probably represents secondary autonomic excitation resulting from the failure to achieve intromission and only indirectly stems from the loss of sensory input. Over many months these reactions gradually dissipated as further adjustments to the situation occurred. The atypical behavior characterized by lying on the side during a mount may also be a secondary reaction, but its basis is complex and varied. The marked interindividual differences and the absence of consistent postoperative trends, points to a complex, multicasual phenomenon of which physical exahustion may be just one factor. In four subjects the gradual increase in this behavior as testing continued suggest that these animals were adjusting to a new and difficult situation by a stereotyped reaction. Rosenblatt and Aronson (unpublished) observed lying on the side behavior in several castrated males that were having long mounts not terminating in intromission.

Beach developed his theory concerning the nonspecific nature of sexual stimulation from experiments involving the deprivation of sensory inputs that have arousal value (Beach, 1942b; Whalen, 1966) but are not directly related to specific motor patterns. In this respect, the long-term effects of our sensory deprivation—the seasonal decline and general decline in sexual arousal—are much more in accord with the mechanism that Beach envisaged.

Nonseasonal Decrease in Sexual Behavior. Our original hypothesis, that sexual activity would gradually decline as a result of lowered sensory input, stemmed from our earlier findings in the cat and the Beach and Levinson (1950) study in the rat showing that changes in penile structure accompany the decline in sexual behavior after castration. These morphological changes presumably affect the sensory receptors in such a way that their sensitivity is lowered, and this, in turn, brings about lowered sexual responsiveness. A recent study of the penile spines (Aronson and Cooper, 1967) raises some doubts about the importance of these structural changes in the maintenance of normal mating behavior. Using neurophysiological techniques we are presently trying to determine whether the sensitivity of the glans is actually impaired by castration. If no sensory changes are found it means that the decline in sexual behavior that we have found is most likely related to the primary effect of the desensitization—loss of intromission. Here the reduction in sensory feedback from the penis is a likely explanation for the drop in sexual excitability, but failure to ejaculate may be a contributory factor.

Rosenblatt and Aronson (1958) found in those castrated male cats persisting in sex behavior for several months after operation that the first decrement is a gradual loss of erection. High levels of mounting without intromission follow, and the situation is then comparable in many respects to our desensitized males. In these males, the dorsal nerve operation leads to disorientation, loss of intromission, and consequently less genital stimulation. By reducing the number of effective tactile receptors the operation also causes a reduction in genital stimulation. This, in turn, brings about a decline in sexual arousal (Fig. 9).

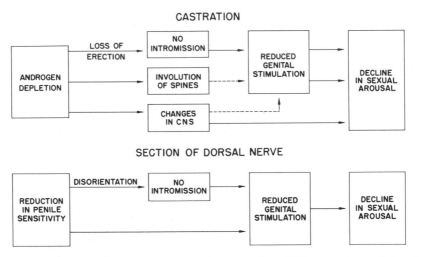

Fig. 9 Schematic diagram comparing the routes by which castration and dorsal nerve section depress sexual arousal. Dashed lines represent suggested functions not verified experimentally.

Following castration, androgen depletion leads to the loss of erection and consequently less genital stimulation. Androgen depletion also causes involution of penile spines, and this may also cause reduced genital stimulation. As in the first case, reduced genital stimulation leads to a reduction in sexual arousal. Androgen depletion also affects the central nervous system (hypothalamus) directly, and this may bring about a reduction in arousal. This direct action of male hormone may account for the more rapid changes in arousal after castration as compared with dorsal nerve section. In Fig. 9, the possibility is also included that the hormone-stimulated hypothalamus may affect genital receptivity through autonomic changes (Livingston, 1959).

Seasonal Cycles in Sexual Arousal. Since male cats mate readily throughout the year, the pronounced seasonal cycles of the desensitized males was unexpected. Apparently we have reversed a physiological process characteristic of domestication through a surgical manipulation. Wild felines, like most mammals, have definite breeding seasons (Matthews, 1941). The Scottish wildcat, for example, breeds only in the spring. With domestication, the breeding season tends to lengthen and becomes less definite in this species and in many other mammals (Amoroso and Marshall, 1960). Although female domestic cats are known to have litters throughout the year, cyclical reproductive activity is well known to cat breeders. Sexual activity is high in winter, most litters are born in March and April, and there is a lull in activity in late summer and fall. Based on histological and physiological evidence, Foster and Hisaw (1935) identified in female cats an anestrous period extending from September to January, and they related this to variations in daylength. This period coincides with the time of minimal sexual activity of our desensitized males.

In domesticated male cats seasonal reproductive activity has almost disappeared, but as noted by Leyhausen (1956) and Michael (1961) and as demonstrated in the present experiment a slight mating cycle is still present. Actually, the histological cycle of the interstitial cells of the testes and tubules of the epididymides is much more pronounced.

The present concept of seasonal cycles in vertebrates suggests an internal rhythm that is modulated by seasonally varying environmental influences such as changing daylength. A major feature of the internal rhythm is the seasonal fluctuation of the brain-pituitary-gonadal axis. Our data indicate that in the cat this system provides high levels of male hormone in the winter, spring, and early summer and low levels in late summer and fall. Since in our colony rooms conditions are kept relatively constant except for daylength, light is thought to be the important environmental variable. Presumably in the males of wild felines, the sensory input from the penis and other sources is insufficient to induce sexual behavior in the fall when the androgen level is low. With domestication, it is possible that the degree to which the testes involute out of season is markedly reduced as is the duration of this period of involution. Domestication may also increase the level of general and sexual stimulation or lower the threshold of sexual behavior so that it is reached even during the period of minimal hormonal output. Thus, under domestication, the breeding cycle in the male is all but obliterated. With the reduction in sensory feedback from the glans of the nerve-cut males and the elimination of intromission and ejaculation, the sensory input is reduced to an extent that is largely insufficient to produce sex behavior during the fall when the androgen titres are low.

Concluding Remarks

It may be seen from this study that sensory information from the glans has a dual role. On the one hand, it energizes the mechanism for sexual excitability, and, on the other hand, it provides precise information for orientation. Although no other examples among mammals have come to our attention, the precise movements that most mammals make when mating suggest that this type of direct sensory-motor integration is common. Since Beach's theory of sexual stimulation, as discussed previously, encompasses only the nonspecific arousal function, it should now be expanded to include orienting processes as well.

The present trend is to consider the central nervous system as the major site of action of gonadal hormones with respect to sexual behavior. This study calls attention to the importance of peripheral stimulation of the genitalia in the maintenance of high levels of sexual arousal. It follows that the depressing effects of castration on arousal should be evaluated in terms of both the central and peripheral mechanism involved.

The seasonal fluctuation in androgen level and the correlated slight decline in sexual behavior of the intact subjects in the fall and early winter indicate that the sexual arousal mechanism is functioning just above threshold level during this period. Any further depression of the arousal system, as through decreased sensory input from the penis, therefore causes a pronounced seasonal decline in sexual behavior. In future experiments this knowledge should provide a suitable means of investigating the effects of various experimental manipulations on the mechanism for sexual arousal.

Summary

The glans penis of 14 sexually experienced male cats was partially desensitized by bilateral section of the nerve dorsalis penis along the shaft of the penis. The immediate effect of the operation was a loss of genital orientation, resulting in failure to achieve intromission when the disoriented but sexually aroused male mounted the estrous female. Erection was not affected by the operation, as shown by behavioral and neurophysiological evidence.

With continued testing three long-term effects of the sensory deprivation were observed:

1. A decided drop in sexual activity occurred in the fall of each year (starting about week 35), with rapid recovery in early winter. In four intact control males only minimal seasonal cycles were seen, but an associated histological study of testes and epididymides showed a definite reduction in androgen available in the fall. The sensory deprivation clearly exaggerated a latent seasonal cycle in the sensory-deprived males.

2. Qualitative changes in behavior were observed; the most prevalent was lying on the side while mounting the female. In this side position the males often thrust vigorously, while the male and female genitalia were separated by a considerable distance.

3. A general nonseasonal decline in sexual behavior was most evident during the third and fourth years of testing.

In respect to Beach's theory concerning the nonspecific and additive nature of sexual stimulation, the disorientation found in this study is considered a special case where the sensory information is required for a precisely oriented motor response which is a critical component of the mating pattern. The long-term effects of the operation, on the other hand, are consistent with Beach's theory. Here the decrease in sensory stimulation resulting from the operation and from the loss of intromission brought about first a reduction in sexual activity in the fall when the androgen level was low, and eventually induced a more general, nonseasonal decline in sexual behavior.

Acknowledgments

Supported by Grants HD-00348 and MH-08600 from the National Institutes of Health. Several students of the American Museum Undergaduate Research Participation Program, supported in part by the National Science Foundation, Special Projects in Science Education, Grant GY-350, assisted in the research. The histological preparations were made by Mrs. A. Marie Tucker. We thank Miss Alba D. Plescia and Mr. Robert Stolberg for technical assistance and Dr. Ethel Tobach, Mrs. Carol Diakow, and Mr. K. K. Cooper for reading the manuscript and for many helpful suggestions.

References

Adler, N. and G. Bermant. 1966. Sexual behavior of male rats: Effects of reduced sensory feedback. *J. Physiol. Psychol.*, 61: 240–243.
Amoroso, E. C., and F. H. A. Marshall. 1960. External factors in sexual period-

icity. In *Marshall's Physiology of Reproduction*, Vol. I (A. S. Parkes, ed.). Longmans, London, pp. 707–831.

Aronson, L. R., and M. L. Cooper. 1966. Seasonal variation in mating behavior in cats after desensitization of glans penis. *Science*, **152**: 226–230.

Aronson, L. R., and M. L. Cooper. 1967. Penile spines of the domestic cat: Their endocrine-behavior relations. *Anat. Rec.*, **157**: 71–78.

Ball, J. 1934. Sex behavior of the rat after removal of the uterus and vagina. *J. Comp. Psychol.*, **18**: 419–422.

Bard, P. 1935. The effects of denervation of the genitalia on the oestrual behavior of cats. *Am. J. Physiol.*, **113**: 5.

Beach, F. A. 1942a. Analysis of factors involved in the arousal, maintenance and manifestation of sexual excitement in male animals. *Psychosomat. Med.*, **4**: 173–198.

Beach, F. A. 1942b. Analysis of the stimuli adequate to elicit mating behavior in the sexually inexperienced male rat. *J. Comp. Psychol.*, **33**: 163–207.

Beach, F. A. 1942c. Central nervous mechanisms involved in the reproductive behavior of vertebrates. *Psychol. Bull.*, **39**: 200–226.

Beach, F. A. 1947a. *Hormones and Behavior*. Hoeber, New York.

Beach, F. A. 1947b. A review of physiological and psychological studies of sexual behavior in mammals. *Physiol. Rev.*, **27**: 240–307.

Beach, F. A., and G. Levinson. 1950. Effects of androgen on the glans penis and mating behavior of castrated male rats. *J. Exptl. Zool.*, **114**: 159–168.

Bechterew, W. von. 1911. *Die Funktionen der Nervencentra*, Vol. III. Gustav Fischer, Jena.

Bessou, P., and Y. Laporte. 1963. Etude de l'erection produite chez le chat, par la stimulation des nerfs hypogastriques. *Arch. Ital Biol.*, **101**: 90–104.

Bonadonna, T. 1956. On some biological and non-biological factors that may affect the collection and quality of semen. Proc. 3rd Intern. Congr. Animal Reproduction, Sec. I, Cambridge, pp. 105–112.

Brooks, C. McC. 1937. The role of the cerebral cortex and of various sense organs in the excitation and execution of mating activity in the rabbit. *Am. J. Physiol.*, **120**: 544–553.

Carlsson, S. G., and K. Larsson. 1964. Mating in male rats after local anesthetization of the glans penis. *Z. Tierpsychol.*, **21**: 854.

Carter, A. C., E. J. Cohen, and E. Shorr. 1947. The use of androgens in women. *In Vitamins and Hormones*, Vol. 5 (R. S. Harris and K. V. Thimann, eds.). Academic Press, New York, pp. 317–391.

Cooper, K. K., M. L. Cooper, and L. R. Aronson. 1964. Physiological and behavioral observations of erection before and after section of the nerve dorsalis penis. *Am. Zoologist*, **4**: 301.

Davidson, J. M. 1966. Activation of the male rat's sexual behavior by intracerebral implantation of androgen. *Endocrinology*, **79**: 783–794.

Diakow, C. A. 1967. The role of genital innervation in the maintenance of sexual behavior of the female cat. Master's thesis, New York University, New York.

Diamond, M. 1965. A critical evaluation of the ontogeny of human sexual behavior. *Quart. Rev. Biol.*, **40**: 147–175.

Dorfman, R. I., and R. A. Shipley. 1956. *Androgens*. Wiley, New York.

Foss, G. L. 1951. The influence of androgens on sexuality in women. *Lancet*, **1**: 667–669.

Foster, H. A., and F. L. Hisaw. 1935. Experimental ovulation and the resulting pseudopregnancy in anoestrus cats. *Anat. Rec.,* **62:** 75–93.

Goltz, F. 1892. Der Hund ohne Grosshirn. *Arch. Ges. Physiol.,* **51:** 570.

Harris, G. W., and R. P. Michael. 1964. The activation of sexual behaviour by hypothalamic implants of oestrogen. *J. Physiol. (London)* **171:** 275–301.

Harris, G. W., R. P. Michael, and P. P. Scott. 1958. Neurological site of action of stilboestral in eliciting sexual behavior. In *Ciba. Foundation Symposium on the Neurological Basis of Behavior* (G. E. Wolstenholme and C. M. O'Conner, eds.). Little, Brown, Boston. pp. 236–251.

Hart, B. L. 1967. Testosterone regulation of sexual reflexes in spinal male rats. *Science,* **155:** 1283–1284.

Herbert, J. 1967. Neural and endocrine stimuli from the female and the sexual behaviour of the male rhesus monkey. *Acta Endocrinol. Suppl.,* **119:** 47.

Kent, C. R., and M. J. Liberman. 1949. Induction of psychic estrus in the hamster with progesterone administered via the lateral brain ventricle. *Endocrinology,* **45:** 29–32.

Kuntz, A. 1953. *The Autonomic Nervous System.* Lea & Febiger, Philadelphia, pp. 290–295.

Langley, J., and H. K. Anderson. 1895. The innervation of the pelvic and adjoining viscera. Part 3. The external generative organs. *J. Physiol. (London)* **19:** 85–121.

Leyhausen, P. 1956. Verhaltensstudien an Katzen. *Z. Tierpsychol. Beiheft,* **2**.

Livingston, R. B. 1959. Central control of receptors and sensory transmission systems. In *Handbook of Physiology, Section I: Neurophysiology,* Vol. 1, Chap. 31, pp. 741–760.

Maes, J. P. 1939. Neural mechanism of sexual behavior in the female cat. *Nature,* **144:** 598–599.

Maes, J. P. 1940. Le méchanisme nerveux de comportement sexuel de la chatte. *Compt. Rend. Biol.,* **133:** 95–97.

Matthews, L. H. 1941. Reproduction in the Scottish wild cat, *Felis silvestris* grampia Miller. *Proc. Zool. Soc. London,* **111:** 59–77.

Michael, R. P. 1961. Observations upon the sexual behaviour of the domestic cat (*Felis catus L.*) under laboratory conditions. *Behaviour,* **18:** 1–24.

Money, J. 1961. Sex hormones and other variables in human eroticism. In *Sex and Internal Secretions.* Vol. 2. (W. C. Young, ed.). Williams & Wilkins, Baltimore, 3rd ed., pp. 1383–1400.

Orbach, J., and A. Kling. 1966. Effect of sensory deprivation on onset of puberty, mating, fertility and gonadal weights in rats. *Brain Res.,* **3:** 141–149.

Palka, Y. S., and C. H. Sawyer. 1966. Induction of estrous behavior in rabbits by hypothalamic implants of testosterone. *Am. J. Physiol.,* **211:** 225–228.

Root, W. S., and P. Bard. 1937. Erection in the cat following removal of lumbo-sacral segments. *Am. J. Physiol.,* **119:** 392–393.

Root, W. S., and P. Bard. 1947. The mediation of feline erection through sympathetic pathways with some remarks on sexual behavior after deafferentation of the genitalia. *Am. J. Physiol.,* **151:** 80.

Rosenblatt, J. S., and L. R. Aronson. 1958. The decline of sexual behavior in male cats after castration with special reference to the role of prior sexual experience. *Behaviour,* **12:** 285–338.

Rosenblatt, J. S., and T. C. Schneirla. 1962. The behavior of cats. In *The*

Behaviour of Domestic Animals (E. Hafez, ed.). Williams & Wilkins, Baltimore, pp. 453–488.

Rubarth, S. 1946. Bidrag till den patologiska anatomin vid betäckningsimpotens hos tjur. *Medd. Vet. Patol. Anat. Avdeln.*, **36**: 732–741.

Schrader, M. G. 1892. Über die Stellung des Grosshirns im Reflexmechanismus des centralen Nervensystems der Werbelthiere. *Arch. Exptl. Pathol. Pharmakol.*, **29**: 55–18.

Semans, J. H., and O. R. Langworthy. 1939. Observations on the neurophysiology of sexual functions in the male cat. *J. Urol.*, **40**: 836–846.

Semmes, J., S. Weinstein, L. Ghent, and H. L. Teuber. 1960. *Somatosensory Changes after Penetrating Brain Wounds in Man.* Harvard University Press, Cambridge.

Shorr, E., G. N. Papanicolaou, and B. F. Stimmel. 1938. Neutralization of ovarian follicular hormone in women by simultaneous administration of male sex hormone. *Proc. Soc. Exptl. Biol. Med.*, **38**: 169–170.

Steinach, E. 1940. *Sex and Life.* Viking Press, New York.

Stone, C. P. 1922. The congenital sexual behavior of the young male albino rat. *J. Comp. Psychol.*, **2**: 95–153.

Stone, C. P. 1923. Further study of sensory functions in the activation of sexual behavior in the young male albino rat. *J. Comp. Psychol.*, **3**: 469–473.

Whalen, R. E. 1966. Sexual motivation. *Psych. Rev.*, **73**: 151–163.

Young, W. C. 1961. The hormones and mating behavior. In *Sex and Internal Secretions,* Vol. 2 (W. C. Young, ed.). Williams & Wilkins, Baltimore, 3rd ed., pp. 1173–1239.

REPRODUCTION AND SEXUAL BEHAVIOR (M. Diamond ed.), 83–131, © Indiana University Press

7

Factors Involved in the Control of Mounting Behavior by Female Mammals

Frank A. Beach

Females of a large number of mammalian species may under certain conditions mount other animals in a manner which to a greater or lesser degree resembles the copulatory pattern of males of the same species. I have not essayed a complete inventory of the phyletic distribution of such behavior, but published reports indicate that it occurs in at least some females of 13 species representing 5 different orders comprising the rodents, lagomorphs, insectivores, ungulates, carnivores, and primates. Some of the accounts refer to single instances, the representativeness of which it is impossible to estimate, but in many cases evidence is sufficient to demonstrate that for some mammals female mounting activity is not "abnormal" or "atypical" but instead represents a predictable and characteristic feature of the species repertoire.

For most species the accounts of feminine mounting behavior are anecdotal and qualitative, but the existence and frequency of the responses in question are nonetheless well established. This is the case, for example, with respect to several types of farm animals of the order Ungulata. The only extensive and controlled investigations

83

of this behavior have dealt with the guinea pig, the rat, and the dog. In preparing the present chapter I have attempted to achieve the following objectives: (1) to summarize such evidence as I have been able to discover concerning the existence and nature of female mounting behavior in various mammals, (2) to review and critically evaluate the principal experimental investigations directly relevant to such behavior and, (3) to formulate as clearly as possible the principal questions or problems involved in achieving a satisfactory interpretation of the phenomena involved.

Observational Evidence

The most liberally documented accounts of mounting by female mammals deal with domestic species, and particularly with those whose breeding has been closely supervised by animal husbandrymen. Unfortunately, despite a general agreement that mounting does occur in various species, very few of the available descriptions include the facts necessary for the interpretation of the behavior involved. In many instances the reproductive status of the mounting animal is assumed rather than positively determined, and in other cases the physiological state or even the sex of the "mountee" is left in doubt. Despite these regrettable lacunae the evidence deserves summarization.

Ungulates

The frequent occurrence of mounting behavior on the part of sows has been reported by a number of observers, and it is often stated that the appearance of such reactions signals the onset of heat or estrus (McKenzie, 1926; Altmann, 1941). According to Hafez et al. (1962) when a sow is in proestrus she may mount the boar, and when she is in either proestrus or estrus her mounting activity is directed toward other sows. The same workers add that sows in anestrus will mount another female when the latter is in estrus, and Burger (1952) agrees that anestrous sows often "ride" those that are in proestrus. These accounts are somewhat contradictory inasmuch as some suggest that a high or rising level of estrogen (estrus or proestrus) is a contributory factor, whereas statements that anestrous sows will mount others indicate that an actively secreting ovary is not essential to the behavior in question. A further source of confusion is the failure of authors to delimit the types of animals most likely to elicit mounting responses.

In the case of cattle it seems firmly established that under specifiable conditions ovarian hormones potentiate or intensify the female's tendency to mount other animals. The literature contains numerous reports to the effect that cows with cystic ovaries are especially prone to mount conspecific individuals frequently and vigorously. In fact, the behavior associated with the presence of ovarian cysts has been termed "nymphomania" (Pearl and Surface, 1915; Calder, 1927; Walton et al., 1940). The responses consist not merely of mounting, but of pawing the ground and bellowing in the manner of the bull (Hafez and Schein, 1962). At the same time such females usually refuse to stand for mounting by other cattle and therefore differ from cows in true estrus (Roberts, 1956).

Hammond and Day (1944) induced similar behavior in anestrous cows by the administration of stilbestrol. Females treated with this estrogenic substance were reported to lower their heads, paw the ground, and pursue and mount heifers which were in estrus. The choice of a stimulus female in heat is noteworthy. Comparable reactions were produced in spayed heifers by estrogen treatment in an experiment reported by de Alba and Asdell (1946). The intensity and vigor of the hormonally induced responses is revealed by the fact that in a study by Folley and Malpress (1944) 20 percent of the estrogen-treated females suffered pelvic fractures as a consequence of mounting activity.

It seems reasonably certain that exogeneous estrogen or endogenous hormone produced by cystic ovaries can stimulate vigorous and persistent male-like responses in cattle, but the behavior which appears under these conditions may not be normal for the species. Hafez and Schein (1962) consider that the combination of pawing, bellowing, and "frantic" mounting which is associated with "nymphomania" differs qualitatively from the mounting behavior shown by untreated cows with normal ovaries. It is well established that normal females do upon occasion exhibit a pattern of mounting which closely resembles the copulatory responses of the bull even to the inclusion of pelvic oscillations. What is less clear is whether this behavior depends upon a high estrogen level, for a number of authorities have recorded the occurrence of mounting behavior on the part of both estrous and anestrous cows (Weber, 1911; Hammond, 1927; de Alba and Asdell, 1946; Roark and Herman, 1950; Hafez and Schein, 1962). Of equal theoretical importance is the fact that most if not all of these authors report that regardless of the reproductive status of the mounting female, the mounted individual is characteristically a second female in estrus.

The only other ungulate in which female mounting behavior has been described is the sheep. According to Hafez and Scott (1962), ewes occasionally mount one another, but such behavior is said to be much less common in this species than in either swine or cattle. Cole et al. (1945) reported that anestrous ewes treated with a combination of chorionic gonadotropin and androgen showed both male-like mounting and feminine receptivity. It is difficult to interpret these findings as well as the rationale for the experimental procedure.

Rodents, Lagomorphs, and Insectivores

Although some rodent species will be dealt with in extenso at a later point in this chapter, it is appropriate here to list all those in which female mounting behavior is known to occur. This is a relatively common form of response in female guinea pigs (Young et al., 1938) and in female rats of some strains (Beach and Rasquin, 1942).

Female rabbits sometimes mount conspecific partners according to Hammond and Marshall (1925) and Hu and Frazier (1940). The only insectivore mentioned in the literature in this connection is the short-tailed shrew. Pearson (1944) avers that females of this species mount other shrews and execute male-like mounts with pelvic thrusting movements.

Carnivores

Cooper observed (1942) that female lions in estrus are sometimes mounted by other females in anestrus, and according to Rosenblatt and Schneirla (1962) the domestic female cat, in heat, may mount other estrous females. It is worth noting that both of the foregoing accounts of feline behavior have as a common element the existence of an estrous condition in the "mountee."

Fuller and DuBuis (1962) have recorded that occasionally a female dog "may be stimulated to make sexual advances by another female in estrus, but such homosexual responses are usually rudimentary and short-lived." Beach et al. (1968) found mounting by both spayed and intact bitches to be somewhat more frequent and complete than the foregoing quotation might lead one to anticipate.

Markley and Bassett (1942) have studied the behavior of captive martens and report that ". . . the female climbs and mounts the male when he is apparently passive" (p. 609).

Primates

In an early observational study Hamilton (1914) noted that adult female monkeys occasionally mounted one another displaying the lip-smacking and pelvic movements .that ordinarily accompany heterosexual coitus. The report includes no statement as to the reproductive condition of either participant. Hamilton's subjects lived in an outdoor compound but were nevertheless confined. However, Carpenter's (1942) field studies of free-living rhesus monkeys revealed that female mounting occurs under natural conditions. He observed frequent mounting of one female by another over a period of several days and concluded that the continuing interaction, ". . . resembled in many respects a male-female consort relation" (p. 149). In a second case Carpenter noted a nonestrous female repeatedly mounting a female which was in estrus. A third example involved two females, both in estrus; and a fourth included one estrous and one proestrous individual. In interpreting all these instances Carpenter reached the following conclusion. "The observations show that the female who is mounted is usually more strongly motivated for sexual behavior than the mounter" (p. 150). This may be relevant to the tentative conclusion based on several other species that the most effective stimulus partner—the type of individual most likely to be mounted—is a second female in estrus.

Premonitory signs of mounting behavior in rhesus macaques of both sexes appear quite early in life according to Harlow's observations (1965). Interaction between animals as young as 1 or 2 months of age sometimes involves rubbing the bodies together and executing thrusting movements of the pelvic region. Beginning in approximately the third month after birth the frequency of this kind of behavior becomes greater in male infants than in females.

Bingham's classic study (1928) of sexual development in chimpanzees includes descriptions of several instances in which 2 immature females "covered" one another, but such behavior was rare in comparison to the relatively numerous instances of heterosexual interaction involving mounting and thrusting by little males directed to little females.

Yerkes (1939) has described female–female mounting in adult chimpanzees. He states that some females confronted with a second female who is in the stage of genital swelling may assume the masculine copulatory position, mounting the estrous individual and displaying thrusting motions. In this case again, as in several mentioned earlier, the most effective stimulus animal seems to be a second female in a state of sexual receptivity.

The evidence is disappointingly incomplete and the accounts are mostly fragmentary, but the record, such as it is, seems to justify the tentative conclusion that mounting behavior by° females is a type of behavior which may be widely distributed throughout the class Mammalia. It may be further suggested that for many species such behavior is not abnormal, does not represent manifestations of "sex reversal," but is instead to be considered a normal element in the behavioral repertoire of the species.

Experimental Evidence

Early in the twentieth century when interest in the secretory functions of the reproductive glands was developing rapidly there was a general tendency to assume that almost any sexually dimorphic behavior could be explained in terms of control by different "sex hormones." It was at that time customary to assume that in the mating patterns of vertebrates there were certain elements which were "male" and others which were "female." As a consequence of these two a priori assumptions the first experimental reports of mounting behavior in female mammals dealt with presumed effects of "male hormone" on the behavior of females.

Effects of Androgen on Adult Females

As early as 1913 Steinach reported that spayed female guinea pigs bearing grafts of testicular tissue sometimes mounted conspecific stimulus animals in masculine fashion. Moore repeated this experiment in 1919 and obtained confirmatory results. A number of years later Young and Rundlett (1939) attempted to induce mounting behavior in female guinea pigs which had been injected with androgenic material. These attempts were unsuccessful, but in 1959 Phoenix et al., whose work is cited later in this chapter, were able to stimulate some mounting in such animals following androgen treatment. The discrepancy almost certainly was due to the more potent androgen used in the later study and the fact that the hormone was administered for a much longer period of time.

Young et al. (1939) injected intact female guinea pigs with 4.0 mg of testosterone propionate daily for 17 days and observed no change in mounting behavior, although clitoral hypertrophy was induced. As noted earlier, Young and Rundlett (1939) were unable to produce mounting in *spayed* animals by administering testosterone.

More recently Diamond (1965) succeeded in eliciting mounting in female guinea pigs by androgen treatment. Testosterone propionate produced this effect in both intact anestrous and spayed individuals, but androgen proved to be much less effective than exogenous ovarian hormones. Spayed females treated with testosterone propionate mounted an average of 4.2 times per test, whereas injection of estrogen and progesterone was followed by a mean frequency of 20.5 mounts per test. At the same time the ovarian hormones produced sexual receptivity in 75 percent of the tests. When testosterone was combined with estrogen and progesterone, both mounting and lordosis were markedly inhibited. Diamond's conclusions were that mounting and lordosis are mediated by different central nervous mechanisms, both of which are sensitive to estrogen plus progesterone. The mechanism for mounting activity is partially responsive to androgen but less so than to ovarian hormones. Finally, androgen is capable of blocking the response of the "lordosis mechanism" to estrogen and progesterone.

The guinea pig belongs to the suborder Hystricomorpha, whereas the rat is a member of the Myomorpha. It is therefore of interest to observe that female rats also show mounting behavior under the influence of testicular hormone.

The earliest report of such behavior was that of Moore (1919), who described it in spayed females bearing testicular transplants. A number of years later Hemmingsen (1933) administered androgen to female rats and produced what he termed "psychical hermaphroditism" because the treated animals exhibited both masculine and feminine responses. Hemmingsen was aware of the fact that some untreated females may mount other rats, but this he attributed to endogenous androgen of undetermined origin. In the same year Kun (1933) proposed that the "lutein tissue" of the ovary secretes androgenic hormone and this is responsible for the occurrence of masculine characters.

The subsequent availability of purified testis hormone made it possible for Ball (1937) to demonstrate that spayed rats given testosterone exhibited frequent mounting responses, although, and this is particularly signifiicant, the treated females did not exhibit the behavioral reflexes associated with ejaculation in the normal male. Stone (1939) obtained similar results, and a second study by Ball (1940) revealed that intact female rats injected with testosterone propionate display not only mounting behavior but also a low degree of receptivity to the male's copulatory attempts.

In reports of two studies, the present writer (Beach, 1938, 1942a) stressed the fact that normal female rats in estrus sometimes mount males, and when this occurs the pattern can include not merely mounting and clasping but also forelimb palpation, pelvic thrusting, abrupt dismounting with a forceful "backward lunge," and subsequent autogenital licking. In fact, the pattern, in its fullest form, is indistinguishable from that seen when a normal male mounts and achieves intromission. The one element lacking is the bodily response normally associated with ejaculation.

Beach (1942b) examined the behavior of prepuberally ovariectomized rats before and after the administration of testosterone propionate in adulthood. When tested for their responses to estrous females before androgen treatment the experimental animals exhibited behavior which consisted chiefly of mounting the stimulus female from the rear and clasping her flanks with the forelimbs. It is to be stressed that these responses occurred in females deprived before puberty of any possible gonadal hormone. Administration of androgen in adulthood occasioned a shift toward a more complex type of mounting that involved more of the elements comprising the male's copulatory pattern. These included the execution of forelimb palpation, pelvic thrusting, and, infrequently, the type of dismounting usually associated with intromission. The behavior of experimental females is compared with that of normal males in Fig. 1. Although he did not describe his findings in comparable detail, Koster (1943) also reported that while untreated female rats show some mounting activity, the frequency of such behavior is greatly increased by injections of testosterone propionate.

Effects of Ovarian Hormones

I have cited first the studies bearing upon mounting behavior in females given androgenic hormone, because in terms of historical development such experiments antedated the ones to be discussed now. It was only after mounting by females was accepted as something other than "abnormal" or "sex-reversed" behavior that it became reasonable to consider the possibility that such behavior might be related to homologous gonadal secretions.

Guinea Pig. Although Avery (1925) appears to have been one of the first investigators to stress the fact that under certain circumstances normal female guinea pigs mount other guinea pigs without any special treatment, the experimental analysis of this behavior was

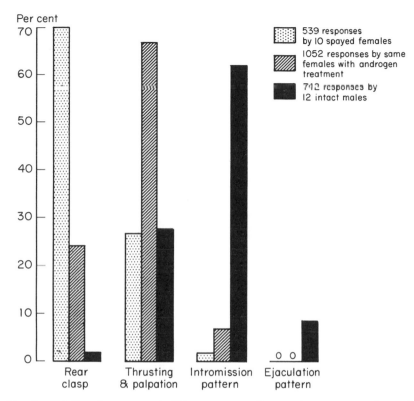

Fig. 1 Relative frequency of different types of mounting responses shown by female and male rats. [From Beach (1942b).]

initiated and carried on for many years by W. C. Young and his associates.

Young et al. (1935) described behavior of females which included pursuit and mounting of both male and female cagemates. This activity, which includes very strong pelvic thrusting, was characterized as being identical to that shown by the normal male. In fact, the authors wrote, "Few if any males are as vigorous as the most active females." This conclusion was based in part on the fact that the latter attempted to mount not only estrous females but those in anestrous and even males. It should be pointed out here that the performance of the mounting females might reflect inferior discrimination rather than superior vigor. Also, although their behavior was said to closely resemble that of the male, two important elements were lacking. In 1939 Young and Rundlett wrote as follows: "When this behavior is being displayed by female guinea pigs, the animals pur-

sue other females or even males, mount them and go through the
motions of copulation except that they do not afterward roll dorsally
and clean their genitalia" (p. 449). In addition, there is no mention
of seeing the behavior normally associated with ejaculation in the
male.

Young et al. believed that mounting in the female guinea pig
". . . is a true proestrous behavior." Their data indicated that these
responses may appear as early as 53 hours before the onset of behavioral estrus as signaled by the first display of lordosis, and that
they tend to drop out from 1 to 3 hours after the appearance of receptivity. Mounting seemed to be most intense a few hours before
females began to receive the male. It was noted that females vary
with respect to the frequency and intensity of their mounting responses, but that individuals tend to behave consistently from one
cycle to the next. A few individuals regularly displayed mounting,
although they never became receptive to the male.

A few years after this initial study, Young et al. (1938) reported
that although many exceptions occur, the frequency of mounting
responses shown by different females generally is proportional to
the number of developing follicles in the ovaries. A subsequent experiment led Young et al. (1939) to reverse the original identification
of feminine mounting as proestrous behavior. Their investigation
showed that although the peak of mounting activity coincides with
the onset of heat, it continues through the period of receptivity. Of 98
females examined, 89 mounted at least once. The frequency of mounts
per estrous period ranged from 1 to 96 with a median of approximately 15 (estimated by present author). No relation could be discerned between length of heat and mount frequency, but extensive
mounting was associated with the presence of more than the average
number of mature ovarian follicles.

Discovery of a positive relationship between follicular development and mounting behavior pointed directly to the possibility that
estrogen is involved, and in 1939 Young and Rundlett demonstrated
that mounting could be reliably induced in spayed guinea pigs by
the administration of estrogen followed after a suitable interval by
progesterone. The most effective hormone treatment was the same
as that which produces sexual receptivity. Injection of estrogen alone
was followed by the appearance of mounting behavior in 23 of
176. spayed females, and the responding individuals mounted an
average of 7.3 times per test. When females were primed with
estrogen and then given progesterone, 108 of 176 animals mounted
for an average of 12.2 times per test. The authors wrote as follows:

". . . mounting activity induced in spayed animals by the injection of estrogen and progesterone is concluded to be identical with that displayed by normal animals" (p. 454).

In agreement with earlier observations on intact females in natural estrus, it was found that spayed animals showed individual differences in their responsiveness to exogenous estrogen and progesterone, but these differences were consistent from test to test. The duration of heat behavior and of mounting were found to be independent, as in the case of normal females. Individuals which proved refractory to the standard hormone dosages did not exhibit any increase in mounting when the amount of estrogen was doubled, but some females which originally failed to show lordosis did display this response under the influence of increased estrogen. When sexually immature spayed animals were injected with estrogen and progesterone it proved possible to evoke lordosis at an earlier age than mounting.

Taken together the foregoing findings led Young and Rundlett to conclude that the mounting performance of female guinea pigs is a separate behavioral entity from heat or receptivity, and that although both categories of response depend upon the same combination of ovarian hormones, they are mediated by different central nervous mechanisms.

If the foregoing interpretation were correct, it might follow that individual differences in the ease and frequency with which mounting can be evoked are due to differences in the responsiveness of target tissues (e.g., neural circuits) to hormonal sensitization. Indirect support for this hypothesis was provided by Goy and Young (1957b), who compared the behavior of guinea pigs from several different genetic strains. This experiment showed that mounting was easily induced when estrogen and progesterone were administered to spayed females from any strain in which such behavior characteristically appeared during natural estrus. It appears that there are strains in which estrous females rarely or never exhibit mounting, although they do exhibit lordosis when mounted by males. Ovariectomized individuals from these genetic stocks are refractory to exogenous ovarian hormones as far as the induction of mounting is concerned.

Still another source of variability in the mounting behavior of female guinea pigs is chronological age. Diamond and Cerny (1966) compared the frequency of mounting in females 3 to 6 months old with that of a second group 13 to 16 months of age. The younger animals showed more mounting reactions (P <0.05), although latency and duration of "heat" responses did not differ in the two groups.

These observations obviously are in accord with the hypothesis that different mechanisms are involved.

Rat. In 1938 the present writer recorded the display of mounting behavior by untreated female rats which were in estrus. Since Young and his collaborators had demonstrated so convincingly that the female guinea pig's mounting behavior is strongly influenced by estrogen and progesterone, a study was undertaken to determine if a similar situation exists in the rat.

Beach and Rasquin (1942) studied the behavior of 15 normally cycling female rats to determine the frequency of mounting activity and of receptive behavior (lordosis) at different stages in the vaginal cycle. The frequency and types of mounting responses shown by females of the strain employed are illustrated in Fig. 2.

As was to be expected, the occurrence of lordosis in response to being mounted by a male was confined to tests conducted when the vaginal smear contained primarily nucleated or nucleated and cornified epithelium. Receptivity was never observed when leukocytes predominated. In contrast, the frequency of mounting reactions did not vary systematically with different stages of the vaginal cycle,

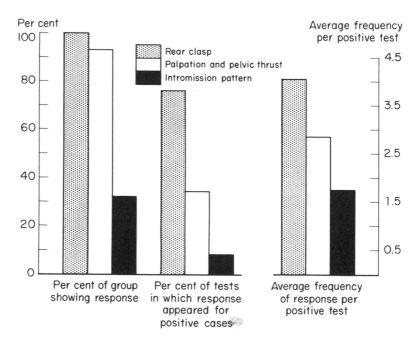

Fig. 2 Mounting responses shown by 15 female rats toward other females in estrus. [From Beach and Rasquin (1942).]

being just as high in diestrus when the smear consisted entirely of leukocytes as it was during procstrus and cstrus.

To test the indicated conclusion that ovarian hormones may not influence mounting in the female rat, 5 of the experimental animals were ovariectomized and later injected with estrogen and progesterone. Removal of the ovaries promptly eliminated all signs of receptivity to the male but had no observable effect on the frequency of mounting responses directed to an estrous female. When the spayed rats were then injected with estrogen and progesterone, the lordosis reflex and other signs of estrus, including ear wiggling and hopping, reappeared temporarily, but mounting of a second female neither increased nor decreased. The relations between vaginal condition and mounting activity in intact and castrated females are illustrated in Fig. 3, which shows that frequency of mounting cor-

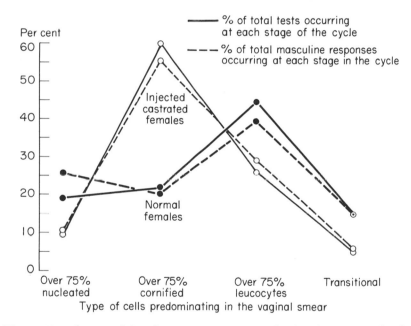

Fig. 3 Distribution of female mounting responses by female rats as related to stages of the vaginal cycle. [From Beach and Rasquin (1942).]

responded with frequency of tests and was not related to hormonal condition as reflected in the vaginal smear.

The spayed animals referred to above had been tested repeatedly for mounting activity before operation. Furthermore, they had experienced a number of ovarian cycles and therefore had been exposed to the influence of ovarian hormones. To eliminate the possibility that either of these variables might have exerted a persisting effect upon postoperative behavior, a second group of rats was ovariectomized. This time the operation was performed when the animals were 21 to 27 days of age and had had no mounting experience.

When these prepuberally ovariectomized females reached adulthood and were tested with stimulus females which were in estrus, the mounting behavior of the spayed females was as frequent and intense as that of animals ovariectomized in adulthood.

Evidence reviewed to this point strongly suggests a clear-cut species difference in the physiological control of mounting responses by female guinea pigs and rats. In the former, the behavior appears to be heavily dependent upon precisely those ovarian hormones that govern the occurrence of lordosis. In the latter sexually receptive behavior is controlled by the same combination of estrogen and progesterone, but mounting seems to be independent of ovarian influences.

None of the evidence to be presented later contradicts this conclusion, but before it can be evaluated certain differences between the experiments on guinea pigs and those on rats need to be taken into consideration. These differences center upon the procedure involved in testing for mounting behavior. In the early work on guinea pigs the female or females to be tested were observed in group cages containing several conspecific animals. Neither the sex nor the reproductive condition of these potential stimulus animals was specified and there is therefore no way of deterining whether, when mounting did occur, it was directed toward males, toward anestrous females, or toward females in estrus. As a matter of fact, it cannot be discovered whether or not estrous females were available for mounting. All the experiments on rats, in contrast, involved testing the experimental animals, one at a time, in a special observation cage with a second female of proved receptivity to serve as the stimulus animal. At this point we wish only to call attention to the procedural discrepancies involved. Their possible bearing upon interpretation of the different results obtained will be discussed later.

Dog. Although mounting has been reported to occur in females of several species of carnivores, the only systematic study within this order is an investigation of the dog by Beach et al. (1968). The first phase of this study involved dyadic tests of 10 adult bitches (3 spayed and 7 intact) when they were in anestrus and when they were in estrus induced by injections of estradiol benzoate. The animals were tested in all possible combinations under each of three conditions:

both in estrus ("EE"), both in anestrus ("AA"), and one in anestrus while the other was in estrus ("AE").

Mounting occurred in 33 percent of the tests under condition AA, in 35 percent of those under condition AE, and in 43 percent of those under condition EE. None of these differences were statistically significant. Investigations of guinea pigs and rats have revealed consistent individual differences in mounting behavior, and the same phenomenon was found in female dogs. The split-half reliability of mount frequency scores during AA tests was 0.88. When the performance of each female during AE tests was compared with that occurring during EE tests, the rank-order correlation was 0.84.

Females were as likely to mount during anestrus as during estrus provided the hormonal state of the stimulus animal was the same under both conditions. Estrous partners were mounted much more frequently than partners in anestrus ($p < 0.01$), but the hormonal condition of the mounting individual had no effect upon frequency of her performance. Table 1 summarizes some of the results and compares the mounting of experimental females with that shown by normal males and males castrated before puberty (Beach, 1968). It

Table 1

Mounting Behavior Shown by Pairs of Female Dogs as a Function of Hormonal Conditions (Beach et al., 1968)

Comparison	Percentage of tests positive	Av. frequency of mounts per positive test
Anestrous female mounted anestrous partner	17	1.8
Anestrous female mounted estrous partner	31	3.0
Estrous female mounted anestrous partner	9	2.8
Estrous female mounted estrous partner	25	3.5
Normal male mounted estrous partner	94	13.5 [a]
Prepuberally castrated male mounted estrous partner	80	9.5 [a]

[a] Data for males taken from Beach (1968) and based upon tests in which locking did not occur.

is apparent that even prepuberally castrated males mount much more frequently than females.

During tests in which two females were involved the endocrinological state of the mountee affected not only the frequency with which she was mounted but also the orientation and completeness of the other bitch's mounting responses. Copulating male dogs occasionally mount the bitch from the anterior or the lateral position, but successful mating depends upon the achievement of the rear orientation and execution of pelvic thrusts which result in intromission. Beach et al. found that when anestrous females were mounted by a second female the various types of mounts were distributed as follows: side mount 53 percent, rear mount without thrusting 37 percent, rear mount with thrusting 10 percent. When the mountee was in estrus the distribution of responses by the mounting bitch was 18 percent side mounts, 18 percent rear mounts without thrusting, 64 percent rear mounts with thrusting.

Results cited to date pertain to the behavior of female–female pairs and to the effects of induced estrus. Observations have also been made of mounting shown by females in natural estrus while they were being tested with potent males. Five bitches were observed repeatedly with five males in the course of two heat periods separated by 8 to 13 months. Under such conditions the male engages in a great deal of mounting and this perforce limits the female's opportunity to mount him. In addition, the occurrence of a successful mating which terminates with the genital lock characteristic of canine copulation automatically puts an end to all mounting by either partner.

In spite of these limitations, the five females studied by Beach et al. mounted the male from the rear in 29 percent of 209 tests. A total of 180 rear mounts was recorded and of these 24 percent included pelvic thrusting. Some of the results are shown in Table 2, which reveals, among other things, the existence of large individual differences in all the measures represented. When performance during the first and second heat periods was compared, there was little consistency with respect to the percentage of tests in which mounting occurred, but the rank-order correlation for average mount frequency per positive test was 0.81 (Spearman–Brown correction).

Four of the five females were tested twice with the same five males when the bitches were in anestrus. No mounting occurred in any of these tests, and in fact there was very little interaction of any kind in any of the pairs. It may be important that all these animals were thoroughly familiar with each other since they lived constantly together in one large field. The test situation therefore

Table 2

Mounting Responses Shown by Female Dogs in Estrus to Potent Males
(Beach et al., 1967)

Female	Total tests	Percent tests with rear mounts	Mean mount frequency per positive test	Percent rear mounts with thrusting
Peggy	51	39	1.92	16
Spot	34	24	0.65	64
Blanche	54	7	0.07	75
Kate	37	51	1.32	23
Dewey	33	33	0.55	39

presented no elements of novelty or strangeness. In the dyadic heterosexual tests while the females were in anestrus a very brief initial period of mutual investigation typically was followed by total disregard for one another throughout the remainder of the observation period.

This study of female dogs indicates that when a female is in estrus she is likely to mount the male and he is certain to mount her. When she is not in estrus neither animal tends to exhibit mounting responses. When the female is in estrus or in anestrus she is likely to mount a second female who is in estrus, and when she is in anestrus she is less likely to mount an anestrous partner.

Effects of Gonadal Hormones during Early Development

Early studies in epigenesis revealed the possibility of experimentally altering the development of the sexual accessory structures derived from the Wolffian and Müllerian systems. In 1938 Dantchakoff reported that neonatal female guinea pigs which had been exposed to androgenic hormone during fetal life possessed two duct systems and a penis. She added that in adulthood these modified females displayed male-like mating responses. W. C. Young deserves special credit for recognizing that this finding implies the existence of sexual differences in the central nervous system which must be established early in ontogenesis and will later be revealed in the form of behavioral differences between adult males and females.

Guinea Pig. Young and his associates were the first to investigate this phenomenon in a series of studies which involved alteration of the normal hormonal conditions of prenatal life and measurement of subsequent changes in adult behavior. Working first with the guinea pig, this group of investigators established the fact that administration of testosterone propionate to pregnant guinea pigs during the proper stages of gestation produces definite modification in female but not necessarily in male offspring.

Genetic females stimulated by androgen during fetal life usually show three signs of masculinization. The external genitals are modified and so closely resemble those of the neonatal male that sex identification at birth often depends upon laparotomy. The display of sexually receptive behavior in adulthood is greatly reduced or eliminated even when the appropriate ovarian hormones are supplied exogenously. The tendency to exhibit mounting behavior and other elements in the masculine copulatory pattern is increased, and the sensitivity of the behavioral mechanisms for such behavior to androgen is much greater than it is in unaltered females which have been spayed at birth.

It is to be stressed that permanent changes of the sort just described are only produced by introduction of androgen into the female organism at the appropriate stage of development. We have already seen that injections of testosterone propionate in adult females of several species may result in the appearance or increase of mounting activity, but this behavioral change lasts only as long as hormonal treatment is continued. With respect to the guinea pig Diamond and Young found that when nonpregnant adult females are injected with testosterone propionate the only effects are temporary masculinization of genital structure and behavior (Young, 1965). When prenatal treatment is employed, androgen is most effective from the beginning of the second trimester, and, if the first injections are delayed until much later in gestation, no permanent effects are produced (Young, 1965).

Phoenix, et al. (1959) compared the mounting responses of neonatally spayed pseudohermaphrodites with those of control females spayed at the same age and of prepuberally castrated males. The results of this study are summarized in Table 3.

Prior to hormone treatment in adulthood male castrates showed a considerable amount of mounting activity. Pseudohermaphrodites mounted occasionally, and control females never did so. Administration of estrogen and progesterone elicited the lordosis response in nearly all control females but in relatively few pseudohermaphrodites and in none of the male castrates. Exogenous ovarian hormones stimulated some mounting activity and the differences between groups in this respect were not statistically significant.

Members of all groups were next injected with 2.5 mg of testos-

Table 3

Behavior of Masculinized Female Guinea Pigs Compared with That of
Gonadectomized Male and Female Control Animals
(Based on Phoenix et al., 1959)

Behavioral measure	Spayed control females	Spayed hermaphroditic females	Castrated males
Percent tests lordosis present with estrogen + progesterone	96	22	0
Mounts per test without hormone treatment in adulthood	0	4.4	11.8
Mounts per test with estrogen + progesterone	10.7	5.6	16.7
Mounts per test with testosterone	5.8	15.4	20.5

terone daily for 16 days and, as shown in the table, castrated males
and pseudohermaphroditic females responded with a marked increase
in mounting frequency. The spayed control females exhibited some
mounting but the frequency of their responses was appreciably below
that of the other two groups.

In a more recent study Gerall (1966) compared the mounting
behavior of pseudohermaphroditic females with that of normal males,
normal females, and spayed females. Some of the pseudohermaphrodites were spayed at birth and others were unoperated. All animals
were first tested for mounting responses to a stimulus female in
induced estrus. Then testosterone propionate was administered and
testing was resumed. Before androgen administration the mounting
frequency of normal males was 0.75 per 15-sec observation period.
This is to be compared with scores of 0.018 for castrated males, 0.32
for normal females, and 0.13 for spayed pseudohermaphrodites. (The
occurrence of any mounting whatsoever in the normal females may
have been due to use of an estrous female as the stimulus animal.)
Spayed females, intact pseudohermaphrodites, and castrated males
showed very little or no mounting.

Following administration of testosterone propionate there was
a definite increase in mounting responses shown by spayed females,
intact pseudohermaphrodites, and normal females. However, the increases in mounting by spayed pseudohermaphrodites and castrated
males were much more pronounced. In addition, some pseudoher-

maphrodites displayed qualitative changes in behavior. "It should be noted that after androgen treatment some of the pseudohermaphrodites exhibited an ejaculatory response during mating tests. Thus, it can be concluded that the pseudohermaphrodite has complete response potentiality to perform as a male." (pp. 367–368).

Rat. Permanent alterations in the female rodent's capacity for feminine and masculine mating responses have been produced in rats as well as guinea pigs.

Harris and Levine (1965) administered testosterone propionate to female rats 5 days after birth and at the same time injected control females with inert oil. In adulthood the control animals were reproductively normal, whereas androgen-treated females displayed constant vaginal estrus but no behavioral receptivity to the male. All females were ovariectomized in adulthood and then injected with testosterone propionate. Experimental castrates exhibited much more mounting activity than did spayed control females. In the same study Harris and Levine found that female rats injected with estradiol benzoate at 5 days of age would not display feminine copulatory reactions in adulthood and exhibited very little mounting activity even when they were injected with androgen. It appears that either androgen or estrogen administered during development may interfere with female mating responses, but only androgen treatment results in an increased capacity for mounting behavior in adulthood.

Goy et al. (1962) injected female rats with 1.0 mg of testosterone propionate for 7 days beginning 1, 10, or 20 days postpartum. The females were ovariectomized at 60 to 80 days and tested for receptive behavior after the administration of estrogen and progesterone. It was found that lordosis was present at normal frequencies in females which had received androgen on the twentieth day of life, but earlier treatment reduced the percentage of animals displaying this response. No observations of mounting behavior were reported, but these findings amplify and confirm those of Harris and Levine with respect to the inhibiting effect of androgen on feminine responses.

Whalen and Nadler (1963) obtained results similar to those of Goy et al. (1962) by treating 4-day-old female rats with estrogen instead of androgen. Experimental and control females were ovariectomized in adulthood, injected with estrogen and progesterone, and tested for sexual receptivity to potent males. Rats injected with inert oil in infancy mated normally, but animals which had received estrogen at 4 days of age either failed entirely to display lordosis, or did so infrequently and sluggishly. Males that mounted these experimental animals experienced great difficulty in achieving intromission although the vaginae appeared normal.

Whalen and Nadler reported no observations on mounting behavior by experimental or control females, but Levine and Mullins (1964) have studied this aspect of behavior in female rats given estrogen in early life. They injected 4-day-old females with estradiol benzoate and tested the animals for sexual receptivity at 120 days of age without any preliminary hormone treatment. After this the females were injected with estrogen and progesterone and retested for the display of lordosis and other signs of receptivity. Finally, starting at 230 days, the experimental females received 100 µg of testosterone per day for 9 days, and during the last 7 days were tested for their tendency to mount normal females in estrus.

Lordosis rarely occurred even when the females had been prepared by administration of ovarian hormones. Under the influence of exogenous testosterone 6 of 13 experimental animals and 4 of 11 control females (injected with oil in infancy) displayed mounting responses. Two of the experimental females exhibited the behavioral pattern which accompanies ejaculation in normal males. This includes a protracted final mount with a deep thrust, slow elevation of the forelegs, and a subsequent cessation of mounting for several minutes. One of these two females displayed the ejaculatory pattern once, resumed mounting, and exhibited the pattern a second time after fewer "intromission" responses than had preceded the first. This resembles the mating performance of males in that the second ejaculation is preceded by fewer intromissions than the first. According to Levine and Mullins, when their experimental females were given androgen in adulthood they showed ". . . extreme masculinization of the genitalia which persisted for at least 30 days after the end of testosterone administration" (p. 186). This may have had a bearing on appearance of the ejaculatory pattern which has not been described by other investigators. Summarizing their findings in a later article, Levine and Mullins wrote as follows. "Paradoxically, females given estrogen in infancy sometimes show complete male sex behavior patterns in response to testosterone in adulthood, while adult animals not given estrogen in infancy only show mounting behavior when given the same amount of testosterone" (1966, p. 1591). Until more evidence is available, it will be difficult to reconcile this statement with Harris and Levine's finding that early treatment with estrogen decreases mounting in adulthood.

Gerall and Ward (1966) have recently described the effects

of prenatal exposure to androgen upon mating behavior in female rats. Testosterone propionate was administered to pregnant rats with the result that their female offspring were pseudohermaphroditic. These animals together with controls of similar age were tested in adulthood for their responses to copulatory attempts by males and for their tendency to mount a receptive stimulus female. Neither control animals nor pseudohermaphrodites showed any significant amount of mounting behavior in adulthood without special hormone treatment. Following the administration of testosterone propionate both control and experimental females exhibited mounting responses to receptive stimulus animals. The increase shown by controls was appreciable but moderate. In contrast, as androgen injections continued the pseudo-hermaphroditic females displayed a progressive increase in the frequency of mounting and thrusting responses, which eventually exceeded that characteristic of the normal male rat. In no instance was the ejaculatory response observed, although the pseudohermaphrodites ". . . developed an evertible penile structure approximately equal in length and diameter to that of a normal male" (p. 372).

Apparently in this experiment prenatal exposure to androgen did not completely suppress ovarian development in all cases because during adulthood before the administration of any exogenous hormones 37 percent of the 30 pseudohermaphroditic females displayed spontaneous estrus. This is to be compared with 83 percent for normal animals. When exogenous estrogen and progesterone were supplied by injection, behavioral estrus was induced in 83 percent of the spayed control females, which had never received androgen, in 71 percent of the females that had been given androgen in adulthood, and in 52 percent of the pseudohermaphrodites that had received androgen both before birth and in adult life. It would seem that androgen administered prenatally may not inhibit development of mechanisms for feminine behavior as completely in the rat as in the guinea pig.

Monkey. Harlow's observations of sexually dimorphic behavior in infant monkeys have been mentioned earlier. It appears (Harlow, 1965) that 2- and 3-year-old males show more mounting and thrusting responses than females of the same age, and in addition males are much more likely than females to indulge in several other forms of social interaction such as "rough and tumble play," "facial threat," etc. It might be supposed that differences in the behavior of little males and females are in part a product of testosterone secreted by the infantile testis, but the inadequacy of this interpretation is revealed by the finding that the behavioral differences appear in males which have been castrated shortly after birth (Goy and Dodsworth, 1962). It is, of course, conceivable that the differences in behavior are related to central nervous system differences induced prenatally by endogenously produced androgen. If this were the case, it might be possible to modify the behavior of genetic females in a masculine direction by applying androgenic stimulation at the appropriate stages of embryonic differentiation (see Chapter 5).

Wells and van Wagenen (1954) demonstrated that pseudo-hermaphroditic female monkeys can be produced by injecting the gestating female with androgen at the appropriate stage of pregnancy. Adopting this procedure, Young et al. (1964) induced the development of pseudohermaphroditic rhesus females and studied their social behavior from infancy. At the time of writing none of these animals has reached the age of sexual maturity, but their behavior as juveniles plainly reflects the influence of prenatal androgen treatment.

"Tests for infantile sexual behavior show conclusively that attempts to mount and the execution of pelvic thrusting appear much more frequently among pseudohermaphrodites than among normal females. Possibly to some workers, although not to those of us who are studying these animals, the most convincing evidence for their masculine bias will be provided by their ability to display erection. . . . Although the erectile organ is very short and otherwise imperfect compared with the normal male phallus, nevertheless its uses and relationship to other behavioral components is entirely appropriate in so far as we have detected" (Goy, in Young, 1965, pp. 100–101).

Effects of Brain Injury

At an earlier point in this chapter we noted the suggestion of Young and Rundlett (1939) to the effect that in the female guinea pig mounting behavior and lordosis are mediated by two separate effector systems which are sensitized or "activated" by the same hormones. If this hypothesis were correct, it might be possible to modify experimentally the functional state of one system without influencing the other, and one obvious method of testing this possibility consists of selectively destroying different parts of the brain and observing the effects of the operation upon both mounting and lordosis responses. This has been done, within limits, in two species.

Guinea Pig. Goy and Phoenix (1963) investigated the effects of injury to the hypothalamus upon mating behavior in female guinea pigs. They found that destruction of brain tissue lying in the midventral region of the hypothalamus was followed by definite changes in copulatory performance. Nine females with such lesions failed to display sexually receptive behavior despite the injection of estrogen and progesterone. Ten additional animals suffering injury to the same area displayed a distinct though not complete post-operative reduction in receptivity. Two ovariectomized females with hypothalamic lesions instead of losing the capacity to exhibit lordosis showed this response without any hormone treatment. Brain injury in these cases may have been slightly more anterior than in other animals.

All animals were observed pre- and postoperatively for the display of mounting responses to a stimulus female in estrus. Of the nine females which became permanently nonreceptive after brain injury, three continued to mount other females although at a reduced frequency. On the other hand, four females exhibiting no post-operative change in feminine behavior nevertheless displayed a reduction in the tendency to mount a second female in estrus. Such mounting behavior as did survive injury to the hypothalamus was of a very low frequency and could not be increased by the administration of ovarian hormones.

"The median number of mounts was 2.4 per animal per test for the eight females that continued to display mounting at a reduced frequency postoperatively. This value did not differ significantly from that obtained from six unoperated spayed females that mounted on tests without oestradiol benzoate and progesterone (median $= 2.2$ mounts per animal per test, $U = 25$, $p > 0.10$). Thus animals that continued to mount postoperatively displayed only that amount which could be obtained from ovariectomized females without hormonal treatment" (p. 20).

Goy and Phoenix also attempted to increase mounting in the brain-operated females by administration of androgen. Daily injections of testosterone propionate for 2 weeks had no clear-cut effect upon the behavior of those animals which had continued to mount after placement of the hypothalamic lesions. However, this treatment did evoke the appearance of low-frequency mounting activity in 6 of 7 females that had ceased entirely to mount after brain operation.

Rat. The present writer was led to investigate the effects of injury to the cerebral cortex upon mounting behavior in female rats as a result of earlier studies involving copulatory behavior of males of this species. It had been established (Beach, 1940) that extensive injury to the neocortex of male rats results in a decreased tendency to copulate with receptive females, and very large cortical lesions totally and permanently abolish mating behavior in the male. Later (Beach, 1943) similar operations were performed on female rats after they had been tested for the display of sexually receptive behavior and for the tendency to mount other females when the latter were in estrus.

Postoperative tests showed that removal of 37 to 65 percent of the neocortex produced no striking change in the ease or frequency with which lordosis and other feminine mating reactions could be elicited during estrus. In fact, in some individuals there seemed to be a slight lowering of the thresholds involved. In contrast, this amount of cerebral injury reduced mounting activity by approximately 50 percent. The motor ability to pursue and mount other rats was unaffected, but the tendency to generate and maintain interest in the stimulus female was noticeably impaired.

Two females survived removal of all neocortical tissues. Both had mounted frequently before operation, but this behavior was completely lacking after decortication. At the same time the copulatory responses of these two females to sexually active males were definitely enhanced after loss of the neopallium. There occurred a marked increase in the percentage of the male's mounts to which the females responded by assuming the lordosis posture. The frequency of ear vibration which accompanies receptivity was markedly increased, and the number of "back-kicks" with which the male is repelled decreased. It seems clear that mounting and the associated acts of palpation and thrusting are influenced by neocortical activity in both male and female rats, whereas lordosis in the female is not dependent upon this part of the central nervous system.

Effects of Experience

There have been no extensive studies of the possible effects of experience upon mounting behavior in female mammals, but two experiments have yielded evidence which suggests that this variable will have to be investigated before a complete understanding of the behavior can be reached.

Goy and Young (1957a) reared female guinea pigs in isolation from all conspecifics except the mother, with whom they remained for 25 days. For those genetic strains in which female mounting was normally of fairly high frequency, isolation until the 150th day of life resulted in a definite reduction in the frequency of mounting reactions. In addition, the duration of heat and the length of the maximum lordosis were shorter in animals isolated from birth than in those raised in groups. The authors' conclusions were in part as follows.

"It is concluded that for the female . . . the organization of the neuromuscular mechanisms mediating sexual behavior depends on a coaction between genetically determined and experiential factors. The experiential factor seems to be more effective when the animals are young" (p. 150).

A suggestion that experience may also influence mounting activity in the female rat comes from a different sort of experiment. Beach and Rasquin (1942) observed 15 normal females in 17 successive tests with estrous females as stimulus animals. As testing progressed there was an increase in the number of individuals that mounted at least once, an increase in the average number of mounts per positive test, and a shift from less complete to more complete forms of mounting. For the group as a whole, the simple rear mount with clasp first appeared after an average of 1.7 tests. Mounting with foreleg palpation and pelvic thrusting was first executed after a mean of 5.5 tests, and the pattern which resembles the male's intromission response was initially displayed after an average of 12.6 tests.

Discussion

In attempting to interpret the mounting behavior of female mammals it is necessary to consider three classes of variables which can be grouped under the following headings: neural mechanisms, hormonal status, and external stimuli. Although they can be considered separately for analytical purposes, the different sorts of variables combined under these rubrics never function independently. Instead they may act in concert, in opposition, or in a "compensatory" fashion to facilitate or inhibit mounting behavior.

For some purposes it is instructive to consider mounting in females as one example of a larger category of responses that includes the behavior of males as well as females. In several species the male may display reactions ordinarily regarded as belonging to the female's repertoire such as "sexual presentation," lordosis, etc. A truly comprehensive interpretation of "coitus-related" responses in any species should include an explanation of the execution of heterologous behavior by both sexes. In this connection the present writer once advanced the following proposal.

"In considering these facts one becomes aware of the possibility of dealing with courtship and copulatory behavior in terms of stimulus-response relationships which are relatively constant in all individuals regardless of sex; and it is apparent that the neuromuscular mechanisms responsible for many such relationships are present in both male and female mammals. In either sex the application of pressure to the dorsolumbar region tends to elicit lordosis and opisthotonus; and in either sex the multi-sensory pattern of stimulation provided by the receptive female tends to evoke pursuit, mounting and palpation with pelvic thrusts" (Beach, 1947, p. 269).

This suggestion was inspired by the results of experiments on the laboratory rat, and for this species the similarities between the sexes appeared to involve not only the neuromuscular but also the hormonal factors controlling coitus-related responses. The extent to which such conclusions can be generalized to include other species must be determined by examination of the evidence, but in principle the attempt to do so seems potentially fruitful. As a working hypothesis, which may well be proved to be partially or totally invalid, it is useful to assume that factors responsible for the male's pursuit, mounting, clasping, and thrusting behavior are the same as those involved in the execution of the same responses by the female. Regardless of its ultimate proof or disproof, such an assumption provides the investigator with several readymade points of departure. For example, an appreciable amount of information is available concerning the central nervous mediation and sensory control of copulatory behavior in males of some species. These findings provide us with the most promising base from which to launch an investigation of the roles of the nervous system and of environmental stimuli in the control of mounting in females of the same species.

Hormonal Control

There are at least two reasons for beginning our analysis with a consideration of hormonal factors that influence the occurrence of mounting in females of different species. First, from the historical point of view, this aspect of the problem was the first to be recognized, and in fact drew attention to the phenomena in question. Second, although there seem to be a number of interspecific similarities in the control of female mounting, the outstanding difference encountered thus far involves species differences in the relative importance of ovarian hormones. It should be explicitly stated that at this point we are considering only the "activational" effects of gonadal hormones (Young, 1961); "organizational" effects exerted during early life will be discussed later.

As noted at the beginning of this review, the interest of experimentalists in mounting by female mammals originated with early studies of the effects of transplanting testicular tissue into females, and later the responses of females to administration of so-called "male" hormone. At that point in the development of endocrinology it was generally simply assumed that "male" hormone produces "male" behavior, and the phenomena observed were interpreted as instances of "sex reversal" in behavior analogous to the temporary or permanent masculinization of accessory and secondary sexual characters which could be induced in genetic females by appropriate manipulation of the endocrine constitution.

Estrogen and Progesterone. W. C. Young and his associates (Young et al., 1935; Young et al, 1939; Young and Rundlett, 1939) deserve credit for being the first to demonstrate that in at least one species mounting responses are a normal element in the behavioral repertoire of the female, occur in close conjunction with sexually receptive responses, and in fact are dependent upon precisely the same ovarian hormones which are responsible for the appearance of heat.

In view of the convincingness of evidence presented by Young and co-workers, it was somewhat surprising to discover that the same behavior is not subject to similar hormonal control in female rats. Although sexual receptivity in the rat, as in the guinea pig, depends upon estrogen and progesterone, the mounting behavior of females of the former species does not seem to be influenced by ovarian secretions (Beach, 1942b; Beach and Rasquin, 1942). Evidence presently available provides no explanation for this apparent difference between the only two rodent species which have been carefully studied.

When examined in one kind of test situation the female dog seems to be similar to the rat (Beach et al., 1968). A bitch will mount other females as readily when she is in anestrus as when she is in estrus, although the frequency of mounting and the "completeness" of the behavior pattern are greatest when the stimulus female is in estrus. On the other hand, when female dogs are tested with males, the mounting responses of the bitch are almost entirely confined to her estrous period. This observation draws attention to the importance of those sources of control which have been referred to under the general heading of "external stimuli" and which will be considered presently. At this point it suffices to note that the role of hormonal factors cannot meaningfully be considered in isolation when other sources of variability are uncontrolled.

Since these additional sources of variability have not been controlled in the nonexperimental accounts of mounting by female mammals of various domesticated species, it is difficult to estimate the probable influence of hormonal conditions in these cases. However, one assumption can be suggested which, if adopted, would simplify the situation considerably. This is that if a female displays mounting responses while she is not in estrus the probability is very high that given the same external stimulus situation she would also mount when she was in estrus. There is evidence for some species that the condition of estrus increases a female's tendency to mount, but there is no evidence to suggest that it decreases such tendencies. The proposed assumption therefore seems justified.

Reports which specify that the mounting individual was in estrus are numerous. This point has been made in descriptions of mounting by female cattle (Hammond and Day, 1944; Hafez and Schein, 1962; Weber, 1911); swine (Altmann, 1941; McKenzie, 1926; Hafez et al., 1962), monkeys (Carpenter, 1942), martens (Markley and Bassett, 1942), and domestic cats (Rosenblatt and Schneirla, 1962). It must be pointed out that for some of these species we lack evidence to the effect that anestrous females *do not* mount, and until this is forthcoming it is of course incorrect to assume that an estrous condition is essential. Furthermore, there are published reports of mounting by anestrous female cattle (Hafez and Schein, 1962; Hammond, 1927; Roark and Herman, 1950; Weber 1911), swine (Burger, 1952), monkeys (Carpenter, 1942), and lions (Cooper, 1942).

It seems that the observational accounts provide us with relatively little convincing evidence regarding the possible contribution of ovarian hormones to a female's tendency to mount other animals. Nonetheless the possibility of stimulation by estrogen should not be discounted, for several writers have stressed the excessive mounting shown by cows with cystic ovaries (Pearl and Surface, 1915; Calder, 1927; Walton et al., 1940; Hafez and Schein, 1962), and comparable behavior is displayed by heifers following administration of exogenous estrogen (de Alba and Asdell, 1946; Folley and Malpress, 1944). It should be recalled that "nymphomaniacal" cows with cystic ovaries rarely are receptive (Roberts, 1956).

Androgen. It is well established that androgenic hormone stimulates the occurrence of mounting behavior in female mammals, but there appear to be marked species differences in the magnitude of such effects. Testosterone propionate regularly and reliably induces mounting reactions in some female rats which have not shown such behavior prior to treatment, and tends to increase the frequency of these responses in all females (Stone, 1939; Ball, 1940). Under the influence of exogenous androgen the pattern of mounting shown by females of this species changes to include a much higher proportion of mounts that mimic the behavior of a male rat when he achieves intromission (Beach, 1942b). Despite its obviously stimulating effects, the administration of androgen has not yet resulted in the display of the ejaculatory pattern by female rats which were anatomically normal at the beginning of treatment.

The only published account of effects of testosterone on behavior of the female dog (Berg, 1944) reveals a marked increase in mounting frequency. Both adult and immature females were found to be responsive to exonegous androgen, and the description of an adult bitch injected with testosterone propionate leaves no doubt that the hormone raised the intensity of such behavior far above levels shown by untreated females either in estrus or anestrus.

Accounts of the responses of female guinea pigs to exogenous androgen are not in complete agreement. The early studies of Young and Rundlett (1939) and of Young et al. (1939) seemed to indicate that testicular hormone has no effect upon mounting behavior in females of this species, but more recent investigations such as those of Phoenix et al. (1959), Diamond (1965), and Gerall (1966) make it clear that both spayed and intact females do exhibit an increase in mounting behavior when appropriate amounts of testosterone are administered. However, the frequency of mounting induced by such treatment is much less than that which occurs in intact animals during estrus or which can be induced in the spayed female by administration of estrogen and progesterone. The full significance of the point is not clear, but it may be important that the one species in which mounting normally depends upon ovarian hormones is also the species least responsive to exogenous androgen.

Neural Control

The spontaneous occurrence of mounting behavior in females of many mammalian species is sufficient evidence to establish the fact that the feminine genotype provides for the development of neuromuscular mechanisms adequate for mediation of some of the elements of the "masculine" pattern of coital behavior. This genetic endowment must include sensory, motor, and integrative elements which are shared by both sexes. Although the precise location and the functional characteristics of most of these elements remain to be established, some pertinent information is available. Thus, in both male and female rats the pursuit and mounting of a stimulus female seems to depend upon some as yet undefined contribution by the cerebral cortex, for extensive injury to this portion of the brain eliminates mounting behavior in both sexes while leaving the female capable of displaying such sexually receptive reactions as lordosis, ear wiggling, and darting or hopping (Beach, 1940; 1943).

Both male and female guinea pigs may fail to mount other animals after placement of lesions in the appropriate region of the hypothalamus, and some females which cease displaying the mounting reaction nevertheless continue to show lordosis when they are in estrus. Conversely, with slightly different lesion loci, some females exhibit loss of receptive responses and retention of mounting behavior (Goy and Phoenix, 1963).

The evidence presently available is extremely limited, but it is consonant with suggestions based upon studies of both the guinea pig (Young and Rundlett, 1939; Young et al., 1939) and the rat (Beach, 1943) to the effect that the female possesses two separate neural systems, one for the mediation of pursuit, mounting, clasping, etc., and the other for the execution of receptive responses. It has also been proposed (Beach, 1945) that a similar duplicate arrangement exists in the case of the male's central nervous system, but investigations of this possibility have been even more limited than in the case of the female.

Strain, Individual, and Sex Differences in Reactivity of Neural Mechanisms. In considering the functional capacity of the central nervous system for the mediation of different kinds of coitus-related behavior patterns, it is important to recognize that the "reactivity" of these mechanisms can vary from species to species, from strain to strain, and even from individual to individual. "Reactivity" is here conceived as independent of the individual's current endocrine status. Differences in the reactivity of various strains of guinea pigs have been intensively studied by W. C. Young and his associates, who have repeatedly demonstrated that such differences are not products of postnatal hormonal activity.

Valenstein et al. (1954) measured "sex drive" in male guinea pigs from two inbred and one genetically heterogeneous strain. Males from both inbred strains had a lower average score than animals from the heterogenous stock, and when the inbred strains were compared with each other they were found to differ significantly on several behavioral measures. Males from strain 13 exceeded those from strain 2 with respect to the frequency of mounts, intromissions, and ejaculations. Strain 2 showed greater frequencies of premounting activity, involving sniffing, nibbling, and nuzzling the female. (These particular strain differences are especially interesting in view of the fact that strain 13 *females* show much more mounting than females from strain 2.) Riss et al. (1955) castrated males from strain 2 and from the heterogeneous strain at 2 days of age and injected them with equal amounts of testosterone propionate in adulthood. Heterogeneous males were much more responsive to exogenous androgen than males from strain 2. The former began to copulate after fewer injections, reacted more intensely in terms of mount frequency, and displayed ejaculation under the influence of a hormone concentration too low to support the same behavior in strain 2 castrates.

Strain differences which are independent of current hormone levels also exist in female guinea pigs. Goy and Young (1957a) compared the frequency of mounting responses shown by spayed animals after the injection of estrogen and progesterone. Heterogeneous females executed an average of 2.9 full mounts and 5.3 abortive mounts per test. Comparable scores for strain 13 females were 8.9 full and 26.4 abortive mounts per test. Females from strain 2 could not be compared with the others because they characteristically engage in "little or no mounting."

To further examine the nature of interstrain differences in female mounting, Goy and Young (1957b) varied the amount of estrogen given to spayed individuals. When they were treated with amounts of hormone adequate to provoke the appearance of sexually receptive behavior, females from strain 2 mounted an average of 1.0 times per test. Females from the heterogeneous group averaged 7.3 mounts per test, and the mean frequency for strain 13 females was 37.7. When the amount of estradiol benzoate injected was increased from 25 to 800 IU, there was no significant change in the frequency of mounting shown by any of the three groups. The evidence just cited is taken to indicate that reactivity of central nervous mechanisms involved in mounting by male and female guinea pigs varies between strains, and that these variations are independent of immediate hormonal effects.

The same conclusion appears applicable to differences between individuals belonging to the same strain. Grunt and Young (1952) found that when male guinea pigs differing in "sex drive" were castrated and given the same amount of exogenous androgen, the preoperative individual differences in copulatory performance were retained. Somewhat similar results were obtained by Beach and Fowler (1959) in an experiment on male rats. Riss and Young (1954) castrated 12 male guinea pigs which had performed very sluggishly in preoperative mating tests. When these castrates were given 20 times the amount of testosterone propionate necessary to restore complete coital performance in normal males after gonadectomy, the mating behavior of the experimental animals was not improved. Apparently the original deficit was not due to androgen insufficiency.

Perhaps the most important differences in the reactivity of central nervous mechanisms which mediate coitus-related behavior are those between males and females. The absence of behavior in one sex which is present in the other could be due to the lack of some critical mechanism. A case in point, which will be discussed in detail later, is the absence of the ejaculatory pattern in female mammals coupled with the lack of an intromittent organ. Other "deficiencies" in the female's mounting performance might be traceable to incomplete development of central nervous circuits essential to the occurrence of other elements in the complete masculine pattern. An alternative possibility is that the brain mechanisms capable of mediating the missing response are present and fully organized in the female, but are relatively insensitive to external stimulation or unresponsive to the normally facilitating effects of critical hormones.

Hormonal Effects on the Developing Nervous System. Some light is thrown upon these problems by experiments which have demonstrated the hormonal control of development in the neural mechanisms which mediate masculine and feminine responses. There is, for example, a good deal of evidence indicating that development of the mechanisms which eventually will mediate mounting and other responses appearing in the copulatory pattern of the male is in part dependent upon the presence of androgen during a specific ontogenetic period. In this respect the "male mechanisms" in the brain are comparable to other masculine sex characters, such as the penis, seminal vesicles, and other derivatives of the Wolffian system in that these also depend upon androgen for their epigenesis.

Functional or surgical castration of male rats within 4 days after birth not only prevents normal development of the penis (Beach and Holz, 1946), but results in incomplete masculine coital behavior when androgen is administered during adulthood (Levine and Mullins, 1966), and simultaneously accentuates the display of lordosis under the influence of exogenous ovarian hormone (Whalen and Nadler, 1963). The female rat treated with androgen just after birth displays permanent masculinization of the genitalia plus an increased tendency to engage in mounting responses when given androgen in adulthood (Harris and Levine, 1965). There also occurs a decrease in the exhibition of sexually receptive reactions under the influence of endogenous or exogenous ovarian hormones (Gerall and Ward, 1966). Evidently in both sexes the reactivity of neural mechanisms involved in mounting and associated reactions is increased by the presence of androgen during a critical stage of development. Conversely, the reactivity of mechanisms mediating lordosis is permanently inhibited by the presence of androgen during the same developmental period.

In the guinea pig the "crucial" phase of development occurs during prenatal life and it is well established that at that time the hormone essential for masculine development is endogenously produced. In this species both the fetal testis and the adrenal cortex secrete measurable amounts of androgen (Zaaijer et al., 1966) beginning as early as 22 days gestational age (Ortiz et al., 1966). Experiments involving prenatal introduction of exogenous androgen show that susceptibility of the guinea pig nervous system to organizational modification is lost by the end of pregnancy (Goy et al., 1964).

When administration of androgen to female guinea pigs and rats leads to permanent deficit in feminine mating responses and to an increase in mounting behavior, and when the elimination of testis hormone in neonatal male rats inhibits the occurrence of masculine copulatory reactions and enhances the display of lordosis during adult life, it seems reasonable to conclude that in both cases two hypothetical systems in the brain have been modified. What is the nature of the modification? Young (1965) referred to the "organizational" effects of androgen upon the developing nervous system and considered these to be "morphogenetic."

Impressive evidence for permanent changes in brain function resulting from hormonal stimulation during early development is provided by experiments on the hypothalamic mechanism which controls gonadotropic functions of the hypophysis. In nonpregnant adult females this mechanism functions cyclically, stimulating the periodic discharge of luteinizing hormone and thus controlling the ovarian rhythm and associated estrous cycles. The male hypothalamus functions acyclically, evoking a more or less constant output of gonadotropic factors by the anterior pituitary. Everett et al. (1949) demonstrated that under normal conditions androgen secreted in infancy induces in the hypothalamus of male rats the differentiation of "an intrinsically acyclic mechanism." In the normal female the absence of testis hormone results in differentiation of a cyclic mechanism in the same brain locus. Male rats castrated at birth develop a cyclic hypothalamus, and in females treated postnatally with androgen the mechanism is acyclic.

As far as behavior is concerned, it is relatively easy to demonstrate that a particular neural mechanism is present, but the problem of proving its absence is more complicated. For example, it is evident that the neural basis for the lordosis response is well organized in neonatally castrated male rats because when they are injected with estrogen and progesterone in adulthood the behavior appears. However, the failure to evoke lordosis in intact males castrated as adults could be due either to a morphological deficit in the central nervous system, or to insensitivity of completely organized mechanisms to ovarian hormones.

Female guinea pigs treated with testosterone propionate at the appropriate stage of fetal development exhibit increased frequency and completeness of mounting behavior when they are injected with androgen in adulthood. Normal females spayed at birth or at maturity also display some enhancement of mounting in response to exogenous androgen, but their reactions are much less marked than those of the pseudohermaphrodites (Gerall, 1966). Has the early hormone treatment of pseudohermaphrodites promoted or perfected the organization of brain mechanisms for mounting, thrusting, etc., or has it merely rendered them more sensitive to the facilitative effects of androgen in adulthood? In other words, when female guinea pigs that have been exposed to androgenic stimulation during the second and third trimesters of pregnancy fail to exhibit lordosis after injections of ovarian hormones, is the failure due to structural or morphogenetic deficiencies in crucial neuromuscular mechanisms or to an abnormally high threshold to ovarian hormones? Young and his colleagues have published rather convincing evidence that makes the first explanation seem unlikely.

Boling et al. (1939) reported that for a few hours after birth both male and female guinea pigs respond to tactile stimulation of the dorsal rump by exhibiting "a response which is similar to if not identical with that given by adult females at the time of heat" (p. 128). The response of the neonates consists of displaying lordosis together with the marked pudendal dilation. The reactions can be evoked only for a few hours immediately after parturition, but even the transitory occurrence of these reflexes in newborn males and females demonstrate the bisexual representation of those central mechanisms which later will mediate the coital performance of the female in estrus. Appearance of lordosis directly after birth does not depend upon placental or ovarian hormones received from the mother; in fact, estrogen and progesterone do not appear to be involved (Beach, 1966). Meidinger (1962) tested the reflexes of newborn guinea pigs which had been masculinized by androgen treatment in utero and found that pseudohermaphroditic females readily executed lordosis and dilation immediately after birth, even though they might never do so in adulthood.

It seems that at birth normal females, experimentally masculinized females and normal males all possess a nervous and muscular organization capable of mediating lordosis and anogenital dilation. Absence of the same responses in adult males and in some pseudohermaphrodites despite, in the latter animals, administration of massives doses of estrogen followed by progesterone could signify that (1) mechanisms present at birth are disrupted before maturity in males and in pseudohermaphrodites but not in normal females; (2) lordosis in infants and in adult estrous females is mediated by different mechanisms; or (3) the same mechanism is involved, is independent of hormonal facilitation in infancy, develops dependency on ovarian hormones during maturation, but is refractory to those hormones in adult males and in masculinized females. Whatever the correct interpretation proves to be, three conclusions seem justified. Male and female guinea pigs are congenitally endowed with a neuromuscular system capable of mediating feminine coital reflexes. Treatment with androgen during prenatal life does not prevent the development and functional organization of the mechanisms involved. During adulthood those mechanisms can be fully activated by ovarian hormones in normal or spayed females but not in males nor in pseudohermaphroditic females.———

Control by External Stimuli

The final category of variables which influence the occurrence of mounting responses in females comprises the environmental stimuli that evoke and maintain such behavior. This problem has not been investigated experimentally but studies have been conducted to identify the sensory basis of mating behavior in males, and if the working hypothesis proposed at the beginning of this discussion is valid, the results of these experiments may provide information pertinent to the understanding of similar behavior in females.

No experiments have been carried out on guinea pigs, but there have been several investigations of the male rat. The initial arousal of the male's interest in and responsiveness to the estrous female appears to depend, not upon any single category of stimulus such as odor or vision, but rather upon a multisensory pattern in which several modalities are involved and no one is essential (Beach, 1942c). It has been suggested that once mounting responses have been initiated the "sensory feedback" resulting from the execution of this behavior contributes to an increasing state of excitement which culminates in occurrence of the ejaculatory response (Beach, 1942d; 1956). One particular element in the total pattern that can be related to a specific type and locus of stimulation is the reaction which normally accompanies the occurrence of ejaculation. This involves much more than the reflexive expulsion of seminal fluid. It includes a complex combination of motor responses and a subsequent period of lowered responsiveness to all forms of sexual stimulation (Beach et al., 1966).

It is well established that ejaculation achieved by the male rat *in copula* depends upon stimulation of the penis which occurs as a result of intromission. Males with abnormally short penes, or those from which a segment of the os penis has been surgically removed mount the estrous female repeatedly, show palpation and pelvic thrusting, but do not display the ejaculatory pattern (Beach and Holz, 1946). In fact, the behavior of such males very closely resembles the mounting performance of female rats which have been injected with large amounts of androgen. Further evidence for the importance of penile sensitivity is provided by reports that ejaculatory responses are temporarily eliminated in male rats following the application of a local anesthetic to the phallus (Adler and Bermant, 1966).

In the light of the foregoing information, it is not surprising that female mammals do not exhibit behavior resembling the male's ejaculatory pattern even when they have been treated with large amounts of androgenic hormone. Lacking an intromittent organ, the female is deprived of an essential source of sensory stimulation, and even if she possesses the central mechanisms capable of mediating this part of the complete copulatory pattern, these mechanisms are not called into action because of an inadequate sensory feedback from the genitals. Two exceptions to this generalization have been reported (Levine and Mullins, 1964; Gerall, 1966), but in both cases the females involved were morphologically modified as a result of early treatment with gonadal hormones and administration of testosterone propionate in adulthood.

In addition to experiments aimed at analyzing the stimuli eliciting separate elements in the coital performance of male animals, there have been other investigations, oriented to a more molar type of approach, intended to identify the kinds of stimulus animals most likely to evoke the display of mounting and associated coital reactions. If similar behavior patterns in the two sexes are dependent upon similar forms of stimulation, results obtained in these studies of the male could yield useful information concerning behavior of the female.

Male rats reared in isolation and tested for mating responses in adulthood tend to mount only the estrous female and to show different responses to females in anestrus, to males, and to animals of a foreign species (Beach, 1942c). This finding certainly is not unexpected, and it might be taken for granted that investigators desiring to elicit mounting in females would employ as stimulus partners other females which were sexually receptive. This has been done in nearly all studies of female rats, but not in all experiments on guinea pigs. In the case of the rat there is convincing evidence demonstrating the superior stimulus value of estrous females.

Beach and Rasquin (1942) studied the mounting activity of 17 prepuberally spayed females. These animals were never given any exogenous hormone. A series of 20 tests was conducted, during the first 15 of which the experimental females were tested in pairs, and each animal thus had as a stimulus partner another ovariectomized, nonreceptive female.

In the course of the first 10 tests the number of individuals exhibiting mounting increased progressively, as did the frequency of mounts per positive test. Both of these indices had reached asymptote by the eleventh test. Upon the occasion of the sixteenth test the situation was changed in one important respect. Each experimental animal was, for the first time, paired with a stimulus female in full behavioral estrus. Some of the effects of presenting the experimental females with a sexually receptive partner are summarized in Table 4. These results strongly indicate that the amount and type of mounting behavior an anestrous female will show depend in part upon the kind of stimulus presented, and, further, that a receptive female is a much more effective stimulus than is a female in anestrus.

Of course these findings do not signify that female rats will mount only estrous females, and in fact evidence to the contrary is available. For example, the present writer (Beach, 1938) has described the mounting of males by females when the latter displayed all the responses normally shown by the male when he mounts and achieves intromission with a receptive female. A very important point is that when females of any species are described as having mounted

Table 4

Mounting Responses Shown by 17 Prepuberally Castrated
Female Rats without Hormone Treatment
(From Beach and Rasquin, 1942)

Succes- sive tests	Females mounting	Total mounting responses	Average no. of mounts per responding female per positive test	Rear clasp only	Total no. each type of response	
					Rear clasp, palpa- tion and thrusts	Clasp, palpate, and thrust with abrupt dismount and genital licking
Stimulus animal: nonreceptive castrated female						
11	15	88	5.9	84	4	0
12	16	117	7.3	103	14	0
13	16	110	6.9	97	13	0
14	13	89	6.8	78	11	0
15	16	104	6.5	94	10	0
Stimulus animal: receptive estrous female						
16	16	235	14.7	158	74	3
17	17	206	12.1	145	54	7
18	16	148	9.3	101	46	1
19	16	143	8.9	103	39	1
20	17	191	11.2	129	62	2

nonestrous females or males, it is probably a safe assumption that
the same animals would have mounted estrous females if these had
been available. The converse is not necessarily true. Absence of
mounting when the only available partners are nonestrous females
or males cannot be taken as proof that mounting would not occur
in response to a stimulus female in a state of sexual receptivity.

Observational accounts of mounting by females of various domesticated species are not always specific in their description of the type
or types of stimulus animals which evoke such responses. However,
reports specifying that the mountee was an estrous female have been
made in connection with the behavior of cows (Hammond, 1927;
Roark and Herman, 1950; Hafez and Schein, 1962), swine (Burger,
1952), monkeys (Carpenter, 1942), chimpanzees (Yerkes, 1939), lions
(Cooper, 1942), and domestic cats (Rosenblatt and Schneirla, 1962).
In none of these accounts is there any direct statement to the effect
that mounting is *not* shown in response to anestrous females, and this
of course would be vital information.

There are numerous reasons for anticipating that females in heat should elicit more mounting behavior than other types of potential partners. The estrous female possesses a number of traits which are lacking in anestrous individuals and in males, and which combine to make her an especially likely target for mounting by other animals of either sex. In the first place, as already emphasized, the female in heat presents a special combination of olfactory, visual, tactile, and, in some species, auditory cues which serve as species-specific "sign stimuli" (Tinbergen, 1951) for the evocation of pursuit and mounting.

Another behavioral feature of possible importance is the hyperactivity that occurs in females of many species when they are in estrus. In the natural environment, increased locomotor activity results in increased mobility and conspicuousness as well as bringing the female into contact with an increased number of potential sexual partners. Hyperactivity of the rat in natural estrus has long been recognized (Slonaker, 1924); and Young and Fish (1945) showed that although ovariectomized females of this species become relatively inactive, high levels of running activity can be elicited postoperatively by estrone administration. (Estradiol benzoate was less effective, and the addition of progesterone had no influence at all.)

Increased locomotor activity accompanies estrus in the sow (Altmann, 1941), the cow (Farris, 1954; Hafez and Schein, 1962), and in at least some chimpanzees (Tinklepaugh, 1933). Interestingly enough the guinea pig is one species in which females do not display cyclic fluctuations in running activity that correlate with ovarian cycles (Young, 1961). This is also a species in which, as will be discussed later, estrous females are no more effective than anestrous females as targets for the mounting responses of other animals of the same gender.

The increased locomotion of females in heat is not by nature random or undirected. Instead it is coupled with a heightened tendency to approach and remain near conspecific individuals of either sex. Anderson (1940) observed that during estrus female rats become less "timid," and LeBoeuf (1967) showed that when a bitch is in estrus she more frequently goes to and remains with a tethered dog of either sex. When estrous females achieve proximity to a conspecific animal they often exhibit special types of behavior that can be construed as solicitation or invitation to mount. This behavior, which is lacking during anestrus, may be indiscriminately oriented to both males and other females.

Solicitational behavior takes different forms in different species. The responses of female rats in estrus have been described by several authors (Ball, 1937; Beach, 1943). The estrous female displays a heightened tendency to approach and investigate other rats if they fail to approach her. When she is investigated by another animal of either sex, the female in heat often darts or hops away for a short distance and then crouches or poses in a special position with the head and rump slightly raised and the middle of the back somewhat depressed. If the other rat does not follow and renew contact, the female returns, reinvestigates the second animal and again exhibits the "pseudoescape" pattern. Usually the temporary retreat evokes pursuit; and assumption of the crouching posture often stimulates mounting responses. Anestrous rats do not engage in any form of solicitation and are therefore less likely to elicit copulatory responses on the part of either males or other females.

The reactions of some bitches in heat to other females have been described by Beach et al. (1968) as follows.

"Females in estrus often directed clear-cut 'solicitation' or 'presentation responses' to their feminine partners. Some estrous bitches approached the partner and positioned themselves directly in front of the second female with the tail deviated and the perineal region exposed. Upon occasion the estrogen-treated animal actively forced her vulva against the muzzle of the other dog, and when the latter responded by nosing and licking the vagina the estrous female's vulva 'tipped' in the direction of stimulation while her hind quarters moved convulsively from side to side."

According to Carpenter (1942), when free-living rhesus monkeys come into estrus they repeatedly approach socially dominant males and persist in remaining near them even when the males attack and wound them. As noted earlier, Carpenter also recorded the occurrence of female–female pairing and mounting in feral monkeys. Young and Orbison (1944) found that during the follicular phase of their cycles most female chimpanzees show more interest in a male in the adjacent cage, move more frequently to join him when permitted to do so, and exhibit the sexual presentation posture more often.

Farris (1954) noted that instead of grazing, the estrous cow not only roams constantly and attempts to mount, but also solicits mounting from other cows. This and other accounts of bovine behavior lead to consideration of still another aspect of the behavior of estrous females which may make them particularly effective stimulus partners for mounting by other females as well as by males. The following description of behavior in cattle is taken from an account by Hafez and Schein (1962).

"Although non-oestrous animals refuse to stand for mounting attempts by oestrous cows, they themselves often mount the latter. In such situations the oestrous cow makes no attempt to escape; instead it either stands quietly or sometimes leans caudally into the mount" (p. 275).

These responses are precisely those which the cow in heat makes when she is mounted by the bull, and it appears that in several other species the estrous female reacts cooperatively when she is mounted by other females. This behavior renders her a more attractive mountee than an anestrous female which attempts to prevent or avoid being mounted. Rosenblatt and Schneirla (1962) state that when a cat in estrus is mounted by another female the first animal, "often performs the entire female sexual pattern." Comparable behavior by the bitch in heat has been described by Beach et al. (1968).

Although there is considerable evidence suggesting that mounting behavior by female mammals is most likely to be elicited by a second female in estrus, this generalization is not applicable to every species. Investigators of mounting in female guinea pigs have been less consistent than students of rat behavior in using estrous females as stimulus animals, but although systematic comparisons are lacking it appears that for the female guinea pig the stimulus properties of the potential mountee are much less important than the current hormonal state of the responding individual. The essential comparisons are difficult to make because they necessitate combining data taken from different experiments, but the attempt is worthwhile.

Goy et al. (1966) reported that intact, anestrous female guinea pigs mounted normal females in anestrus an average of 1.3 times per test. In another study it was shown that 1.5 mounts per test were executed by untreated, spayed females when the stimulus animal was a female in estrus (Goy et al., 1964). Apparently the estrous condition of the partner did not result in any increase in mounting by the anestrous, spayed females. However, in this same experiment when the experimental females were brought into heat by injections of estrogen and progesterone they mounted other estrous females an average of 12.5 times per test. From these comparisons it would appear that an estrous condition in the stimulus animal is without effect, but estrus in the responding individual results in a marked increase in mounting frequency.

Diamond and Young (1963) studied mounting behavior of pregnant and nonpregnant guinea pigs which had been treated with testosterone propionate and the description of methods includes the following statement.

"The only criterion for selection of the stimulus animal was that she must not be larger than the experimental animal. Most often the stimulus female was not in heat; however, estrous females were used occasionally but without noticeable effect on the performance of the experimental female" (p. 430).

More direct evidence on this point is provided in the results of an unpublished study by Dr. Robert Goy, who has generously allowed the writer to summarize some of his findings. Eight female guinea pigs from strain 13, which is characterized by a high frequency of mounting in females, were examined for their tendency to mount other females when the latter were in estrus and in anestrus. During all tests the responding females were in induced estrus. The average mean frequency of mounts per test when stimulus females were in anestrus was 15.9, and when they were in estrus it was 15.2. Obviously both types of partners were equally effective.

One would like to know whether the same lack of differential responsiveness would have obtained when the responding females were in anestrus, but all the evidence taken together strongly supports the conclusion that the condition of sexual receptivity in the stimulus partner has relatively little effect upon the tendency of female guinea pigs to display mounting behavior, and in this respect females of this species are distinctly different from those of other species, including the rat and dog. Another extremely relevant but unanswered problem is whether the male guinea pig discriminates between estrous and anestrous females as targets for his mounting activity. Such discriminatory behavior is known to characterize the copulatory behavior of male rats and dogs, but unless males of a species clearly show selective responsiveness in such a situation females could scarcely be expected to do so.

Concluding Remarks

Descriptive and experimental reports reviewed in the foregoing pages make it clear that mounting behavior by female mammals is a fairly widespread phenomenon occurring in at least some species of several different orders within the class. It is evident that the behavior demands systematic analysis, and I have attempted to indicate the kinds of evidence needed to advance our understanding of the mechanisms involved.

One of the first problems is to determine the distribution of the behavior. Nearly all the available evidence pertains to domesticated species and selectively bred strains, and even within these limits the record is fragmentary. Knowledge is needed concerning the presence or absence of mounting responses in commonly studied species such as the inbred mouse and the Syrian hamster. Obtaining such information will depend upon creating optimal conditions for the occurrence of the responses in question. It is also important to gather evidence relating to additional domesticated species and to feral animals which are more likely to be seasonal breeders.

A second objective is more accurate and detailed specification of the endocrinological state of the mounting female. Specifically it is important to learn whether the tendency of normal females to mount other individuals is strongly influenced by ovarian hormones. This entails the gathering of evidence pertaining to mounting during both estrus and anestrus.

Third, there is need for information that will help to define the stimulus factors involved in the elicitation of mounting on the part of females. This will involve recording the sex of the mountee and, if females are mounted their hormonal status should be indicated.

All the foregoing questions can be attacked on the basis of controlled observation. For more detailed analysis experimental procedures will be necessary. It is highly desirable to investigate the effects of exogenous androgen on mounting in females of many different species. The contributions of the nervous system deserve serious study via experiments involving selective ablation, stimulation, and recording.

In short, this type of behavior should be studied in the same way that "feminine" and "masculine" copulatory behavior has already been investigated. For some species at least it is just as much a part of the female's repertoire as lordosis. Since it includes responses that are essential elements of the male's coital pattern, a complete analysis of female mounting should greatly increase our understanding of neural and hormonal mechanisms that have bisexual representation.

Acknowledgment

Studies conducted by the writer since 1960 were supported by Public Health Service Research Grant MH-04000 from the National Institute of Mental Health.

References

Adler, N., and G. Bermant. 1966. Sexual behavior of male rats: Effects of reduced sensory feedback. *J. Comp. Physiol. Psychol.*, **61**: 240–243.
de Alba, J., and S. A. Asdell. 1946. Estrous behavior and hormones in the cow. *J. Comp. Psychol.*, **39**: 119–124.

Altmann, M. 1941. Interrelations of the sex cycle and the behavior of the sow. *J. Comp. Psychol.*, **31**: 481–489.

Anderson, E. E. 1940. The sex hormones and emotional behavior. I. The effect of sexual receptivity upon timidity in the female rat. *J. Genet. Psychol.*, **56**: 149–158.

Avery, G. T. 1925. Notes on reproduction in guinea pigs. *J. Comp. Psychol.*, **5**: 373–396.

Ball, J. 1937. The effect of male hormone on the sex behavior of female rats. *Psychol. Bull.*, **34**: 725–732.

Ball, J. 1940. The effect of testosterone on the sex behavior of female rats. *J. Comp. Psychol.*, **29**: 151–165.

Beach, F. A. 1938. Sex reversals in the mating pattern of the rat. *J. Genet. Psychol.*, **53**: 329–334.

Beach, F. A. 1940. Effects of cortical lesions upon the copulatory behavior of male rats. *J. Comp. Psychol.*, **29**: 193–244.

Beach, F. A. 1942a. Execution of the complete masculine copulatory pattern by sexually receptive female rats. *J. Genet. Psychol.*, **60**: 137–142.

Beach, F. A. 1942b. Male and female mating behavior in prepuberally castrated female rats treated with androgen. *Endocrinology*, **31**: 673–678.

Beach, F. A. 1942c. Analysis of stimuli adequate to elicit mating behavior in the sexually inexperienced male rat. *J. Comp. Psychol.*, **33**: 163–207.

Beach, F. A. 1942d. Analysis of factors involved in the arousal, maintenance and manifestation of sexual excitement in male animals. *Psychomat. Med.*, **4**: 173–198.

Beach, F. A. 1943. Effects of injury to the cerebral cortex upon the display of masculine and feminine mating behavior by female rats. *J. Comp. Psychol.*, **36**: 169–199.

Beach, F. A. 1945. Bisexual mating behavior in the male rat: Effects of castration and hormone administration. *Physiol. Zool.*, **18**: 390–402.

Beach, F. A. 1947. A review of physiological and psychological studies of sexual behavior in mammals. *Physiol. Rev.*, **27**: 240–307.

Beach, F. A. 1956. Characteristics of masculine "sex drive." In *Nebraska Symposium on Motivation* (M. Jones, ed.). Univ. Nebraska Press, Lincoln.

Beach, F. A. 1966. Ontogeny of "coitus-related" reflexes in the female guinea pig. *Proc. Natl. Acad. Sci. U.S.*, **56**: 526–533.

Beach, F. A. 1968. Coital behavior in dogs. V. Long-term effects of castration in males. Manuscript in preparation.

Beach, F. A., and H. Fowler. 1959. Individual differences in the response of male rats to androgen. *J. Comp. Physiol. Psychol.*, **52**: 50–52.

Beach, F. A., and A. M. Holz. 1946. Mating behavior in male rats castrated at various ages and injected with androgen. *J. Exptl. Zool.*, **101**: 91–142.

Beach, F. A., and P. Rasquin. 1942. Masculine copulatory behavior in intact and castrated female rats. *Endocrinology*, **31**: 393–409.

Beach, F. A., C. M. Rogers, and B. LeBoeuf. 1968. Coital behavior in dogs. II. Effects of estrogen on mounting by females. *J. Comp. Physiol. Psychol.* In press.

Beach, F. A., W. H. Westbrook, and L. G. Clemens. 1966. Comparisons of the ejaculatory response in men and animals. *Psychosomat. Med.*, **28**: 749–763.

Berg, I. A. 1944. Development of behavior: The micturition pattern in the dog. *J. Exptl. Psychol.*, **34**: 343–368.

Bingham, H. C. 1928. Sex development in apes. *Comp. Psychol. Monogr.,* **5:** 1–165.

Boling, J. L., R. J. Blandau, J. G. Wilson, and W. C. Young. 1939. Post-parturitional heat responses of newborn and adult guinea pigs. Data on parturition. *Proc. Soc. Exptl. Biol. Med.,* **42:** 128–132.

Burger, J. F. 1952. Sex physiology of pigs. *Onderstepoort J. Vet. Res. Suppl.,* **2** (cited by W. C. Young, 1961).

Calder, A. 1927. A case of partial sex-transformation in cattle. *Proc. Roy. Soc. Edinburgh,* **47:** 222–229.

Carpenter, C. R. 1942. Sexual behavior of free ranging rhesus monkeys (*Macaca mulatta*). II. Periodicity of estrus, homosexual, autoerotic and non-conformist behavior. *J. Comp. Psychol.,* **33:** 143–162.

Cole, H. H., G. H. Hart, and R. F. Miller. 1945. Studies on the hormonal control of estrous phenomena in the anestrous ewe. *Endocrinology,* **36:** 370–380.

Cooper, J. B. 1942. An exploratory study on African lions. *Comp. Psychol. Monogr.,* **17:** 1–48.

Dantchakoff, V. 1938. Rôle des hormones dans la manifestation des instincts sexuel. *Compt. Rend.,* **206:** 945–947.

Diamond, M. 1965. The antagonistic actions of testosterone propionate and estrogen and progesterone on copulatory patterns of the female guinea pig. *Anat. Rec.,* **151:** 449 (Abstr.).

Diamond, M., and V. A. Cerny. 1966. The effect of age on female sexual behavior in the guinea pig. *Am. Zoologist,* **6:** 301 (Abstr.).

Diamond, M., and W. C. Young. 1963. Differential responsiveness of pregnant and nonpregnant guinea pigs to the masculinizing action of testosterone propionate. *Endocrinology,* **72:** 429–438.

Everett, J. W., C. H. Sawyer, and J. E. Markee. 1949. A neurogenic timing factor in control of the ovulatory discharge of luteinizing hormone in the cyclic rat. *Endocrinology,* **44:** 234–250.

Farris, E. J. 1954. Activity of dairy cows during estrus. *J. Am. Vet. Med. Assoc.,* **125:** 117–120.

Folley, S. J., and F. H. Malpress. 1944. Artificial induction of lactation in the bovine by subcutaneous implantation of synthetic oestrogen tablets. *J. Endocrinol.,* **4:** 1–22.

Fuller, J. L., and E. M. DuBuis. 1962. The behavior of dogs. In *The Behavior of Domestic Animals* (E. S. E. Hafez, ed.). Williams & Wilkins, Baltimore, pp. 415–452.

Gerall, A. A. 1966. Hormonal factors influencing masculine behavior of female guinea pigs. *J. Comp. Physiol. Psychol.,* **62:** 365–369.

Gerall, A. A., and I. L. Ward. 1966. Effects of prenatal exogenous androgen on the sexual behavior of the female albino rat. *J. Comp. Physiol. Psychol.,* **62:** 370–375.

Goy, R. W., and R. O. Dodsworth. 1962. Failure of early castration to prevent the development of masculine patterns of social behavior or the display of infantile sexual behavior by young rhesus males. *Am. Zoologist,* **2:** 411–412 (Abstr.).

Goy, R. W., and C. H. Phoenix. 1963. Hypothalamic regulation of female sexual behaviour: Establishment of behavioural oestrus in spayed guinea pigs following hypothalamic lesions. *J. Reprod. Fertility,* **5:** 23–40.

Goy, R. W., and W. C. Young. 1957a. Somatic basis of sexual behavior patterns in guinea pigs. *Psychosomat. Med.,* 19: 144–151.

Goy, R. W., and W. C. Young. 1957b. Strain differences in the behavioral responses of female guinea pigs to a-estradiol benzoate and progesterone. *Behaviour,* 10: 340–354.

Goy, R. W., C. H. Phoenix, and W. C. Young. 1962. A critical period for the suppression of behavioral receptivity in adult female rats by early treatment with androgen. *Anat. Rec.,* 142: 307 (Abstr.).

Goy, R. W., W. E. Bridson, and W. C. Young. 1964. Period of maximal susceptibility of the prenatal female guinea pig to masculinizing actions of testosterone propionate. *J. Comp. Physiol. Psychol.,* 57: 166–174.

Goy, R. W., C. H. Phoenix, and W. C. Young. 1966. Inhibitory action of the corpus luteum on the hormonal induction of estrous behavior in the guinea pig. *Gen. Comp. Endrocrinol.,* 6: 267–274.

Grunt, J. A., and W. C. Young. 1952. Differential reactivity of individuals and the response of the male guinea pig to testosterone propionate. *Endocrinology,* 51: 237–248.

Hafez, E. S. E., and M. W. Schein. 1962. The behaviour of cattle. In *The Behaviour of Domestic Animals* (E. S. E. Hafez, ed.). Williams & Wilkins, Baltimore, pp. 247–296.

Hafez, E. S. E., and J. P. Scott. 1962. The behaviour of sheep and goats. In *The Behaviour of Domestic Animals* (E. S. E. Hafez, ed.). Williams & Wilkins, Baltimore, pp. 297–333.

Hafez, E. S. E., L. J. Sumption, and J. S. Jakway. 1962. The behaviour of swine. In *The Behaviour of Domestic Animals* (E. S. E. Hafez, ed.). Williams & Wilkins, Baltimore, pp. 334–369.

Hamilton, G. V. 1914. A study of sexual tendencies in monkeys and baboons. *J. Animal Behavior,* 4: 295–318.

Hammond, J. 1927. *The Physiology of Reproduction in the Cow.* Cambridge Univ. Press, New York.

Hammond, J., Jr., and F. T. Day. 1944. Oestrogen treatment of cattle: Induced lactation and other effects. *J. Endocrinol.,* 4: 53–82.

Hammond, J., and F. H. A. Marshall. 1925. *Reproduction in the Rabbit.* Oliver & Boyd, London.

Harlow, H. F. 1965. Sexual behavior in the rhesus monkey. In *Sex and Behavior* (F. A. Beach, ed.). Wiley, New York, pp. 234–265.

Harris, G. W., and S. Levine. 1965. Sexual differentiation of the brain and its experimental control. *J. Physiol. (London),* 181: 379–400.

Hemmingsen, A. M. 1933. Studies on the oestrous-producing hormone. *Skand. Arch. Physiol.,* 65: 97–250.

Hu, C. K., and C. N. Frazier. 1940. Masculinization of adult female rabbit following injection of testosterone propionate. *Proc. Soc. Exptl. Biol. Med.,* 42: 820–823.

Koster, R. 1943. Hormone factors in male behavior of the female rat. *Endocrinology,* 33: 337–348.

Kun, H. 1933. Psychische Feminierung und Hermaphrodisierung von Männchen durch Weiblicher Sexualhormon. *Endocrinology,* 13: 311–323.

LeBoeuf, B. J. 1967. Interindividual behavior in dogs. *Behaviour,* 29: 268–295.

Levine, S., and R. F. Mullins, Jr. 1964. Estrogen administered neonatally affects adult sexual behavior in male and female rats. *Science,* 144: 185–187.

Levine, S., and R. F. Mullins, Jr. 1966. Hormonal influences on brain organization in infant rats. *Science,* 152: 1585–1592.

Markley, M. H., and C. F. Bassett. 1942. Habits of a captive marten. *Am. Midland Naturalist,* 28: 604–610.

McKenzie, F. F. 1926. The normal oestrous cycle in the sow. *Missouri Univ. Agr. Expt. Sta. Res. Bull.,* 86: 1–48.

Meidinger, R. 1962. Differential effect of testosterone propionate given prenatally on sexually dimorphic and sexually isomorphic measures of behavior in the guinea pig. *Am. Zoologist,* 2: 540 (Abstr.).

Moore, C. R. 1919. On the physiological properties of the gonads as controllers of somatic and psychical characteristics. I. The rat. *J. Exptl. Zool.,* 28: 137–160.

Ortiz, E., Price, D., and J. J. P. Zaaijer. 1966. Organ culture studies of hormone secretion in endocrine glands of fetal guinea pigs. II. Secretion of androgenic hormone in adrenals and testes during early stages of development. *Koninkl. Ned. Akad. Wetenschap. Proc. Ser. C,* 69: 400–408.

Pearl, L. R., and F. M. Surface. 1915. Sex studies. VII. On the assumption of male secondary sex characters by a cow with cystic degeneration of the ovaries. *Maine Agr. Expt. Sta. Bull.,* 237: 65–80.

Pearson, O. P. 1944. Reproduction in the shrew (*Blarina brevicauda* Say). *Am. J. Anat.,* 75: 39–93.

Phoenix, C. H., R. W. Goy, A. A. Gerall, and W. C. Young. 1959. Organizing action of prenatally administered testosterone propionate on the tissues mediating mating behavior in the female guinea pig. *Endocrinology,* 65: 369–382.

Riss, W., and W. C. Young. 1954. The failure of large quantities of testosterone propionate to activate low drive male guinea pigs. *Endocrinology,* 54: 232–235.

Riss, W., E. S. Valenstein, J. Sinks, and W. C. Young. 1955. Development of sexual behavior in male guinea pigs from genetically different stocks under controlled conditions of androgen treatment and caging. *Endocrinology,* 57: 139–146.

Roark, D. B., and H. A. Herman. 1950. Physiological and histological phenomena of the bovine estrual cycle with special reference to vagino-cervical secretions. *Missouri Univ. Agr. Expt. Sta. Res. Bull.,* 455.

Roberts, S. J. 1956. *Veterinary Obstetrics and Genital Diseases.* Edwards, Ann Arbor, Mich.

Rosenblatt, J. S., and T. C. Schneirla. 1962. The behaviour of cats. In *The Behaviour of Domestic Animals* (E. S. E. Hafez, ed.). Williams & Wilkins, Baltimore, pp. 453–488.

Slonaker, J. R. 1924. The effect of pubescence, oestruation and menopause on the voluntary activity in the albino rat. *Am. J. Physiol.,* 68: 294–315.

Steinach, E. 1913. Feminierung von Männchen und Maskulierung von Weibchen. *Zentr. Physiol.,* 27: 717–723.

Stone, C. P. 1939. Sex drive. In *Sex and Internal Secretions* (E. Allen, C. H. Danforth, and E. A. Doisy, eds.). Williams & Wilkins, Baltimore, 2nd ed., pp. 1213–1262.

Tinbergen, N. 1951. *The Study of Instinct.* Oxford, New York.

Tinklepaugh, O. L. 1933. Sex cycles and other cyclic phenomena in a chimpanzee during adolescence, maturity and pregnancy. *J. Morphol.,* 54: 521–547.

Valenstein, E. S., W. Riss, and W. C. Young. 1954. Sex drive in genetically heterogeneous and highly inbred strains of male guinea pigs. *J. Comp. Physiol. Psychol.*, **47**: 162–165.

Walton, A., J. Edwards, and J. Hammond. 1940. Fertility in farm animals. *J. Roy. Agr. Soc. Engl.* **100**: 1–12.

Weber, E. 1911. Untersuchungen über die Brunst des Rindes. *Arch. Wissenschap. Prakt. Tierheilk.*, **37**: 382–454.

Wells, L. J., and G. van Wagenen. 1954. Androgen-induced female pseudohermaphroditism in the monkey (*Macaca mulatta*): anatomy of the reproductive organs. *Contrib. Embryol.*, **35**: 93–106.

Whalen, R. E., and R. D. Nadler. 1963. Suppression of the development of female mating behavior by estrogen administered in infancy. *Science*, **141**: 273–274.

Yerkes, R. M. 1939. Social dominance and sexual status in the chimpanzee. *Quart. Rev. Biol.*, **14**: 115–136.

Young, W. C. 1961. The hormones and mating behavior. In *Sex and Internal Secretions* (W. C. Young, ed.). Williams & Wilkins, Baltimore, 3rd ed., pp. 1173–1239.

Young, W. C. 1965. The organization of sexual behavior by hormonal action during the prenatal and larval periods in vertebrates. In *Sex and Behavior* (F. A. Beach, ed.). Wiley, New York, pp. 89–107.

Young, W. C., and W. R. Fish. 1945. The ovarian hormones and spontaneous running activity in the female rat. *Endocrinology*, **36**: 181–189.

Young, W. C., and W. D. Orbison. 1944. Changes in selected features of behavior in pairs of oppositely sexed chimpanzees during the sexual cycle and after ovariectomy. *J. Comp. Psychol.*, **37**: 107–143.

Young, W. C., and B. Rundlett. 1939. The hormonal induction of homosexual behavior in the spayed female guinea pig. *Psychosomat. Med.*, **1**: 449–460.

Young, W. C., E. W. Dempsey, C. W. Hagquist, and J. L. Boling. 1939. Sexual behavior and sexual receptivity in the female guinea pig. *J. Comp. Psychol.*, **27**: 49–68.

Young, W. C., E. W. Dempsey, and H. I. Myers. 1935. Cyclic reproductive behavior in the female guinea pig. *J. Comp. Psychol.*, **19**: 313–335.

Young, W. C., E. W. Dempsey, H. I. Myers, and C. W. Hagquist. 1938. The ovarian condition and sexual behavior in the female guinea pig. *Am. J. Anat.*, **63**: 457–487.

Young, W. C., R. W. Goy, and C. H. Phoenix. 1964. Hormones and sexual behavior. *Science*, **143**: 212–218.

Zaaijer, J. J. P., D. Price, and E. Ortiz. 1966. Organ culture studies of hormone secretion in endocrine glands of fetal guinea pigs. I. Androgenic secretion as demonstrated by a bioindicator method. *Konikl. Ned. Akad. Wetenschap. Proc. Ser. C*, **69**: 389–399.

Discussion

REPRODUCTION AND SEXUAL BEHAVIOR (M. Diamond ed.), 135–137, © Indiana University Press

8

Gonadotropins and Endometrial Cups

H. H. Cole

One of the questions still unresolved is the significance of the secretion of gonadotropin in the pregnant mare. Is the presence of pregnant mare serum gonadotropin (PMSG) essential for normal pregnancy in this species? We do know that an accessory set of corpora lutea are formed in consequence to its presence. On the other hand, there is evidence that high levels of PMSG are not required. For example, we have shown (Clegg et al., 1962) that a mare carrying a horse fetus has approximately 18 times more PMSG than does the same mare carrying a mule fetus. In other words, the average concentration of hormone at the sixtieth day of pregnancy was found to be 170 IU per ml when the mare was bred to a stallion as compared to 10 IU per ml when bred to a jack. Pregnancy progresses normally in both instances.

The endometrial cups of the pregnant mare are interesting structures in that PMSG is secreted into the blood stream of the mare (an endocrine secretion) and at the same time is secreted into the lumens of the uterine glands (an exocrine secretion). Presumably, this exocrine PMSG passes across the chorion and enters the allantoic blood vessels. Strangely, the presence of PMSG in the fetal circulation has never been established, but it has been presumed on the basis of the remarkable hypertrophy of the fetal gonads coincident with high levels in the maternal circulation.

PMSG has both follicle-stimulating and lutenizing activities. Four IU of PMSG will double the weight of the seminal vesicles of the hypophysectomized male rats (Cole et al., 1940). In the hypophysectomized female, 4 IU produces a marked interstitial cell response and a slight increase in ovarian weight, but the follicles are not noticeably affected. With larger doses marked follicular development and luteinization occur. Thus it is scarcely correct to refer to PMSG as predominately follicle-stimulating.

How does PMSG differ from gonadotropins derived from other sources? Human chorionic gonadotropin (HCG) is predominately a luteinizing hormone, but according to our findings it also has intrinsic follicle-stimulating activity (Cole and Bigelow, 1967). Although a luteinizing fraction essentially devoid of FSH activity can be prepared from pituitary extracts, no one has prepared, to my knowledge, FSH fractions from any source (pituitary, blood, or urine) which are devoid of LH activity. Thus it is still unclear whether luteinizing capacity is an intrinsic property of follicle-stimulating hormone or whether the luteinization is due to contamination with LH.

Finally, I should like to say a word about terminology of the gonadotropin in the blood of the pregnant mare, in the endometrial cups, and in endometrial cup secretion. My own early suggestion of "equine gonadotropin" is entirely inadequate because this term does not distinguish between the hormone produced by the endometrial cups and that produced by the pituitary of the mare. The terms pregnant mare serum (PMS) or pregnant mare serum gonadotropin (PMSG) are unsuitable because one could hardly justify reference to the hormone found in the endometrial cup secretion as "pregnant mare serum." Catchpole (1964) has recently attempted to revive the term equine cyonin. Astwood and Greep (1939) suggested that the term cyonin (Gr. kuo, pregnancy + protein) be used for all protein hormones of placental origin. Strictly speaking, however, PMSG is not a placental hormone, because at the site of the endometrial cup there is no contact between fetal and maternal tissues. They suggested that PMSG be designated as equine cyonin, human chorionic gonadotropin as human cyonin, and the luteotropin in the rat as murine cyonin. However, the term has received little acceptance in the 27 years since its launching, even by its proponents, and thus there is little hope of its survival.

Past failures to find a suitable designation for the hormone secreted by the endometrial cups of the mare should not deter further efforts. Consequently, I am suggesting the term endometrial cup gonadotropin (ECGH). Logically the abbreviation would be "ECG" but inasmuch as this abbreviation has a widely accepted connotation it would appear preferable to add an "H" for hormone.

References

Astwood, E. B., and R. W. Greep. 1939. Nomenclature of gonad-stimulating hormones of placental origin. *Science,* **89:** 81.

Catchpole, H. R. 1964. Physiology of the gonadotropic hormones. In *Gonadotropins: Their Chemical and Biological Properties* (H. H. Cole, ed.). Freeman, San Francisco.

Clegg, M. T., H. H. Cole, C. B. Howard, and H. Pigon. 1962. The influence of foetal genotype on equine gonadotrophin secretion. *J. Endocrinol.,* **25:** 245–248.

Cole, H. H., and M. Bigelow. 1967. Follicle stimulation as an intrinsic property of human chorionic gonadotropin. *Anat. Rec.,* **157:** 19–26.

Cole, H. H., R. I. Pencharz, and H. Goss. 1940. On the biological properties of highly purified gonadotropins from pregnant mare serum. *Endocrinology,* **27:** 548–553.

REPRODUCTION AND SEXUAL BEHAVIOR (M. Diamond ed.), 139–143, © Indiana University Press

9

The Female Reproductive System

S. R. M. Reynolds

Several years ago, I had the privilege of visiting the Beaverton Laboratory. I met some of the people who talked today, as well as Dr. Young, whom I had known for many years. They then were organizing programs, facilities, and criteria for their work on the study of primates; observing, measuring, and recording. I was impressed by what we heard today and with the great progress that has been made in really only the few months that have elapsed since that time.* The research has gone in several directions in a most effective and productive manner.

When some of us attend meetings of this sort for several days, I guess we're rather hard put to summarize and crystallize the experience in terms of, "What did I learn?" I'll explain the problem that impedes us in getting the facts we are after. In a session, after hearing a paper I wanted to hear, a second paper started. I did not leave the room in order not to embarrass the speaker or listeners and not to make a fuss by falling over some of the people in the audience. We dilute our learning progress by accessory experiences of variable value to us.

This second speaker said something that perhaps was the one

* See Chapter 5.

thing I will remember from that meeting, as he gave a correlation which should perhaps have preceded a 45-minute sermon. I'll pass it on to you again because there is truth in it and I think it bears on what we're discussing this afternoon. He said, "We all drink deep at the wells which others have dug." Then he went on with his parable. The same is true, of course, in the fields of our professional associations yet we don't always know on whom we depend. The future, however, grows out of the past, inevitably.

I would like to mention in this connection one or two things that touch on areas that I think need to be explored further. They have, in a sense, lain somewhat dormant since Dr. Young was the first to make particular observations relevant to them. I know they have been extended since then to other animals and reproductive phenomena.

I refer first to the fact that Dr. Young was the first investigator to show (Young, 1961) that the full copulatory response in certain labortary animals depends not upon estrogen alone, but upon estrogen in combination, and at the right time, with small amounts of progesterone.

There was already in the literature (Reynolds and Friedman, 1930; Lloyd, 1937; Crandall, 1938; Schmidt, 1943; Gillman and Gilbert, 1944), at the time when Dr. Young made this discovery, plenty of evidence that pointed to this conclusion, but Dr. Young first put his finger on the point; after that many people recognized the phenomenon in other contexts.

We have accepted the fact that progesterone of ovarian origin plays an important role before ovulation. I raise a question, however, which seems to have escaped most people concerned with fundamental biology. We take it for granted that an endocrine organ is commonly supposed to be a specialized type of epithelial tissue which elaborates a specific product or products transmitted by blood or body fluids to a target organ—or target organs—where it has—or they have—a specific effect. This is a reasonably accurate conventional definition of an endocrine gland, but if this definition is true, how can progesterone be produced by an endocrine organ before the epithelium of a corpus luteum exists? This is true in the observation Dr. Young first recognized and that other people had also made. In this light we must modify and revise our idea of what an endocrine organ really is.

It is the tissue that secretes a given product—a specific product—and has an effect on a target organ. I raise a further question: How is it that the theca cells of the Graafian follicle elaborate estrogen and then, prior to ovulation, begin to transform their energies to secrete, in addition to estrogen, a small amount of progesterone before ovulation? These two hormones acting in concert produce in the female the necessary conditions for the copulatory behavioral response. I think that there is need for a study of this particular phenomenon.

Several years ago at the meeting of the Anatomists, I happened to preside at a session (I only hear papers when I preside at a session) in which a beautifully timed sequence of the development of the ultrastructure of the corpus luteum was given (Blanchette, 1963). It was the first significant paper on this subject that I had heard. It was beautifully definitive work. There was not one word, however, to relate, structure to function. I suspect that 10 to 12 minutes is too short a time to discuss such important physiological and behavioral changes in relation to morphology. But to put my finger on the point, I would say that in this area, a study of the ultrastructure, molecular biology, cytochemistry, ultramicrochemistry—I don't care how you put it—maybe of the ribosomal content or the organelles of the theca interna, under the appropriate stimuli and at well-chosen times, needs to be done by investigators in order to reach into the cells being described to find the mechanism by which gonadotropic hormones exert their influence on the structure of the Graafian follicle. All at once, before ovulation in rats, guinea pigs, rabbits, and other unknown species, the beginning of a new kind of synthesis, that of progestin, i.e., substances, takes place.

I submit that this kind of thing must apply also to the study of certain types of placentas which produce steroid hormones such as estrogens and progesterone. Why are these hormones elaborated by syncytial trophoblast cells in hemochorial placentas (Wislocki and Bennett, 1943) and not, as far as I know, by cytotrophoblast cells? And yet syncytial trophoblast is derived from cytotrophoblast (Hertig, 1962).

We don't as yet really know anything about processes of this sort. They are all part and parcel of the same thing. I'm saying that advances in the field of molecular biology, whether to understand behavior, pregnancy mechanisms, or many other things pertaining to reproduction, will resolve themselves, when boiled down, to appropriate correlated studies in the field of ultramicrochemistry, molecular biology, and fine structure. These, however, can be understood only when one knows the organ structure at a relatively gross level.

One additional point I would like to make along the foregoing lines refers to something that I heard discussed yesterday. Dr. Charles Hooker made an observation (Hooker and Wooten, 1966) that if one removes the cervical ganglia of the rat's uterus early in pregnancy, the pregnancy goes on but the mechanism of parturition is prevented. The animal is incapable of delivery. This is a difficult thing to explain. To put this in a meaningful sense one has to go back to the work of Ludwig and Lenz in 1923 when they described the mechanism of labor in terms of coordinated uterine activity as Dr. Richard Blandau* showed today with respect to the uterine tubes in the transport of the ova and as was described more crudely by Westman in 1929. We saw clearly on film today as a group what Westman described in words, as an individual. The techniques have improved and so has our understanding. The advances come when techniques improve and we proceed from one plateau of comprehension to another.

In Dr. Hooker's experiments he also described something else of great interest. He mentioned that if one removes the cervical ganglia of mice the mice will have normal estrous cycles, but they will never copulate. As a result of this, our comprehension of copulatory behavior is challenged. We heard things today about behavioral copulatory mechanisms in relation to the physiology concerned. We heard about feedback mechanisms today. We've talked about sensory input to the central nervous system. We've talked about a number of mechanisms but we have failed so far to relate these to actual pathways and integrated physiology and endocrinology. I think we have failed to relate the behavioral deficiency, whatever it is, to the response that we're studying, be it behavior, parturition, or what not.

To get a tipoff on what is missing one has to go back to the work of Kennedy in 1929, on the uterine cervical ganglia of the mouse and similar descriptive work since then in other animals; hamsters and rats (Redmond, 1962). Only at the time of heat or under the influence of estrogen does one find large aggregations of Nissl substance in the uterine cervical ganglia. Other parts of the CNS are not so affected. There is something going on here, at this precise focal point in the peripheral CNS, that affects copulatory behavior and affects parturitional mechanisms and feedback controls to the hypothalamus as well as the endocrine complex of pseudopregnancy (Meyer et al., 1929).

These are but some of the things that we need to know. I believe that the future always grows out of the past, and if one wants to understand the future one must understand the past. I think the

---

* The original symposium program started with a movie and talk about ova transport presented by Dr. Richard Blandau, University of Washington, Seattle.

understanding of Dr. Young's work and the wide ramifications of what we heard today is testimony to this point.

References

Blanchette, E. J. 1960. The fine structure of the luteal cell of the rabbit during pregnancy and following parturition. *Anat. Rec.,* **145:** 208.

Crandall, W. R. 1938. Effect of progesterone on cell division in the circular muscle of the rabbit's uterus. *Anat. Rec.,* **72** :195–210.

Gillman, J., and C. Gilbert. 1944. A case report of hysterectomy on ovarian activity in the baboon. *J. Obstet. Gynaecol. Brit. Empire,* **51:** 495–498.

Hertig, A. T. 1962. Some new observations on an old organ. *Obstet. Gynecol.,* **20:** 859–866.

Hooker, C. W., and R. N. Wooten, Jr. 1966. The ganglia of the cervix uteri in the non-pregnant mouse. *Anat. Rec.,* **154:** 360.

Kennedy, W. P. 1929. The ganglia cervicalis and the oestrous hormone. *Trans. Edinburgh Obstet. Soc.,* **36:** 75–88.

Lloyd, C. W. 1937. Effect of progesterone on cell division in uterine epithelium. *Proc. Soc. Exptl. Biol. Med.,* **36:** 190–191.

Ludwig, F., and E. Lenz. 1923. Über Bauchfenstergeburten. *Z. Geburtschilfe Gynaekol.,* **86:** 589–598.

Meyer, R., S. L. Leonard, and F. L. Hisaw. 1929. Effects of anesthesia on artificial production of pseudopregnancy in the rat. *Proc. Soc. Exptl. Biol. Med.,* **27:** 340–342.

Redmond, W. C. 1962. Ovarian influence on the uterine cervical ganglia. Thesis, University of Illinois, Urbana.

Reynolds, S. R. M., and M. H. Friedman. 1930. Studies on the Uterus. III. The activity of the uterine fistula in unanesthetized rabbits following coitus and during pseudopregnancy. *Am. J. Physiol.,* **94:** 696–707.

Schmidt, I. G. 1943. Proliferation in the genital tract of the normal mature guinea pig treated with colchicine. *Am. J. Anat.,* **73:** 59–80.

Westman, A. 1929. Untersuchungen über die Physiologie der Tube Uterini bei Macacus–Rhesus Affen. *Acta Obstet. Gynecol. Scand.,* **8:** 307–314.

Wislocki, G., and H. S. Bennett. 1943. The histology and cytology of the human and monkey placentae, with special reference to the trophoblast. *Am. J. Anat.,* **73:** 335–423.

Young, W. C. 1961. The hormones and mating behavior. In *Sex and Internal Secretions* (William C. Young, ed.). Williams & Wilkins, Baltimore, 3rd ed., pp. 1173–1239.

10

Neuroendocrine Factors in the Control of Reproduction

Berta Scharrer

As I look back at this afternoon's impressive array of papers, I am conscious of the exceptional range of interests and competence that characterizes Dr. Young's work. I am proud and happy to participate in this program honoring him as a scientific colleague, teacher, and friend. However, as a comparative endocrinologist concentrating on invertebrates, one might wonder what justification there is for my being here. Perhaps it is my interest in the relationships between the nervous and the endocrine systems that comes closest to Bill Young's sphere of activities. Since the time is running short, I should like to comment on just a few aspects of this topic whose broad implications have become so evident in both parts of this afternoon's program.

The study of the functional interdependence of the two integrative organ systems in existence encompasses a variety of phenomena which fall into two major categories: (1) the effects of hormonal stimuli on the nervous system, and (2) the influence of neural activities on the endocrine apparatus (see Scharrer and Scharrer, 1963; Bajusz and Jasmin, 1964; Weitzman, 1964–1968; E. Scharrer, 1966; B. Scharrer, 1967). Both are equally involved in the complex control mechanism of the timed events in reproductive physiology.

145

If we examine the effects of hormones on the nervous system or, more specifically, on nerve cells, we are struck by the great difference in the types of response we can observe. One type concerns the initiation or reactivation of complex neural phenomena that result in changes of what we call behavior, as discussed in the second part of this program by Dr. Beach and others. As to the effects of circulating gonadal hormones on the brain, we may observe, in the adult, predictable behavioral patterns that involve not only reproductive, but other activities as well. Among the latter are various forms of social behavior, motor activity, etc., and it is generally accepted that circulating hormones activate predetermined patterns of activity. Of particular interest are the lasting effects on behavioral orientation caused by pre- and postnatal hormonal milieus, as discussed in Chapter 5 (also see Chapters 20 and 25).

The other type of effect is exemplified by the control exerted by circulating gonadal steroids on gonadotropin release. We know that this involves the recording of sex hormone titers by special "hormone-sensitive cells" in the hypothalamus. This information conditions signals to the adenohypophysis that are responsible for the withholding or release of pituitary gonadotropins (or perhaps their synthesis) according to a definite time schedule, as discussed in Chapters 3 and 4. The result is a series of endocrine events which assures, for example, the periodic functions of the ovary and uterus of primates.

The most intriguing step in this sequence of commands is the switch from nerve cell to endocrine cell, a step which is made possible by the existence, within the nervous system, of special neurons with dual capacities, cells that are capable of receiving nervous stimuli and of dispatching hormonal messages to endocrine centers (E. Scharrer, 1952, 1965; Gabe, 1966; Knowles and Bern, 1966). Much attention is being given to the characterization of the hormones derived from these neurosecretory cells, their mode of action, and the manner in which they are released from their cells of origin. It is now well established that more than one type of neurosecretory hormone exists. These can be distinguished by morphological, chemical, and functional criteria.

The "classical" neurosecretory cell contains cytoplasmic granules with a characteristic staining pattern; selective methods for their light-microscopic demonstration are Gomori's chrome-hematoxylin phloxin or aldehyde fuchsin, Adams and Sloper's alcian blue technique, and Schiebler and Sterba's pseudoisocyanin-fluorescence method. Electron microscopically such cells show membrane-bounded granules in their cytoplasm that are variably, but as a rule highly, electron dense and fall into characteristic size ranges. These cellular products are polypeptides (presumably bound by a carrier protein, called neurophysin). To date the best known examples of polypeptide hormones of neurosecretory origin are the "posterior lobe hormones" vasopressin and oxytocin.

While these are directly dispatched to their "terminal targets" (kidney, uterus) and thus exemplify first-order neuroendocrine phenomena, other hormonal substances of neural origin act on glands of internal secretion (second- or third-order neuroendocrine activities). Among these are active principles destined for the control of adenohypophysial functions. Several chemically distinct entities of hypothalamic origin have been identified, each earmarked for a specific "target," among them the gonadotropin-producing cells of the pituitary. The substances responsible for the liberation (or withholding) of such "tropic hormones" are often referred to as "releasing factors" (examples: FSH-RF, LH-RF, C-RF), but more broadly applicable terms, such as hypothalamic "regulating factors" or "hypophysiotropic principles," would seem preferable.

Whatever their designation, these active principles reach their destinations within the adenohypophysis by a special vascular route, the hypophysial portal system. Thus they must be able to travel over some distance, i.e., from the site of release (median eminence, etc.) to the sites of localization of their respective target cells. The responses involved are relatively sustained.

These two characteristics liken the hypothalamic "regulating factors" to hormones rather than neurotransmitters the latter being characterized by *in loco* action of very much shorter duration. A number of known "regulating factors" (including those in charge of gonadotropin control) can be further distinguished from known neurotransmitters by their polypeptide nature (see Fraschini et al., 1966).

However, the possibility that substances of nonproteinaceous character released from neural elements may act in the manner of hormones has not been ruled out. One of the current interests centers on the detection of nerve fibers with rich stores of catecholamines in the median eminence, i.e., the very area where "regulating factors" enter the portal circulation. The analysis of this and related observations is greatly aided by the use of modern techniques of microscopy such as fluorescence histochemistry, in combination with ultrastructural methods (Falck and Owman, 1965). It has been found that axons containing a characteristic class of vesicles, the presumed intracellular storage sites of biogenic amines, establish "synaptoid" contacts with "classical," i.e., polypeptide-granule-carrying, axons.

This leaves two possibilities as to the manner in which catecholamine-rich fibers participate in the control of adenohypophysial functions. They may monitor, at the level of the median eminence, the discharge of hypothalamic "regulating factors" of polypeptide character, or they may themselves furnish one or more hypophysiotropic principles with distinctive tasks of their own to perform.

If the latter alternative can be substantiated by future experimentation, i.e., if catecholamines can be shown to elicit sustained effects in target cells at some distance via vascular channels, such biogenic amines would come to represent another class of neurosecretory hormones. One of their main distinctions, as compared with the known classical types, would be the nonpolypeptide character of their active cellular products.

The establishment of such a new class of neurosecretory neurons would, however, not extinguish the widely recognized borderline between neurohormones and neurohumors or, differently expressed, between "ordinary" and "neurosecretory" neurons. The fact remains that "neurosecretory" neurons are especially endowed to fulfill distinctive endocrine tasks for which ordinary neurons, even though capable of secreting active principles, are unsuited. The very nature and effectiveness of classical impulse transmission hinges on the speed with which precisely localized neurohumors are destroyed. Endocrine activities, on the other hand, by definition, have to bridge distances and to control multiple target cells simultaneously for relatively sustained periods of time. The need for such a means of communication apparently has led to the development within the nervous system of a distinctive class of neurosecretory cells whose products are a special type of endocrine substances, the neurohormones. Their decisive role in reproductive physiology is firmly established.

References

Bajusz, E., and G. Jasmin (eds.). 1964. *Major Problems in Neuroendocrinology.* Karger, Basel.

Falck, B., and C. Owman. 1965. A detailed methodological description of the fluorescence method for the cellular demonstration of biogenic amines. *Acta Univ. Lund, Sect. II,* 7: 1–23.

Fraschini, F., M. Motta, and L. Martini. 1966. Methods for the evaluation of hypothalamic hypophysiotropic principles. In *Methods in Drug Evaluation* (P. Mantegazza and F. Piccinini, eds.). North-Holland, Amsterdam, pp. 424–457.

Gabe, M. 1966. *Neurosecretion.* Pergamon Press, New York.

Knowles, F., and H. A. Bern. 1966. The function of neurosecretion in endocrine regulation. *Nature,* **210**: 271–272.

Scharrer, B. 1967. The neurosecretory neuron in neuroendocrine regulatory mechanisms. *Am. Zoologist,* **7:** 161–169.

Scharrer, B. 1968. Neurohumors and neurohormones: definitions and terminology. *J. Neuro-visc. Rel.* In press.

Scharrer, E. 1952. The general significance of the neurosecretory cell. *Scientia (Milan),* **46:** 177–183.

Scharrer, E. 1965. The final common path in neuroendocrine integration. *Arch. Anat. Microscop. Morphol. Exptl.,* **54:** 359–370.

Scharrer, E. 1966. Principles of neuroendocrine integration. *Res. Publ. Assoc. Nervous and Mental Disease,* **43:** 1–35.

Scharrer, E., and B. Scharrer. 1963. *Neuroendocrinology.* Columbia Univ. Press, New York.

Weitzman, M. (ed.). 1964–1968. *Bibliographia Neuroendocrinologica,* Vols. 1–5. Albert Einstein College of Medicine, New York.

Volume Contributions

REPRODUCTION AND SEXUAL BEHAVIOR (M. Diamond ed.), 153–160, © Indiana University Press

11

Contraception

Gregory Pincus *

Consideration of present-day contraceptive practice indicates clearly the emergence of physiological control methods. Nonetheless its emergence does not signify by a long shot worldwide acceptance. The fact is that the practice of any type of contraception is far from worldwide in extent or dimensions. The problems of the acceptability of contraception is not a biological one but the nature of conception control, its future, and some facts concerning its use are indeed in the biologist's purview. This review, therefore, will concern itself with (1) recent biologically significant methods of fertility control, (2) methods in the making, and (3) some physiological actions and mechanisms of current and future methods.

Recent Developments in Contraception

In 1951 Mrs. Margaret Sanger, then President of the International Planned Parenthood Federation, visited The Worchester Foundation for Experimental Biology and asked if a contraceptive pill might not be devised, since the methods then current were far from foolproof

---

* Although originally scheduled as a speaker for the afternoon program, Dr. Pincus, due to ill health, was unable to attend. His position in the program was graciously filled by Dr. E. C. Amoroso, who spoke on "The Role of Endometrial Cups in Pregnancy." This chapter was submitted subsequently. Dr. Pincus died August 22, 1967.

and also impractical in many areas of the world. Dr. Chang and I informed her that enough facts were available to justify an investigation into the inhibition of ovulation. It was clear from early studies that sterility in the rabbit might be induced by the administration of either estrogen (Pincus and Kirsch, 1936) or progesterone (Makepeace et al., 1937), the latter being obviously inhibitory of ovulation, as we were able to confirm (Pincus and Chang, 1953) and extend to the rat (Slechta et al., 1954). Since progesterone by mouth was less effective than on injection, we sought and found orally active progestins (Pincus et al., 1956). These were found by all available indications to be active ovulation inhibitors in the human and, used in combination with an estrogen, also excellent regulators of menstrual cyclicity (see Pincus, 1965a, Chap. 11). It is this use of estrogen and progestin which is the basis for the present-day oral contraceptives. Appropriate combinations, e.g., 1 to 5 mg of the progestin plus 0.08 to 0.15 mg of the estrogen (mestranol), are taken for 20 to 21 days successively, beginning on day 5 of the menstrual cycle (called combined therapy) or the estrogen is taken from day 5 to 25 and the progestin taken along with it either from day 11 to 25 or day 20 to 25 (called sequential therapy). The efficiency of the combined therapy appears to be nearly 100 per cent and somewhat superior to sequential therapy (Pincus, 1965b) (see Chapter 12).

A variant on the foregoing recently studied experimentally has been the oral administration of a progestin continuously at a low dose which appears not to be inhibitory of ovulation in most cycles but which nonetheless is fairly effective as an antifertility measure and which disturbs menstrual function to a limited extent (Rudel and Martinez-Manautou, 1966). Another variant involves the injection of a depot progestin with or without added estrogen (Gold et al., 1963, Siegel, 1963) at approximately monthly intervals.

A development of a long-known contraceptive technique is the insertion of an intrauterine device (IUD). Because of their relative cheapness and apparent nontoxicity, plastic devices are used. Contraceptive efficiency is not as great as with the oral contraceptives, particularly if account is taken of the occurrence of pregnancies following expulsion of the IUD (cf. Pincus 1965a, Chap. 13). This method is now being tested on a fairly wide scale in a number of areas with statistics still being gathered as to side effects, e.g., menstrual disturbances, infections, inflammations, etc., and as to rates of rejection.

Future Developments

A number of possibilities for fertility control are under active investigation primarily in experimental animals. These include (1) potential sterilizing measures in the male, (2) nonsteroidal agents affecting ovulation, (3) measures affecting the sperm and eggs in the female reproductive tract. I have reviewed most of these in a recent book (Pincus, 1965a). Here I will briefly recount some of the more significant procedures.

The Male

Spermatogenesis inhibition may be accomplished by using sperm or certain sperm proteins as antigens or by use of certain nonsteroidal chemical agents such as the nitrofuranes or dithiocarbamides or by the use of steroids, particularly progestins and estrogens. Practical application has thus far been unattained in view of the problems attendant on the development of isoimmunity in men, the toxicity of some of the nonsteroidal agents at effective doses, and the fact that most steroidal inhibitors of spermatogenesis appear to be also inhibitors of libido. Nonetheless, the possibility of useful antifertility for males is still potent. Antispermatogenetic agents lacking significant toxicity are being sought, as are steroids which may affect sperm production without affecting androgenesis. Agents which may be lethal to epididymal sperm without having general toxicity are conceivable. The use by males of nonspermicidal substances that might prevent sperm fertility is also a possibility. An excellent review by Jackson (1965) is recommended.

Ovulation Control

The mechanisms involved in the induction of ovulation are clearly delineated in this book (see Chapters 2, 3, and 4). The isolation and chemical identification of the hypothalamic gonadotropin-releasing factors might afford a number of new leads to control by the use of appropriate antagonists. The use of gonadotropins as antigens may also offer a useful approach, although menstrual-cycle problems associated with anovulation may prove to be unmanageable except with supplementary steroid regimens. Most interesting to us has been the finding of agents in brain extracts which stimulate and others which inhibit induced ovulation (Pincus, 1966). As naturally occurring compounds they may prove to be useful in affecting the act of ovulation without other effects, i.e., inhibition of ovarian steroidogenesis.

It is well known that a large number of pharmacological agents block ovulation (Everett, 1965; Walpole, 1965). These vary from various centrally active drugs having diverse functions, e.g., dibenamine, atropine, barbitals, reserpine, morphine, to triphenylethylene derivatives and derivatives of bis-thiourea. Practical clinical application has not been made for obvious reasons with the centrally active drugs; e.g., their central effects dominate over the ovulation-inhibiting one. With some of the others, side effects varying from obvious toxicities to undesirable amenorrheas have been observed.

The Gametes and Fertilized Ova in the Fallopian Tubes and Uterus

Spermatozoa deposited in the genital tract of the female of most species thus far studied must be capacitated for fertilization (Chang, 1953; Austin, 1961) and this capacitation is inhibited in vivo in the pseudopregnant uterus or on progesterone administration or reversed in vitro by suspension of the sperm in dilute seminal plasma (Chang, 1957, 1958). It is possible that the anticonceptional effect of low doses of progestins in the human may be due to prevention of sperm capacitation. Since the operation of capacitation in the human is still in doubt (Blandau, 1961), a thorough investigation of the phenomenon in the human would be very worthwhile.

The ovulated mammalian ovum, whether it is fertilized or not, usually takes several days to traverse the fallopian tubes. The rate of traverse is clearly affected by ovarian hormones. In the mouse, the rat, and the rabbit estrogens administered during the period of travel will, depending upon the dose used, either induce premature expulsion into the uterus or cause retention beyond the normal time, i.e., "tube-locking." We have observed premature expulsion from the uterus as well as the fallopian tubes occurring with estrogen treatment and indeed have found that certain steroids with weak estrogenic action are quite potent as ovum expeller (Pincus, 1965c). This ovum-expelling effect may be the means of sterilization with postcoital estrogen administration observed in the monkey by Morris and van Wagenen (1966). Data for similar effects in the human are lacking, but quite high doses of some standard estrogens are suggested as being needed for this effect. Effective ovum-expelling compounds with minor or no estrogenic action would (as described by us above) be most suitable for practical application, and chemical ingenuity will undoubtedly lead to the production of a number of them. Chang (1966) has recently described a similar expelling effect on tubal ova in the rabbit when active progestins are administered in doses failing to prevent ovulation during the 3 days preceding ovulation. He has called this the "before the fact" effect. Its study in various species is obviously called for.

Some Modes of Action and Physiological Effects of Present and Future Contraceptives

As is evident in the preceding summary and as may be deduced from my more detailed accounts (Pincus, 1965a), interference with normal mechanisms of reproduction may be accomplished by a variety of methods. Until the advent of the oral contraceptives, such interference was accomplished either by so-called "barrier" methods (e.g., the use of the condom or the cervical cap) or by intravaginal spermicidal action (e.g., by douche or antiseptic foams and jellies). The newer methods tend to imitate natural inhibitory mechanisms. The roles of ovarian steroids in natural regulation are various. Ovulation is prevented from occurring at undesired times and with undesired frequency by the negative feedback upon hypothalamic centers controlling the release of essential gonadotropins. This would appear clearly to be the mode of operation of progestin–estrogen treatment in women. Yet we are still pretty much in the dark concerning the details of this mechanism, e.g., the means of transport and quantities of steroid delivered to the critical loci, the nature of the chemical reactions occurring with the steroids at the critical loci, problems of binding and metabolism at the site, and so on.

If this type of ignorance of modes of action is true for the most used of modern contraceptives, it is even more evident for others Thus the best explanation I have found for the sterilizing action of IUD is that some stimulated uterine humoral agent acts in some way to induce an ovum-expelling secretion of ovarian estrogen. Actual interference with decidiualization and nidation may indeed occur in some species but not in all and just what happens in the human is inevident. The nature of the stimulus and the biochemical events underlying the presence of IUD and repercussions to this presence are unknown.

In the case of spermatogenesis inhibitors two modes of action appear possible: (1) direct action upon tubular cells, or (2) prevention of adequately sustaining pituitary gonadotropin output. The latter may indeed be involved in the antispermatogenic action of hormonal steroids or of clomiphene citrate and certain indene and hydrazine derivatives (Nelson and Patanelli, 1965), the former in the action of some of the nonsteroidal drugs mentioned. These nonsteroidal drugs may interfere with intratubular energy, producing enzyme systems, or they may have any of a number of effects on nucleic acid and protein synthesis in spermatogenetic cells. Certainly, known antimitotic agents and antimetabolites are quite effective as spermatogenesis inhibitors (Jackson, 1965).

The action of the postovulatory contraceptive agents described above would appear to involve effects either upon myometrial contraction or upon the fluid content of the oviducts or both. In connection with the myometrial mechanisms we need a reinvestigation of the role of the biogenic amines and of prostaglandins upon tubal and uterine contraction processes. Although a little is known of the alteration in tubal secretions induced by estrogen and progestin administered to rabbits and rats (Mastroianni and Wallach, 1961; Mastroianni et al., 1961), intensive study of the nature of the secretory products, their effects on ova in vitro, and the source of the fluid all require establishment. Similar considerations apply to uterine secretions. The possibility of a uterine or tubal barrier to certain plasma constituents clearly needs ascertainment, especially since certain agents may be directly ovicidal if they can actually reach the ova.

I should like to add a few words about the so-called adverse effects of modern contraceptives. In the course of use of the steroidal contraceptives by women various phenomena observed in users have been described as effects of the administered drugs. These phenomena vary from occasional episodes of nausea, headache, or dizziness to fatal thromboembolism. We have demonstrated the psychogenic origin of transient episodes by the use of double-blind studies with placebos and variations in the nature of patient admonition (cf. Pincus, 1965a, Chapter 13). Several committees have inquired into a number of the pathological phenomena with the verdict of no scientific evidence for steroidal causation (see the Report of the Advisory Committee on Oral Contraceptives, 1966). More serious are allegations of potential carcinogenic effects of exogeneous estrogenic steroid (Hertz and Bailar, 1966). But this is speculation unsustained by any scientific data demonstrating estrogen-induced cancer in the human. Indeed, available evidence suggests reduction in precancerous conditions in target tissues (e.g., the cervix, Pincus and Garcia, 1964; Hillemans et al., 1964) and of tumor incidence in the breast. Certainly long-term studies of adequately controlled populations of users should be made along with appropriate animal studies, but thus far the advantages would appear to far outweigh possible adverse actions (cf. Pincus, 1965b).

What applies to the oral ovulation inhibitors which are so widely used and extensively tested applies also to the newer methods now under study. Careful scientific inquiry should be made into the possible establishment of modified hormonal balance systems and into the consequences of such modified endocrine or other biochemical equilibria. In our daily lives the fluctuations in the endocrine milieu may be remarkably varied, what with hormonal responses to all sorts of stress and with limitations upon such responses imposed by everything from genes to personality. To these endogenous regulatory factors may be added the influence of exogenous agents such as tranquilizers, analgesics, narcotics, antibiotics, and numerous other drugs. The remarkable feature of continued human existence is the relatively minor occurrence of overt endocrinopathies in the face of these hormonal fluctuations. We are provided with extraordinary margins of safety and within their limits variability is the rule.

Acknowledgments

Investigations by the author and his colleagues were aided by research grants from Mrs. Stanley McCormick, Mrs. James Faulkner, G. D. Searle Co., and Merck, Sharp and Dohme, the Andre and Bella Meyer Foundation, the Population Council and the American Cancer Society.

References

Austin, C. R. 1961. *The Mammalian Egg*. Thomas, Springfield, Ill.

Blandau, R. J. 1961. Biology of eggs and implantation. In *Sex and Internal Secretions*, Vol. II (W. C. Young, ed.). Williams & Wilkins, Baltimore, 2nd ed., pp. 797–882.

Chang, M. C. 1953. Fertilizability of rabbit germ cells. In *Mammalian Germ Cells* (G. E. W. Wolstenholme, ed.). Little, Brown, Boston, pp. 226–242.

Chang, M. C. 1957. A detrimental effect of seminal plasma on the fertilizing capacity of sperm. *Nature,* **179:** 258–259.

Chang, M. C. 1958. Capacitation of rabbit spermatozoa in the uterus with special reference to the reproductive phases of the female. *Endocrinology,* 63: 619–628.

Chang, M. C. 1966. Effects of oral administration of medroxyprogesterone acetate and ethinyl estradiol on the transportation and development of rabbit eggs. *Endocrinology,* **79:** 939–948.

Everett, J. W. 1965. In *Agents Affecting Fertility* (C. R. Austin and J. S. Perry, eds.). Churchill, London, p. 244.

Gold, J. J., L. Smith, A. Scommegna, and S. Borushek. 1963. The efficacy of provest in inhibiting ovulation. *Intern. J. Fertility,* 8: 725–735.

Hertz, R., and J. C. Bailar, III. 1966. Estrogen-progestogen combinations for contraception. *J. Am. Med. Assoc.*, **198**: 1000–1006.

Hillemans, H. G., J. E. Ayre, and J. M. LeGuerrier. 1964. Die Einwirkung von Steroiden auf Krebsvorstadien an der Cervix. *Arznemittel-Forsch.*, **14**: 784–791.

Jackson, H. 1965. In *Agents Affecting Fertility* (C. R. Austin and J. S. Perry, eds.). Churchill, London, p. 62.

Makepeace, A. W., G. L. Weinstein, and M. H. Friedman. 1937. The effect of progestin and progesterone on ovulation in the rabbit. *Am. J. Physiol.*, **119**: 512–516.

Mastroianni, L., Jr., and R. C. Wallach. 1961. Effect of ovulation and early gestation on oviduct secretions in the rabbit. *Am. J. Physiol.*, **200**: 815–818.

Mastroianni, L., Jr., F. Beer, U. Shah, and T. H. Clewe. 1961. Endocrine regulation of oviduct secretions in the rabbit. *Endocrinology*, **68**: 92–100.

Morris, J. M., and G. van Wagenen. 1966. Compounds interfering with ovum implantation and development. III. The role of estrogens. *Am. J. Obstet. Gynecol.*, **96**: 804–815.

Nelson, W. O., and D. J. Patanelli. 1965. In *Agents Affecting Fertility* (C. R. Austin and J. S. Perry, eds.). Churchill, London, p. 78.

Pincus, G. 1965a. *The Control of Fertility*. Academic Press, New York.

Pincus, G. 1965b. Control of conception by hormonal steroids. *Science*, **153**: 493–500.

Pincus, G. 1965c. In *Preimplantation Stages of Pregnancy* (G. E. W. Wolstenholme and M. O'Connor, eds.). Churchill, London, p. 378.

Pincus, G. 1968. International Colloquium on the Physiology of Reproduction in Mammals, Paris, 1966. *Arch. Anat. Microscop. Morphol. Exptl.* In press.

Pincus, G., and M. C. Chang. 1953. Effects of progesterone and related compounds on ovulation and early development in the rabbit. *Acta Physiol. Latinoam*, **3**: 177–183.

Pincus, G., and C. R. Garcia. 1964. Ovulation inhibition by progeston-estrogen combination. *Intern. J. Fertility*, **9**: 95–105.

Pincus, G., and R. E. Kirsch. 1936. Sterility in rabbits produced by injections of oesterone related compounds. *Am. J. Physiol.*, **115**: 219–228.

Pincus, G., and M. C. Chang, M. X. Zarrow, E. S. E. Hafez, and A. P. Merrill. 1956. Studies of the biological activity of certain 19 nor-steroids in female animals. *Endocrinology*, **59**: 695–707.

Report on the Oral Contraceptives of the Advisory Committee on Obstetrics and Gynecology, Food and Drug Administration, August 1, 1966.

Rudel, H. W., and J. Martinez-Manautou. 1966. *Excerpta Med. Intern. Congr. Ser.*, **547**: 73.

Siegel, I. 1963. Conception control by long-acting progestogens: Preliminary report. *Obstet. Gynecol.*, **21**: 666–668.

Slechta, R. G., M. C. Chang, and G. Pincus. 1954. Effects of progesterone and related compounds on mating and pregnancy in the rat. *Fertility Sterility*, **5**: 282–293.

Walpole, A. L. 1965. In *Agents Affecting Fertility* (C. R. Austin and J. S. Perry, eds.). Churchill, London, p. 159.

REPRODUCTION AND SEXUAL BEHAVIOR (M. Diamond ed.), 161–175, © Indiana University Press

12

Control of Fertility
with Mestranol

Ralph I. Dorfman and Wendell H. Rooks, II

Professor William C. Young made many important contributions to the field of reproductive physiology and particularly did pioneer work on the influence of steroid sex hormones on the hypothalamic–anterior pituitary system. A few years after Pfeiffer (1936, 1937) showed that testes grafted to female rats in early infancy and removed before puberty produced constant estrus in the adult host animal, Professor Young took up the study of this phenomenon with his associates and showed that testosterone propionate injected over a 28-day period starting on either the first, fifth, or tenth postnatal day prevented the proper development of the reproductive systems of these female rats (Wilson, 1943; Wilson and Young, 1941; Wilson et al., 1940, 1941). This treatment produced adult females with small ovaries containing cystic and atertic follicles and without corpora lutea. The uteri were small, the animals did not show an estrus cycle, and were sterile when mated with males of known fertility. These experiments were followed by a report by Professor Young's associate, Dr. Wilson (1943), which dealt with the effects of estrogens in this test system. In this second study, female albino rats were injected three times weekly for a total of 12 treatments over a 28-day period beginning at various prepuberal ages between birth and the fortieth day. The reproductive ability of these animals was studied at 3 or more months after the start of the estrogen treatment. If estradiol dipropionate treatment was initiated after the fifteenth day of age, the adult females were essentially normal and produced normal litters. When the estrogen treatment was started on day 10 or earlier, the sexual development of the animals was seriously modified. Wilson (1945) describes, for the first-day-treated animals, loss of spontaneous sexual behavior, persistent diestrus, small ovaries, no corpora lutea, abnormally thickened mammary ducts, and complete infertility.

In Wilson's (1943) study, a dose of 1.2 mg of estradiol dipropionate administered over a 28-day period starting on days 20, 30, or 40 did not modify the mating behavior of any of these females; representative animals became pregnant and bore normal litters.

These findings have since been confirmed in many laboratories and in mice as well as rats (Merklin, 1953; Barraclough and Gorski, 1961; Hale and Weichert, 1944; Weichert, 143; and Kincl et al., 1965).

This chapter describes some of our efforts in adapting some of the findings on the infant rodent, as well as other estrogenic effects for the development of methods for the control of certain rodent and bird populations. In the present review we shall deal with the activity of the antifertility agent mestranol (17α-ethynyl-3-methoxyestra-1,3,5 (10)-trien-17β-ol) in this effort. This steroid is a unique orally active estrogen which has particularly interesting properties as an inhibitor of the hypothalamic–anterior pituitary–gonadal system. This compound is about one fourth as active as estrone by subcutaneous injection in the immature mouse using the weight of the uterus as the indicator of estrogenicity and some 11 times the same standard when administered by gavage and judged by the same end point (Dorfman and Kincl, 1966).

Various studies have demonstrated that mestranol has an antipituitary effect, probably by way of the hypothalamic area. In a 10-day test in the rat, Falconi and Ercoli (1963) found a significant pituitary inhibition when mestranol was administered orally at a dose of 1.48 μg. Miyake et al. (1961) studied the influence of mestranol in a mouse parabiosis assay and found that this steroid was active by both subcutaneous and oral administration. By the latter route the compound was some 100 times more active than estrone and 10,000 times that of an androgen-like methyltestosterone. Kincl et al. (1964) used intact female-castrated parabionts and evaluated mestranol as having an antipituitary activity 1 times ethynyl estradiol and some 13 times that of estradiol-17β.

The compound has a high antifertility activity, as demonstrated by Overbeek et al. (1962) and by Kincl and Dorfman (1965). The latter study utiilzed a method by which daily mestranol treatment started as proestrus and continued for 7 consecutive days with observations at 9 days. The subcutaneous injection dose of 15 μg was 100 percent effective in preventing pregnancy, while 45 μg by the oral route was also completely effective.

Mestranol is effective in influencing both androgen formation by the testis as well as spermatogenesis (McGinty and Djerassi, 1958; and Patanelli and Nelson, 1959). As indicated earlier, the administration of single doses of sex hormones to rodents within the first few days of life causes serious permanent changes in the sexual development of both males and females. These changes are essentially modifications which render the females anovulatory and the males deficient in testicular function. Mestranol is uniquely effective both by injection and oral administration. This steroid is 10 times more active than ethynyl estradiol and 1000 times more active than 17β-estradiol by subcutaneous injection. The high activity of orally administered mestranol is illustrated by the report of Rudel and Kincl (1966). When concentrations of 0.0003 percent mestranol were fed to lactating rats for 5 days, the fertility of the developing females showed dramatic changes at 45 days of age. At this time the mean ovarian weights differed from 43.3 ± 2.8 g in the control animals to 23.1 ± 0.06 g in the treated animals and the ovaries of the treated animals showed no corpora lutea.

Antifertility Studies in Rats

Rooks and Dorfman (1968a) studied adult male and female rats which were caged together from day 1 and treated by gavage with varying concentrations of mestranol. The rats usually received the daily dose in three portions at 9 A.M., 4 P.M., and at 10 P.M. Each cage contained three females and one male. The control group received only the aqueous vehicle.

In one experiment (PC-2), the mestranol dose was 2 mg and three different dosage schedules were used. The steroid was administered on days 1 and 2; days 1, 2, 15, and 16; or on days 1, 2, 8, 9, 15, 16, 22, and 23. The vehicle-treated animals showed 100 percent fertility with a mean littering day of 25 days and a mean of 11 normal young cast. The total dose of 4 mg of the estrogen, that is, 2 mg in each of days 1 and 2, delayed fertility only 2 weeks, since all females had born normal young by the 44th day of the study, and the mean littering day was 40, with a mean of 13 young. A further delay in littering was observed in the group receiving a total of 8 mg over the first 16 days. The mean littering day was 52, and this was further extended to a mean littering day of 65, when the total dose of mestranol was increased to 16 mg delivered in eight doses within the first 23 experimental days: on days 1, 2, 8, 9, 15, 16, 22, and 23. Mestranol, under the conditions of experiment PC-2, modified the total fertility of the rats for a limited period of time.

In a second study (PC-3) the experimental design was similar to that of PC-2 in that both males and females were treated and only first-litter observations were recorded, but differed by the fact that both the schedule of treatment days and daily doses were changed. Males and females were treated for an initial 4 days, for 8 days within the first 18 days (days 1 to 4, and 15 to 18), or for 16 of the first 25 days (days 1 to 4, 8 to 11, 15 to 18, 22 to 25). The daily dose was varied from 2, 4, 8, or 16 mg. First-litter data were observed for a total of 200 days. When mestranol was administered daily for 4 days using doses from 2 to 16 mg, relatively minor changes in fertility could be established on the basis of delay in mean littering day or the maximum percentage littering observable at various times up to 200 days.

At a dosage of 2 to 16 mg per day for 8 days over an 18-day period some decrease in overall fertility was observed above and beyond that seen for treatment only during the first 4 days, but the change was not striking. At the 2-mg daily dose level for 4 days, the delay in the day on which 50 percent of the females littered was from 33 to 49. Increasing the daily dosage to 4 mg neither improved the 50 percent littering day nor the maximum littering attained. Further increases in dosage to 8 and 16 mg daily did not produce striking increases in the infertility periods.

Impressive reduction in fertility resulted from daily mestranol treatment with 4, 8, or 16 mg of mestranol on days 1 to 4, 8 to 11, 15 to 18, and 22 to 25. Under these conditions less than 59 percent of the animals littered at 200 days. The maximum littering at 200 days was 22 percent at the daily dose of 4 mg, 44 percent at 8 mg/day, and only 11 percent at the 16-mg daily dose level.

Experiment PC-4 was planned to study the effect of mestranol treatment on first and second littering efficiency. The design of this study included the administration of the steroid by gavage to both the males and females and observations of all animals for 81 days. After 81 days, selected groups were observed at 127, 151, and 172 days after the start of the experiment. Treatment was 1, 2, or 4 mg of mestranol daily and the treatment days were 1, 2; 1, 2, 31, 32; or 1, 2, 31, 32, 61, 62.

At a 1-mg daily dose of mestranol for days 1 and 2, little antifertility effect was noted. When the daily dosage was continued at 1 mg but the treatment days extended to include days 31 and 32, real effectiveness in preventing the casting of the first litter was not achieved, but at 81 days inhibition of reproduction was clearly observable on the basis of second-litter data. Extending the treatment to include days 61 and 62 at 1 mg per day did not result in a striking improvement in fertility control.

At the 2- and 4-mg daily dose levels and 2 days of administration, very little effect was noticed. At the dosage of 2 mg per day for the day 1, 2, 31, 32, 61, and 62 schedule there was a considerable decrease in fertility. At 81 days only 40 percent of the females littered and 0 percent were in the second-littering stage. This is to be contrasted to the control group, which had shown a 92 percent efficiency for the first litter and 89 percent for the second litter.

When the daily dose was increased to 4 mg the four-dose schedule of treatment on days 1, 2, 31, and 32 was highly effective in decreasing the number of litters cast within the 81-day study period, but this design was no better than the 2-mg dosage schedule for the 6-day schedule. Increasing the daily dosage of mestranol by administering the 4-mg daily dose for 6 days did not intensify the effect.

In experiment PC-4 the first litter data on the control animals did not change after day 46 of the study, at which time 22 of the 24 rats had littered. Two females were apparently sterile, since no change occurred. Each of the 22 fertile females cast an additional litter by day 81.

At a daily mestranol dosage of 2 mg administered on days 1, 2, 31, 32, 61, and 62, reasonable fertility control of the first litter was demonstrated. With rats treated on the same time schedule but increasing the dosage to 4 mg, a maximum of 7 to 15 litters were observed on day 127 and no further litters were found even at day 172. It is unlikely that sufficient mestranol was in circulation to restrain the hypothalamus by the usually described mechanisms for this extended period of time.

Both the 2- and 4-mg daily doses of mestranol over the 6-day period (days 1, 2, 31, 32, 61, and 62) showed some highly significant antifertility responses for second littering. In the control group 17 of 24 cast second litters by day 71 and 22 of 24 cast second litters by day 81. At the 2-mg level no litters were cast by day 81 but 10 of the 12 females had littered at 127 days. The data on the 4-mg dosage levels indicate complete second-litter inhibition until day 127, at which time only 4 of 15 females had young. This number increased to 5 at 151 days and was unchanged at day 172.

Antifertility Studies in Mice

Study PC-5 (Dorfman and Rooks, 1968) was an attempt to control fertility in mice by administering mestranol by gavage to both males and females on a twice-daily basis. Treatment days were 1, 2; 1, 2, 31, 32; or 1, 2, 31, 32, 61, 62; and the daily dose was 0.1, 0.2, and 0.4 mg per day.

The incidence of first litters was not influenced by mestranol treatment on days 1, 2. When days 30 and 31 were included in the dosage schedule, there was a tendency of the percent littering to be somewhat inhibited. The remarkable finding, however, was the littering percentage observed for the group treated on days 1, 2, 30, 31, 60, 61. This more intense treatment schedule, at the 0.1-mg daily dose level, resulted in a fertility equal to or greater than the control group. An even more unexpected result was found in the second-litter result. The reproductive efficiency, progressing from the least to the greatest, was treatment on days 1, 2; 1, 2, 30, 31; and 1, 2, 30, 31, 60, 61.

Data from PC-5 at 0.2 and 0.4 mg of mestranol indicated again that increasing the concentrations of mestranol or the number of days of administration did not necessarily guarantee increased infertility.

Experiment PC-8 on the control of fertility in mice was identical to that described under PC-5 except for dosage of mestranol. The daily dosage was 0.4, 0.8, and 1.6 mg and the treatment schedule was 1, 2; 1, 2, 31, 32; and 1, 2, 31, 32, 61, 62 days of treatment.

At 100 days, 38 to 98 days after the last day of mestranol treatment, only minor differences were found in the mean littering day or percentage of live litters cast. Differences in fertility were observed in animals which received mestranol at daily dosage of 1.6 mg per day for days 1, 2, 31, 32, and for days 1, 2, 31, 32, 61, 62, which showed inhibition of litter bearing at the rate of 47 and 33 percent respectively. One hundred percent littering was found for the control group.

Somewhat more significant reductions in fertility were observed for second-littering efficiency. At all doses of mestranol for 6-day treatment periods significant reductions were observed. Decreases of 40, 80, 67, and 73 percent were recorded for the groups treated under the following treatment conditions, respectively: 0.4 mg per day for

6 days, 0.8 mg per day for 6 days, 1.6 mg per day for 4 days, and finally, 1.6 mg per day for 6 days.

The third- and fourth-litter data show even more dramatic inhibition of reproduction. Control data at 100 days for the third littering shows 18 for the 24 females and 11 of 24 casting the fourth litter. The group treated with 0.4 mg of mestranol on days 1, 2, 31, 32, 61, and 62 showed the severe reduction to 2 of 15 and 0 of 15 litters for the third and fourth litters, respectively. Increasing the daily dosage to 0.8 and 1.6 mg resulted in the same intense decreases in third and fourth littering and reasonable decreases when the 4-day dosage schedule including days 1, 2, 31, and 32 were employed. Similar observations have been made at 170 days.

Of the 15 females treated with 0.8 mg per day on days 1, 2, 31, 32, 61, and 62, 19 cast a first litter and 3 a second litter within the first 100 days. Six animals died and, as with most of the deaths, this was usually due to some irregularities during delivery of the young. At 170 days there was a gain of three second litters, meaning that three females had not littered for the second time. At the daily dosage of 1.6 mg for days 1, 2, 31, 32 at 100 days, seven live first litters were cast and five live second litters. This did not change during the following 70 days.

When the same dose was administered for the 6-day period of 1, 2, 31, 32, 61, and 62, five and four live litters resulted for the 100-day observation period for the first and second litters, respectively. At 170 days there was a gain in the number of litters but at this time four females had failed to cast live first litters and two failed to produce live second litters.

Antifertility Studies in Coturnix Quail

In addition to the mammal, birds too were studied (Rooks and Dorfman, 1968b). Thirty-five-day-old Coturnix quail were placed on a diet of Game Bird Startena supplemented with 5 percent sesame oil. The treated birds received mestranol incorporated in the diet. The egg-laying observation period covered 65 days from 35 to 100 days of age.

The control level of 39 eggs per 100 quail days in experiment A was significantly depressed when the birds were fed a diet containing 0.01 percent mestranol. At 0.02 percent mestranol the suppression was intensified to 87 percent. Mestranol in the diet at 0.04 and 0.08 percent resulted in egg-laying depressions of 85 and 90 percent. In this experiment the 0.02 percent mestranol in the diet maximally inhibited ovulation.

In Experiment B a mean of 52 eggs were laid per 100 quail days in the absence of treatment. As in experiment A, the rate of egg laying decreased with increasing concentrations of mestranol in the diet. As little as 0.0025 percent mestranol produced a 44 percent decrease in eggs laid. The egg-laying capacity was further decreased to 67, 60, and 98 percent, respectively, for 0.005, 0.01, and 0.16 percent of the antifertility agent in the diet.

Mestranol causes antifertility in the quail for many days after cessation of treatment. In the case of the 0.0025 percent mestranol in the diet, 21 days of infertility resulted from the 10-day treatment. When 0.08 percent mestranol was fed for 10 days, 35 days of anovulation resulted, and increasing this dose to 0.16 percent yielded 43 infertile days after cessation of treatment.

Discussion

Rat Fertility Control

Tables 1, 2, 3, and 4 summarize the efficiency of mestranol as an agent to control fertility in the rat, dealing only with first-littter data. Tabe 1 summarizes the rank order from most effective to least effective treatment schedules to produce 70 percent fertility control from the last day of mestranol treatment. Better than 175 days of fertility control were obtained when 64 mg of the steroid was administered for 16 days during the first 25 days. This was by far the most prolonged control of fertility observed. When 64 mg of mestranol was administered as 8-mg daily doses on days 1 to 4 and 15 to 18, considerably less efficiency was seen; only 70 percent control for more than 35 but less than 74 days. Reasonably good fertility control resulted from treatment from days 1 to 4 at 4 mg per day. Under these conditions, 70 percent fertility control was achieved for more than 38 and less than 49 days.

Table 2 deals with the rank order from most effective to least effective treatment schedule to produce 100 percent fertility control from the last day of mestranol treatment. One hundred and twenty-eight mg of mestranol given in eight daily doses for 16 of the first 25 days inhibited littering for more than 49 and less than 74 days. At 4 mg per day under the same conditions, something more than 49 days of fertility control was achieved. The same total dose, but given

Table 1

Rank Order of Treatment Schedules
(Listed in Order of Decreasing Intensity)
to Produce 70% Fertility Control
Counted from Last Day of Mestranol Treatment [a]
(Rat; first litter data only)

Days of control, 70% level	Total mestranol, mg	Daily dose, mg	Treatment, days	Experiment no.
>175	64	4	1–4, 15–18, 8–11, 22–25	PC-3
>38 <49	16	4	1–4	
>38 <49	32	8	1–4	
>35 <74	64	8	1–4, 15–18	
>29 <42	16	2	1, 2, 8, 9, 15, 16, 22, 23	PC-2
>24 <31	8	2	1, 2, 15,16	
>19 <65	24	4	1, 2, 31, 32, 61, 62	PC-4

[a] Rooks and Dorfman (1968a).

over 4 days at 16 mg per day, resulted in 100 percent inhibition for at least 38 days and less than 56 days.

For fertility control for at least 31 days but less than 38 days, it was possible to use a total of 32 mg of mestranol administered by gavage as 4 mg per day for 8 treatment days, or 8 mg per day for 4 treatment days. Tables 3 and 4 indicate similar data except that the calculations give the total days for 70 percent (Table 3) and 100 percent (Table 4) fertility control from the start of the experiment rather than only the 70 or 100 percent free period from the last day of treatment, as was illustrated in Tables 1 and 2, respectively.

Mouse Fertility Control

Table 5 is a composite of the two mouse studies and is based on the total first and second litters cast per potential female. The expression "potential female" recognizes the fact that some female mice died and it is assumed that their death was due to abnormalities during pregnancy. A ratio of total number of first and second litters per female has been calculated and is represented in Table 5. The composite control ratio of 1.87 was only modestly decreased when the

Table 2

Rank Order of Treatment Schedules
(Listed in Order of Decreasing Intensity)
to Produce 100% Fertility Control
Counted from Last Day of Mestranol Treatment [a]
(Rat; first litter data only)

Days of control, 100% level	Total mestranol, mg	Daily dose, mg	Treatment, days	Experiment no.
>49 <74	128	8	1–4, 15–18, 8–11, 22–25	PC-3
>49 <74	256	16	1–4, 15, 18, 8–11, 22–25	
>49 <64	64	4	1–4, 15–18, 8–11, 22–25	
>38 <49	64	16	1–4	
>35 <56	128	16	1–4, 15–18	
>31 <38	32	8	1–4	
>31 <38	32	4	1–4, 15–18	
>28 <49	32	2	1–4, 15–18, 8–11, 22–25	
>25 <35	64	8	1–4, 15–18	
>24 <35	32	4	1–4, 15–18	
>24 <35	16	2	1–4, 15–18	
>17 <29	16	2	1, 2, 8, 9, 15, 16, 22, 23	PC-2

[a] Rooks and Dorfman (1968a).

daily dose of mestranol was 0.1 mg and any of the three different dosage schedules were used. At 0.2 mg, only the day 1, 2, 31, 32 treatment schedule showed some reasonable decrease in ratio from the control of 1.87 to 0.87. Three additional ratios showed some significant decrease. These were 0.67 for the 0.8 mg per day for the 6-day treatment schedule, the 1.06 value for the 4-day schedule and 1.6 mg, and the most intense effect when 1.6 mg of mestranol was administered daily for days 1, 2, 31, 32, 61, and 62, yielding a ratio of 0.27, or a decrease in fertility by this index of 86 percent.

Table 6 analyses the effect of mestranol when observations of 100 days of the study PC-8, involving four litterings, are considered. Again the dramatic effect of the antifertility steroid was seen when the compound was administered over the 62 days on the 6-day treatment schedule. Total litters per female were reduced from 3.16 in the

Table 3

Rank Order of Treatment Schedules
(Listed in Order of Decreasing Intensity)
to Produce 70% Fertility Control from Day 1 [a]
(Rat; first litter data only)

Days of control, 70% level	Total mestranol, mg	Daily dose, mg	Treatment, days	Experiment no.
200	64	4	1–4, 15–18, 8–11, 22–25	PC-3
81	24	4	1, 2, 31, 32, 61, 62	PC-4
53	64	8	1–4, 15–18	PC-3
52	16	2	1, 2, 8, 9, 15, 16, 22, 23	PC-2
42	32	8	1–4	PC-3
42	16	4	1–4	
40	8	2	1, 2, 15, 16	PC-2

[a] Rooks and Dorfman (1968a).

control group to 1.46, 0.93, and 0.6 for the daily doses of 0.4, 0.8, and 1.6 mg, respectively. At the highest daily dose of 1.6 mg for the 4 days 1, 2, 31, and 32, an intense antifertility effect was observed with a value of 1.2 litters per female.

The antifertility effect of mestranol measured, not in absolute reduction of progeny, but rather by balance of antilittering effectiveness per unit of mestranol employed, is seen when the percent reduction in young born was evaluated per milligram of mestranol used (Table 7). There appears to be a particularly high efficiency for the use of 0.4 mg of mestranol over the 6-day period.

Fertility Control of Coturnix Quail

Mestranol appears to have an intense and prolonged inhibitory effect on the hypothalamic–anterior pituitary–ovarian system. Relatively minimum amounts of orally administered steroid produced this effect. Ten days feeding of a diet containing 0.16 percent of the antifertility agent resulted in 43 days of anovulation in the birds.

Table 4

Rank Order of Treatment Schedules
(Listed in Order of Decreasing Intensity)
to Produce 100% Fertility Control from Day 1 [a]
(Rat; first litter data only)

Days of control, 100% level	Total mestranol, mg	Daily dose, mg	Treatment, days	Experiment no.
74	64	4	1–4, 15–18, 8–11, 22–25	PC-3
74	128	8	1–4, 15–18, 8–11, 22–25	
74	256	16	1–4, 15–18, 8–11, 22–25	
53	128	16	1–4, 15–18	
43	32	2	1–4, 15–18, 8–11, 22–25	
43	64	8	1–4, 15–18	
42	64	16	1–4	
42	16	2	1–4, 15–18	
40	16	2	1, 2, 8, 9, 15, 16, 22, 23	PC-2
35	16	4	1–4	PC-3

[a] Rooks and Dorfman (1968a).

Summary

Studies on the antifertility activity of mestranol have been conducted in albino rats, Swiss-Webster albino mice, and in the Coturnix quail. In each of these studies immediate and prolonged antifertility has been demonstrated with the intensity of fertility control being dependent upon the number of days of treatment and the daily dose.

References

Barraclough, C. A., and R. A. Gorski. 1961. Evidence that the hypothalamus is responsible for androgen-induced sterility in the female rat. *Endocrinology*, 68: 68–79.

Dorfman, R. I., and F. A. Kincl. 1966. Uterotrophic activity of various phenolic steroids. *Acta Endocrinol.*, 52: 619–626.

Dorfman, R. I., and W. H. Rooks, II. 1968. Control of fertility by mestranol in the Swiss-Webster albino mouse. In press.

Falconi, G., and A. Ercoli. 1963. 3-Cyclopentyl ether of 17α-ethynylestradiol: a

Table 5

Composite First and Second Litter Data of Experiments
PC-5 and PC-8 in Mice [a]
(Observations at 74 days)

Daily dose, mg	Treatment, days	No. of mice	Live litters		Total first and second litters in 74 days per female
			First litter	Second litter	
0	0	48	47	43	1.87
0.1	1, 2	15	15	5	1.33
	1, 2, 31, 32	15	12	10	1.47
	1, 2, 31, 32, 61, 62	15	15	11	1.7
0.2	1, 2	15	15	15	2.0
	1, 2, 31, 32	15	11	2	0.87
	1, 2, 31, 32, 61, 62	15	15	6	1.40
0.4	1, 2	30	22	30	1.73
	1, 2, 31, 32	30	28	10	1.26
	1, 2, 31, 32, 61, 62	30	23	21	1.46
0.8	1, 2	15	15	13	1.86
	1, 2, 31, 32	15	13	10	1.53
	1, 2, 31, 32, 61, 62	15	9	1	0.67
1.6	1, 2	15	15	9	1.60
	1, 2, 31, 32	15	11	5	1.06
	1, 2, 31, 32, 61, 62	15	4	0	0.27

[a] Dorfman and Rooks (1968).

potent anti-gonadotrophic and contraceptive agent in rodents. *Experientia,* **19:** 249–250.

Hale, H. B., and C. K. Weichert. 1944. Ovarian tumors in adult rats following prepuberal administration of estrogens. *Proc. Soc. Exptl. Biol. Med.,* **55:** 201–202.

Kincl, F. A., and R. I. Dorfman. 1965. Antifertility activity of various steroids in the female rat. *J. Reprod. Fertility,* **10:** 105–113.

Kincl, F. A., A. J. Birch, and R. I. Dorfman. 1964. Pituitary gonadotropic inhibitory activity of various steroids in ovariectomized-intact female rats in parabiosis. *Proc. Soc. Exptl. Biol. Med.,* **117:** 549–552.

Table 6

Summation of Live Litters Cast in 100 Days in Mice [a] (PC-8)

Daily mg dose,	Treatment, days	No. of females	Live litters cast				Total litters	Total litters per female
			First	Second	Third	Fourth		
0	0	24	24	23	18	11	76	3.16
0.4	1, 2	15	11	15	14	4	44	2.94
	1, 2, 31, 32	15	13	12	8	1	34	2.26
	1, 2, 31, 32, 61, 62	15	11	9	2	0	22	1.46
0.8	1, 2	15	15	15	14	5	49	3.27
	1, 2, 31, 32	15	13	13	7	1	34	2.26
	1, 2, 31, 32, 61, 62	15	10	3	1	0	14	0.93
1.6	1, 2	15	15	10	9	2	36	2.40
	1, 2, 31, 32	15	7	5	5	1	18	1.20
	1, 2, 31, 32, 61, 62	15	5	4	0	0	9	0.6

[a] Dorfman and Rooks (1968).

Kincl, F. A., A. Folch Pi, M. Maqueo, L. Herrera Lasso, A. Oriol, and R. I. Dorfman. 1965. Inhibition of sexual development in male and female rats treated with various steroids at the age of five days. *Acta Endocrinol.*, 49: 193–206.

McGinty, D. A., and C. Djerassi. 1958. Some chemical and biological properties of 19-nor-17α-ethynyltestosterone. *Ann. N.Y. Acad. Sci.*, 71: 500–515.

Merklin, R. J. 1953. Reproductive performance of female mice treated prepuberally with a single injection of estradiol dipropionate. *Endocrinology*, 53: 342–343.

Miyake, T., K. Horibe, E. Itoga, Y. Nomura, H. Kakushi, K. Odaguchi, and M. Kadowaki. 1961. Inhibitory effect of various steroids on gonadotrophin hypersecretion in parabiotic mice. *Endocrinology*, 69: 534–546.

Overbeek, G. A., Z. Madjerek, and J. de Visser. 1962. The effect of lynestrenol on animal reproduction, *Acta Endocrinol.*, 41: 351–370.

Patanelli, D. J., and W. O. Nelson. 1959. The effect of certain 19-nor-steroids and related compounds on spermatogenesis in male rats. *Arch. Anat. Microscop. Morphol. Exptl.*, 48 (*Suppl.*): 199–222.

Pfeiffer, C. A. 1936. Effects of ovarian transplants upon the development and maintenance of the seminal vesicle and prostate gland of the albino rat. *Anat. Rec.*, 65: 213–237.

Pfeiffer, C. A. 1937. Alterations in the percentage of cell types in the hypophysis by gonad transplantation in the rat. *Endocrinology*, 21: 812–820.

Rooks, W. H., II, and R. I. Dorfman. 1968a. Control of fertility in rats by mestranol. In press.

Table 7

Relative Efficiency of Various Dosage Schedules
and Daily Doses of Mestranol in Mice [a] (PC-8)
(100 days of observations)

Daily dose, mg	Treatment, days	Litters per female	Young per female	% Reduction in young per mg of mestranol
0	0	3.16	31.6	—
0.4	1, 2	2.94	29.4	9
	1, 2, 31, 32	2.26	22.6	18
	1, 2, 31, 32, 61, 62	1.46	10.9	27
0.8	1, 2	3.27	29.4	4.3
	1, 2, 31, 32,			
	1, 2, 31, 32	2.26	20.3	11.1
	61, 62	0.93	6.5	16.6
1.6	1, 2	2.4	21.6	14.5
	1, 2, 31, 32	1.2	10.8	10.3
	1, 2, 31, 32, 61, 62	0.6	3.6	9.2

[a] Dorfman and Rooks (1968).

Rooks, W. H., II, and R. I. Dorfman. 1968b. Influence of mestranol on egg laying efficiency in coturnix quail. In press.

Rudel, H. W., and F. A. Kincl. 1966. The biology of antifertility steroids. *Acta Endocrinol.*, **51** (Suppl.): 105.

Weichert, C. K. 1943. Effect of environmental stilbestrol in shortening prolonged gestation in the lactating rat. *Proc. Soc. Exptl. Biol. Med.*, **53**: 203–204.

Wilson, J. G. 1943. Reproductive capacity of adult female rats treated prepuberally with estrogenic hormone. *Anat. Rec.*, **86**: 341–359.

Wilson, J. G., and W. C. Young. 1941. Sensitivity to estrogen studied by means of experimentally induced mating responses in the female guinea pig and rat. *Endocrinology*, **29**: 779–783.

Wilson, J. G., W. C. Young, and J. B. Hamilton. 1940. A technique suppressing development of reproductive function and sensitivity to estrogen in the female rat. *Yale J. Biol. Med.*, **13**: 189–202.

Wilson, J. G., J. B. Hamilton, and W. C. Young. 1941. Influence of age and presence of the ovaries on reproductive function in rats injected with androgens. *Endocrinology*, **29**: 784–789.

REPRODUCTION AND SEXUAL BEHAVIOR (M. Diamond ed.), 177–186, © Indiana University Press

13

Perspectives in Human Fertility

Robert W. Noyes

Before seriously attempting to solve his reproductive problems, man should develop a deeper perspective and a better definition of human fertility than he has at the present time. Patients, practitioners, and researchers are all limited by current frontal views of the reproductive process, which—let's face it—is by no means man's highest evolutionary attainment. This chapter will give examples of how slight differences in perspective may lead to large differences in solutions of some of man's fertility problems. The chapter will conclude with an attempt at a general perspective and a comprehensive definition of fertility that is relevant to the human race as well as to the individual from both within and beyond present evolutionary bounds.

The following common gynecological problem exemplifies one way in which perspective influences clinical treatment. An unmarried, 24-year-old patient with a history of infrequent and inadequate menses, asked her physician if she was fertile. Believing that his patient's fertility depended upon regular ovulation, he systematically pursued the generally accepted diagnostic and therapeutic measures and succeeded in inducing regular menses and biphasic temperature curves. He then assured the patient that her fertility had been improved. His perspective equated fertility with normal function of the reproductive organs.

A second practitioner saw fertility as an equilibrium in which the function of an organ or system might vary widely from normal yet contain compensatory factors powerful enough to maintain normal fertility. He had observed that many apparently poorly functioning reproductive systems could come through with large families, while many apparently normal ones might produce nothing. For these reasons, when he was confronted with an exactly similar problem to the one presented above, he simply examined the patient thoroughly to rule out organic disease and gave this advice: If you don't become pregnant within six months after commencing regular intercourse return for an infertility study. He was tempted but did not add: and don't let anyone try to make you ovulate until the ovum has a chance to get fertilized.

A second example involves perspectives in the laboratory as well as in the clinic. A condition known variously as *underdeveloped secretory endometrium, luteal deficiency, secretory hypoplasia,* and a host of other synonyms has been blamed for the reproductive problems of from 7 to 66 percent of patients (Noyes, 1959). How does one evaluate secretory endometrial development? One way is to allow maturation to proceed as far as possible, take an endometrial biopsy just before menses, and observe whether or not a *maximal* secretory response has occurred. Or one can take the biopsy any time after ovulation and compare the endometrial response with histological standards that have been established for each day of the secretory phase of the cycle (Noyes, et al., 1950). A very different conclusion about endometrial development will be reached if one pursues one of these slightly different viewpoints rather than the other.

Biopsies of late premenstrual or early menstrual endometrium are expected to show secretory exhaustion of the glands and a marked predecidual response in the stroma. These are end stages of development and no criteria have been described for overdevelopd secretory endometrium. For this reason all deviations from normal have to be recorded as underdevelopment, even though some of the deviations are certain to have been caused by errors in tissue sampling, sectioning, staining, or interpretation.

When biopsies are taken at various times during the secretory phase of the cycle, deviations from the expected development will be observed in the direction of over as well as underdevelopment (Noyes and Haman, 1953). Figure 1 shows that in about 21 percent of 1007 biopsies the histological date coincided exactly with the maturation date calculated from the shift in basal body temperature (no deviation = 0 on abscissa), about 54 percent appeared to be one or more days underdeveloped (left of 0 on abscissa), and about 25 percent appeared to be one or more days overdeveloped (right of 0 on ab-

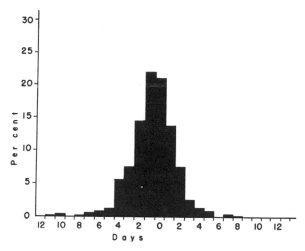

Fig. 1 Distribution of deviations between the observed histological development of 1007 endometrial biopsies and the calculated day of the secretory phase on which the endometrial biopsy was taken. [From Noyes et al. (1950).]

scissa). However, the apparent preponderance of underdeveloped endometria was found to be due to a sampling error and disappeared when a statistical test for linearity of regression was performed. The error consisted of taking more biopsies beyond than before the midsecretory point. This tends to accumulate random errors along with the truly underdeveloped endometria and skews the distribution erroneously. There is no evidence that in an infertile population more patients have underdeveloped than overdeveloped endometria.

The proponents of *"underdeveloped secretory endometrium"* advocate postovulatory progesterone therapy. However, when progesterone was given in one cycle and a placebo in another cycle (Fig. 2) progesterone neither advanced nor retarded endometrial development significantly (Noyes, 1959). Estrogen significantly retarded endometrial development, but chorionic gonadotropin (HCG) and various combinations of estrogen, progesterone, and HCG had little effect.

What one would really like to know about endometrial development is what are the limits within which the ovum can implant and develop normally. What might be called an "egg's eye view" of the endometrium has not been obtained as yet in women. But in animals, the technique of transferring donor ova into the uterus of recipient hosts at precisely defined times after ovulation has yielded some new and interesting perspectives (Noyes and Dickmann, 1960). In rats, ova enter the uterus on day 4 of pregnancy and implant during the

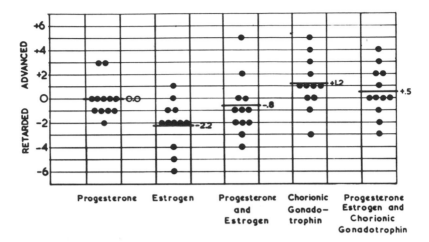

Fig. 2 Effect on endometrial development of hormones administered between ovulation and endometrial biopsy on about the eighth postovulatory day. The ordinate is calibrated in days of histological advancement of retardation. [From Noyes (1959).]

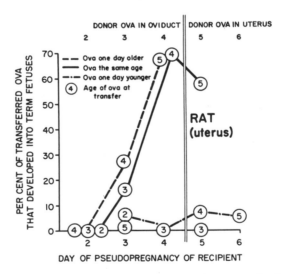

Fig. 3 Effect of endometrial development on the survival of rat ova. The abscissa gives the stage of endometrial development in days, the ordinate the percent of ova surviving. The solid line represents the normal endometrial-ovular relationship, the dashed line endometrial underdevelopment, and the dash-dot line endometrial overdevelopment. [From Noyes and Haman (1953).]

afternoon of day 5. If day 4 ova are transferred into the uterus on day 5 (endometrium relatively overdeveloped), none of the ova become term embryos (Fig. 3). Instead they degenerate within a few hours (Fig. 4). However, when day 5 ova are transferred into the

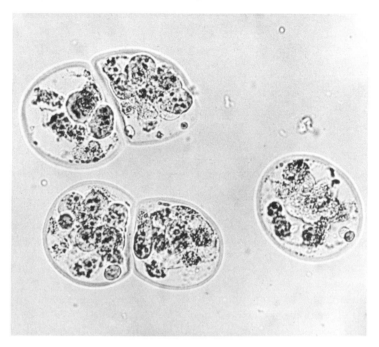

Fig. 4 Ova recovered 12 hours after transfer of day 4 ova into the uterus of a recipient rat on day 5 of pseudopregnancy, showing the extent of damage caused by overdeveloped endometrium. [From Dickmann and Noyes (1960).]

uterus on day 4 of pregnancy they survive as well as controls (Fig. 3). Although the ova are chronologically mature, they are unable to implant until endometrial maturation "catches up" on day 5. During the delay in implantation in the relatively underdeveloped endometrium, the ova continue to mature, and this preimplantation maturation gives them such a head start that by the end of pregnancy the fetuses weigh 25 percent more than their litter-mate controls (Noyes, et al., 1961a; Noyes, et al., 1961b) (Fig. 5).

Instead of being the cause of infertility as previously suspected, underdeveloped endometrium may thus be a better environment than even normal endometrium for embryonic development. The previously neglected overdeveloped endometrium is so toxic to ova that it is worthy of careful consideration as a contraceptive method. A com-

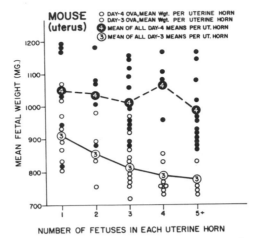

Fig. 5 Mean weights of mouse fetuses in each of 70 uterine horns, 15 days after transfer of day 3 ova into one horn and day 4 ova into the other horn on day 3 following ovulation. The day 4 ova continued to mature in the underdeveloped endometrial environment, and, although they both implanted at the same time, by the time of term pregnancy the fetuses resulting from the day 4 ova weighed 25 percent more than their day 3 litter-mate controls. [From Noyes et al. (1961b).]

plicating factor is that the same hormones that alter endometrial development also change the tubal transport rate of ova. This is as important a factor in determining implantation as either ovular or endometrial development. Two of the three critical determinants of implantation—ovular maturation, endometrial development, and tubal transport—will have to be controlled independently before fertility can be controlled at the postfertilization phase.

Treatment for males is also biased by perspective, as witness the problem of how many spermatazoa an ejaculate should contain to be compatible with normal fertility. For many years the only data available were from studies of infertile couples, and from this experience 60 million sperm per milliliter was considered to be the minimal number. Then MacLeod and Gold (1951) studied the semen of husbands awaiting the birth of their children and found that 20 million sperm per milliliter was compatible with pregnancy. It would seem that increasing numbers of sperm compensate in some way for decreased fertility, but the exact compensatory mechanisms remain unknown in both male and female. In animal experiments the number of sperm required for normal fertility following artificial insemination is 500 times less than in the normal ejaculate (Cheng and Casida, 1948).

Less well documented is the reported infertility in man associated with abnormally high sperm counts (MacLeod, et al., 1955; MacLeod and Gold, 1957). And still less has been said about whether or not fertility could be restored by simple dilution of the hyperspermic semen followed by artificial insemination. These uncertainties make it difficult, if not impossible, to evaluate the fertility of the husband in a given couple, assuming that he has at least a few sperm in the ejaculate. One is not justified in reassuring the oligospermic husband of an infertile couple that he could father a child if he cohabited with a large enough number of fertile women. Some oligospermic men may be normally fertile, others may not. Practitioners of artificial insemination tend to reject oligispermic donors whether or not they have apparently fathered children, so we may never find out whether or how sperm numbers actually correlate with human fertility.

A final example of how perspective may affect clinical management is the problem of psychogenic infertility. Although an impressive array of psychic states has been associated with variations in fertility, only two have been objectively studied (Noyes and Chapnick, 1964). In both cases, the clinical impression was found to be incorrect: adoption does not increase fertility and frigidity does not decrease fertility. Psychic influences can stop ovulation (war amenorrhea) and cause impotence, but there is as yet no firm evidence that the psyche can cause occult infertility in otherwise normal couples. The perspective held by some researchers that "psychogenic sterility can be defined as sterility in a couple in whom no pathology or dysfunction can be demonstrated by any method available to us today" (Fischer, 1953) is of little use in identifying causes or mechanisms of action of psychic influences. Psychogenic causes of occult infertility are well worth looking for, however, because suggestion techniques might be used to control the population growth rate.

Granting that the handling of today's fertility problems are confused by variability of outlook and lack of clear definition, is it possible to evolve a general perspective and a comprehensive definition of human fertility for the future? The deeper one looks the more difficult this becomes. Starting with the present evolutionary state of man's reproductive processes and the current trend to go always for the "most," *fertility* could be defined in terms of the largest number of living children a couple could have in one lifetime. Maximally fertile women would not menstruate because they would be pregnant from menarche to menopause. They would have multiple rather than single births and the reproduction age span might extend from age 9 to 50.

Many people would consider this a reasonable definition for animal breeders but not for application to modern man.

Volition and control are important adjuncts to a comprehensive definition of fertility for man, and the concept of maximum fertility is superseded by that of optimum fertility. What needs to be defined might best be termed *eufertility*, i.e., the ability of a couple to have as many healthy children as they wish, whenever they wish, and with complete reproductive efficiency. *Hyperfertility* would be more children at shorter birth intervals than desired, *hypofertility* would be longer intervals or fewer children than desired, and *sterility* would remain the permanent inability to reproduce. Couples who wanted no children but were "surprised" would be hyperfertile and so would couples who wanted two children as soon as possible and had triplets. Couples who wanted three children as soon as possible and had twins would be hypofertile, as would couples who wanted 14 children and had only 13.

Dysfertility would be reproductive inefficiency and would include menstruation, hyperejaculation (more than one ejaculate needed per ovulation), hyperspermia (more than perhaps 20 million sperm per ejaculate), failure of gamete transport, failure of fertilization and of implantation, abortion, morning sickness, toxemia, prematurity, and birth defects. A hypothetical example of eufertility would be the case of an amenorrheic woman who married an oligospermic man on a 1-day furlough. They wanted three children as soon as possible. By prearrangement ovulation had been induced, there was time for but a single intercourse, and after 9 pleasant months healthy triplets were born. The husband later returned to his still amenorrheic wife, no one tried to make her menstruate, and in due time each of their three offspring had children of his own. The requirements for volition, control, and efficiency have been adhered to within the rather stringent definition of eufertility.

A truly comprehensive definition of fertility would, by extension, include the needs of the race as well as the needs of the individual, and fertility would become the ability of humans to reproduce "themselves" efficiently. This sounds simple but isn't. Assuming that what man wants is a stable population with randomly distributed genes, "themselves" are eufertile couples who *must* produce one male and one female child and *must* have by each child one grandson and one granddaughter. A couple who produces two boys or two girls is not strictly reproducing "itself" and is transmitting more than its share of sex-linked genes to the future population. To be sure of reproducing themselves, couples must have their children as early as possible. If a son or daughter dies or is hypofertile, the parents must produce a fertile replacement or they will have failed to reproduce "themselves" and hence are technically hypofertile. Furthermore, the spouse of an infertile child would have to divorce, remarry, and have a son and daughter in order to qualify her own parents for eufertility. Artificial insemination in this context would be dysgenic. An alternative way to make up for a second-generation deficiency would be to have the fertile child produce all the required four grandchildren, but this would introduce an excess of genes of the fertile child and his spouse into the population. Even if a couple could replace a defaulting son or daughter by having a third child a generation later, this child might also die or be hypofertile. For these reasons, the eufertile couple, to reproduce "themselves," must have control of the number, sex, and fertility of their offspring—a very difficult equilibrium to maintain throughout the population. Either the concept of volition must be discarded from the definition or else a means for replacing defaulted children must be found from outside the population.

Man does not have to be bound by the current dimensions of evolution. In vitro reproduction is well within our grasp. By this means, genetic variation could be fostered or inhibited, euphenic conditions ensured, random errors rejected, and the vacillating law of supply and demand obeyed. Fertility in this type of future might then be defined as the continuous availability of a wide assortment of gametes which when combined in a one sperm/one ovum ratio would produce normal zygotes.

It can be concluded that any comprehensive perspective or definition of fertility formulated for man in his current evolutionary state will need to be modified in the future. In vitro reproduction, either alone or as a supplement to the continuing in vivo efforts of the conservatives among us, offers the best chance of solving man's fertility problems without sacrificing volition, control, or the individual to society. Perhaps the main value of continuing to seek new perspectives in the old surroundings is to keep from confusing evolutionary norms with optimal human reproduction. We will never know how "deep" fertility is until we look at side views as well as the front.

Acknowledgments

This work was supported in part by the National Institutes of Child Health and Human Development, Grant HD-02066, and by the Ford Foundation.

References

Cheng, P., and L. E. Casida. 1948. Fertility in the rabbit as affected by the dilution of semen and the number of spermatozoa. *Proc. Soc. Exptl. Biol. Med.,* **69:** 36–39.

Dickmann, Z., and R. W. Noyes. 1960. The fate of ova transferred into the uterus of the rat. *J. Reprod. Fertility,* **1:** 197–212.

Fischer, I. C. 1953. Psychogenic aspects of sterility. *Fertility Sterility,* **4:** 466–472.

MacLeod, J., and R. Z. Gold. 1951. Spermatazoa counts in 100 men of known fertility and in 100 cases of infertile marriages. *J. Urol.,* **66:** 436–442.

MacLeod, J., and R. Z. Gold. 1957. The male factor in fertility and infertility. IX. Semen quality in relation to accidents of pregnancy. *Fertility Sterility,* **8:** 36–49.

MacLeod, J., R. Z. Gold, and C. M. McLane. 1955. Correlation of the male and female factors in human infertility. *Fertility Sterility,* **6:** 112–143.

Noyes, R. W. 1959. The underdeveloped secretory endometrium. *Am. J. Obstet. Gynecol.,* **77:** 929–945.

Noyes, R. W., and E. M. Chapnick. 1964. The literature on psychology and infertility. *Fertility Sterility,* **15:** 543–558.

Noyes, R. W., and Z. Dickmann. 1960. Relationship of ovular age to endometrial development. *J. Reprod. Fertility,* **1:** 186–196.

Noyes, R. W., and J. O. Haman. 1953. Accuracy of endometrial dating. *Fertility Sterility,* **4:** 504–517.

Noyes, R. W., A. T. Hertig, and J. Rock. 1950. Dating the endometrial biopsy. *Fertility Sterility,* **1:** 3–25.

Noyes, R. W., L. L. Doyle, and D. L. Bentley. 1961a. Effect of preimplantation development on fetal weight in the rat. *J. Reprod. Fertility,* **2:** 238.

Noyes, R. W., L. L. Doyle, A. H. Gates, and D. L. Bentley. 1961b. Ovular maturation and fetal development. *Fertility and Sterility,* **12:** 405–416.

REPRODUCTION AND SEXUAL BEHAVIOR (M. Diamond ed.), 187–205, © Indiana University Press

14

A Critique of our Progress Toward Understanding the Biology of the Mammalian Ovary

H. W. Mossman

"There is no tissue of the body in which the changes are as conspicuous and as dramatic as those in the ovary and there is no tissue which presents more variable aspects." "We have learned much about the functioning of the ovary, but there is little that we can explain." These quotations from Dr. William C. Young in the summary of his chapter on the mammalian ovary (Young, 1961) are in each case statements of fact that are for reproductive physiologists both a stimulus to proceed with ovarian study and a warning to be humble and conservative in assumptions as to their past and future accomplishments.

It is not my purpose to attempt to review the work on the mammalian ovary that has appeared since the publication of the 3rd edition of *Sex and Internal Secretions*. Rather, I shall take a somewhat "dog in the manger" attitude to point out some of the "variable aspects," particularly those related to what one might call the "functional anatomy" of the ovary, aspects which we have neglected and which in the long run must be investigated and recorded if we are ever to fully understand and explain much of the biology of this complex and puzzling organ.

The Uniqueness and Variability of the Female Reproductive Process

The female reproductive organs of viviparous animals must not only provide eggs and a place for them to be fertilized and to develop, a mechanism for birth, and in mammals postnatal nourishment by lactation for an appreciable period, but all these processes must occur in proper sequence. Among the most remarkable of these mechanisms is placentation, with its cooperation between genetically different maternal and fetal tissues to form a smoothly differentiating, long-lasting, functional organ. How is developmental "information" passed between these two tissues to account for their precise integration? Why, especially in species where maternal and fetal tissues are intimately intermingled in the placenta as in endotheliochorial and hemochorial types, is there so little manifestation of immunological antagonism? Can it be that the functioning of the ovary–oviduct–uterus–embryo complex is basically different from that of other complexes of organs and systems? It is obvious that some way must have been worked out to avoid tissue antagonism, for, if this had not been done, viviparous forms with intimate fusion of maternal and fetal tissues could not have evolved. But what of the other finely regulated sequences and cycles characterizing this complex? Are they not also unique in animal biology and far more intricate than those of the male? I think we must admit that they are.

One need only contemplate the great variations in mammalian reproductive processes and adaptations to appreciate how widely the ovaries of representatives of the numerous orders and families must differ from one another to function properly in each situation. We have little reason to expect that the ovary of the polyestrus, polytocous rat with its 5-day estrous cycle, 21-day gestation period, very immature newborn, and a 3- to 4-week lactation period, will very closely resemble the ovary of the nearly monestrous, monotocous Canadian porcupine with its 7-month gestation period, very precocious newborn, and months-long lactation period. But even this degree of difference is much less than that between the rat and man, or such variant conditions as those of animals like the weasel or bear with "delayed implantation" periods of several months. One could go on citing cases of wide variation in female reproductive biology, such as the elephant shrew which ovulates an average of 60 eggs but implants and bears only 2 (Horst and Gillmann, 1941). But the point is clear without more evidence that to really understand mammalian reproduction we need many more comparative data on both ovarian anatomy and function. These data must become complete, and readily available for many representative forms. They must consist of more than simply demonstrations of the existence of variant or bizarre conditions, which is all that much of our existing literature is. We must have information in depth, at least on the basic morphology and function of these ovaries.

Inadequacies of our Knowledge

Paucity of Forms Studied

On first thought it may seem that we do have many more adequate data than I have indicated, and indeed the amount of literature on the anatomy and function of the mammal ovary covered by such recent reviews as those of Brambell (1956), Young (1961), and Zuckerman (1962) does impress one with the great extent of our present knowledge. It does until, among other things, one equates it with the number of existing families of mammals, and realizes that for every family about which we have useful information there are several times as many about which we know little or nothing. Actually most of our knowledge of the mammalian ovary is based on a few laboratory and domestic animals, including three myomorph rodent genera, the mouse, rat, and hamster; one hystricomorph, the guinea pig; one lagomorph, the domestic rabbit; one canid, the dog; two primates, the macaque monkey and man; and three artiodactyls, the pig, cow, and sheep.* It is true that there is much accurate and useful literature on several other laboratory and domestic forms and indeed on many wild and even rare or difficult species such as the African elephant (Perry, 1953) and the tenrec (Setifer), in the latter of which there is no follicular antrum, and in which intrafollicular fertilization is normal, and the egg is already in the pronuclear stage when it is ovu-

---

* Simpson (1945) recognizes the following numbers of living families and genera in the groups mentioned here: Myomorpha—9 families, 216 genera; Hystricomorpha—16, 59; Lagomorpha—2, 10; Carnivora—10, 113; Anthropoidea—5, 36; Artiodactyla—9, 81. (He recognizes a total of 18 orders and 121 families of living mammals.)

lated (Strauss, 1938). But thorough and excellent as much of this work is, it is almost always too incomplete for full understanding, and is only a start toward a sound and comprehensive knowledge of the functional morphology of the ovaries in the approximately 120 families of living mammals.

Basic Information Lacking or Incomplete

There is a surprising range of basic things about ovarian functional morphology that cannot be found in the literature. Nowhere is there a complete account of the changes in the ovary of any species from its embryonic development through its first pregnancy and lactation cycle. van Wagenen and Simpson's (1965) account of the macaque and human ovary has helped greatly to fill some of the gaps for these two species, but contains little on the adult ovaries. Hertig (1964) offers good illustrations of human corpora lutea up to the seventeenth day of pregnancy, but says nothing about interstitial gland tissue. There are few good descriptions of human ovaries from known periods in later gestation. Most, like one of our own (Mossman et al., 1964), deal with some specific problem and leave much else unsaid. Even with a species as much studied as the laboratory rat, it is impossible to find a record of many important features. Although the thecal gland is reputed to be the source of estrogens, there is no account of the basic histology of the theca interna during the growth of a rat follicle. Also there is no account of the interstitial cell cycle in this species during pregnancy. In spite of all the interest in reproduction in farm animals there is not even a complete description of the classical histology of the ovary of the sheep or cow during their estrous cycle, pregnancy, and lactation periods. If one wants to know the nature of the follicle or corpus luteum or interstitial gland tissue of any mammal at a particular period, this can rarely be found in the literature. There is no detailed study of the correlation of the morphology of the ovaries of juveniles with that of the uterus or vagina or with possible behavioral rhythms or blood levels of steroid hormones, hence little clear evidence of the probable cyclic changes that may occur before full puberty. Only by piecing together information from a variety of sources can one manage to obtain at best a fragmentary account of the life history of the ovary of a few laboratory and domestic species and man. But now let us turn from generalities to specific neglected ovarian problems.

The development of the mammalian ovary is reasonably well known in a number of genera, but there are still basic problems upon which there is disagreement, or at least still some reasonable doubt. One of these is the question of the origin, migration, and significance of the primordial germ cells. It is generally agreed that they arise from yolk sac endoderm, and that their migration in mammals is by their own amoeboid movement (Blandau et al., 1963), not by the blood stream as in birds. It is still not always accepted that they are the direct parent cells of definitive germ cells, but Blackler and Fischberg (1961) have given strong evidence that in *Xenopus* some of the germ cells are direct descendants of them. Nor is it always accepted that all potential oocytes of mammals are present before or soon after birth, in spite of such excellent work as that of Mintz (1960a, 1960b) and Rudkin and Griech (1962), which provides very convincing evidence for this in mice. One must always ask whether these results would be repeatable in other rodent families or other orders of mammals. Might there not be marked differences between short-lived and long-lived species, even within a family? If it is reasonable on the basis of what is known of cell physiology to expect germ cells to exist in a state of "dormancy" with no cell division in the prophase of the first meiotic division for 1 or 2 years in a mouse, is it also reasonable to expect them to remain in a similar state in woman for 45 to 50 years? I do not believe it is, but there is little evidence yet available to support my doubt. There are, however, mammals such as the mink and some of the squirrels which have large numbers of follicles of all sizes during proestrus and estrus, yet which during late pregnancy and lactation have very few primary follicles and no vesicular ones. One wonders where the late-prophase stages of the oocytes are at this time, for they reappear in abundance before the next estrus. Careful quantitative studies, such as those of Mandl and Zuckerman (Franchi et al., 1962), have never been made on these species, but should be.

A less important, yet basic feature of ovarian development about which much uncertainty exists (although one would not be aware of it from the glibness of most textbook descriptions) is the manner of development of ovarian cortex and its relation to the medulla. In many species the classical concept of proliferation of a new outer zone or cortex at the time of sex differentiation is a fact. The medullary cords become reduced and apparently take no significant part in the mature ovary. In other species, however (the man and the macaque are among these), there is very little evidence that the cortex is really distinct from the medulla at the time of sex differentiation, although the figures of van Wagenen and Simpson (1965) do show an indistinct demarcation between the two parts. The juvenile eastern chipmunk (*Tamias striatus*) and red squirrel (*Tamiasciurus hudsonicus*) quite clearly produce their first ovulatory follicles from medullary cords while their ovarian cortex is still infantile in character (Mossman, 1966). How can this situation be harmonized with Burns' (1955) findings that the opossum medulla is stimulated by androgens and the cortex by estrogens? What actually is the significance of the cortex and medulla of a mammalian ovary? There seems to be no lead, even for the forming of a sensible theory for the existence of these two ovarian entities, which appear to be so important and specific in some cases and so unimportant and nonspecific in others. We certainly need to know far more about comparative ovarian development and the reaction of cortical and medullary regions to hormonal stimuli during development.

Special Problems

Ovarian assymtery is another phenomenon which is known to occur normally in several patterns in different mammals: certain bats (Ramaswamy, 1961), the viscacha (Pearson, 1949), and in a more limited manner in the Canadian porcupine (Mossman and Judas, 1949). In fact, a minor predominance of one ovary in weight and in ovulatory activity is known for several species (Ramaswamy, 1961). At whatever period of development or maturity these ovaries react to gonadotropic hormones circulating in the general blood stream, why should the right react differently from the left? When the difference appears in the fetus or juvenile, one can more readily rationalize it on the basis of genetically determined differences in vascular and nerve supply; but when it occurs only after pregnancy has started, as in the case of the porcupine, then it seems that some direct influence from either the pregnant or nonpregnant horn of the uterus on the ipsilateral ovary must enter into the explanation. Clearly these things have not been explained, and they may well hold important keys to our full understanding of development and differentiation.

Of even more direct interest to the reproductive physiologist is the evidence that has accumulated in the last few years that in several mammals there is some control of ovarian morphology by the uterus, both in pregnant and nonpregnant animals (Anderson et al., 1963; Moor and Rowson, 1966; Fischer, 1967). It should also be of interest that there is evidence that no such relationship occurs in some species. In other words, this is another example of major differences in female reproductive physiology in different groups, and again points to the need for wide-ranging comparative studies of the problem. There is no clear clue to the pathway by which the uterus affects the ipsilateral ovary only. Both neural and vascular mechanisms have been implicated but proof of either is lacking (see Chapter 2).

The rete ovarii and epoophoron tubules are considered vestiges of little significance in the female. However, one occasionally sees oocytes in the epithelium of both areas in adults. Also both epithelia are often well developed, resembling closely those of the male, where at least some absorptive functions are becoming known (Mason and Shaver, 1952). Rete cysts are almost normal in the guinea pig and very common in woman. In at least two genera of bats (*Tadarida* and *Uroderma*) the rete epithelium is highly developed, certainly suggestive of an active function, probably glandular (Fig. 1). In view of these clues, it would seem worth the effort to examine the retia and epoophorons of these genera more carefully by histochemical and electronmicroscopial techniques. Anatomical vestiges are also physiological vestiges and under certain circumstances may become very important functionally or pathologically.

"Hilus cell" is a term often seen in the literature, particularly in respect to human ovarian pathology, yet at least two different cellular entities have been so designated. These are the sympathicotroph cells or cells of Berger (van Campenhout, 1946), and the adrenal cortex-like cells that are almost universally associated with the epoophoron tubules near the hilus. The latter may be called the "genital adrenal," as they also often occur in the homologous position in the male (Seliger et al., 1966), and have been demonstrated to assume adrenocortical function after adrenalectomy. In contrast, the Berger cells produce active masculinizing tumors (German et al., 1961; and Green and Maqueo, 1966), and cytologically closely resemble testicular interstitial cells. Clearly neither of these tissues is adequately known, either from the anatomical or functional standpoint. Clearly also, "hilus cell" is a nonspecific term.

Major Glandular Tissues

While we have glandular cells in mind, it is appropriate to point out that there is only one ovarian gland tissue, the corpus luteum, that is reasonably well understood as to anatomy and function. Yet there is still much divergent opinion about it; whether theca interna or stomal cells contribute to its luteal cell population; whether all its cells are alike in function; whether the two or more cell types that

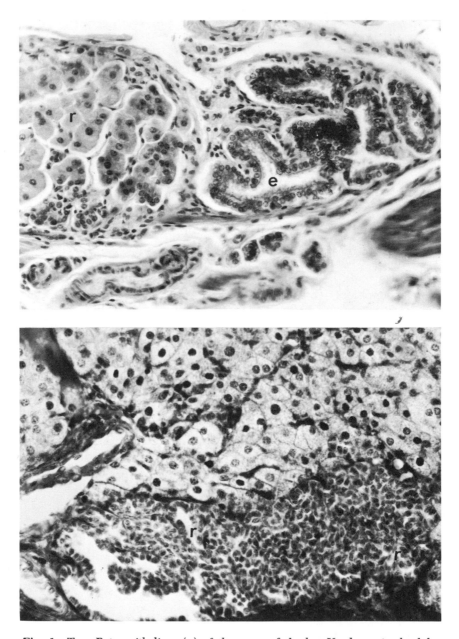

Fig. 1 Top: Rete epithelium (r) of the ovary of the bat *Uroderma* is glandular and only identifiable as rete by study of serial sections which show its direct continuity with the eoophoron tubules (e). × 235. Bottom: Most of the rete (r) of the bat *Tadarida* is a hyperplastic mass of small epithelial cells which completely obscure the lumina but are not glandular in appearance in the reproductive stages available in my material. Similar hyperplasia of rete epithelium also occurs in the bats *Myotis* and *Eptesicus*. Interstitial gland tissue above. × 350.

often occur are simply different phases of the same cells; whether certain cytological characteristics are trustworthy as indicators of active secretion; and whether secondary and accessory corpora lutea function as do primary ones.

Also it is generally considered sufficient to state that "the follicles secrete estrogens," but there is much evidence that it is only the thecal gland cells of the theca internae of nearly "ripe" follicles that actually do the work. They are the only fully differentiated steroid-secreting type cells of the ripe follicle. These have been studied (Dubreuil, 1957; Falck, 1959; Stafford et al., 1942), but certainly their development, functional state, and fate (after ovulation) deserve much more thorough investigation.

At the same time that thecal gland and early luteal gland tissue is present, all mammalian ovaries so far studied are well populated with atretic follicles, and the thecae internae of at least most of the vesicular and some of the secondary ones of these have differentiated into another type of steroid secreting tissue, the interstitial gland cells. These usually are distinctly different by ordinary light microscopy from either thecal gland or luteal gland cells, although in a few species, the rat unfortunately being one, they closely resemble certain stages of luteal cells. Besides originating from the theca interna of degenerating secondary and vesicular follicles, as happens in all mammals so far investigated, there are many species such as the rabbit, bat, and bear where additional large amounts of this cell type seem to differentiate directly from the cortical stroma (Figs. 2 and 3). Then there are others, mainly carnivores (especially obvious in the mink), where medullary cord epithelium persists in quantity and in the adult differentiates into extensive cords or tubules of interstitial gland cells, again apparently identical to those differentiated from atretic follicles in the same ovary (Fig. 4). Since atresia takes place in infantile and juvenile ovaries as well as in those of adults, and also in postmenopausal ovaries of women, interstitial gland tissue is distributed much more widely throughout the life cycle than the thecal gland or luteal gland (Mossman et al., 1964). Stromal-type interstitial gland cells are abundant in fetal life in human ovaries, and extremely abundant in some other species, notably the fetal horse (Cole et al., 1933). Yet in spite of the conspicuousness of interstitial gland tissue, its universal occurrence in all mammals studied, and its presence in the fetal, juvenile, and senile periods of life as well as at maturity, surprisingly little is known about its function. There is some evidence in the rabbit that it is a progesterone secretor (Hilliard et al., 1963), and in the rat that it is an estrogen secretor (Falck, 1959). None of the

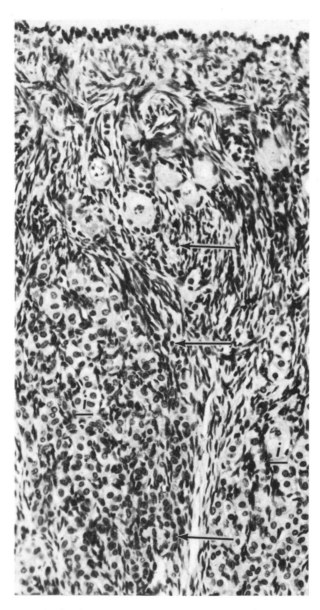

Fig. 2 Interstitial gland tissue (i) of the domestic rabbit showing numerous transitional stages (some indicated by arrows) between stromal cells and glandular cells. × 230.

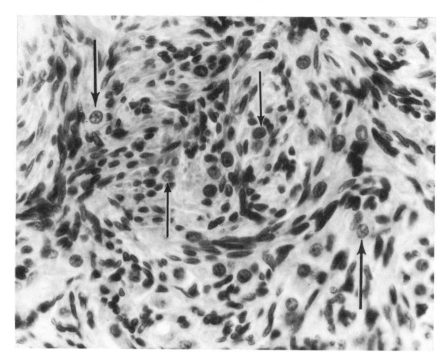

Fig. 3 Stroma immediately deep to the tunica albuginea of the ovary of a grizzly bear, showing numerous cells in transition (small arrows and elsewhere) between undifferentiated stromal cells and well-differentiated interstitial gland cells (large arrows). × 495.

work is conclusive. It may be that interstitial gland function is different from either thecal gland or luteal gland, and it may be that it is supplemental to one or the other. Certainly interstitial gland cell abundance and universal occurrence in all mammals warrants serious study, for we have no right to assume that we understand ovarian function while we still know practically nothing of the physiology of this tissue.

Atresia of Follicles

After discussing interstitial gland tissue we can logically go back to the problems associated with follicular atresia, for it is this peculiar phenomenon in a certain range of follicle sizes that initiates, through some unknown inducing mechanism, the differentiation of much of the interstitial gland tissue. Atresia itself is among the least understood

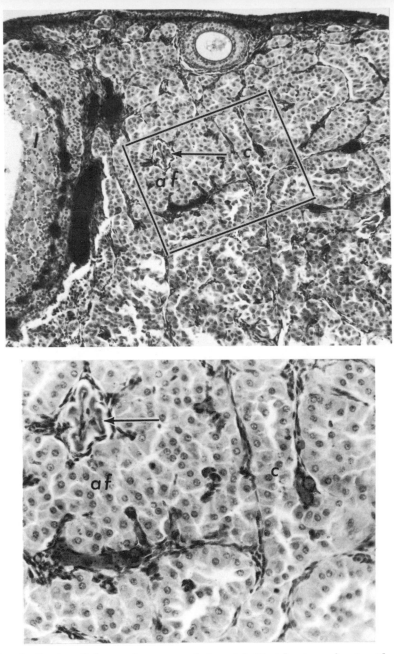

Fig. 4 Portion of the ovarian cortex of the mink *Mustela vison*, showing identical interstitial gland tissue derived from the theca interna of an atretic follicle (af) and from epithelial cortical and medullary "tubes" and "cords" (c). Top: General view. Partially luteinized epithelium (1) of follicle in early atresia. Remnant of zona pellucida (arrow) of follicle in late atresia. The cords and tubes of interstitial gland tissue extend throughout the cortex and medulla and can be shown to be continuous with the rete. × 95. Bottom: Higher magnification of the area outlined in top photo. × 235.

of ovarian phenomena. Why do some follicles, regardless of size or apparent age, undergo degeneration while others persist or grow to maturity under what appear to be exactly the same immediate environmental conditions? It seems that there are three categories of follicles at the period when atresia is taking place in adult ovaries: first, one or more secondary or small vesicular follicles which respond to stimuli, presumed to be mainly from gonadotropic hormones, by growing rapidly to form mature folicles; second, many follicles which respond to these stimuli in varying degrees and for variable lengths of time, but sooner or later degenerate; and third, a large group of primary and presumably secondary and perhaps even small vesicular follicles which at the time are apparently completely unresponsive to these stimuli. Explanations such as favorable or unfavorable location in relation to vascular supply do not give much comfort when one considers the richness of the capillary net in the ovarian cortex, the efficiency of diffusion through intercellular substance, and the small size and close proximity of follicles to one another at the time response of some begins. Another important unknown concerning atresia is how long it takes a follicle to reach a certain stage of degeneration, or to disappear entirely. This is important in estimating the number of follicles and eggs produced by the ovary, and also in understanding the formation and replacement of interstitial gland tissue differentiated from the thecae internae of atretic follicles. It is a common observation that a certain segment of the granulosa of a vesicular follicle may be in early degeneration while another area may be entirely normal. In fact, the first signs of atresia are usually pyknosis, karyorrhexis, and shedding of cells into the liquor folliculi, all taking place in the most central stratum of the follicular epithelium, while in the middle and outer strata of the same segment mitotic proliferation may still be very active (Fig. 5). This certainly suggests a deleterious effect of the follicular liquor, but to my knowledge this element of normal and atretic follicles has never been subjected to comparative analyses.

General Discussion

The Nature of the Dilemma

Being fully aware of the extensive and brilliant investigations involving the endocrinology and chemistry of the ovary which have been carried on for the last 50 years, and which are still expanding

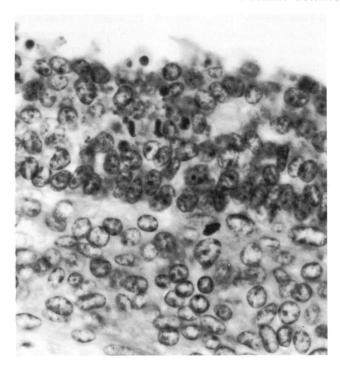

Fig. 5 Segment of the wall of a vesicular ovarian follicle in early atresia from a guinea pig, showing mitotic activity in the outer epithelial zone despite cell degeneration along the inner surface. × 685.

rapidly in many directions, and with alert application of the newest and most sophisticated instrumentation and techniques, I have attempted to confine my remarks to the more prosaic and yet basic areas that can be categorized as "functional anatomy." These involve principally microscopic and ultramicroscopic morphology, and its physiological and biochemical interpretation. Because the ovary is a cyclic organ closely integrated into cyclic reproductive phenomena of the rest of the reproductive system and accessory organs, observations on its morphology and chemistry usually have little meaning unless correlated with the conditions in the other organs involved. These of course include the mammary glands, the pituitary and its related neural and neurosecretory mechanisms, and, during pregnancy, the embryo and the fetal membranes. Often, for full meaning, all of this must also be related to the individual's behavior.

One measure of the degree of understanding of a science is how effectively it can be applied. Certainly the applications of our knowledge of the physiology of reproduction are numerous and effective, yet there are many problems in the area of control of reproduction for which the critical physiological mechanisms are still obscure or totally unknown. One of the most interesting of these problems, because it involves so many disciplines, is that of successful breeding of animals in captivity. To reproduce the environment to which a species is reproductively sensitized and adapted is usually impossible, so what we need to know is how to turn on or off the critical reproductive mechanisms at the correct times. We need to be able to reach and control these basic physiological mechanisms by direct means in ways which will produce the effects of the normal environment of the species and negate the effects of the abnormal environment. We are a long way from this goal.

It is obvious that to obtain complete data needed on even a limited period in the reproductive history of a species is a long, meticulous, time-consuming task even with a small laboratory animal as the subject, and far more so with a large one or a wild species. This accounts for the relatively fragmentary and scattered data that we do have on the functional anatomy of mammalian reproduction. Most investigators are neither by nature nor by academic environment equipped to systematically accumulate the great masses of fully documented data that are needed. Divided interests and duties, limited facilities and space, and dozens of other factors interfere.

A Possible Mitigation of Much of the Dilemma

It is of importance to consider what could be done to assure the more rapid accumulation of the type of information needed. One solution would be the establishment of separately supported centers or institutes dedicated to this type of investigation. Their aim should be the accumulation of material—gross, microscopic, and ultramicroscopic—in the form of permanent reference collections of preserved specimens, microscopic slides, and photomicrographs from which investigators could obtain completely documented data either for publication, or as background for less anatomically oriented investigations. Since it is never possible to publish much more than a summary of the information actually available in good anatomical material, and since with advancing knowledge viewpoints as to what may be important are constantly changing, the preservation of such material in the form of catalogued reference collections would be invaluable.

At present we are in an era of severe competition for advancement in the academic community in which so many of us find ourselves, so severe that at least the younger ones of us are forced into lines of research that are currently fashionable. Not only that, but the same pressures seem to favor those who merely skim the "cream," and to penalize those whose curiosity impels them to the more difficult task of analyzing the far more complex "whey" and "curd," which often constitute the main substance of a problem, and hence may eventually yield the most fundamental and useful information.

Another defect in our present system is its wastefulness of valuable anatomical material. It is tragic to contemplate the years of effort that have been devoted by individual scholars to the building up of reference collections of anatomical material, only to have the whole thing actually thrown into the trash cans when they retire. This procedure is partially justified by the need for space to start new programs and by the lack of any facilities for making such material useful to other investigators.

A working anatomical museum, associated with a good university, but independent of it for space, staff, and financial support, would do much to give the continuity, coordination, and encouragement necessary to assure the development of a broad and profound knowledge of the biology of reproduction. It could serve in many valuable ways: as a repository for specialized collections of material, unpublished notes and reprints, all of which are now almost always discarded upon the retirement or death of an investigator; as a live research institution for expansion and completion of sets of such material and for the accumulation and study of new material, especially of a comparative nature; and as an invaluable source of reference and teaching of background material for those from other institutions engaged in or about to engage in new research which would profit by a sound anatomical background.

To my knowledge there are only two embryological museums that in part meet these criteria. One is part of the Hubrecht Laboratory at Utrecht, Holland, the other is in the Department of Embryology of the Carnegie Institution at Baltimore. Both of these institutions are devoting almost all their energy, space, and resources to experimental work, hence their reference material, although well housed and available, has remained almost completely static for the last 15 to 20 years. To serve the needs I have outlined, working museums of anatomical material would need to be much larger, much more heavily staffed and financed, and should have as their prime aims the continuing accumulation of a reference collection of anatomical material dealing with the biology of reproduction, the making of this material available for reference and research, and an active research program by the resident staff on problems that could best make use of this type of material—that is, by the approach of functional morphology.

Summary

An attempt has been made to point out some of the deficiencies in our present knowledge of the basic functional anatomy of mammalian reproduction, particularly as it applies to the ovary. There are two general flaws in the present status of our knowledge of this subject: lack of completeness and depth of understanding of the basic functional morphology of the species that have been investigated, and lack of broad comparative coverage. Our lack of knowledge of the function of ovarian interstitial gland tissue and of its occurrence in relation to the various phases in the life of an individual is an example of the first. Our lack of knowledge of reproductive phenomena in numerous important groups of mammals, coupled with the general failure to recognize that what we do know is based on so few species, is an example of the second. It is suggested that the establishment of a reference and working museum of anatomical materials dealing with the biology of reproduction would go far toward eventually correcting these defects and assuring rapid and sound advancement in this important field.

References

Anderson, L. L., A. M. Bowerman, and R. M. Melampy. 1963. Neuro-utero-ovarian relationships. In *Advances in Neuroendocrinology* (A. V. Nalbandov, ed.). Univ. Illinois Press, Urbana.

Blackler, A. W., and M. Fischberg. 1961. Transfer of primordial germ-cells in *Xenopus laevis. J. Embryol. Exptl. Morphol.,* 9: 634–641.

Blandau, R. J., B. J. White, and R. E. Rumery. 1963. Observations on the movements of the living primordial germ cells in the mouse. *Fertility Sterility,* 14: 482–489.

Brambell, F. W. R. 1956. Ovarian changes. In *Marshall's Physiology of Reproduction* (A. S. Parkes, ed.). Longmans, Green, London, Chap. 5.

Burns, R. K. 1955. Urogenital system. In *Analysis of Development* (B. H. W. Willier, P. A. Weiss, and V. Hamburger, eds.). Saunders, Philadelphia.

Cole, H. H., G. G. Hart, W. R. Lyons, and H. R. Catchpole. 1933. The development and hormonal content of fetal horse gonads. *Anat. Rec.,* 56: 275–293.

Dubreuil, G. 1957. Le déterminisme de la gland thecale de l'ovaire. Induction morphogéne à partir de la granulosa folliculaire. *Acta Anat.,* 30: 269–274.

Falck, B. 1959. Site of production of oestrogen in the rat ovary as studied in microtransplants. *Acta Physiol. Scand.,* 47, *Suppl.,* 163: 1–101.

Fischer, T. V. 1967. Local uterine regulation of the corpus luteum. *Am. J. Anat.,* 121: 425–442.

Franchi, L. L., A. M. Mandl, and S. Zuckerman. 1962. The development of the ovary and the process of oogenesis. In *The Ovary* (S. Zuckerman, ed.). Academic Press, New York, Chap. I.

German, E., H. Horowitz, R. van de Wiele, and R. M. Torack. 1961. Leydig-cell tumor of the ovary: Case report and review. *Clin. Endocrinol. Metab.*, 21: 91–97.

Green, J. A., and M. Maqueo. 1966. Histopathology and ultrastructure of an ovarian hilar cell tumor. *Am. J. Obstet. Gynecol.*, 96: 478–485.

Hertig, A. T. 1964. Gestational hyperplasia of endometrium, and corpora lutea during early pregnancy. *Lab. Invest.*, 13: 1153–1191.

Hilliard, J., D. Archibald, and C. H. Sawyer. 1963. Gonadotrophic activity of pre-ovulatory synthesis and release of progestin in the rabbit. *Endocrinology*, 72: 59–66.

Horst, C. J. van der, and J. Gillmann. 1941. The number of eggs and surviving embryos in *Elephantulus*. *Anat. Rec.*, 80: 443–452.

Mason, K. E., and S. L. Shaver. 1952. Some functions of the caput epididymis. *Ann. N.Y. Acad. Sci.*, 55: 585–593.

Mintz, B. 1960a. Formation and early development of germ cells. *Symposium on Germ Cells and Development*. Inst. Intern. d'Embryologie and Fondazione A. Baselli, pp. 1–24.

Mintz, B. 1960b. Embryological phases of mammalian gametogenesis. *J. Cellular Comp. Physiol.*, 56, *Suppl.*, 1: 31–48.

Moor, R. M., and L. E. A. Rowson. 1966. Local maintenance of the corpus luteum in sheep with embryos transferred to various isolated portions of the uterus. *J. Reprod. Fertility*, 12: 539–550.

Mossman, H. W. 1966. The rodent ovary. In *Comparative Biology of Reproduction in Mammals* (J. W. Rowlands, ed.). Academic Press, New York, pp. 455–470.

Mossman, H. W., and I. Judas. 1949. Accessory corpora lutea, lutein cell origin, and the ovarian cycle in the Canadian porcupine. *Am. J. Anat.*, 85: 1–39.

Mossman, H. W., M. J. Koering, and D. Ferry. 1964. Cyclic changes of interstitial gland tissue of the human ovary. *Am. J. Anat.*, 115: 235–256.

Pearson, O. P. 1949. Reproduction of a South American rodent, the mountain viscacha. *Am. J. Anat.*, 84: 143–174.

Perry, J. S. 1953. The reproduction of the African elephant (*Loxodonta africans*). *Phil. Trans., Roy. Soc. London*, B237: 93–149.

Ramaswamy, K. R. 1961. Studies on the sex-cycle of the Indian vampire bat, *Megaderma* (*Lyroderma*) *lyra lyra* (Geoffroy). Pt. I. Breeding habits. *Proc. Nat. Inst. Sci. India*, 27: 287–307.

Rudkin, G. T., and H. A. Griech. 1962. On the persistence of oocyte nuclei from fetus to maturity in the laboratory mouse. *J. Cell Biol.*, 12: 169–176.

Seliger, W. G., A. J. Blair, and H. W. Mossman. 1966. Differentiation of adrenal cortex-like tissue at the hilum of the gonads in response to adrenalectomy. *Am. J. Anat.*, 118: 615–630.

Simpson, G. G. 1945. The principles of classification and a classification of mammals. *Bull. Am. Mus. Natural History*, 85.

Stafford, W. T., R. F. Collins, and H. W. Mossman. 1942. The thecal gland in the guinea pig ovary. *Anat. Rec.*, 83: 193–207.

Strauss, F. 1938. Die Befruchtung und der Vorgang der Ovulation bei *Ericulus* aus der Familie der Centetiden. *Biomorphosis*, 1: 281–312.

van Campenhout, E. 1946. The epithelioneural bodies. *Quart. Rev. Biol.*, **21:** 327–347.

van Wagenen, G., and M. E. Simpson. 1965. *Embryology of the Ovary and Testis, Homo Sapiens and Macaca mulatta.* Yale Univ. Press, New Haven, Conn.

Young, W. C. 1961. The mammalian ovary. In *Sex and Internal Secretions* (W. C. Young. ed.). Williams & Wilkins, Baltimore, 3rd ed., pp. 449–496.

Zuckerman, S. (ed.). 1962. *The Ovary.* Academic Press, New York.

REPRODUCTION AND SEXUAL BEHAVIOR (M. Diamond ed.), 207–230, © Indiana University Press

15

Enzymology of the Uterus
and Mammalian Reproduction

E. S. E. Hafez

Introduction

Enzymes have a wide and characteristic distribution in the female reproductive tract. The pattern of distribution and the levels of specific activity vary with the species, endocrine condition, and stage of reproductive cycle. Qualitative and quantitative studies of the enzyme systems have been undertaken on the uterus, embryo, and placenta of several mammalian species. Qualitative methods dealing with enzymorphology are based on histochemical and cytochemical techniques in which the enzymes are preserved in frozen tissue sections to retain their activity toward natural or synthetic substrates. Quantitative enzyme analysis of tissue homogenates involve microcolorimetry, microspectrophotometry (Glick, 1963), microfluorometry (Lowry et al., 1956; Greengard, 1956), micromanometry (Holter and Linderstrom-Lang, 1951; Brachet, 1957), and microchromatography (Edström and Hyden, 1954; Edström, 1956).

The techniques used to measure the rate of enzyme reactions are reviewed by Bergmeyer (1963). Methods of separating uterine, placental, and embryonic tissues are shown on Figs. 1 and 2.

The purpose of this chapter is to discuss the role of uterine and placental enzymes in relation to metabolic patterns, the reproductive cycle, implantation, and prenatal development in mammals.

The Uterus

Metabolic Patterns

The endometrium metabolizes carbohydrates, lipids, and proteins required for cell nutrition, rapid proliferation of the uterine tissue, and for the development of the conceptus. Cyclical variations in the metabolic patterns are associated with changes in the rate of nucleic acid synthesis, the availability of glucose, and glycogen reserve. These reactions depend on four phenomena correlated with the ovarian cycle: (1) the enzymatic reactions necessary for glucose metabolism, (2) the increase in circulating blood through the network of spiral arterioles, (3) the histological and cytological changes which occur in the endometrium and myometrium, and (4) the stimulating action of the ovarian hormones and other hormones (Jacquot and Kretchmer, 1964).

Estrogen-induced growth of the uterus and the stimulation of protein synthesis and mitoses require the utilization of ATP. The biochemical mechanisms between the estrogenic activation and subsequent responses of target organs are not fully understood. Villee and Gordon (1956) have shown, in the human endometrium and placenta, a direct "in vitro" stimulation by estradiol of a cell-free diphosphopyridine nucleotide–requiring isocitric dehydrogenase preparation. This specific action of estradiol would increase the rates of Krebs' cycle of other energy-obtaining enzymes.

The establishment of a progestational response involves major growth of the endometrium, a striking increase in DNA and RNA, and a water loss in the endometrium. The endometrium at this secretory phase has a higher synthetic capacity than that of pregnancy. During pregnancy, the uterus hypertrophies extensively and increases in connective tissue ground substances and in fibrillar elements, with very little muscular hyperplasia (Maibenco, 1960). Energy requirements of the uterus rise throughout gestation.

Glucose and glycogen are of special significance in uterine metabolism. In the endometrium the glucose changes into glucose-6-phosphate by hexokinase action as it passes through the cell wall; some of the glucose-6-phosphate changes back into glucose by the action of glucose-6-phosphatase. The glucose-6-phosphate breaks down through the Embden-Meyerhof and Krebs' citric acid pathway to generate ATP, which produces the energy not only for the glucose metabolism but also for the buildup of protein into RNA and DNA and other anabolic processes (Szego and Lawson, 1964). Some of the glucose-6-phosphate is stored in the endometrial glands as glycogen.

Phosphorylase forms the 1,4 linkage between glucose molecules, producing straight-chain polymers of the amylose type, while amylo-1, 6-glucosidase forms the 1,6 linkage necessary to form the branching side chains. Both enzymes are necessary for the formation of glycogen. Since phosphorylase is concerned with the process of glycogenesis, the presence of glycogen in a tissue is considered to be indirect evidence of the presence of the enzyme. Glycogen has been observed in the uterus of the cyclic rat only in the muscle cells, where it occurs in greatest amount at proestrus and in least amount at diestrus (Bo and Atkinson, 1952).

Glycogen can be attacked by both β- and α-amylase. β-Amylase catalyzes a hydrolysis of alternate linkage in a chain of 1,4 linkage residue, thereby liberating maltose. Its action ceases when a glycosidic linkage other than D-1,4 linkage is encountered. α-Amylase catalyzes random hydrolysis of D-1,4 linkage in both exterior and interior chains of glycogen, yielding maltose as the main product, and also of some 1,6 glusosidic linkage compounds (cf. Sumawong et al., 1962).

The gonadal hormones play a major role in regulating uterine metabolism (Mounib and Chang, 1965a). Estrogen causes an increase in uterine weight in mammals. This weight gain is associated with hyperaemia and is follow by an increase in amino acid incorporation, nucleic acid synthesis, and nitrogen retention. Estrogen also stimulates phosphorus incorporation, oxidative metabolism, aerobic and anaerobic glycolysis, and glycogen deposition (Leathem, 1959). The activity of lysosomal enzymes increases in biological processes involving intracellular digestion by cells or autolysis of cells. In some cell types, increased activity appears to be under hormonal control (Lobel et al., 1961).

Uterine Enzymes and the Reproductive Cycle

The synthetic, secretory, and reabsorptive activities of the luminal and glandular epithelia of the endometrium undergo cyclical changes according to the reproductive cycle. Analogous changes occur in the localization and specific activity of certain enzymes in these epithelia (Likar and Likar, 1964).

In the human endometrium, certain dehydrogenases (lactic and malic) exhibit more activity during the progestational phase of the menstrual cycle, whereas certain transaminases are more active during the estrogenic phase. In the rabbit endometrium, the progestational environment results in decreased activity of lactic dehydrogenase and an increase in glutamic oxalacetic transminases (Delgado and Fridhandler, 1964). Similar cyclical variations occur in the activity of alkaline phosphatase, adenosine triphosphatase, and β-glucoronidase of the mouse endometrium (Thiery and Willighagen, 1963).

Gonadal hormones are the specific catalysts which stimulate blood flow, cause cellular changes, and stimulate the enzyme and coenzyme systems responsible for energy production. The activity of endometrial enzymes is affected by ovariectomy and the administration of steroid hormones (reviewed by Gross, 1961, and Hafez, 1964). Following estradiol administration in ovariectomized rats, there is a marked alteration in the intensity and location of β-glucuronidase, esterase, and alkaline phosphatase in the vagina; on the other hand, the change in diphosphopyridine nucleotide diaphorase or acid phosphatase appears much slower (Hayashi, and Fishman, 1961). It has been suggested that the mobilization of certain uterine enzymes by estrogen affects lipid and carbohydrate metabolism in the uterus.

Species differences exist in the response of uterine enzymes to the estrous cycle and the prevailing endocrine condition (Table 1). Also the hormonal condition affects the various regions of the uterus in a characteristic fashion. For example, in the mouse there is a differential response of succinic dehydrogenase and TPN-diephorase to steroid stimulation (Rosa, 1959). These differential responses may be related to the specific permeabilities of ovarian hormones by such structures as epithelium, muscle, or stroma (cf. Rosa and Velardo, 1959b). In nonpregnant sheep, the caruncles contain higher levels of succinic dehydrogenase, glucose-6-phosphate dehydrogenase, and glutamic-oxalacetic transaminase than the intercarunclar mucosa. Meanwhile the carunclar mucosa contains less alkaline phosphatase and lactic dehydrogenase than the intercarunclar areas (Hafez and White, unpublished data).

Carbonic Anhydrase. Carbonic anhydrase, discovered by Meldrum and Roughton (1933) in red blood corpuscles, catalyzes both phases of the reversible reaction of carbonic acid. Carbonic anhydrase has a wide and characteristic distribution in the female reproductive tract, mainly in the uterine endometrium, placental tissue, oviducts, and, to a small degree, ovarian lutein tissue.

In the endometrium of the nonpregnant rabbit the concentration of carbonic anhydrase is low. Following the mating, the enzyme con-

Table 1

Summary of the Relationship between the Reproductive Cycle
and the Activity of Endometrial Enzymes

Species	Enzyme levels increase during estrogenic phase	Enzyme levels increase during progestational phase	Ref.
Man		α-Amylase	Hughes, 1945
		Phosphorylase	Zondek and Hestrin, 1947
	Phosphatase		Arzac and Blanchet, 1948
	Glutamic-oxalacetic transaminase	Aldolase	Lindenschmidt, 1960
	Glutamic-pyruvic transaminase	Lactic dehydrogenase Malic dehydrogenase	
Mouse		Aminopeptidase	Thiery and Willighagen, 1963
	Carbonic anhydrase		Madjerek and van der Vies, 1961
	Alkaline phosphatase		Jeener, 1948
Rabbit	Lactic dehydrogenase	Glutamic-oxalacetic transaminase	Delgado and Fridhandler, 1964
		Carbonic anhydrase	Lutwak-Mann and Adams, 1957; Madjerek and van der Vies, 1961; Tsuji, 1963
Rat	Succinic dehydrogenase		Rosa and Velardo, 1959a, 1959b
Sheep		Amylase	Hafez and White, unpublished data
		Glucose-6-phosphate dehydrogenase	

tent does not increase before the fourth day; from then the activity increases to a maximum about the eighth day and declines with advancing pregnancy (Lutwak-Mann, 1955). Carbonic anhydrase is particularly active in the uterine mucosa of adult sheep. The enzymic activity is limited almost entirely to the intercaruncular mucosa and the caruncles exhibit only traces of carbonic anhydrase (Lutwak-Mann and Averill, 1954). The activity in the sheep uterine mucosa, unlike that in the rabbit, is not related to pregnancy. Moreover, there is no difference in activity between estrous and anestrous ewes (Lutwak-Mann and Averill, 1954).

The dependence of rabbit endometrial carbonic anhydrase on progestational agents is well established and has been used as a bioassay for luteotropic activity (Lutwak-Mann and Adams, 1957). This quantitative relationship does not apply to all species. In mice estrogens raise uterine carbonic anhydrase, whereas progesterone antagonizes the effect of estrogen (Madjerek and van der Vies, 1961; Ogawa and Pincus, 1962). In immature rats estradiol causes a marked increase in uterine carbonic anhydrase (Bialy and Pincus, 1962).

β-Glucuronidase. Substantial evidence supports the relationship between estrogens and the distribution and concentration of β-glucuronidase (Fishman and Fishman, 1944; Knobil, 1952). The characteristic alterations in β-glucuronidase of endometrial and glandular epithelia as a function of the estrous cycle have been described in several species. In a mouse there is a synchronous increase of β-glucuronidase activity during proestrus which reaches a maximum in estrus and then decreases (Thiery and Willighagen, 1963).

The activity of the uterine β-glucuronidase decreases following ovariectomy in mice (Fishman and Fishman, 1944; Fishman, 1947), and rats (Leonard and Knobil, 1950; Knobil, 1952). The administration of estrogens in physiological doses increases β-glucuronidase in the uterine tissue of ovariectomized mice (Fishman, 1947; Kerr et al., 1949; Harris and Cohen, 1951) and rats (Szego and Roberts, 1953; Beyler and Szego, 1954).

Saccaric acid inhibits the β-glucuronidase activity "in vitro" (Karunairatnam and Levvy, 1949; Mills and Paul, 1949). The saccarate ion per se has no effect on β-glucuronidase, but the inhibitory factor is most likely the saccaro-1,4-lactone, which is formed in the aqueous solution of the saccharate; the saccharic acid possesses an inhibitory effect only if it has a carboxyl group at C-6 (Levvy, 1952). The "in vivo" inhibitory effect of potassium hydrogen saccharate (as a lactone ester) on the uterine β-glucuronidase activity was studied in the ovariectomized rat. Estradiol increased this enzyme activity, whereas the inhibitory suspension caused a less marked increase in the uterine enzyme activity (Salmi et al., 1959).

Phosphatase. Alkaline and acid phosphatases are common in many organs of the body and have been the object of several studies concerning hormone–enzyme relationships. Most often the following relations have been seen. The enzymorphology of alkaline phosphatase in the uterus has been described in several species (Wislocki and Dempsey, 1945). Changes in alkaline phosphatase distribution are observed during the menstrual cycles in the human endometrium (Arzac and Blanchet, 1948). In the bovine endometrium, alkaline phosphatase is present in the intercaruncular areas of the upper densely cellular stroma, in the fibrous sheaths of gland tubules and blood vessels, and in the distal borders of the surface epithelial and superficial gland cells (Moss et al., 1954).

The activity and distribution of alkaline phosphatase in the bovine uterus during the estrous cycle are partially controlled by gonadal hormones. The injection of estradiol into ovariectomized mice is followed by a marked increase in the enzyme activity of the uterine glands, luminal epithelium, and of the circular layer of the myometrium (Atkinson and Elftman, 1947). A positive correlation is also observed, following treatment with progesterone, between the progestational reaction and the amount of alkaline phosphatase in the endometrium (Giering and Zarrow, 1958). The concentration of alkaline phosphatase in the immature mouse was increased sixfold by estradiol, but androgen and progesterone were without effect.

Several hydrolytic enzymes having neutral or acid pH optima are associated with the "lysosomes," a class of cytoplasmic particles (De Duve et al., 1955; De Duve, 1959). These bodies are localized with the staining reaction for acid phosphatase. Particles with the chemical and the histochemical properties of lysosomes occur in many cell types (Novikoff, 1961), and the proportions of enzymes in the lysosomes may differ from tissue to tissue.

Dehydrogenases. The cyclical changes in the activity of succinic acid dehydrogenase in the endometrial epithelium, demonstrated histochemically (Rosa and Velardo, 1959a) and biochemically (Bevar et al., 1954) in the rat, supports the concept (Foraker et al., 1954) that the activity of this enzyme in an index of the functional status of the epithelial cell. Maximal activity for the enzyme appears to coincide with the estrogenic phase of the cycle in the rat (Rosa and Velardo, 1959b). A drop in enzyme activity follows the peak activity of proestrus.

Superovulation by gonadotropins causes subtle changes in the activity of succinic dehyrogenase in the rabbit endometrium (Biddulph et al., 1959).

Other enzymes. In the rabbit endometrium there is a sharp rise in the dipeptidase activity from estrus to day 4 of pseudopregnancy. This is followed by a steady increase until a plateau is reached on day 8 and maintained until day 12. Thereafter the activity falls steadily until a level slightly lower than that of estrus is reached on day 17 (Albers et al., 1961). The sudden increase in aminopeptidase activity at the end of the cycle may be the expression of intense catabolic phenomena which characterizes this phase.

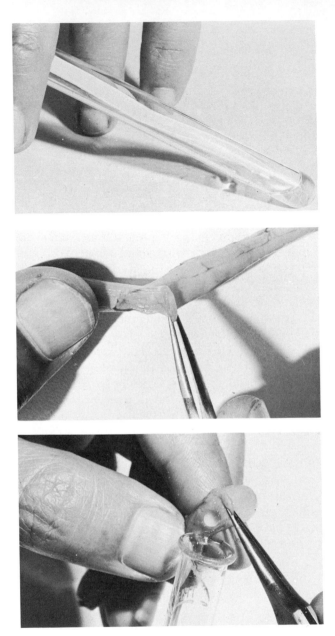

Fig. 1 Techniques Used to Prepare Embryonic Tissues for Enzyme Analysis. Top: Six-day old rabbit blastocysts are flushed from the uterus using the same buffer designed for homogenization. The blastocysts are then transferred to the homogenizing tube and the buffer removed using a thin piece of filter paper. The blastocysts are weighed collectively, then the homogenizing buffer added. Center: To collect 7-day old rabbit blastocysts the uterine horn is dissected from the mesosalpinx and a strip of the uterus is peeled off until the blastocyst is located. Bottom: When the blastocyst is located, it is transferred to the homogenizing tube.

During the progestational response, endometrial succinoxidase increases two- to threefold over the estrus level; castration atrophy diminishes succinoxidase activity in both the endometrium and myometrium (Telfer and Hisaw, 1957).

Estrone, testosterone, and progesterone administration, which stimulates activity in the uterus of the immature rats, increases transaminase activity in this organ. Growth hormone also stimulates growth of the uterus but reduces its transaminase activity (Eckstein and Shain, 1963), This indicates a difference between the growth-promoting action of growth hormones and the sex hormones on the uterus.

In the endometrial epithelium of the mouse the 5-nucleotidase and adenosine triphosphatase show distinct cyclical changes in intensity and localization (apical migration) which parallel the growth intensity of this tissue and the titer of circulating estrogens (Thiery and Willighagen, 1963). Like acid and alkaline phosphatase, 5-nucleotidase and adanosine triphosphatase show a typical "secretion cycle."

Endometrial Secretions

The luminal fluids of the female reproductive tract provide a favorable environment for gamete survival, fertilization, and prenatal differentiation. For example, the luminal fluids of the oviduct seem to stimulate the respiration of sperm (Olds and VanDemark, 1957; Hamner and Williams, 1963) and capacitated sperm respire at a much greater rate than freshly ejaculated sperm. The exact physiological and biochemical mechanisms are still unknown.

The rate of secretory activity of these fluids varies with the stage of the reproductive cycle. Such activity is higher during estrus than any other phase of the cycle. (Bishop, 1956; Clewe and Mastroianni, 1960, for rabbit; Black et al., 1963, for sheep). The secretory activity is regulated by ovarian steroid hormones (Bishop, 1956; Mastroianni et al., 1961; Mastroianni and Wallach, 1961).

The results of Albers and Castro (1961) on the protein components of rat uterine fluid using immunoelectrophoresis suggest that the uterine fluid is not produced from the serum by simple diffusion but is actively secreted by the hormone-influenced endometrium. The increased glycine and serine content of the secretions in progesterone-treated animals may indicate an anabolic effect necessary for the growth and development of the embryo (Gregoire et al., 1961). Uterine and cervical fluid and extracts from endometrial and cervical mucosa in the rabbit contained 5-nucleotidase, ATPase, and purine

Fig. 2 Techniques Used to Prepare Endometrial Tissues for Enzyme Analysis.
Top: The uterus of the rabbit is opened and placed on a piece of filter paper.
The uterine secretions are removed by pressing another piece of filter paper over
the endometrium. The superficial layer of the endometrium is dissected using fine
scissors and samples are collected in containers immersed in crushed ice. Bottom:
The uterus of the sheep is opened and the superficial layers of the caruncles are
dissected and collected in containers immersed in crushed ice.

nucleosidase (Leone et al., 1963). Ribonucleoprotein is closely associated with the secretory activities of uterine glands.

The enzyme levels of the uterine secretions are also influenced by the reproductive cycle (Ringler, 1961; Leone et al., 1963; White et al., 1963). The presence of a glycerylphosphorylcholine-splitting enzyme was first demonstrated in the luminal fluid of the uterus of the ewe (White and Wallace, 1961). Subsequent studies on the rat indicate that the level of the diesterase is greater in proestrus and estrus than in diestrus and metestrus (White et al., 1963; Wallace et al., 1964). Estrogen can cause an increase in β-glucuronidase (Leonard and Knobil, 1950), glucose-6-phosphate, phosphogluconate, and alkaline phosphatase of rat uterine luminal fluid (Ringler, 1961). The enzymes in the luminal fluids of the uterus may play major roles in several reproductive phenomena such as capacitation and decapacitation of sperm and the nutrition of the morulae and blastocyst.

Endometrial Enzymes and Implantation

Changes in the activity of uterine enzymes at implantation may be responses to mechanical as well as to endocrine stimuli. These include alterations in the connective tissues (Harkness and Harkness, 1956; Reynolds, 1959, Maibenco, 1960), hypertrophy of muscle fibers, and vascular adaptations (Ramsey, 1954).

At implantation in the rabbit (8 days *postcoitum*), carbonic anhydrase activity is markedly lower at the implantation sites than in other parts of the endometrium (Bialy and Pincus, 1960). Prior to implantation there is a sudden increase in glutamic oxalacetic transaminase of the endometrium, while at implantation there is a rise in lactic dehydrogenase and a decline in malic dehydrogenase (Delgado and Fridhandler, 1964). In the rat, there is a marked rise in uterine β-glucuronidase (Prahald, 1962) and endometrial peptidase at implantation (Albers and Castro, 1961). Certain proteolytic enzymes extractable from the uterus can digest collagens as well as muscle protein (Morione and Seifter, 1962; Woessner and Brewer, 1963). Such enzymes may play a function in implantation.

Myometrial Enzymes

The significance of glycogen breakdown in energy transformations during muscle contraction is well established. Its significance may be even greater in uterine muscle than in skeletal muscle contraction, owing to the low content of ATP and phosphocreatine. The dependence of uterine contractility on steroid hormones suggests the determination of energy substances under different hormonal influences (Bo and Smith, 1964a, 1964b). Injection of estrogen increases the glycogen content of uterine muscle in rats, while no significant effect on the mucosa is found (Walaas, 1952). Injection of progesterone, testosterone propionate, or adrenal cortex extract does not promote glycogen formation in uterine muscle. During pregnancy the glycogen content of uterine muscle increases.

Estradiol markedly increases phosphorylase activity and simultaneously raises myometrial glycogen (Leonard, 1958). In castrate progesterone-treated rats, enzymic activity is observed in the outer longitudinal layer. In rats that receive estrogen and progesterone concurrently, phosphorylase activity is heavy in the outer longitudinal muscle layer and weak in the inner circular muscle layer (Bo, 1959).

At implantation, in the rabbit myometrium, there is a rise in lactic dehydrogenase and a decline in malic dehydrogenase (Delgado and Fridlandler, 1964).

The Embryo

Metabolic Patterns

The development and differentiation processes of the embryo are controlled by complex enzyme systems. Prenatal metabolism comprises of two major processes: energy production and protein biosynthesis. Energy-rich phosphate bonds which are required for protein biosynthesis are associated with dehydrogenation, the transfer of hydrogen and electrons, and glycolysis. Energy is supplied mainly by glycolysis, but the process of glucose degradation varies with the stage of development. In the tubal ova, energy is derived from the hexose monophosphate shift and some dehydrogenase systems. After blastocyst formation, the Embden-Meyerhof and TCA cycle are the route of energy production (reviewed by Sugawara and Hafez, 1968).

Little is known of the energy sources required for development in mammalian ova which contain small quantities of yolk materials. The concept that the ova at the stage of preimplantation develop nutritively in a closed system has been supported by recent investigations. The oxygen consumption of ova was measured in media to which several substrates were added. The rate of the respiratory activity did not increase during the early stage of ova from one cell to morula when some substrates belonging to the TCA cycle were added to the incubating media (Sugawara, 1962). At the early blasto-cyst stage, respiratory activity is increased by the addition of sub-strates. The rate of increase varies with the substrate. This indicates that mammalian ova, during the early stage of development, are not capable of oxidizing suitable substrates via aerobic respiration.

The utilization of various substrates "in vitro" varies with the species and the stage of ova development (Mounib and Chang, 1965b). In the rabbit, pyruvate, cystine, and glutathione stimulate blastocyst growth, wherease glucose and lactate do not. Mouse ova are successfully cultured and develop into a blastocyst "in vitro" when lactate is present in the medium (Brinster, 1963). Brinster (1965) studied the amino acid requirement of two-celled mouse ova in culture and demonstrated that the omission of no single amino acid from the medium completely prevented the development of some two-cell ova into blastocysts. The omission of cystine, however, resulted in a significant decrease in development. This may suggest that sul-phydril compounds such as cystine are essential for activity and for synthesis of enzyme systems of the developing embryo.

Enzyme Systems and Cleavage

The rate of metabolic activity varies with the stage of develop-ment and the nature of endogenous metabolites within the vitellus. For example, the cytochemical features of DNA, RNA, PAS-positive materials, and lipids in the tubal ova of rodents change during cleav-age and development (Dalcq and Mulnard, 1953; Ishida, 1954; Austin and Amoroso, 1959). In general, the mammalian ova are classified into three categories according to the amount of glycogen and lipids in the ova (Ishida, 1960): type I (the ova of cows, sheep, goats, pigs, and dogs) contains none to small amounts of glycogen and a large amount of lipids; type II (the ova of rats, mice, hamsters) contains none to large amounts of glycogen and none to small amounts of lipids; type III (the ova of rabbits) contains none to small amounts of glycogen and small amounts of lipids. Differences in the relative amounts of these metabolites within the vitellus are associated with different levels of enzymic activity. The activity of alkaline and acid phosphatase and ATPase, as judged histochemically, varies with the stage of development (Dalcq, 1954, 1955, 1959; Tondeur, 1959). The activity levels of amylase, succinic dehydrogenase, glucose-6-phos-phate dehydrogenase, and glutamic-oxalacetic transaminase, as estimated spectrophotometrically in homogenates of blastocysts, vary with the species and stage of development (Hafez and White, unpublished data).

The Placenta

Metabolic Patterns and Functions of Placental Enzymes

The placenta contains more glycogen than any other components of the conceptus. During late pregnancy the placental glycogen content falls as the glycogen content of the fetal liver rises sharply. The decline in placental glycogen coincides with the onset of the hepatic glycogenic function in the fetus (Tuchmann-Duplessis and Bortolami, 1954). In the rabbit, glycogen is localized exclusively in the decidua of the maternal placenta; the fetal placenta, including the yolk sac, is devoid of glycogen (Loveland et al., 1931).

The placenta of some species, e.g., sheep, contains isomerase and is able to form fructose. Hers (1960a, 1960b) suggested that the sheep's placenta converts glucose to sorbitol with an aldose reductase.

The giant cells of the trophoblast perform several functions, including invasiveness and synthesis of luteotropic and steroid hormones. The histologic appearances at the margin of the growing trophoblastic shell of the human placenta in the early months of gestation suggest that the cells and matrix of the decidua are attacked and slowly destroyed by the action of the advancing, growing cytotrophoblast (Wislocki and Padykula, 1961). Fragmentation of collagen fibers in the vicinity of the trophoblast has been noted in the placenta of rodents (Wislocki et al., 1946). Proteolytic activity has been demonstrated experimentally in the presence of fertilized mouse ova transferred to various extrauterine sites, including the anterior chamber of the eye.

The passage of many substances across the placental barrier is chemically regulated (Huggett and Hammond, 1952; Wislocki and Padykula, 1961). Dempsey and Wislocki (1945) suggested that a layer of different phosphatases located in the placental barrier may participate in the transfer of metabolites. For example, alkaline phosphatase may be associated with the absorption of phosphorylated compounds in the microvilli. In the placenta of a wide variety of species the presence of carbonic anhydrase has led to the assumption that this substance is involved in fetal metabolism (Zarrow, 1961) and in the transfer of calcium across the placenta (Lutwak-Mann, 1955).

The giant cells of the trophoblast exhibit a remarkable capacity to generate TPNH via oxidation of glucose-6-phosphate. TPNH is now thought to be essential for a number of hydroxylations in the synthesis of cholesterol from acetate and in its conversion to the various functional hormones (cf. Block., 1957). $\triangle^5$-3-hydroxysteroid dehydrogenase activity (Levy et al., 1959), as well as generation of a continuous supply of TPNH through glucose-6-phosphate dehydrogenase activity, is involved in the synthesis of all known steroid hormones.

Implantation sites of rats (pregnant 10 to 21 days) and mice have been assayed for $\triangle^5$-3-hydroxysteroid dehydrogenase activity by histochemical and biochemical methods (Deane et al., 1962). Histochemically, activity was limited to the peripheral giant trophoblasts of the fetal placenta and in rats rises to a peak at about 13 to 15 days of gestation and thereafter declines. This enzyme is required for oxidation of D_{19} and $C_{21}\triangle^5$-3-hydroxysteroids to $\triangle^4$-3-ketosteroids and thus plays a key role in the biosynthesis of the active steroid hormones. Other features of the giant cells which indicate their function in the production of steroid hormones are a conspicuous amount of cytoplasmic lipid and a high capacity for making reduced triphosphopyridine nucleotide (TPNH) as a result of the oxidation of glucose-6-phosphate.

Marked changes occur in the enzyme levels of the endometrium following parturition. Immediately postpartum, increased enzymic activity develops around the placental detachment sites, in the epithelial cells, and in macrophages and stromal cells. The activity of lysosomal acid phosphatase was studied both by a cell-standing technique during postpartum involution of the rat uterus, and by its regression following hormone withdrawal (Lobel and Deane, 1962). Little enzymic activity was detectable in uteri from virgin and pregnant rats; immediately postpartum marked enzyme activity developed among the placental detachment sites.

Enzyme Systems in the Placenta

The chemical morphology of the placenta has been studied in several species including ruminants and man (Dempsey and Wislocki, 1945; Wislocki and Dempsey, 1945, 1946a, 1946b, 1946c; Wimsatt, 1951; Moss et al., 1954). The mammalian placenta contains a wide variety of enzyme systems, e.g., oxidative enzymes (Reale and Pipino, 1959), succinic dehydrogenase (Seligman and Rutenburg, 1951; Telkkä and Lehto, 1954; Reale and Pipino, 1957; Padykula,

1958), and cholinesterase (Torda, 1942; Ord and Thompson, 1950). In sheep, the placenta contains aldose reductase, which catalyzes the reduction by TPNH of a great number of aldoses or related substances, and of several aliphatic and cyclic aldehydes (Hers, 1960a, 1960b).

The human placental enzymes have been classified into five major groups: (1) *hydrolases:* esterases, glycosidases, amidases, peptidases, phosphomidases, polyphosphatases, haloganeses, carbon–sulfur hydrolases, and carbon–carbon hydrolases; (2) *transferases:* transmethylases, transacylases, transglycosylases, transphosphatases, transaminases, transadenlases, and transsulfurases; (3) *oxidoreductases:* aerobic transhydrogenases, anaerobic transhydrogenases, oxidases, anaerobic transelectronases, peroxidases, and catalases; (4) *lyases and syntheases:* carbolyases and carbosyntheases, hydratases and dehydratases, carbon–sulfur lyases, carbon–nitrogen lyases and syntheases, and hydrogenases and hydrogenlyses; and (5) *isomerases and racemases* [classified by Page and Glendening (1954) using the terminology of Hoffman-Ostenhof (1953)]. Other enzymes are reported to be absent from the human placenta, e.g., lipase, uricase, histidase, renin, and DOPA decarboxylase.

The trophoblast and the blastocoelic fluid in sheep and rabbits contain varying amounts of alkaline phosphatase, acid phosphatase, amylase, glucose-6-phosphate dehydrogenase, lactic dehydrogenase, and glutamic-oxalacetic transaminase (Hafez and White, unpublished data). The levels of these enzymes vary prior to implantation.

Localization of Placental Enzymes

The localization of enzymes in the placenta varies with the type of placentation. In the epitheliochorial placenta of pigs, succinic dehydrogenase is localized in the whole trophoblastic epithelium and particularly in that of the areolae and of the bottom of the chorial fossae. In the placenta of cows and sheep, the enzymes are localized in the trophoblastic epithelium of the intercarunclar chorion and that of the bases of the villi (Reale and Pipino, 1959).

Alkaline phosphatase is widely distributed in all types of placenta but, ironically, in maximal concentration in those species producing no fructose, and in minimal concentration in the fructogenic species (Ainsworth et al., 1951). This enzyme is found histologically in sheep's maternal placenta and absent in the chorionic villi and other fetal parts. In the rat placenta, a moderate alkaline phosphatase reaction is found in the decidua, and an intense reaction is found in the junctional zone, syncytial trophoblast, and trophoblastic giant cells. The enzyme is not demonstrated in the labyrinth in the early stage of development. Alkaline phosphatase occurs in the syncytial trophoblast (Buno and Curi, 1945; Dempsey and Wislocki, 1945; Wimsatt, 1951).

The various maternal and fetal components of the allantochorion and inverted yolk sac placentae of the rat have different patterns of glycogen storage and glucose-6-phosphatase activity and these vary at different times. Glucose-6-phosphatase activity of the disc in the rat is localized mainly in the labyrinthine trophoblast and glucose secretion may occur in this fetal layer during the last half of gestation. This would indicate that there are two placental regions, the decidua and the labyrinthine trophoblast, which may be involved in glucose secretion at different times during gestation (Padykula and Richardson, 1963).

Future Research

Further research is needed to study the biochemical mechanism of the transfer of energy in the form of electron potential to that of energy-rich phosphate bonds within the cells of the trophoblast. Comparative investigations in uterine and placental enzymes on a variety of species are recommended. These studies might provide useful information for "dating" of the endometrium, and the diagnosis of reproductive abnormalities and congenital fetal malformations (cf. Homburger and Fishman, 1956; Gross and Danziger, 1957; Humke, 1963; Stark and Oweis, 1963). Changes in enzyme levels may reflect alterations in uterine metabolism.

Implantation involves the local suspension of the normal capacity of the endometrial tissue to reject homologous foreign tissue—the trophoblast. The biochemical mechanisms associated with implantation and early stages of placentation are little known. The changes in endocrine environment and trophoblast differentiation during implantation are associated with certain changes in enzyme patterns. Whether these enzymes are essential for implantation and prenatal development still awaits further investigation. Studies are also needed on the enzymology of the uterine luminal fluid and the myometrium.

The enzymorphologic study of tissues provides a different kind of information than do the biochemical analysis of the homogenates. The advantages of visualizing the actual tissue and cellular sites of enzyme responses to hormones are emphasized. On the other hand, enzymic reaction within the cell may not represent the actual distribution on "in vivo," since the reaction products may migrate from the cytopalsm to the nucleus (Herman and Deane, 1953). Biochemical studies based on homogenate analysis should be carefully interpreted, since such studies are influenced by several factors, such as (1) solubility of the enzyme in the homogenizing medium, (2) the total amount of soluble protein in the tissue, (3) stability of the enzyme under experimental conditions, (4) the histological makeup of the tissues, (5) the possible presence of endogenous activators or inhibitors (Delgado and Fridhandler, 1964) and (6) the relative degree of vascularity of the tissue and the contamination with blood cells. The use of tissue-culture techniques may be employed to study the cytochemical characteristics of endometrial and trophoblastic cells (cf. Weiss and Fawcett, 1953).

Acknowledgments

Unpublished results in this paper are part of an investigation supported by U.S. Public Health Service Research Grant HD-00585-03 of National Institute of Child Health and Human Development. Scientific Paper No. 2800, College of Agriculture Research Center, Project 1698.

References

Ainsworth, I. N., C. W. Parr, and F. L. Warren. 1951. Fructose formation in the placenta. *J. Endocrinol.,* 7: 63–64.

Albers, H. J., and M. E. Castro. 1961. The protein components of rat uterine fluid. An analysis of its antigens by immunoelectrophoresis and outchterlony gel diffusion technic. *Fertility Sterility,* 12: 142–150.

Albers, H. J., J. M. Bedford, and M. C. Chang. 1961. Uterine peptidase activity in the rat and rabbit during pseudopregnancy. *J. Physiol. (London),* 201: 554–556.

Arzac, J. P., and E. Blanchet. 1948. Alkaline phosphatase and glycogen in human endometrium. *J. Clin. Endocrinol.,* 8: 315–324.

Atkinson, W. B., and H. Elftman. 1947. Mobilization of alkaline phosphatase in the uterus of the mouse by glycogen. *Endocrinology,* 40: 30–36.

Austin, C. R., and E. C. Amoroso. 1959. The mammalian egg. *Endeavour,* 18: 130–141.

Bergmeyer, H. U. 1963. *Methods of Enzymatic Analysis.* Academic Press, New York.

Bever, A. T., J. T. Velardo, M. A. Telfer, F. L. Hisaw, and C. M. Goolsby. 1954. Changes in enzyme activity in uterus of rats during estrus cycle. *Federation Proc.,* 13: 13–14.

Beyler, A. L., and C. M. Szego. 1954. Correlation of ovarian cholesterol levels with changes in β-glucuronidase activity of reproductive tract during the estrous cycle and pregnancy. *Endocrinology,* 54: 323–333.

Bialy, G., and G. Pincus. 1960. Carbonic anhydrase activity of rat uterine tissues. *Endocrinology,* 67: 728–729.

Bialy, G., and G. Pincus. 1962. Effects of estrogen and progestin on the uterine carbonic anyhdrase of immature rats. *Endocrinology,* 70: 781–785.

Biddulph, C., M. San Martin, S. C. Becker, and W. H. McShan. 1959. Succinic dehydrogenase and adenosinetriphosphatase activities of corpora lutea, ovarian interstitial tissue and endometrium from pseudopregnant rabbits and rabbits treated with gonadotrophic hormones. *J. Endocrinol.*, **18**: 125–131.

Bishop, D. W. 1956. Active secretion in the rabbit oviduct. *Am. J. Physiol.*, **187**: 347–352.

Black, D. L., R. T. Duby, and J. Riesen. 1963. Apparatus for the continuous collection of sheep oviduct fluid. *J. Reprod. Fertility*, **6**: 257–260.

Block, K. 1957. The biological synthesis of cholesterol. *Vitamine Hormone*, **15**: 119–150.

Bo, W. J. 1959. Distribution of phosphorylase in the uteri of cyclic and hormone treated rats. *J. Histochem. Cytochem.*, **7**: 403–408.

Bo, W. J., and W. B. Atkinson. 1952. Histochemical studies on glycogen deposition in the uterus of the rat. I. In intact cyclic animals and in castrates treated with ovarian hormones. *Anat. Rec.*, **113**: 91–100.

Bo, W. J., and M. S. Smith. 1964a. Histochemical observations on the glycogen synthesizing enzyme in the decidual cells (rats). *Anat. Rec.*, **148**: 262–263.

Bo, W. J., and M. S. Smith. 1964b. Glycogen synthetase in the rabbit tongue and uterus. *Anat. Rec.*, **148** 503–505.

Brachet, J. 1957. In *Biochemical Cytology* (G. H. Bourne and J. F. Danielle, eds.). Academic Press, New York.

Brinster, R. L. 1963. A method for "in vitro" cultivation of mouse ova from two-cell to blastocyst. *Exptl. Cell. Res.*, **32**: 205–208.

Brinster, R. L. 1965. Studies on the development of mouse embryos "in vitro." *J. Exptl. Zool.*, **158**: 49–68.

Buno, W., and C. R. Curi. 1945. Distribucion de la fosfatase en la placenta humana. *Ciencia (Mex.)*, **6**: 59.

Clewe, T. H., and L. Mastroianni, Jr. 1960. A method for continuous volumetric collection of oviduct secretions. *J. Reprod. Fertility*, **1**: 146–150.

Dalcq, A. M. 1954. Functions cellulaires et cytochimie structurale dans l'oeuf de quelques Rongeures. *Compt. Rend. Soc. Biol.*, **148**: 1332–1373.

Dalcq, A. M. 1955. Processes of synthesis during early development of rodent eggs and embryos. *Studies Fertility*, **7**: 113–128.

Dalcq, A. M. 1959. La localisation cytochimique de l'adenosine-triphosphatase dans les oeufs des Mammifers et a relation avec leur organisation morphogenetique. *Bull. Acad. Roy. Med. (Belg.)*, **24**: 825.

Dalcq, A. M., and J. Mulnard. 1953. Localisation de la phosphatase alcaline dans les ebauches dentaires des Rongeurs. *Compt. Rend. Soc. Biol.*, **147**: 2040–2042.

Deane, H. W., B. L. Rubin, E. C. Driks, B. L. Lobel, and G. Leipsner. 1962. Trophoblastic giant cells in placentas of rats and mice and their probable role in steroid hormone production. *Endocrinology*, **70**: 407–419.

De Duve, C. 1959. Lysosomes—a new group of cytoplasmic particles. In *Subcellular Particles* (T. Hayashi, ed.). Ronald Press, New York, pp. 128–159.

De Duve, C., B. C. Pressman, R. Gianetto, R. Wittiaux, and F. Applemans. 1955. Tissue fractionation studies. Intracellular distribution patterns of enzymes in rat liver tissue. *Biochem. J.*, **60**: 604–617.

Delgado, R., and L. Fridhandler. 1964. Enzyme changes in the rabbit uterus in early pregnancy. *Exptl. Cell Res.*, **34**: 45–53.

Dempsey, E. W., and G. B. Wislocki. 1945. Histochemical reactions associated with basophilia and acidophilia in the placenta and pituitary gland. *Am. J. Anat.*, **76**: 277–301.

Eckstein, B., and H. Shain. 1963. The development of the ovary of the rat. III.

The effect of gonadotrophins on glutamic-oxalacetic transaminase. *Acta Endocrinol.*, **42**: 389–394.

Edström, J. E. 1956. Separation and determination of purines and pyrimidine nucleotides in picogram amounts. *Biochim. Biophys. Acta,* **22**: 378–388.

Edström, J. E., and H. Hyden. 1954. Ribonucleotide analysis of individual nerve cells. *Nature,* **174**: 128–129.

Fishman, W. H. 1947. β-glucuronidase—its relation to the action of estrogenic hormones. *J. Biol. Chem.,* **169**: 7–15.

Fishman, W. H., and L. W. Fishman. 1944. The elevation of uterine β-glucuronidase activity by estrogenic hormones. *J. Biol. Chem.,* **152**: 487–488.

Foraker, A. G., P. A. Celi, and S. W. Denham. 1954. Dehydrogenase activity in normal and hyperplastic endometrium. *Cancer,* **7**: 100–105.

Giering, J. E., and M. X. Zarrow. 1958. Changes in uterine morphology and phosphatase levels induced by chronic stimulation with the ovarian hormones. *Acta Endocrinol.,* **29**: 499–507.

Glick, D. 1963. *Techniques of Histo- and Cytochemistry.* Wiley-Interscience, New York.

Greengard, P. 1956. Determination of intermediary metabolites by enzymic fluorimetry. *Nature,* **178**: 632–634.

Gregoire, A., T. D. Gongsakdi, and A. E. Rakoff. 1961. The free amino acid content of the female rabbit genital tract. *Fertility Sterility,* **12**: 322–327.

Gross, M. 1961. Biochemical changes in the reproductive cycle. *Fertility Sterility,* **12**: 245–262.

Gross, S. J., and S. Danziger. 1957. Histochemical techniques applied to the study of benign and malignant squamous epthelium of the cervix uteri. *Am. J. Obstet. Gynecol.,* **73**: 94–119.

Hafez, E. S. E. 1964. Uterine and placental enzymes. *Acta Endocrinol.,* **46**: 217–229.

Hamner, C., and W. Williams. 1963. Composition of rabbit oviduct secretions. *Fertility Sterility,* **16**: 170–176.

Harkness, M. L. R., and R. D. Harkness. 1956. The distribution of the growth of collagen in the uterus of the pregnant rat. *J. Physiol. (London),* **132**: 492.

Harris, R. S., and S. L. Cohen. 1951. The influence of ovarian hormones on the enzymatic activities of tissues. *Endocrinology,* **48**: 264–272.

Hayashi, M., and W. H. Fishman. 1961. Enzymorphologic observations in the uterus and vagina of castrate rats receiving ovarian hormones. *Acta Endocrinol.,* **38**: 107–120.

Herman, E., and H. W. Deane. 1953. A comparison of the localization of alkaline glycero-phosphatase, as demonstrated by the Gomori-Takarmatan method in frozen and in paraffin sections. *J. Cellular Comp. Physiol.,* **41**: 201–224.

Hers, G. 1960a. Le mechanisme de la formation du fructose seminal et du fructose foetale. *Biochim. Biophys. Acta,* **37**: 127–138.

Hers, G. 1960b. L'aldose reductase. *Biochim. Biophys. Acta,* **37**: 120–126.

Hoffmann-Ostenhof, O. 1953. Suggestions for a more rational classification and nomenclature of enzymes. *Advan. Enzymol.,* **14**: 219–260.

Holter, H., and K. Lindstrøm-Lang. 1951. Micromethods and their application in the study of enzyme distribution in tissues and cells. *Physiol. Rev.,* **31**: 432–448.

Homburger, F., and W. H. Fishman. 1956. The laboratory diagnosis of cancer of the cervix. *Symposia on Research Advances Applied to Medical Practice,* No. 2. Karger, Basel.

Huggett, A. St. G., and J. Hammond. 1952. Physiology of the placenta. In *Marshall's Physiology of Reproduction,* Vol. 2 (A. S. Parkes, ed.). Longmans, London, 3rd ed., pp. 312–397.

Humke, W. 1963. Isolation and behaviour of alkaline phosphatase in the normal and pathological placenta. *Arch. Gynaekol.,* **198:** 184–186.

Ishida, K. 1954. Histochemical studies of rat tubal ova. *Tohoku J. Agr. Res.,* **5:** 1–8.

Ishida, K. 1960. Histochemical studies of lipids in the ovaries of domestic animals. *Saibo Kaku Byorigaku Zasshi,* **19:** 547–563.

Jacquot, R., and N. Kretchmer. 1964. Effect of fetal decapitation on enzymes of glycogen metabolism (rats). *J. Biol. Chem.,* **239:** 1301–1304.

Karunairatnam, M. C., and G. A. Levvy. 1949. The inhibition of β-glucuronidase by saccharic acid and the role of the enzymes in glucuronidase synthesis. *Biochem. J.,* **44:** 599–604.

Kerr, L. M. H., J. G. Campbell, and G. A. Levvy. 1949. β-glucuronidase activity in the mouse. *Biochem. J.,* **46:** 278–284.

Knobil, E. 1952. The relation of some steroid hormones to β-glucuronidase activity. *Endocrinology,* **50:** 16–28.

Kraicer, P., and M. C. Shelesnyak. 1959. The induction of deciduomata in the pseudopregnant rat by systemic administration of histamine and histamine-releasers. *J. Endocrinol.,* **17:** 324–328.

Leathem, J. H. 1959. Some biochemical aspects of the uterus. *Ann. N.Y. Acad. Sci.,* **75:** 463–471.

Leonard, S. L. 1958. Hormonal effects on phosphorylase activity in the rat uterus. *Endocrinology,* **63:** 853–859.

Leonard, S. L., and E. Knobil. 1950. β-glucuronidase activity in the rat uterus. *Endocrinology,* **47:** 331–337.

Leone, E., M. Libonati, and C. Lutwak-Mann. 1963. Enzymes in uterine and cervical fluid and in certain related tissues and body fluids of the rabbit. *J. Endocrinol.,* **25:** 551–552.

Levvy, G. A. 1952. The preparation and properties of β-glucuronidase. 4. Inhibition by sugar acids and their lactones. *Biochem. J.,* **52:** 464–472.

Levy, H., H. W. Deane, and B. L. Rubin. 1959. Visualization of steroid-3β-01-dehydrogenase activity in tissues of intact and hypophysectomized rats. *Endocrinology,* **65:** 932–943.

Likar, I. N., and L. J. Likar. 1964. Acid mucopolysaccharides and mast cells in the bovine uterus at different stages of the sexual cycle. *Acta Endocrinol.,* **46:** 493–506.

Lobel, B. L., and H. W. Deane. 1962. Enzymic activity associated with post-partum involution of the uterus and its regression after hormonal withdrawal in the rat. *Endocrinology,* **70:** 567–578.

Lobel, B. L., R. M. Rosenbaum, and H. W. Deane. 1961. Enzymic correlations of physiological regression of follicles and corpora lutea in ovaries of normal rats. *Endocrinology,* **68:** 232–247.

Loveland, G., E. F. Maurer, and F. F. Snyder. 1931. The diminution of the glycogen store of the rabbit's placenta during the last third of pregnancy. *Anat. Rec.,* **49:** 265–275.

Lowry, O. H., N. R. Roberts, and C. Lewis. 1956. The quantitative histochemistry of the retina. *J. Biol. Chem.,* **220:** 879–892.

Lutwak-Mann, C. 1955. Carbonic anhydrase in the female reproductive tract. Occurrence, distribution and hormonal dependence. *J. Endocrinol.*, 13: 26–38.

Lutwak-Mann, C., and C. E. Adams. 1957. Carbonic anhydrase in the female reproductive tract. II. Endometrial carbonic anhydrase as indicator of lutoid potency: Correlation with progestational proliferation. *J. Endocrinol.*, 15: 43–55.

Lutwak-Mann, C., and R. L. W. Averill. 1954. Carbonic anhydrase activity in the uterus and fallopian tube of the ewe. *J. Endocrinol.*, 11, xii.

Madjerek, Z., and J. van der Vies. 1961. Carbonic anhydrase activity in the uteri of mice under various experimental conditions. *Acta Endocrinol.*, 38: 315–320.

Maibenco, H. C. 1960. Connective tissue changes in postpartum uterine involution in the albino rat. *Anat. Rec.*, 136: 59–72.

Mastroianni, L., Jr., and R. C. Wallach. 1961. Effect of ovulation and early gestation on oviduct secretions in the rabbit. *Am. J. Physiol.*, 200: 815–819.

Mastroianni, L., Jr., F. Beer, U. Shah, and T. H. Clewe. 1961. Endocrine regulation of oviduct secretion in the rabbit. *Endocrinology*, 68: 92–100.

Meldrum, N. U., and F. J. K. Roughton. 1933. Carbonic anhydrase: Its preparation and properties. *J. Physiol. (London)*, 80: 113–142.

Mills, G. T., and J. Paul. 1949. The properties of β-glucuronidase. *Biochem. J.*, 44: 34.

Morione, T., and S. Seifter. 1962. Alteration in the collagen content of the human uterus during pregnancy and postpartum involution. *J. Exptl. Med.*, 115: 357–365.

Moss, S., T. R. Wreen, and J. F. Sykes. 1954. Alkaline phosphatase, glycogen, and periodic acid-Schiff positive substances in the bovine uterus during the estrous cycle. *Endocrinology*, 55: 261–273.

Mounib, M. S., and M. C. Chang. 1965a. Metabolism of endometrium and fallopian tube in the estrous and the pseudopregnant rabbit. *Endocrinology*, 76: 542–546.

Mounib, M. S., and M. C. Chang. 1965b. Metabolism of glucose, fructose and pyruvate in the 6-day rabbit blastocyst. *Exptl. Cell Res.*, 38: 201–215.

Novikoff, A. B. 1961. Lysosomes and related particles. In *The Cell*, Vol. 2 (J. Brachet and A. E. Mirsky, eds.). Academic Press, New York, p. 423.

Ogawa, Y., and G. Pincus. 1962. Estrogen effects on the carbonic anhydrase content of mouse uteri. *Endocrinology*, 70: 359–364.

Olds, D., and N. L. VanDemark. 1957. Physiologic aspects of fluids in the female genitalia with special reference to cattle. *Am. J. Vet. Res.*, 18: 587–602.

Ord, M. G., and R. H. S. Thompson. 1950. Nature of placental cholinesterase. *Nature*, 165: 927–928.

Padykula, H. A. 1958. A histochemical and quantitative study of enzymes of the rat's placenta. *J. Anat.*, 92: 118–129.

Padykula, H. A., and D. Richardson. 1963. A correlated histochemical and biochemical study of glycogen storage in the rat placenta. *Am. J. Anat.*, 112: 215–241.

Page, E. W., and M. B. Glendening. 1954. *Gestation* (L. B. Flexner, ed.). Josiah Macy, Jr., Foundation, New York, p. 225.

Prahald, K. V. 1962. A study of the rat uterine β-glucuronidase prior to implantation of the ovum. *Acta Endocrinol.*, 39: 407–410.

Ramsey, E. M. 1954. Circulation in the maternal placenta of primates. *Am. J. Obstet. Gynecol.,* **67:** 1–14.

Reale, E., and G. Pipino. 1957. Les variations de la repartition histochimique de la succino-dehydrogenase au cours de la placentation chorion-allantoidienne et vitelline etudiées dans le *Mus musculus albinus. Compt. Rend. Acad. Anat.,* **44:** Reunion-Leyde.

Reale, E., and G. Pipino. 1959. La distribuzione della succino-deidrogenasi nella placenta di alcuni mammiferi. Studio istochimico. *Arch. Ital. Anat. Embriol.,* **64:** 318–356.

Reynolds, S. R. M. 1959. V. Aspects of the gravid uterus: gestation mechanisms. *Ann. N.Y. Acad. Sci.,* **75:** 691–699.

Ringler, I. 1961. The composition of rat uterine luminal fluid. *Endocrinology,* **68:** 281–291.

Rosa, C. G. 1959. Cytochemical demonstration of diphosphopyridine nucleotide-diaphorase activity in cells of vaginal secretions of mice. *Proc. Soc. Exptl. Biol. Med.,* **102:** 198–201.

Rosa, C. G., and J. T. Velardo. 1959a. Histochemical localization of vaginal oxidative enzymes and mucins in rats treated with estradiol and progesterone. *Ann. N.Y. Acad. Sci.,* **83:** 122–144.

Rosa, C. G., and J. T. Velardo. 1959b. Histochemical observations of oxidative enzyme systems in the uterus and vagina of the rat. *Ann. N.Y. Acad. Sci.,* **75:** 491–505.

Salmi, H. A., A. M. Salmi, and K. Hartiala. 1959. Inhibition of uterine β-glucuronidase activity in the rat by local application of potassium hydrogen saccharate. *Acta Endocrinol.,* **30:** 147–153.

Seligman, A. M., and A. M. Rutenburg. 1951. The histochemical demonstration of succinic dehydrogenase. *Science,* **113:** 317–320.

Stark, G., and E. Oweis. 1963. Transaminases (GOT, GPT) and dehydrogenases (LDH, MDH) in normal and pathological placentas. *Arch. Gynaekol.,* **199:** 124–133.

Sugawara, S. 1962. Metabolism in the mammalian ova. *Nippon Chikusangaku Kaiho,* **33:** 1–10.

Sugawara, S., and E. S. E. Hafez. 1968. Metabolism of mammalian ova. *Acta Endocrinol.* In press.

Sumawong, V., A. T. Gregoire, W. D. Johnson, and A. E. Rakoff. 1962. Identification of carbohydrates in the vaginal fluid of normal females. *Fertility Sterility,* **13:** 270–280.

Szego, C. M., and D. A. Lawson. 1964. Influence of histamine on uterine metabolism: Stimulation of incorporation of radioactivity from amino acids into protein, lipid and purines (rat). *Endocrinology,* **74:** 372–381.

Szego, C. M., and S. Roberts. 1953. Steroid action and interaction in uterine metabolism. *Recent Progr. Hormone Res.,* **8:** 419–469.

Telfer, M. A., and F. L. Hisaw, Jr. 1957. Biochemical responses of the rabbit endometrium and myometrium to oestradiol and progesterone. *Acta Endocrinol.,* **25:** 390–404.

Telkkä, A., and L. Lehto. 1954. Histochemically demonstrable succinic dehydrogenase activity of placental tissues. *Ann. Med. Exptl. Biol. Fenniae (Helsinki),* **32:** 292–296.

Thiery, M., and R. G. J. Willighagen. 1963. Enzymatic-histochemical study of the corpus uteri of the mouse. *Anat. Rec.,* **146:** 263–279.

Tondeur, M. 1959. Effets de l'impregnation osmique in toto des oeufs vierges, fecondes ou segmentes du rat et de la souris. *Bull. Classe Sci. Acad. Roy. Belg.,* **45:** 487–512.

Torda, C. 1942. Choline esterase content of tissues without innervation (placenta). *Proc. Soc. Exptl. Biol.,* **51:** 398–400.

Tsuji, J. H. 1963. Carbonic anhydrase in the endometrium of the rabbit. *Japan. Obstet. Gynecol. Soc.,* **15:** 1001–1010.

Tuchmann-Duplessis, H., and R. Bortolami. 1954. Les Constituants histochimique de l'allentoplacenta du lapin. *Bull. Microscop. Appl.,* **4:** 73–88.

Villee, C. A., and E. E. Gordon. 1956. The stimulation by estrogens of DPN-linked isocitric dehydrogenase from human placenta. *Bull. Soc. Chim. Belg.,* **65:** 186–201.

Walaas, O. 1952. Effect of oestrogens on the glycogen content of the rat uterus. *Acta Endocrinol.,* **10:** 175–192.

Wallace, J. C., G. M. Stone, and I. G. White. 1964. The influence of some oestrogens and progestogens on the activity of glycerylphosphorylcholine diesterase in rinsing of the rat uterus. *J. Endocrinol.,* **29:** 175–184.

Weiss, L. P., and D. W. Fawcett. 1953. Cytochemical observations on chicken monocytes, macrophages and giant cells in tissue culture. *J. Histochem. Cytochem.,* **1:** 47–65.

White, I. G., and J. C. Wallace. 1961. Breakdown of seminal glycerylphosphorylcholine by secretions of the female reproductive tract. *Nature,* **189:** 843–844.

White, I. G., J. C. Wallace, and G. M. Stone. 1963. Studies on the glycerylphosphorylcholine diesterase activity of the female genital tract in the ewe, cow, sow and rat. *J. Reprod. Fertility,* **5:** 298.

Wimsatt, W. A. 1951. Observations on the morphogenesis cytochemistry and significance of binucleatic giant cells of the placenta of ruminants. *Am. J. Anat.,* **89:** 233–281.

Wislocki, G. B., and E. W. Dempsey. 1945. Histochemical reactions of the endometrium in pregnancy. *Am. J. Anat.,* **77:** 365–403.

Wislocki, G. B., and E. W. Dempsey. 1946a. Histochemical reactions in the placenta of the cat. *Am. J. Anat.,* **78:** 1–41.

Wislocki, G. B., and E. W. Dempsey. 1946b. Histochemical age-changes in normal and pathological placental villi (Hydatiform mole, eclampsia). *Endocrinology,* **38:** 90–109.

Wislocki, G. B., and E. W. Dempsey. 1946c. Histochemical reactions of the placenta of the pig. *Am. J. Anat.,* **78:** 181–219.

Wislocki, G. B., and H. A. Padykula. 1961. Histochemistry and electron microscopy of the placenta. In *Sex and Internal Secretions* (W. C. Young, ed.). Williams & Wilkins, Baltimore, 3rd ed., Chap. 15.

Wislocki, G. B., H. W. Deane, and E. W. Dempsey. 1946. The histochemistry of the rodent's placenta. *Am. J. Anat.,* **78:** 281–345.

Woessner, J. F., Jr., and T. H. Brewer. 1963. Formation and breakdown of collagen and elastin in the human uterus during pregnancy and post-partum involution. *Biochem. J.,* **89:** 75–82.

Zarrow, M. X. 1961. Gestation. In *Sex and Internal Secretions* (W. C. Young, ed.). Williams & Wilkins, Baltimore, 3rd ed., pp. 958–1034.

Zondek, B., and S. Hestrin. 1947. Phosphorylase activity in human endometrium. *Am. J. Obstet. Gynecol.,* **54:** 173–175.

REPRODUCTION AND SEXUAL BEHAVIOR (M. Diamond ed.), 231–239, © Indiana University Press

16

Molecular Action of Estrogens

Claude A. Villee

In the past decade some half-dozen theories have been advanced regarding the mechanism of action of hormones, each with experimental data to buttress it. Implicit in all these theories is the assumption that every hormone has a single, primary site of action and that its multiple physiologic effects stem from this single, primary site of action. Some of these theories have been discarded as newer data have made them untenable; others still provide a reasonable explanation for one or more aspects of hormonal action. Careful review at this time suggests that there may well be no single, primary molecular site of action from which all the physiologic effects of hormones follow. Indeed, an extensive series of experiments in our laboratory (Channing and Villee, 1966a, 1966b) showed that luteinizing hormone has three separate and distinct actions on the luteinized cells of rat ovaries. These include (1) an effect on the cell membrane—a stimulation of the uptake of glucose and certain other hexoses; (2) a stimulation of the enzyme phosphorylase, perhaps analogous to that of adrenal phosphorylase by ACTH and of liver phosphorylase by glucagon; and (3) an increased conversion of cholesterol to pregnenolone, apparently by a stimulation of 20α-hydroxylase. ACTH has a comparable effect on the 20α-hydroxylase of the adrenal.

The physiologic and morphologic effects of estrogens are primarily a stimulation of the growth of target organs, and the target

organs studied in greatest detail are the uterus and vagina of the
rat and human endometrium. Growth is a symphony of energy-
requiring processes involving the synthesis of nucleic acids, proteins,
lipids, and other substances. In a given tissue at a particular moment,
growth might occur at less than the maximal rate if one of the substrates for the synthesis of protein, nucleic acids, or lipids were
present in less than optimal concentrations or if the activity of some
key enzyme in one of these biosynthetic pathways were depressed.
A hormone could then stimulate growth by increasing either the
amount or the activity of an enzyme or a group of enzymes, by increasing the uptake and hence the amount of some substrate or cofactor, or by decreasing the concentration of an inhibitor or repressor.
Growth could also be less than maximal if the amount of biologically
useful energy for these synthetic processes were rate-limiting, and
growth could be stimulated under these conditions if some system for
increasing the availability of biologically useful energy were increased
in activity. When estrogen is administered to an intact animal, only
some of its tissues, and not all, respond with an increased rate of
growth. The question of what distinguishes these responsive tissues
from the unresponsive or relatively less responsive tissues is part
of the general problem of the biochemical basis of cell differentiation.
Indeed the whole question of the biochemical basis of the cellular
and enzymatic specificity of hormonal action remains a challenge for
the future.

The growth of the uterus or endometrium stimulated by estrogen is characterized by a proliferation of previous cell types rather
than the appearance of new cell types that might indicate a hormonal effect on cell differentiation and the development of new
cellular characteristics. In addition, estrogens have widespread, general effects on skin, bone, and many other tissues; and any theory
of estrogen action must provide an explanation for these effects as
well as the effects on the primary target organs. Estrogens affect not
only a wide spectrum of tissues but a wide variety of metabolic
activities within each tissue. Thus Mueller and his colleagues (cf.
Mueller et al., 1958, for a review) have demonstrated that estradiol
injected in vivo increases a host of metabolic functions in the uterus
of the castrate rat when the uterus is subsequently incubated in vitro.
Among the enzymes of the uterus which have been shown to decrease
in activity when a rat is castrated and to increase in activity when the
castrate rat is subsequently injected with estrogens are serine aldolase,
phenol-activated DPNH oxidase, alkaline phosphatase, phosphorylase,
glucose-6-phosphate dehydrogenase, and 6-phosphogluconic acid de-

hydrogenase. With each of these the increased activity is detected in vitro only when the estrogen has been administered in vivo some time before. Thus it is not possible to determine whether the increased enzymatic activity is a direct effect of the estrogen or an indirect effect of a generalized increase in the rate of protein synthesis which follows upon the addition of estrogen.

Most investigators have suggested that hormones, in general, and estrogens, in particular, must interact with some specific receptor site, a site usually postulated to be some sort of macromolecule, a protein, or perhaps a nucleic acid. Jensen and Jacobson (1962), Toft and Gorski (1966), and others have attempted to isolate and identify such macromolecular receptors. There is evidence to suggest that at least some of the macromolecular receptors specific for estrogens are located in the nucleus of the target cell.

Under the appropriate experimental conditions estrogens have been found to enhance or depress almost every metabolic process that has been investigated in target cells such as those of the rat uterus or human endometrium. This would not be unexpected, since growth involves a coordinated increase in many, if not most, of the cell's metabolic processes. It is not yet known for certain whether estrogen causes an acceleration only of existing cell processes or whether its presence initiates new metabolic reactions.

The experiments of Jensen and Jacobson (1962) with highly labeled estrogens have defined the physiologic levels of estrogens more precisely than before and have shown that estrogens are effective in vivo at concentrations of $10^{-8}M$ or less. Thus studies in purified systems should conform to this level of estrogens if they are to shed light on the physiologic mechanism of action of hormones. The results of Jensen and his collaborators make it perfectly clear that no metabolic conversion of estradiol is involved in, or results from, the action of the steroid in the rat uterus. The experiments of Gorski et al. (1965) and of Segal et al. (1965) provide some information about the chemical nature of the receptor sites within the rat uterus, and knowledge of the properties of these receptors may ultimately lead to clarification of this problem.

Having agreed that the initial step in the mechanism of action of estrogen is its combination with some receptor site, investigators differ markedly in their hypotheses regarding the nature of the site, the intracellular location of the site, and the sequelae of the hormone–receptor interaction. One theory states that the hormone alters the permeability of the cell membrane or the membrane of some subcellular structure. By stimulating a specific permease or by some general effect on the architecture of the substance of the cell membrane the hormone would increase the transport of a material, make either substrate or cofactor more readily available, and thus increase the overall rate of some metabolic sequence. The importance of estrogenic effects on cellular permeability via the release of histamine has been stressed repeatedly by Szego (1965), Spaziani (1963), and others. An increased permeability of membranes does appear to be a significant component of the overall response of the target organ, such as the rat uterus, to estrogens; but this increased permeability may be a secondary effect which follows the primary effect of the estrogen rather than the initiating step in the process.

Another suggestion is that the hormone is involved as a coenzyme or cosubstrate in a particular enzyme system. Some investigators have been attracted by the possibility that the physiologic action of the hormone involves a reaction in which the hormone itself undergoes some change. This mechanism was invoked originally by Quastel and Woodridge (1928) and elaborated subsequently by Talalay and Williams-Ashman (1958), who suggested that the physiologic effects of all steroid hormones involve their reversible oxidation and reduction by enzymes with dual pyridine nucleotide specificity. A large body of experimental evidence has accumulated since this suggestion was made, which has led to the rejection of the theory that substrate-mediated transhydrogenation has any physiologic importance (Hechter and Halkerston, 1964). Bush and Mahesh (1959) showed that the action of progesterone in tissues does not involve a ketone-alco-version at carbon 11 of the steroid. Wiest (1959) demonstrated that the action of progesterone in tissues does not involve a ketone-alchohol interconversion at carbon 20. Neither the 20α-hydroxy nor the 20β-hydroxy steroid dehydrogenase is involved. The claim by Hurlock and Talalay (1958) that androsterone stimulates transhydrogenation in the liver by a 3α-hydroxy steroid dehydrogenase was not confirmed by the experiments of Stein and Kaplan (1959) or by those of Bloom (1960). Jensen and Jacobson's (1962) experiments show that the physiologic effects of estrogens do not involve any interconversion of estrone and estradiol. The transfer of hydrogen from one pyridine nucleotide to another by a system of two 17-hydroxysteroid dehydrogenases in guinea pig liver can occur by a substrate-meditated transhydrogenation utilizing testosterone and androstenedione, but only at concentrations of enzyme, cofactors, and hormones that greatly exceed physiologic levels (Villee and Spencer, 1960). Thus, although a purified enzyme from the placenta can be made to carry out substrate-mediated transhydrogenation with estradiol, this appears to be an enzymologic artifact of no physiologic significance. The fact that most steroid hormones occur in pairs which differ in the presence of an —OH or an =O at a specific point—estradiol-estrone, testosterone-androstenedione, cortisol-cortisone, 20-hydroxypregn-4-ene-3-one-pro-gesterone—together with the simplicity of this theory made it very appealing, and it was widely held.

Another general hypothesis states that a hormone may alter the activity of a preformed protein, converting an inactive protein to one with full enzymatic activity. Studies in our laboratory have shown that estradiol stimulates an estrogen-dependent pyridine nucleotide transhydrogenase in the placenta, endometrium, myometrium, and pituitary and converts an inactive protein to one with full enzymatic activity. This pyridine nucleotide transhydrogenase was separated from the estradiol dehydrogenase in our laboratory in 1958 (Villee and Hagerman, 1958), and this separation has been confirmed more recently by Karavolas and Engel (1966). Thus it is clear that in the organ in which this enzyme system has been studied most intensively, the human term placenta, there are two separate and distinct enzyme systems, one a true estrogen-dependent pyridine nucleotide trans-hydrogenase and the second a system which carries out substrate-mediated transhydrogenation catalyzed by estradiol dehydrogenase.

A series of experiments using preparations from human myome-trium showed that this tissue does not carry out the dehydrogenation of estradiol nor the hydrogenation of estrone when tested with suit-able radioactive substrates (Abe et al., 1964). A conversion of as little as 0.5 percent of the original estradiol to estrone by the system could readily have been detected. This same enzyme preparation from human myometrium showed estrogen-dependent pyridine nucleotide transhydrogenase activity similar to that found in the placenta. When estradiol-4-^{14}C was used to activate the enzyme, it could be demon-strated after transhydrogenation had been stimulated that the estra-diol remained as estradiol. When labeled estrone was used in other experiments the system was stimulated, transhydrogenation occurred, but there was no conversion of estrone to estradiol.

These experiments provide the in vitro counterpart to the in vivo studies of Jensen and agree that no metabolic conversion of estradiol occurs during the stimulatory process. Jensen and Jacobson (1962) demonstrated that essentially all the estradiol taken up by the rat uterus and vagina remains unconjugated and unconverted—it remains as estradiol. In contrast, much of the estradiol taken up by the liver is converted to estrone and 2-methoxyestrone and is conjugated to water-soluble products such as the glucosiduronates and sulfates.

In the past year Doctor Kato, working in my laboratory, has shown that labeled estradiol injected into castrate rats is taken up not only by the anterior pituitary as had been shown before by others (Jensen and Jacobson, 1962) but by a specific region in the anterior hypothalamus (Kato and Villee, 1967a, 1967b). The nature of the receptor site in this tissue is, as yet, unknown (as is the receptor site in other tissues), but the specificity of the region of the brain that takes up the estradiol, correlated with the known role of the hypothalamus in regulating the secretion of gonadotropins by the pituitary, suggests that this uptake may be of physiologic significance in the complex interrelations of hormones regulating the estrous and menstrual cycles. Diamond and Dale (1967) have shown a comparable uptake of testosterone-^{3}H by the hypothalamus of the neonatal rat.

A third general mechanism of action of estrogens and of other hormones that has been postulated states that the hormone alters the rate at which enzyme molecules are synthesized from small precursors by affecting either the transcription or the translation processes of gene action. There are several different ways in which estrogens might interact with the various parts of the genetic apparatus, and one must distinguish between the derepression of a specific segment of the genome, either by the hormone or by a hormone–receptor complex which leads to the synthesis of new enzymes, and the activation of preexisting enzymes involved in the replication, the transcription, or the translation processes.

The experiments of Segal et al. (1965) showed that RNA preparations from the endometrium of estrogen-stimulated rats, when infused into the lumen of the uterus of other rats, lead to effects which mimic those of estrogen on the cells. This suggests that the nucleic acid provides some kind of final common pathway by which information is transferred in the expression of estrogen action.

In comparable experiments, Doctor Fujii and I have found that RNA preparations from the seminal vesicles of androgen-treated immature rats will, when injected into the seminal vesicle of other immature rats, cause significant increases in the weight of the organ and in the synthesis of total protein (Fujii and Villee, 1966, 1967). In contrast, RNA obtained from the liver or prostate of these same androgen-treated rats did not cause increased weight when injected into the seminal vesicles. The RNA preparations lose their activity when heated or treated with ribonuclease. Appropriate experiments in which highly labeled testosterone was injected into the rats demonstrated that the RNA preparations are not contaminated with androgen. These experiments, which indicate that RNA is involved somewhere along the line in mediating the effect of the androgen, do not reveal the primary interaction which initiates the whole process but do indicate that specific RNA moieties are involved.

The experiments of Clever and Karlson (1960), Karlson (1965), Beerman (1958), and others have suggested that the hormone ecdysone stimulates molting and metamorphosis in insects by activating specific genes. This leads to the production of specific messenger RNA, evident in the "puffing" of certain regions in the chromosome, and this leads to the synthesis of specific proteins which may in turn lead to further gene activation. In these experiments and in those of Ui and Mueller (1963) with the uterus of the rat, the experimental design has included injecting inhibitors of RNA synthesis or of protein synthesis such as puromycin, actionomycin, and cycloheximide and observing the interruption of the sequence of events which may occur. The difficulties in interpreting such experiments are clear.

These experiments with ecydsone led to the suggestion that steroids as a group may serve as "activators" of genes. This view has attracted a great deal of attention, and Means and Hamilton (1966) have recently shown that the synthesis of nuclear RNA is stimulated within 2 minutes after the injection of estrogen in the uterus of the ovariectomized rat. This is direct evidence that one of the earlier effects of the hormone occurs at the transcriptional level in the uterine cell. This stimulation occurs more promptly than other reported effects of estrogen at the level of translation or of the mobilization of histamines. Gorski and others (1965) had suggested that the stimulation of RNA synthesis by estrogens depends upon a preceding synthesis of protein, but the findings of Means and Hamilton would suggest that the effect on the synthesis of nuclear RNA occurs prior to the enhanced synthesis of either nuclear or cytoplasmic proteins. The same experiments showed that the uptake of precursors of RNA by the uterus also increases very rapidly, within 2 minutes after the administration of estrogen to the ovariectomized adult rat. Thus both the transcription of DNA and the permeability of the cell membranes would appear to be affected within a very short time, but these experiments did not permit a decision as to which was first and which was second.

Thus we return to the conclusion that it seems unlikely at the present time that any single site or mechanism of action of estrogens on cell metabolism could account satisfactorily for all the physiologic consequences of the presence of the steroid in the cell. No single intracellular receptor site will account for all the observations. Instead, it seems more reasonable to conclude that estrogens and perhaps other hormones as well have multiple receptor sites within the cell, each specific for the hormone and each modifying in some fashion some special aspect of cell metabolism; and it is the sum of these individual sites all of which are mechanisms of action of the hormone, that together comprise the physiologic response to the hormone in target tissues and other organs. This conclusion does not simplify the problem, but then nature is not simple.

References

Abe, T., D. D. Hagerman, and C. A. Villee. 1964. Estrogen dependent pyridine nucleotide transhydrogenase of human myometrium. *J. Biol. Chem.,* **239:** 414–418.

Beermann, W. 1958. In *Developmental Cytology,* 16th Growth Symposium (D. Rudnick, ed.). Ronald Press, New York, pp. 83–103.

Bloom, B. 1960. An evaluation of hormonal augmented transhydrogenase activity in rat liver cells. *J. Biol. Chem.,* **235:** 857–858.

Bush, I. E., and V. B. Mahesh. 1959. Metabolism of 11-oxygenated steroids. 2. 2-Methyl steroids. *Biochem. Jr.,* **71:** 718–742.

Channing, C. P., and C. A. Villee. 1966a. Luteinizing hormone: Effects on uptake and metabolism of hexoses by luteinized rat ovaries. *Biochim. Biophys. Acta,* **115:** 205–218.

Channing, C. P., and C. A. Villee. 1966b. Stimulation of cholesterol metabolism in the luteinized rat ovary by luteinizing hormone. *Biochim. Biophys. Acta,* **127:** 1–17.

Clever, U., and P. Karlson. 1960. Induktion von Puff-veranderungen in den Speicheldrusenchromosomen von Chironomus tentans durch Ecdyson. *Exptl. Cell Res.,* **20:** 623–626.

Diamond, M., and E. Dale. 1967. Distribution of radiolabeled steroid after administration to the neonatal rat. *Anat. Rec.,* **157:** 234 (Abstr.).

Fujii, T., and C. A. Villee, 1966. Effects of testosterone on nucleic acid metabolism in tissues of immature rats. 2nd Intern. Congr. Hormonal Steroids, Milan, May (Abstr.).

Fujii, T., and C. A. Villee. 1967. The mediation by RNA of testosterone-stimulated growth of seminal vesicle and prostate. *Proc. Natl. Acad. Sci.,* **57:** 1468.

Gorski, J., W. D. Noteboom, and J. A. Nicolette, 1965. Estrogen control of synthesis of RNA and protein in the uterus. *J. Cellular Comp. Physiol.,* **66** (*Suppl. 1*): 91–109.

Hechter, O., and I. D. K. Halkerston. 1964. On the action of mammalian hormones. In *The Hormones,* Vol. 5 (G. Pincus, K. V. Thimann, and E. B. Astwood, eds.). Academic Press, New York, pp. 697–826.

Hurlock, B., and P. Talalay. 1958. 3α-Hydroxysteroids as coenzymes of hydrogen transfer between di- and triphosphopyridine nucleotides. *J. Biol. Chem.,* **233:** 886–893.

Jensen, E. V., and H. I. Jacobson. 1962. Basic guides to the mechanism of estrogen action. *Recent Progr. Hormone Res.,* **18:** 387–414.

Karavolas, H. J., and L. L. Engel. 1966. Human placental 17β-estradiol dehydrogenase. III. The separation of a 17β-estradiol-dependent transhydrogenase. *J. Biol. Chem.*, **241**: 3454–3456.

Karlson, P. 1965. Biochemical studies of ecdysone control of chromosomal activity. *J. Cellular Comp. Physiol.*, **66** (*Suppl. 1*): 69–75.

Kato, J., and C. A. Villee. 1967a. Preferential uptake of estradiol by the anterior hypothalamus. *Endocrinology*, **80**: 567–575.

Kato, J., and C. A. Villee. 1967b. Factors affecting uptake of estradiol-6,7-^{3}H by the hypophysis and hypothalamus. *Endocrinology*, **80**: 1133–1138.

Means, A. R., and T. H. Hamilton. 1966. Early estogen action: Concomitant stimulations within two minutes of nuclear RNA synthesis and uptake of RNA precursor by the uterus. *Proc. Natl. Acad. Sci.*, **56**: 1594–1598.

Mueller, G. C., A. M. Herranen, and K. F. Jervell. 1958. Studies on the mechanisms of action of estrogens. *Recent Progr. Hormone Res.*, **14**: 95–139.

Quastel, J. H., and W. R. Woodridge 1928. Some properties of the dehydrogenating enzymes of bacteria. *Biochem. J.*, **22**: 698–702.

Segal, S. J., O. W. Davidson, and K. Wada. 1965. Role of RNA in the regulatory action of estrogen. *Proc. Nat. Acad. Sci.*, **54**: 782–787.

Spaziani, E. 1963. Relationship between early vascular responses and growth in the rat uterus: Stimulation of cell division by estradiol and vasodilating amines. *Endocrinology*, **72**: 180–191.

Spaziani, E., and C. M. Szego. 1959. Further evidence for mediation by histamine of estrogenic stimulation of the rat uterus. *Endocrinology*, **64**: 713–723.

Stein, A. M., and N. O. Kaplan. 1959. Relationship of 3α-hydroxysteroid dehydrogenase to pyridine nucleotide transhydrogenases. *Science*, **129**: 1611–1612.

Szego, C. M. 1965. Role of histamine in mediation of hormone action. *Federation Proc.*, **24**: 1343–1352.

Talalay, P., and H. G. Williams-Ashman. 1958. Activation of hydrogen transfer between pyridine nucleotides by steroid hormones. *Proc. Natl. Acad. Sci.*, **44**: 15–26.

Toft, D., and J. Gorski. 1966. A receptor molecule for estrogens: Isolation from the rat uterus and preliminary characterization. *Proc. Natl. Acad. Sci.*, **55**: 1574–1581.

Ui, H., and G. C. Mueller. 1963. The role of RNA synthesis in early estrogen action. *Proc. Natl. Acad. Sci.*, **50**: 256–260.

Villee, C. A., and D. D. Hagerman. 1958. On the identity of the estrogen-sensitive enzyme of human placenta *J. Biol. Chem.*, **233**: 42–48.

Villee, C. A., and J. M. Spencer. 1960. Some properties of the pyridine nucleotide-specific 17β-hydroxysteroid dehydrogenases in guinea pig liver. *J. Biol. Chem.*, **235**: 3615–3619.

Wiest, W. G. 1959. Conversion of progesterone to 4-pregnen-20α-ol-3-one by rat ovarian tissue *in vitro*. *J. Biol. Chem.*, **234**: 3115–3121.

REPRODUCTION AND SEXUAL BEHAVIOR (M. Diamond ed.), 241–260, © Indiana University Press

17

Problems in the Molecular Biology of Androgen Action

H. G. Williams-Ashman and Jun Shimazaki

Elucidation of the chemical nature of mammalian sex hormones was unquestionably one of the greatest triumphs of reproductive physiology in the second quarter of our century. More recently, the biosynthesis of sex and adrenocortical hormones has been clarified. It is evident that all these hormones can be regarded as degradation products of cholesterol. In addition, the major metabolic transformations of mammalian steroid hormones that occur in the liver and other organs have now been delineated. As Talalay (1957, 1965) has pointed out, the complexities of the reactions involved in steroid hormone biosynthesis and metabolism are readily comprehensible in terms of the specificities and tissue distribution of a relatively small family of enzymes for which steroids serve as substrates, and whose properties are presently the subject of active investigation.

The central problem of sex hormone biochemistry is now the molecular basis of their action. Unfortunately, it can safely be said that the impressive volume of experimental effort directed toward this problem over the last decade has yielded much information and hardly any understanding. This situation is reminiscent of the state of research on water-soluble vitamins prior to the realization that the biological actions of these substances result from their serving as precursors for group-transferring coenzymes. Until this important generalization was established, studies on the biochemical concomitants of deficiencies of water-soluble vitamins were only symptomological in nature and often dealt with happenings that were many steps removed from the primary site of action of the vitamins. Failure to appreciate that a wide variety of symptoms can result from perturbation of one or a few types of biochemical mechanisms can lead to a preoccupation with secondary events which may actually obscure the basic issues. Today research on the molecular basis of steroid hormone action remains almost entirely in the realm of phenomenology. We propose here to discuss certain aspects of this problem with particular reference to the action of androgens on male accessory genital organs such as the prostate gland.

Androgens influence the prostate in two principal ways. In the first place, fetal testicular hormones are essential for the embryonic differentiation of prostatic buds out of the urogenital sinus (Price and Ortiz, 1965; Burns, 1961; Wells, 1965). Such "organizational" or "morphogenetic" actions are manifest only during very restricted periods of embryonic life, and they are essentially irreversible. Second, androgenic hormones initiate and maintain the growth and functional differentiation of the prostate postnatally (Huggins, 1945; Price and Williams-Ashman, 1961; Williams-Ashman et al., 1964). The latter "activational" or "excitatory" effects of androgens are readily reversible, as evidenced by the fact that the prostates of castrated or hypophysectomized animals can be made to wax or wane ad infinitum by administration or withdrawal of androgenic steroids. The pioneer investigations of W. C. Young and his collaborators (Phoenix et al., 1959; Young, 1961; Young et al., 1965; Diamond, 1965) established that androgens exert comparable "organizational" actions in fetal or early neonatal periods, and "activational" effects in adulthood, with respect to male modes of sexual behavior in various mammals (cf. Harris, 1964). From a mechanistic standpoint, one wonders whether the molecular processes which underlie expression of the "organizational" actions of androgens may, at least to some extent, be recapitulated whenever the "activational" effects of these hormones take place in any particular androgen-sensitive organ (Mann, 1964).

The only known function of the male accessory genital glands is to secrete the fluids that comprise the seminal plasma. This is carried out by the epithelial cells, which in the case of the rat ventral prostate represent the predominant cellular element. The most striking effect of androgen withdrawal is to cause the tall columnar prostatic epithelial cells of the sexually mature male to shrivel up, with a marked loss in endoplasmic reticulum and ribosomes, and fragmentation of the Golgi apparatus. The nuclei become small and pyknotic (Price and Williams-Ashman, 1961), and, as discussed below, synthesis of ribonucleic acids and some other nuclear functions is "turned off" to a considerable extent. Following castration, there is a gradual decline in the level of certain respiratory (but not glycolytic) enzymes, and also of the activity of various enzymes concerned with the synthesis of secretory products. The latter specialized enzymatic machinery naturally varies greatly from one accessory gland to another in different species.

Prostatic growth that follows treatment of orchiectomized mammals with testosterone is the net result of (1) hypertrophy of epithelial cells, (2) the formation of secretion and retention of secretory products in the glandular acini, and (3) hyperplasia of various cellular elements. The degree to which cell hyperplasia contributes to the overall growth of various androgen-sensitive tissues varies greatly from one organ to another. For example, in neuter mice, androgens induce growth of the levator ani muscle at constant cell population, i.e., without occurrence of any cell division (Venable, 1966). Again, growth of the cock's comb following androgen treatment is largely due to the water retention which follows from a massive elaboration of hyaluronic acid, accompanied by little or no cell hyperplasia (Szirmai, 1962). As we shall consider later, hyperplasia can contribute markedly to rat ventral prostate growth under certain experimental conditions, although restrictions to further cell division are quickly brought into play regardless of the intensity or duration of the androgenic stimulus.

Utilization of Oxygen

The original observation reported in 1944 by Barron and Huggins that the respiration (but not the anaerobic glycolysis) of canine prostate slices diminishes after orchiectomy has since been confirmed with slice preparations of various male accessory glands from many species (Nyden and Williams-Ashman, 1953; Levey and Szego, 1955; Butler and Schade, 1958). Treatment with testosterone restores the defective respiration of prostatic slices from castrated animals. But a lag period of at least 10 hours elapses between injection of the hormone and the first detectable increase in oxygen consumption. The factors which limit the respiration of prostatic intact-cell preparations in vitro remain to be clarified. It is noteworthy that when ventral prostate slices are incubated in Krebs–Ringer phosphate buffers containing glucose, addition of small quantities of 2, 4-dinitrophenol increases the respiration with preparations from both normal and orchiectomized rats to about the same extent, even though oxygen uptake by slices from the castrates is abnormally low (Nyden and Williams-Ashman, 1953). This suggests that the overall consumption of oxygen by the prostate slices is restricted by availability of adenine nucleotide phosphate acceptors within the mitochondria (cf. Greville, 1966). But the levels of some respiratory enzymes (Williams-Ashman, 1954) and the mitochondrial population density (Edelman et al., 1963; Williams-Ashman, 1962) in rat ventral prostate are dependent on the circulating levels of androgenic hormones. Alterations in the synthesis of various respiratory enzymes and of carriers such as cytochrome c therefore seem to contribute to the observed enhancement of respiration of prostate tissue slices which occurs within a day or so after treatment of castrates with testosterone.

More swift effects of testosterone treatment on the levels of adenine and pyridine nucleotides in the rat ventral prostate were recently reported by Ritter (1966). He found that a fortnight after orchiectomy of adult rats, the levels of ATP and of NADP(H) and NAD(H) in the prostate were within the normal range. But within half an hour after intramuscular injection of free testosterone into the castrates, there occurred a marked decline in the levels of ATP, which reached a maximum at about 1 hour, followed by a rise in the content of ATP toward the normal value. Similar oscillations in the levels of NAD(H) and NADP occurred during the first 10 hours after administration of testosterone, involving an increase in the total levels of NAD(H). Various lines of evidence suggested that gross alteration of pyridine nucleotide transhydrogenase reactions could not explain the changes in pyridine nucleotide levels. The changes in NAD observed 8 hours after testosterone treatment were about the same in animals poisoned with massive doses of puromycin or actinomycin D, which suggests that new RNA or protein synthesis was not necessary for occurrence of these oscillations in pyridine nucleotides. Ritter (1966) concluded that increased NAD biosynthesis is an important early event in the action of testosterone on the prostate, leading to a redirection of energy production toward a more oxidative direction and hence a more efficient production of ATP.

Using different analytical methods, Coffey, Ichinose, and Shimazaki (personal communication) in this laboratory confirmed that a large yet transitory decline in rat ventral prostate ATP levels occurred within 1 hour after injection of free testosterone into orchiectomized rats. A similar decline in total ATP content was reported to occur in the uterus during the early phases of response to estrogens (Aaronson et al., 1965). In this laboratory, however, only marginal changes in prostatic NAD and NADH levels were observed to occur during the first 8 hours after treatment of castrated rats with testosterone. Moreover, during this time there was no change in the activity of prostatic nuclear NMN adenyltransferase, an enzyme which may play a rate-limiting role in NAD biosynthesis. These findings do not support Ritter's contention (1966) that an increased synthesis of NAD is an important early part of the action of androgens on the prostate. In this connection it is worth noting that the rat ventral prostate is rich in enzymes that degrade pyridine nucleotides (Williams-Ashman et al., 1958) and that no information is available to decide whether hormone-induced alterations in the levels of these nucleotides reflect changes in their rate of synthesis or degradation. However, minor changes in NAD levels and large fluctuations in ATP do indeed occur in the prostate after treatment of castrates with androgens much sooner than earlier described alterations of the oxygen consumption of tissue slice preparations, and in the levels of certain respiratory enzymes. Also pertinent to the relation of cell respiration to the androgen-dependent functional differentiation of the prostate is the theory of Warburg (1956) that biologically useful energy (i.e., ATP) generated by mitochondrial-linked respiratory processes may somehow support cell differentiation much better than can energy derived from anaerobic fermentations.

Ribosomal Protein Synthesis

The notion that "differential gene action" plays a central role in the process of cell differentiation has become more amenable to experimental scrutiny as a result of recent developments in molecular biology. It is now a commonplace that genetic information stored in the form of linear sequences of nucleotide bases in DNA is ultimately expressed in terms of the linear amino acid sequences of specific proteins. Moreover, the immediate gene products formed under normal conditions are ribonucleic acids of one form or another (transfer, messenger, and ribosomal RNAs), all of which are components of the principal protein-synthesizing machinery of the cytoplasm, whose workhorses are the polyribosomes, which are largely associated with the endoplasmic reticulum. There are, in essence, three major processes involved in gene expression which can be regarded as points of control: (1) the synthesis of various RNAs that are copies of specific regions of the nuclear DNA genome, (2) the translocation of these RNAs to the sites of protein biosynthesis in the cytoplasm, and (3) the reading of genetic messages by the polyribosomes, in which various transfer RNAs serve as aminoacyl carriers. Each of these processes involves, of course, the interplay of many complex enzymatic reactions; the latter, in turn, are often associated with membranous structures by virtue of which they can be extremely sensitive to alterations in the local environment. The functional differentiation of the prostate under the stimulus of androgens entails gross alterations in genetically determined polynucleotide- and protein-synthesizing systems.

The rapid dwindling of male accessory glands of reproduction which occurs after castration of adult mammals is accompanied by a pronounced fall in the amount of RNA extractable from the organs per unit quantity of DNA. In the rat ventral prostate, for example, the RNA/DNA ratio declines from a normal value of about 3 to a level of 0.5 or even lower within a few days after orchiectomy. Injection of replacement doses of testosterone restores this value to normal levels. Values of the RNA/DNA quotient as high as 4 can be observed after treatment of castrates with hyperphysiological amounts of androgens. Under these conditions, androgen stimulation does not significantly alter the RNA/DNA ratio of isolated rat ventral prostate nuclei, which remains at a value of about 0.25 (Williams-Ashman et al., 1964; Liao, 1965).

Approximately 80 percent of the total prostatic RNA is comprised of cytoplasmic ribosomal RNA. In all animal tissues that have been studied up to now, mature cytoplasmic ribosomes contain at least one molecule of the three major categories of ribosomal RNA with sedimentation constants in the vicinity of 28S, 18S, and 5S. All these ribosomal RNAs have a guanosine and cytosine $(G + C)$ content which is higher than that of the nuclear DNA. Sucrose density-gradient analyses have shown that animal ribosomal RNAs are derived from a 45S precursor molecule which is synthesized in the nucleus, and probably in the nucleoli, with which are associated the ribosomal RNA cistrons of the nuclear DNA genome. This 45S ribosomal RNA precursor appears to be degraded in the nucleolus to one molecule of 18S ribosomal RNA and one molecule of a 32S ribosomal RNA precursor. In turn, this 32S RNA undergoes a further transition (probably in the nucleoplasm) to form one 28S ribosomal RNA molecule. Recent evidence suggests that, in at least some animal species, the 45S ribosomal RNA precursor is truly polycistronic with respect to the 18S and 28S RNA components of the mature cytoplasmic ribosomes, both of which are the products of separate genes (Brown, 1967). In addition, there exist a wide variety of messenger RNAs for each of the various proteins (some of which may be polycistronic messengers) as well as some 40 to 50 different types of transfer RNAs.

The most striking effect of androgens on the prostate of castrated mammals is to induce a rapid formation of many new cytoplasmic ribosomes which occurs *pari passu* with elaboration of an extensive endoplasmic reticulum. A variety of experiments on aminoacyl transfers by isolated ribonucleoprotein particles also indicated that testosterone increased the levels of template RNAs in the prostate (Williams-Ashman et al., 1964; Liao, 1965; Liao and Williams-Ashman, 1962). Such investigations naturally focused attention on the enzymatic synthesis of RNA by prostatic cell nuclei. The latter contain an active RNA polymerase system which is largely bound to the chromatin material and difficult to extract therefrom in a soluble form or free of DNA. Initial experiments disclosed that within a few days after treatment of castrated rats with testosterone, there occurred marked increases in the RNA polymerase activity of crude prostatic nuclear extracts. The effects of the hormone were greatest when the reactions were carried out in media of relatively low ionic strength (Hancock et al., 1960). Increasing the ionic strength of the medium enhanced the base-line RNA polymerase activities while diminishing the effect of hormone administration. Detectable elevation of RNA polymerase activity of prostatic nuclei can be observed within 1 hour after injection of testosterone into recently orchiectomized rats, and the maximal change in polymerase reaction is found within 12 hours (Liao et al., 1965). In marked contrast to the recent report by Lukacs and Sekeris (1967) that testosterone (and cortisol) directly stimulate RNA synthesis by isolated rat liver nuclear extracts, other workers have uniformly failed to detect any influence of testosterone and other androgens in vitro on prostatic RNA polymerase reactions (Williams-Ashman et al., 1964; Hancock et al., 1960; Doly et al., 1965). At low ionic strengths, the RNA polymerase activities of prostatic nuclear preparations seem to be limited more by the priming ability of the DNA bound to the preparations than by the catalytic activity of the RNA polymerase activating protein. The latter may be more rate-limiting to complementary RNA synthesis when the reactions are carried out at high ionic strengths. From experiments conducted at varying ionic strengths, it has been concluded that testosterone treatment in vivo enhances the RNA polymerase activity of prostatic nuclei in vitro by increasing in some fashion the template activity of the DNA in addition to increasing the levels of the polymerase protein (Williams-Ashman et al., 1964; Doly et al., 1965).

That this picture is an oversimplified one is evident from a series of important experiments from Liao's laboratory (Liao et al., 1966a, 1966b; Liao and Lin, 1967). These investigations revealed that in media of low ionic strength, the increased prostatic RNA polymerase activity induced by testosterone is far more sensitive to inhibition by low levels of actinomycin D in vitro than is the base-line RNA nucleotide incorporation. Actinomycin D given in vivo also counteracted the enhancement of RNA synthesis due to androgen treatment. From nearest-neighbor base frequency analyses of the RNA products synthesized by these nuclear preparations, it was evident that the additional RNA synthesized after testosterone administration was qualitatively different from the RNA formed by prostatic nuclei obtained from control castrates. A value for the ratio (C + G/A + U) of 1.75 was found for the ^{32}P-labeled RNA formed by prostatic nuclei from the testosterone-treated animals as compared with a ratio of 1.35 for the controls. Addition of small quantities of actinomycin D to the nuclear preparations abolished these differences, giving a uniform C + G/A + U of 1.23. The corresponding value of this ratio for normal prostatic ribosomal RNA is 1.63. (The RNA synthesized by these prostatic nuclear extracts in vitro is somewhat asymmetric in base composition.) It is well established that in mammalian cells, low concentrations of actinomycin D preferentially inhibit synthesis of ribosomal RNA precursor molecules at nucleolar sites with little or no effect on formation of nonribosomal RNA at extranucleolar regions of the chromatin. Liao and co-workers (1966a, 1966b) therefore concluded that the normal function of prostatic nucleoli is androgen-dependent, and that the nucleolus plays a central part in the androgenic control of RNA and protein biosynthesis. They further hypothesized that the demonstrable increase in template activity (for protein synthesis) per unit quantity of phenol-extracted prostatic nuclear RNA or ribosomal RNA which results from testosterone treatment of castrates (Liao, 1965), is not so much due to any selective enhancement by the hormone of synthesis of messenger RNAs as compared with ribosomal or transfer RNAs, but instead represents an increase in the formation of newly formed ribonucleoprotein particles rich in messenger RNA over older ribosomes poor in messenger RNA content.

Very recently, Liao and Lin (1967) have studied RNA synthesis by prostatic nuclei in the absence and presence of exogenous

RNA polymerase purified from *Micrococcus lysodeikticus*. In the presence of an excess of the latter enzyme, the differences in RNA synthesis due to testosterone treatment are no longer apparent. From a study of nearest-neighbor frequencies of the RNA synthesized by these preparations under different conditions, Liao and Lin concluded that prostatic nuclear chromatin can be classified into four categories: (1) M regions, which occupy 70 to 80 percent of the total nuclear DNA, and which are accessible to neither actinomycin D nor exogenous RNA polymerase; (2) R regions, occupying 20 to 30 percent of the total nuclear DNA; here the DNA is available to bind actinomycin D and can serve as a template for RNA synthesis by bacterial RNA polymerase when the nuclei are disrupted; (3) Ch regions, containing about 1 percent of the total nuclear DNA, which support RNA synthesis even after withdrawal of androgens; and (4) No regions, with which less than 1 percent of the nuclear DNA is associated, and where androgens in vivo provoke selective enhancement of RNA synthesis. It is interesting that the deoxycytidyl $(3', 5')$ deoxyguanosine sequence in prostatic DNA seems to have a striking nonrandom distribution among these various districts of the genome. Liao and Lin (1967) reckon that this dG-dC sequence in the No region is about 24, 8, and 2 times that found in the M, R, and Ch regions, respectively.

Any interpretation of these findings must take into account that they are based on experiments with cell-free nuclear extracts. It remains to be proved whether the RNA synthesized under these artificial conditions is significantly related to RNA synthesized by prostatic nuclei in vivo, and particularly to various RNAs which ultimately enter the cytoplasm of prostatic cells and there function in protein biosynthesis. For it must be remembered that in vivo, considerable amounts of rapidly turning over RNA may be formed in the nucleus and then degraded therein without ever entering the cytoplasm (Harris, 1963). Nevertheless, these findings emphasize that if template masking factors limit RNA synthesis by isolated prostatic nuclei from castrated rats, then these "repressor substances" mask only tiny segments of actinomycin-binding cistrons that are available to the endogenous RNA polymerase of the nuclei. This is borne out by the finding (Liao and Lin, 1967) that the amount of actinomycin D that is *readily* bound by the DNA associated with prostatic nuclei is about 20 to 30 percent of that bound by refined rat DNA, and that the binding of the antibiotic to prostatic nuclei is not affected by alterations in the androgenic status of the animals.

Control of Nuclear RNA Synthesis

The foregoing raises further questions as to the mechanisms by which the RNA polymerase system of isolated prostatic cell nuclei is altered by administration of testosterone in such a fashion as to synthesize an increased quantity of RNA which is richer in guanosine and cytosine than the RNA formed by preparations from control castrates. This brings us face to face with the fact that such effects of androgens on prostatic nuclear RNA polymerase are detectable only after a lag period of about 1 hour. It is therefore entirely possible that they represent secondary events which may be many steps removed from the primary locus of action of the hormone. In this regard it must be emphasized that there are indications that there exist in mammalian cells complex coupling mechanisms between (1) the synthesis of ribosomal RNAs, on the one hand, and of messenger and transfer RNAs, on the other; and (2) active protein biosynthesis by polyribosomes in the cytoplasm, and the fabrication of ribonucleic acids in the nucleus. The chemical basis of these coupling mechanisms remains utterly mysterious (Tata, 1966; Williams-Ashman, 1965).

Liao and Lin (1967) have pointed out that although some combination of androgens with hypothetical "repressors" of specific RNA synthesis in the nucleus is intriguing, other mechanisms for the androgen-induced changes in prostatic RNA polymerase can be imagined. They suggest that the RNA polymerase protein may be sequestered by specific regions of the DNA genome (possibly as a consequence of some association of the DNA with membranous structures in the nucleus), and that stimulation of the gland by the hormone could result in some translocation of the polymerase protein to the ribosomal RNA cistrons, which apparently reside in the nucleoli. They hypothesize: "The specific association of polymerase and DNA template may involve a 'conformational fit' of molecules required for the initiation of polynucleotide formation and the restricted distribution of certain nucleotide sequences may serve an important function in directing polymerases to a specific part of the DNA template or regulating the rate of RNA synthesis."

We would like to draw attention to another possibility. Most considerations of the control of RNA synthesis in living cells have centered around considerations of the differential transcription of RNA copies of specific regions of the DNA genome. It is often rather dogmatically assumed that there is maintenance of a complete genome in all haploid differentiated cells, and that the total information content in all nuclei of a given species is equivalent. Although there is considerable evidence to support the notion of constancy of the nuclear DNA genome, this is by no means rigorously proved for all cells (Ebert and Kaign, 1966). Indeed, recent experiments by Brown (1967) and co-workers make it likely that during oogenesis in *Xenopus levis* there may occur a differential replication of the specialized nucleolar DNA which serves to direct the synthesis of ribosomal RNAs. It may be enlightening to examine, by suitable DNA-RNA hybridization and perhaps other techniques, whether there is an actual constancy of nucleolar ribosomal RNA cistrons of the DNA in the prostatic nuclei of animals of varying androgenic status.

Considerable interest attaches to recent reports that testosterone may associate with various histones (Bonner and Ts'o, 1964; Sluyser, 1966a, 1966b), and also with protein constituents of the nuclei of some androgen-sensitive tissues (Wilson and Loeb, 1965). In a recent publication (Williams-Ashman and Shimazaki, 1967) we have discussed the possible functions of nuclear histones and polyamines with respect to the androgenic control of nuclear RNA synthesis in the prostate. The limited experimental evidence available does not point to any unique role being played by these basic molecules, but further studies in this direction are clearly warranted.

Mitochondrial Protein Synthesis

The vast majority of contemporary studies on the hormonal control of specific protein synthesis have centered around consideration of the formation, intracellular translocation, translation, and stability of RNAs which are complementary to various districts of the nuclear DNA genome. Over the last few years, however, there has accumulated considerable evidence that the mitochondria of nucleated cells contain a unique DNA, and that this mitochondrial DNA may, at least in part, play a directive role in the synthesis of certain (although by no means all) mitochondrial proteins. Isolated mitochondria from a number of mammalian cells have been shown to support the incorporation of labeled amino acids into protein-like material. These processes exhibit very different requirements for cofactors as compared with protein biosynthesis by isolated polyribosomes. In particular, mitochondrial "protein synthesis" (1) does not necessitate addition of exogenous transfer RNAs and soluble transfer enzymes, (2) is very sensitive to the inhibitory action of chloramphenicol in vitro (in marked contrast to mammalian as opposed to bacterial polyribosomal systems), and (3) is not inhibited by ribonuclease. The bulk of labeled amino acids incorporated by isolated mitochondria appear to enter the "structural protein" of these particles, and certain mitochondrial respiratory enzymes are clearly synthesized outside the mitochondria (Kadenbach, 1967).

Pegg and Williams-Ashman (1968) have found that isolated rat ventral prostate mitochondria promote a vigorous incorporation of labeled isoleucine or phenylalanine into protein. Conditions were established under which the incorporations were linear with time at 37°C for at least 1 hour, were proportional to the amount of mitochondria added (using protein or cytochrome oxidase activity as indices), and were clearly not accounted for by the presence either of bacteria or of adventitious polyribosomes from the endoplasmic reticulum or other parts of the cytoplasm. These incorporations could be made completely dependent upon an external energy source (exogenous ATP and an ATP-generating system) so that any changes resulting from hormonal treatments could be studied independently of any alterations in the energy transducing systems that are coupled with the mitochondrial respiratory chain. Within 2 days after orchiectomy of adult rats, the ability of isolated prostate mitochondria to catalyze incorporation of isoleucine or phenylalanine into protein was diminished. At this time after androgen withdrawal, there is no change in the amount of mitochondrial material extractable from the rat ventral prostate, and the ability of the mitochondria to carry out oxidations of the tricarboxylic acid cycle and coupled phosphorylations is unimpaired. Five days after castration the prostate mitochondrial protein synthesis is virtually annulled. It was shown that this was not accompanied by any increase in destruction of ATP by the mitochondria. Interpretation of these findings is complicated by the fact that, at present, it is not possible analytically to distinguish between effects of the hormone on the formation of activated amino acids, on the one hand, or on the final stages of peptide bond formation, on the other. Recent experiments in this and other laboratories have suggested that intramitochondrial transfer RNAs indeed serve as aminoacyl carriers in mitochondrial protein synthesis. Moreover, an interval of about 1 day elapses between the time of administration of androgens to castrated rats and the first signs of restoration of prostatic mitochondrial protein synthesis. The latter process is unaffected by addition of testosterone in vitro. Nevertheless, these findings indicate that androgens exert a profound influence on the incorporation of amino acids by prostate mitochondria, and raise the question as to whether expression of genes encoded in mitochondrial DNA may be regulated by the hormones independently of the nuclear DNA genome and its ribonucleic acid products.

Replication of DNA and the Hyperplastic Element of Prostatic Growth

There is a growing realization that a cell carrying out complete replication of its DNA is generally a cell that has already taken the decision to divide (Baserga, 1965). The factors involved in the initiation and completion of DNA synthesis are therefore of critical importance in the control of cell division. Very little attention has been given to the biochemistry and hormonal control of DNA synthesis in male accessory genital glands. Early studies on mitotic rates during rat ventral prostate growth showed that these attained a maximum about 43 hours after a single injection of testosterone propionate into castrated rats, and that mitotic activity did not begin until about 35 hours (Burkhart, 1942). Mitosis thus represents a comparatively late event in the process of androgen-induced prostatic growth. This is also true of the incorporation of various precursors into DNA by seminal vesicle in comparison with earlier alterations in RNA synthesis and various metabolic systems (Wicks and Villee, 1964).

We have recently studied changes in the activity of a "replicative" DNA polymerase in rat ventral prostate which accompany the growth of the prostate resulting from single or multiple daily injections of hyperphysiological doses of testosterone propionate into rats that were castrated 7 days previously (Kosto et al., 1967; Coffey et al., 1968). The amounts of androgen administered were such that they induced about the maximal possible ventral prostate growth after about 12 daily injections. When a single 2-mg dose of testosterone propionate was given, only insignificant changes in DNA polymerase occurred during the first 24 hours, by which time maximal increases in prostatic nuclear RNA polymerase had already taken place. By 48 hours the polymerase levels had risen two- to threefold, and attained a maximal level of about 15 times the control values some 3 to 5 days after injection of the androgen. After this time the DNA polymerase activities declined, and returned essentially to the normal base line. Similar massive changes (up to 50-fold) in prostatic DNA polymerase also occur in hypophysectomized rats after a *single* injection of androgen, and that they are transitory in character is not at all surprising. However, virtually the same large yet transitory increases in polymerase levels occur in castrates to which testosterone is administered every day in excessive amounts. Here again, maximal polymerase activities were observed on about the fourth day after beginning the hormone treatments, and subsequently declined, returning to normal at about the twelfth, at which time the total prostatic DNA content had attained a stable plateau level. Measurements of the incorporation of thymidine into ventral prostate DNA either in vivo, or by prostate minces in vitro, showed that these indices of DNA replication pretty much paralleled the alterations in DNA polymerase activity. This provides yet another example of the finding, made with a number of other mammalian cells (cf. Williams-Ashman and Shimazaki, 1967; Baserga, 1965; Kosto et al., 1967), that large quantities of enzymes that may be involved in the synthesis of DNA are elaborated by mammalian cells only when they are in the "S" phase of the cell cycle, or shortly thereafter. Many experiments (Coffey et al., unpublished) indicated that the increased prostatic DNA polymerase resulting from the androgen treatments (1) occurred largely in soluble cytoplasmic rather than nuclear fractions of prostate homogenates, and (2) had many properties in common with the polymerase in the prostates of untreated castrates or normal animals (requirement for all four deoxyribonucleoside triphosphates, activation by glycerol, etc.), although the polymerase in extracts from the androgen-treated animals showed an even more stringent requirement than normal for single-stranded DNAs as templates. Naive experiments involving the mixing of prostatic extracts from the various groups of animals showed that the transitory increases in polymerase activities due to androgen administration could not be accounted for by removal or inactivation of substances present in the prostates of castrates that might inhibit DNA polymerase reactions.

Concurrent administration of actidione or actinomycin D largely prevents the rise in ventral prostate DNA polymerase which occurs 48 hours after injection of testosterone into castrated rats. This suggests that the rise in DNA polymerase requires new protein synthesis. Further studies on factors which determine the turnover of prostatic DNA polymerase(s) and other enzymes that may be involved in DNA replication would undoubtedly give much insight into both the hyperplastic element of prostatic growth and the mechanisms responsible for the ultimate restrictions on prostatic size, which are somehow imposed regardless of the degree and extent of androgenic stimulation. Such investigations would have important bearing on the vexatious problem of benign prostatic growths in man.

Metabolism of Androgens in Relation to Their Actions

Whether any of the metabolic transformations undergone by sex hormones in the body are related to their biological actions is a long-standing problem in sexual physiology. It has been established that, under certain conditions, very low concentrations of certain steroids which exhibit either estrogenic or androgenic activities can serve as hydrogen carriers for transhydrogenations between pyridine nucleotides that are catalyzed by refined hydroxysteroid dehydrogenases (Talalay and Williams-Ashman, 1960). But little if any physiological significance seems to be attached to such "coenzyme-like" properties of these steroids, which appear to be of the nature of test-tube artifacts (Williams-Ashman, 1965; Talalay and Williams-Ashman, 1960). The pioneer studies of Jensen (1965) demonstrated that, at least in some species, both natural and synthetic estrogens can promote the growth of organs of the female genital tract without suffering any chemical change.

One of us (J.S.) has recently reviewed the extensive transformations of testosterone to a variety of products (notably androst-4-ene-3, 17-dione and 5α-androstan-17β-ol-3-one) which are carried out by the prostate (Shimazaki et al., 1965a, 1965b). This raises the question of the possible "active forms" of androgens in their target organs. Recently Farnsworth (1965) has reported that slices of benign human prostate catalyze a small conversion of testosterone to 19-nortestosterone, and he suggested that the latter scroid might be the active form of testosterone in the prostate. The yields of 19-nortestosterone were minuscule, however, and Farnsworth's hypothesis is lacking in any solid experimental foundation. Very recently, Bruchovsky and Wilson (1968) and Liao and Anderson (personal communication) have observed that dihydrotestosterone (5α-androstan-17β-ol-3-one) is the major transformation product of testosterone in the rate prostate following injection of the labeled hormone. In particular, these occurs a preferential association of dihydrotestosterone with the chromatin of cell nuclei of the rat ventral prostate, but not of some other organs such as the liver. Prostatic nuclei as well as cytoplasm contain an NADPH-dependent reductase which catalyzes the reduction of testosterone to dihydrotestosterone. These interesting findings raise the possibility that dihydrotestosterone may be an "active form" of testosterone in the prostate gland.

Epilogue

The aspects of prostatic biochemistry discussed here have shed no light on the very fundamental problem of the chemical nature and intracellular location of the primary receptors for androgens. Rather, they deal exclusively with secondary amplification mechanisms involved in the growth and functional differentiation of male accessory genital glands. Naturally, the precise details of this amplificatory biochemical machinery will depend very much on the particular androgen-sensitive tissue which one chooses to study, and in the last analysis, they may be determined largely by restrictions on expression of parts of the genome that are imposed during embryonic life, and remain inviolate thereafter. Yet it must be remembered that androgens appear to be essential for the embryonic differentiation of the male accessory glands. In any event, impressive changes in the function of the genetically determined protein-synthesizing apparatus of the prostate which occur after androgenic stimulation have now been delineated, and these events clearly play a central role in the functional differentiation of this organ. But many of the enigmas of androgen physiology—factors which determine whether a tissue is competent to be influenced by androgens, the basis of the antagonism of androgen action by estrogens and other steroids, the mechanism of the inhibitory actions of androgens on gonadotropin release and certain lymphoid tissues, and so on—are likely to remain very foggy until insight is gained into the chemistry of the primary receptors for androgenic hormones. Solution of the latter problem clearly demands the development of novel experimental approaches which may in turn be contingent on advances in quite different areas of chemical physiology.

Acknowledgments

Work from the author's laboratory was supported by a Research Grant (HD-01453) from the U.S. Public Health Service. Dr. Shimazaki is the recipient of a Bio-Medical Research Fellowship from the Population Council, Inc.

References

Aaronson, S. A., Y. Natori, and H. Tarver. 1965. Effects of estrogen on uterine ATP levels. *Proc. Soc. Exptl. Biol. Med.*, **120**: 9–10.
Barron, E. S. G., and C. Huggins. 1944. Metabolism of isolated prostatic tissue. *J. Urol.*, **51**: 630–634.

Baserga, R. 1965. The relationship of the cell cycle to tumor growth and control of cell division: A review. *Cancer Res.*, **25**: 581–595.

Bonner, J., and P. O. P. Ts'o. 1964. *The Nucleohistones.* Holden-Day, San Francisco.

Brown, D. D. 1967. The genes for ribosomal RNA and their transcription during development. In *Current Topics in Developmental Biology* (A. Moscova and A. Monroy, eds.). Academic Press, New York.

Bruchovsky, N., and J. D. Wilson. 1968. The conversion of testosterone to 5α-androstan-17β-ol-3-one by rat prostate *in vivo* and *in vitro. J. Biol. Chem.*, **243**: 2012–2021.

Burkhart, E. Z. 1942. A study of early effects of androgenic substances in the rat by aid of colchicine. *J. Exptl. Zool.*, **89**: 135–165.

Burns, R. K. 1961. Role of hormones in the differentiation of sex. In *Sex and Internal Secretions* (W. C. Young, ed.). Williams & Wilkins, Baltimore: 3rd ed., pp. 76–158.

Butler, W. W. S., III, and A. L. Schade. 1958. The effects of castration and androgen replacement on the nucleic acid composition, metabolism and enzymatic capacities of the rat ventral prostate. *Endocrinology*, **63**: 271–279.

Coffey, D. S., J. Shimazaki, and H. G. Williams-Ashman. 1966. Polymerization of deoxyribonucleotides in relation to androgen-induced prostatic growth. *Arch. Biochem. Biophys.*, **124**: 184–198.

Diamond, M. 1965. A critical evaluation of the ontogeny of human sexual behavior. *Quart. Rev. Biol.*, **40**: 147–175.

Doly, J., M. Ramuz, P. Mandel, and P. Chambon. 1965. Soluble DNA-dependent RNA polymerase from prostate nuclei. *Life Sci.*, **4**: 1961–1966.

Ebert, J. D., and M. E. Kaign. 1966. The keys to change: Factors regulating differentiation. In *Major Problems in Developmental Biology* (M. Locke, ed.). Academic Press, New York, pp. 29–84.

Edelman, J. C., H. Brendler, A. W. Zorgniotti, and P. M. Edelman. 1963. Effects of castration on mitochondria of rat ventral prostate. *Endocrinology*, **72**: 853–858.

Farnsworth, W. E. 1965. 10-Demethylation of testosterone by human prostate. *Steroids*, **6**: 519–530.

Greville, G. O. 1966. Factors affecting the utilization of substrates by mitochondria. In *Regulation of Metabolic Processes in Mitochondria* (J. M. Tager, S. Papa, E. Quagliariello, and E. C. Slater, eds.). Elsevier, Amsterdam, pp. 86–106.

Hancock, R. L., R. F. Zelis, M. Shaw, and H. G. Williams-Ashman. 1960. Incorporation of ribonucleoside triphosphates into ribonucleic acid by nuclei of the prostate gland. *Biochim. Biophys. Acta*, **55**: 257–260.

Harris, G. W. 1964. Sex hormones, brain development and brain function. *Endocrinology*, **75**: 627–648.

Harris, H. 1963. Nuclear ribonucleic acid. *Progr. Nucleic Acid Res.*, **2**: 19–59.

Huggins, C. 1945. The physiology of the prostate gland. *Physiol. Rev.*, **25**: 281–295.

Jensen, E. V. 1965. Mechanism of estrogen action in relation to carcinogenesis. *Proc. 6th Canadian Cancer Research Conference.* Pergamon Press, New York, pp. 143–165.

Kadenbach, B. 1967. Synthesis of mitochondrial proteins: Demonstration of a transfer of proteins from microsomes to mitochondria. *Biochim. Biophys. Acta,* **134:** 430–442.

Kosto, B., H. I. Calvin, and H. G. Williams-Ashman. 1967. Fluctuations in prostatic DNA polymerase activity induced by testosterone. *Advan. Enzyme Regulat.,* **5:** 25–37.

Levey, H. A., and C. M. Szego. 1955. Effects of castration and androgen administration on metabolic characteristics of the guinea pig seminal vesicle. *Am. J. Physiol.,* **183:** 371–376.

Liao, S. 1965. Influence of testosterone on template activity of prostatic ribonucleic acids. *J. Biol. Chem.,* **240:** 1236–1243.

Liao, S., and A. H. Lin. 1967. Prostatic nuclear chromatin: An effect of testosterone in the synthesis of ribonucleic acid rich in cytidyl (3′,5′) guanosine. *Proc. Natl. Acad. Sci.,* **57:** 379–386.

Liao, S., and H. G. Williams-Ashman. 1962. An effect of testosterone on amino acid incorporation by prostatic ribonucleoprotein particles. *Proc. Natl. Acad. Sci.,* **48:** 1956–1964.

Liao, S., K. R. Leininger, D. Sagher, and R. W. Barton. 1965. Rapid effect of testosterone on ribonucleic acid polymerase activity of rat ventral prostrate. *Endocrinology,* **77:** 763–765.

Liao, S., R. W. Barton, and A. H. Lin. 1966a. Differential synthesis of ribonucleic acid in prostatic nuclei: Evidence for selective gene transcription induced by androgens. *Proc. Natl. Acad. Sci.,* **55:** 1593–1600.

Liao, S., A. H. Lin, and R. W. Barton. 1966b. Selective stimulation of ribonucleic acid synthesis in prostatic nuclei by testosterone. *J. Biol. Chem.,* **241:** 3869–3871.

Lukacs, I., and C. E. Sekeris. 1967. On the mechanism of hormone action. IX. Stimulation of RNA polymerase activity of rat-liver nuclei by cortisol in vitro. *Biochim. Biophys. Acta,* **134:** 85–90.

Mann, T. 1964. *The Biochemistry of Semen and of the Male Reproductive Tract.* Wiley, New York.

Nyden, S. J., and H. G. Williams-Ashman. 1953. Influence of androgens on synthetic reactions in ventral prostate tissue. *Am. J. Physiol.,* **172:** 588–600.

Pegg, A. E., and H. G. Williams-Ashman. 1968. Effects of androgens on incorporation of labeled amino acids into proteins by isolated prostate mitochondria. *Endocrinology,* **82:** 603–610.

Phoenix, C. H., R. W. Goy, A. A. Gerall, and W. C. Young. 1959. Organizing action of prenatally administered testosterone propionate on the tissues mediating mating behavior in the female guinea pig. *Endocrinology,* **65:** 369–382.

Price, D., and E. Ortiz. 1965. The role of fetal androgen in sex differentiation in mammals. In *Organogenesis* (R. L. DeHaan and H. Ursprung, eds.). Holt, Rinehart and Winston, New York, pp. 629–652.

Price, D., and H. G. Williams-Ashman. 1961. The accessory reproductive glands of mammals. In *Sex and Internal Secretions* (W. C. Young, ed.). Williams & Wilkins, Baltimore, 3rd ed., pp. 366–488.

Ritter, C. 1966. NAD biosynthesis as an early part of androgen action. *Mol. Pharmacol.,* **2:** 125–133.

Shimazaki, J., H. Kurihara, Y. Ito, and K. Shida. 1965a. Metabolism of testosterone in prostate (2nd report). Separation of prostatic 17β-ol-dehydrogenase and 5α-reductase. *Gunma J. Med. Sci.,* **14:** 326–333.

Shimazaki, J., H. Kurihara, Y. Ito, and K. Shida. 1965b. Testosterone metabolism in prostate: Formation of androstan-17β-ol-3-one and androst-4-ene-3, 17-dione, and inhibitory effect of natural and synthetic estrogens. *Gunma J. Med. Sci.*, **14**: 313–325.

Sluyser, M. 1966a. Binding of testosterone and hydrocortisone to rat-tissue histones. *J. Mol. Biol.*, **22**: 411–414.

Sluyser, M. 1966b. Effect of testosterone on the binding of prostate histone to DNA in vitro. *Biochem. Biophys. Res. Commun.*, **22**: 336–339.

Szirmai, J. A. 1962. Histological aspects of the actions of androgens and estrogens. In *Protein Metabolism* (F. Gross, ed.). Springer, Berlin, pp. 45–74.

Talalay, P. 1957. Enzymatic mechanisms in steroid metabolism. *Physiol. Rev.*, **37**: 362–389.

Talalay, P. 1965. Enzymatic mechanisms in steroid biochemistry. *Ann. Rev. Biochem.*, **34**: 347–380.

Talalay, P., and H. G. Williams-Ashman. 1960. Participation of steroid hormones in the enzymatic transfer of hydrogen. *Recent Prog. Hormone Res.*, **16**: 1–47.

Tata, J. R. 1966. Hormones and the synthesis and utilization of ribonucleic acids. *Progr. Nucleic Acid Res.*, **5**: 191–250.

Venable, J. H. 1966. Constant cell populations in normal, testosterone-deprived and testosterone-stimulated levator ani muscles. *Am. J. Anat.*, **119**: 263–270.

Warburg, O. 1965. On the origin of cancer cells. *Science*, **123**: 309–314.

Wells, L. J. 1965. Fetal hormones and their role in organogenesis. In *Organogenesis* (R. L. DeHaan and H. Ursprung, eds.). Holt, Rinehart and Winston, New York, pp. 673–680.

Wicks, W. D., and C. A. Villee. 1964. Studies on the course of action of testosterone propionate on the rat seminal vesicle. *Arch. Biochem. Biophys.*, **106**: 353–359.

Williams-Ashman, H. G. 1954. Changes in the enzymatic constitution of the ventral prostate gland induced by androgenic hormones. *Endocrinology*, **54**: 121–129.

Williams-Ashman, H. G. 1962. Chemical approaches to the function of the prostate gland and seminal vesicles. In *On Cancer and Hormones: Essays in Experimental Biology*. Univ. of Chicago Press, Chicago, pp. 325–346.

Williams-Ashman, H. G. 1965. New facets of the biochemistry of steroid hormone action. *Cancer Res.*, **25**: 1096–1120.

Williams-Ashman, H. G., and J. Shimazaki. 1967. Some metabolic and morphogenetic effects of androgens on normal and neoplastic prostate. In *Endogenous Factors in Tumor-Host Balance* (R. W. Wissler, T. Dao, and S. Woods, eds.). Univ. Chicago Press, Chicago, pp. 31–41.

Williams-Ashman, H. G., S. Liao, and G. S. Gotterer. 1958. A direct effect of testosterone on interactions between pyridine nucleotides in male accessory sexual tissues. *Proc. 4th International Congress of Biochemistry, Vienna*. Pergamon Press, New York, p. 114.

Williams-Ashman, H. G., S. Liao, R. L. Hancock, L. Jurkowitz, and D. A. Silverman. 1964. Testicular hormones and the synthesis of ribonucleic acids and proteins in the prostate gland. *Recent Progr. Hormone Res.*, **20**: 247–301.

Wilson, J. D., and P. Loeb. 1965. Estrogen and androgen control of cell biosynthesis in target organs. In *Developmental and Metabolic Control Mechanisms and Neoplasia*. Williams & Wilkins, Baltimore, pp. 375–390.

Young, W. C. 1961. The hormones and mating behavior. In *Sex and Internal Secretions* (W. C. Young, ed.). Williams & Wilkins, Baltimore, 3rd ed., pp. 1173–1239.

Young, W. C., R. W. Goy, and C. H. Phoenix. 1965. Hormones and sexual behavior. *Science,* **143:** 212–218.

18

Testicular Enzymes as Fingerprints in the Study of Spermatogenesis

David W. Bishop

Writing about the nongerminal aspects of the testis some forty years ago, Carl Moore (1927) observed that "Lack of progress in the study of the organs of internal secretion has often been due to the fact that sufficiently dependable, easily read indicators for the products of their activity, were not available." In a reverse sense, the germinal epithelium stands in an analogous position today—the cellular products are clear enough, but sufficiently dependable, easily read indicators of the causes and events associated with germ-cell elaboration have not been available. Indeed, the entire process of spermatogenesis, despite its role in both reproduction and behavior, has been treated, until recently, rather as a stepchild in the broad sweep of reproductive physiological investigations.

Several significant areas of research activity lately do, to be sure, indicate that interest in germ-cell differentiation is being rekindled as new approaches are adopted and useful implements fashioned: (1) the application of specific cytochemical procedures to studies of the testicle, about which more comment will follow; (2) the reactivation of the old wave-cycle concept of classical cytologists, stimulated perhaps by Moree (1947) and Roosen-Runge and co-workers (1950, 1953) and elegantly developed into a sound, quantitative basis for kinetic analysis of germ-cell cycles, register, and programming by Leblond, Clermont, Heller, and colleagues (1952, 1957, 1960, 1962, 1964, 1966); (3) the successful reemployment of in vitro methods, particularly organ culture, in studies of testis from both invertebrate and vetebrate sources, including man, Although tissue culture is not a new idea (see Goldschmidt, 1915; Lewis and Robertson, 1916; Champy, 1920), modern refinements have proved rewarding in the partial elucidation of various control mechanisms at play during differentiation of the male germ cells (Schneiderman et al., 1953; Haffen, 1960; Wolff and Haffen, 1965; Basu et al., 1966; Steinberger and Steinberger, 1967).

It is not the intent of this contribution to review spermatogenesis in terms of these advances, or to survey the full spectrum of enzymic reactions present in either complex testicular homogenates or suspensions of the single-cell type, spermatozoa. Rather, the aim is to indicate a new dimension by outlining evidence which suggests that selected enzyme systems (1) can possibly serve as functional indicators of spermatogenic activity, (2) may be limited to, or associated with, key stages in the process, and (3) could eventually prove, in some instances, to operate in a causal relation with specific steps in the unique and complex changes involved in germ-cell differentiation. Fingerprinting, as used in better known biological contexts, implies a highly sophisticated and refined method of analysis; as employed here, the term implies the limitation to, or identification with, germinal elements in general and, quite possibly, specific key reaction systems. An additional objective of such an overview is to provoke additional thought and investigation of enzyme systems, patterns, and distribution which might lead to enhanced understanding of spermatogenesis and any behavioral activity which either stems from, or contributes to, variations in the germinal epithelium.

Spermatozoal Enzymes

Spermatozoa are replete with a wide variety of enzymic systems which have been extensively investigated, by both biochemical and cytochemical methods, as catalytic effecters of metabolic processes. The stimulus for these studies has arisen from concern with both the gametes' over-all role in reproduction and the special functional characteristics intrinsic to these cells; as a further incentive for analysis, spermatozoa constitute a readily available homogeneous cell population, with singular manifestations of cellular activity. Whatever mature sperm may lack in enzyme activity normally associated with division cycles and biosynthesis—being a relatively stable, if not resting, cell population—they make up, in part, by special enzyme systems related to flagellation, metabolic adaptation, and egg penetration. A survey of enzymic and other biochemical components of sperm may be found in Mann's monograph on male reproduction (1964), to which the reader is referred.

A cataloguing of the enzymes of spermatozoa, the end product of differentiation, without adequate information as to how or when they got there, will hardly serve our immediate purpose. It may suffice to point out, however, that mammalian sperm are equipped with a full assortment of enzymes associated with the familiar Embden–Meyerhof glycolytic pathway, the citric acid cycle, and the cytochrome–cytochrome oxidase electron-transport system (Mann, 1967). Considerable species variation exists in both enzyme distribution and relative activities; many invertebrate sperm and those of vertebrate animals which reproduce by external fertilization show, for example, a reduction in, or absence of, glycolytic activity and presumably are deficient in enzymes required for these reactions. Enzymatic systems involved in sperm motility have been recently reviewed by Nelson (1967), and the sperm lysins associated with prefertilization changes and possible egg penetration are discussed by Dan (1967). The extent of biosynthetic activity in mature sperm seems, at best, marginal, and evidence for relevant enzymes is less than compelling (Bishop, 1961). In sum, however, the complete spectrum of enzymes of these cells is striking. Studies of the origin and elaboration of these catalysts should be very revealing; for the present, in few instances have their cytobiochemical beginnings been revealed. One can only assume that, if not incorporated from outside the germ cell during spermiogenesis, they have already been established in the developing cell during a stage of active protein synthesis, probably not later than the so-called resting (growth) stage of the primary spermatocyte, that is, prior to meiosis (Chandley and Bateman, 1962; Monesi, 1962; Muckenthaler, 1964).

Germinal Epithelial Enzymes

Most of the enzymes present in spermatozoa occur also in immature germ cells, and many have been demonstrated in tissue homogenates of whole testes, young and old. However, the testicle generally is a complex mixture of tissues and cell types, and biochemical analysis of the entire organ is not apt to afford great insight into the distribution and characterization of cellular components without further means of localization. This can be accomplished in part by the employment of histochemical procedures; an unexplored area of biochemical investigation could also make use of gonadal material from animals in which relatively large and discrete lobes or follicles of the testis display synchronous patterns of differentiation and therefore constitute homogeneous, experimentally advantageous, cell populations (e.g., in certain amphibia, elasmobranchs, and insects). To serve as a spermatogenic probe, an enzyme must be related if not limited to the germinal epithelium and preferably to a specific stage of differentiation or physiological reaction unique to the process. The rest of the testis is far from inert, as has been amply demonstrated by many penetrating studies of steroid biosynthesis on the part of the interstitium (see Eik-Nes, 1964; Dorfman et al., 1967; Grant et al., 1967) and by recent investigations of Sertoli-cell activity in, for example, normal and cryptorchid rats (Firlit and Davis, 1966). Some enzyme systems have been demonstrated in testes which include only early spermatogonia and appear to be associated with all stages of spermatogenesis, as, for example, acid phosphatase, nucleoside diphosphatase, and lactic acid dehydrogenase (Fox and Fox, 1967). Others, such as phosphamidase, glycerophosphate dehydrogenase, and hyaluronidase, cannot be detected in significant quantity until the spermatocyte or spermatid stage of differentiation.

As information accrues in regard to the mechanisms of action of various drugs and inhibitors on specific stages of spermatogenesis, it may be expected that these tools will aid in the further pinpointing of testicular enzyme activity (Fox and Fox, 1967). Certain spermatogenic inhibitors, for example triethylenemelamine (TEM), block early spermatogonial divisions (Steinberger, 1962), whereas the sulfonates, diamines, dinitropyrroles, and nitrofurans seem to affect principally the late stages in the process, i.e., spermatocytes and spermatids (Fox and Jackson, 1965; Drobeck and Coulston, 1962; Featherstone et al., 1955). As a case in point, Featherstone and co-workers concluded that the primary action of furadroxyl in inhibiting rat spermatogenesis is the impairment of pyruvate oxidation at the level of the primary spermatocyte.

What can be learned from a survey of germ-cell enzymes as visualized by cytochemical procedures? It may be observed in Table 1 (admittedly a first approximation) that some systems are present throughout development, appearing early in spermatogenesis, whereas

Table 1

Cytochemical Demonstrations of Germinal Epithelial Enzymes [a]

Enzymes	Species	Ref. [b]
Active throughout spermatogenesis		
Lactic dehydrogenase	Rat, man, bull	1, 2, 3, 4
Malic dehydrogenase	Rat	1
Succinic dehydrogenase	Rat, man, bull	1, 2, 4, 5
Glutamic dehydrogenase	Bull	4
Alcohol dehydrogenase	Man	2
Glu-6-P dehydrogenase	Man, bull	2, 4
Acid phosphatase	Rat, man	2, 6
Alkaline phosphatase	Man, frog	2, 7, 8, 9
Nucleoside diphosphatase	Rat	6, 10
5-Nucleotidase	Rat	6
Increased activity in late stages [c]		
Lactic dehydrogenase	Man, bull	3, 11
Succinic dehydrogenase	Rat	12
Glutamic dehydrogenase	Bull	4
Glu-6-P dehydrogenase	Bull	4
Acid phosphatase	Rat, deer	13, 14
Alkaline phosphatase	Man, deer	7, 14
Activity limited to late stages [c]		
β-Hydroxybutyrate dehydrogenase	Bull	4
Sorbitol dehydrogenase	Guinea pig	15
α-Glycerophosphatase	Rat	16
Phosphamidase	Rat	17
Hyaluronidase	Bull	5, 18, 19

[a] Does not include enzymic demonstrations in mature gametes.

[b] 1, Ambadkar and George, 1964; 2, Koudstaal et al., 1967; 3, Stallcup and Roussel, 1965; 4, Blackshaw and Samisoni, 1967; 5, Fox and Fox, 1967; 6, Tice and Barrnett, 1963; 7, Montagna, 1952; 8, Mancini et al., 1952; 9, Burgos, 1955; 10, Niemi and Kormano, 1964; 11, Jirásek and Raboch, 1963; 12, Pósalaky et al., 1961; 13, Niemi and Kormano, 1965; 14, Wislocki, 1949; 15, Bishop, 1967; 16, Mietkiewski and Lukaszyk, 1966; 17, Meyer and Weinmann, 1957; 18, Mancini et al., 1964; 19, Yamane, 1956.

[c] Late stages refer to spermatocytes and spermatids.

others show activity virtually only at late stages of differentiation. Such a summary, however, is offered with reservation and should be viewed with some degree of caution. Most of these enzyme systems are not limited to germ cells and therefore can be expected to play important roles in anabolic or catabolic activities characteristic of all cells, regardless of type or state of differentiation. Moreover, considerable variation exists among species, as well as in the stages subjected to scrutiny in any given investigation, noted in Table 1. Finally, the techniques employed, although hopefully precise, are not always absolute in their designation of specificity, particularly if intracellular localization is at stake. The demonstration, for example, of dehydrogenase activity, which generally makes use of the visualization of reduced tetrazolium (formazan) as hydrogen acceptor, depends not only on a specific NAD-dependent dehydrogenase to produce $NADH_2$, but also on the latter's enzymic reduction by diaphorase (tetrazolium reductase). $NADH_2$-diaphorase, a component of mitochondria, correctly localizes such mitochondrial enzymes as succinic, malic, and isocitric dehydrogenases of liver cells (Walker and Seligman, 1963) and their counterparts in the midpieces of sperm (Gupta and Kamboj, 1962; Balogh and Cohen, 1964; Hrudka, 1965). The tetrazolium-reduction procedure fails, however, to demonstrate dehydrogenases located in nonmitochondrial compartments of these cells (see Novikoff, 1960).

As additional enzymes may be added to this list and their individual features become known, particularly those with unique and unusual biochemical characteristics, and as other methods of identification are employed in parallel (e.g., electron micrographic, fluorescent-antibody labeling, and specific enzyme inhibition), one may anticipate some eventual clarification of the relation of ultrastructure to biochemical pattern in the spermatogenic process. One is reminded of the prediction of Lars Ernster (1959) in this connection, here taken slightly out of context: "To map the relationship between structural alterations and the patterns in which cellular enzymes react and interact may come to be, I believe, one of the most important achievements of future biochemistry." Of the numerous enzymes which have been identified in germinal epithelium and which may serve as enzymatic keys to particular features of spermatogenesis, three systems have special value and are singled out for more detailed consideration: hexokinase, lactic dehydrogenase, and sorbitol dehydrogenase.

Testis-Specific Hexokinase

In Drosophila, a testis-specific isozyme, apparently associated with the germinal epithelium, has been identified by electrophoretic procedures by Murray and Ball (1967). "Hex-t" makes its appearance in preparations of males only and is limited to the gonads of pupae and adults, in which spermatogenic activity is greatest. This enzymic band is electrophoretically distinct from the several major isozymes of hexokinase found generally in Drosophila tissues, and it separates clearly from yet another sex-associated isozyme, one limited to the male accessory gland tissue. Whereas, the Hex-t band is present in pupae already producing spermatozoa, the isozyme is more closely associated with spermatogenesis than with spermiogenesis, since it appears in testes of genetic stocks with either immotile (XO male) or no (*tra/tra* transformed female) mature spermatozoa. The further pinpointing of this distinctive molecular form of enzyme in the framework of spermatogenesis could seem to provide a most useful and enlightening biochemical marker with significant implications. It should, at the same time, be noted that Hex-t may be of provincial importance only, since it appears to be species-specific and occurs in the testes of *Drosophila melanogaster* but not in those of *D. pseudoobscura.*

Katzen (1967) has found evidence for a "testis-specific" hexo-kinase component also in the rat. But little is as yet known about its distribution, its relation to particular stages of differentiation, or its value for further analysis of spermatogenesis. This isozyme may indeed be associated with mature sperm only, but it is more likely characteristic of spermatocytes and spermatids as well.

Although somewhat meager, such demonstrations represent a beginning. Moreover, the fundamental role played by hexokinase in the conversion of glycolytic substrate suggests that the presence of singular, germ-cell specific isozymes may, in these species, be of considerable significance to both the processes of differentiation and metabolic adaptation.

The X-Band of Lactic Dehydrogenase

The concept of multiple molecular form in enzymes developed during the 1950s. Of approximately 100 enzymes that have now been shown by electrophoretic methods to display separate isozymes, the one probably most explored is lactic dehydrogenase (LDH) (Kaplan and Ciotti, 1961). The penetrating studies of Markert and colleagues, particularly, have elucidated many biochemical, physicochemical, and developmental features of LDH and its constituent isozymes (Markert and Møller, 1959; Markert and Appella, 1961; Markert and Ursprung, 1962; Markert, 1963, 1964). The five major isozymes of mammalian LDH have been characterized with respect to their tissue specificity, species affinity, polypeptide makeup, genetic control, and ontogenetic sequence. Developmental studies on avian LDH have been contributed by Cahn et al. (1962), Lindsay (1963), and Blanco et al. (1964). Attention is here focused on the singular isozyme, the X-band, which appears in the postpubertal testes of some birds and mammals (Fig. 1). This molecular form of LDH is sex-limited and testis-specific; it is confined to the germinal epithelium, and does not occur in the interstitium, of the mature testis (Zinkham et al., 1964; Goldberg and Hawtrey, 1967; see also Stambaugh and Buckley, 1967). First appearing in very late spermatogonial and/or spermatocyte stages of germ-cell differentiation, LDH-X is the predominant isozyme in the mature sperm of man, mouse, and the rabbit and, in the rabbit, accounts for about 90 percent of the total LDH activity. Owing perhaps to its molecular variation and genetic control, LDH-X may occur as a single (e.g., man, mouse rabbit, dog) or complex band (e.g., rat, bull, guinea pig, pigeon); in the testes of some species, however, it cannot be demonstrated with routine electrophoretic procedures (e.g., cat, boar, chicken, duck). In those forms in which

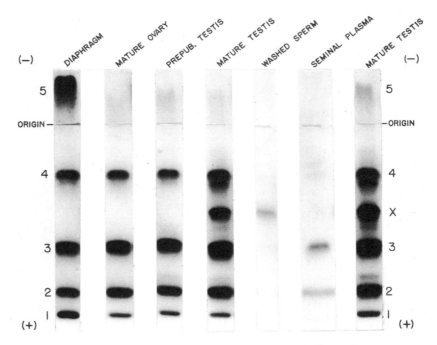

Fig. 1 Zymogram of LDH in human tissue; starch gel electrophoretic patterns visualized by incubation in presence of lactate, NAD, phenazine methosulfate, and nitro-blue tetrazolium. Note X-band in mature testis and, faintly, in sperm. [From Zinkham et al., 1966; by permission of the American Academy of Pediatrics.]

LDH-X can be recognized in the germinal epithelium, it offers promise as an effective basis for quantitative evaluation of germ-cell content in normally developing and in impaired testes. Zinkham and co-workers (1964), for example, have used this as an assay system on immunologically impaired guinea pig testes in which the germinal epithelium is destroyed, but in which the interstitium remains functional (Bishop and Carlson, 1965).

Two biochemical features of LDH-X help to single out this isozyme from among the usual five and therefore tend to pinpoint its precise site or stage of activity in the germinal epithelium:

1. One of these characteristics has to do with relative reaction rates of the various isozymes when NAD is replaced by NAD analogues. In the presence of acetyl pyridine adenine dinucleotide (AP-NAD), for example, human band-X shows a marked increase in activity, whereas that of the other five isozymes is depressed (Zinkham et al., 1964). Although this response of human LDH-X is not shared by band-X isozymes from various other mammals (rabbit, mouse, dog, bull), it does sharpen the tool by which LDH may serve, in man at least, as an indicator of spermatogenic activity, as well as to enunciate enzyme-specific differences in related species (Blanco and Zinkham, 1963).

2. The substrate specificity of band-X isozyme is such as to utilize not only lactate but DL-α-hydroxybutyrate and DL-α-hydroxyvalerate as well (Allen, 1961). Goldberg and Hawtrey (1967) have taken advantage of this to localize LDH-X rather accurately in mouse germinal epithelium. By employing α-hydroxyvalerate as substrate, these investigators demonstrated by electrophoretic, histochemical, and spectrophotometric methods that the testis-specific isozyme first shows activity in mice between 14 and 16 days of age, at a time when spermatocytes begin to appear in the seminiferous tubules. Activity then increases with age as more and more mature germ cells are produced.

The band-X isozyme of LDH can thus serve as a marker in the process of spermatogenesis, albeit late in the series of cell changes. Its occurrence—in some birds and mammals—is rather limited, but its uniqueness would seem to warrant further investigation in quantitative and molecular studies of germ-cell formation. Additional means of localization, e.g., by fluorescent-antibody labeling, should be encouraged. A comparative approach to the problem also would prove instructive, particularly with respect to analogous isozymes in invertebrate and lower chordate animals which breed by means of internal fertilization. At the present time, the functional emphasis on

LDH-X centers upon the role this isozyme may play in the mature gamete: some special capacity to bring about more effectively the catalytic conversion of pyruvate to lactate and, more importantly, to regulate the $NAD:NADH_2$ balance, since the coenzyme is essential for many energy-requiring biological processes. It is not unreasonable to speculate that LDH-X, like LDH-5 in other tissues, may be associated with a high rate of anaerobic glycolysis and constitutes a metabolic adaptation to the singular conditions enjoyed by the spermatozoa of higher animals. This emphasis on sperm metabolism is as it should be, perhaps, but a point to remember is that the enzyme may also play a significant role in the processes of spermatogenesis and/or spermiogenesis themselves (see below).

Testicular Sorbitol Dehydrogenase

Unlike the testis-specific hexokinase isozymes, thus far found in two species, and the LDH-X bands of some avian and mammalian testes, sorbitol dehydrogenase (SDH) is found associated with spermatogenesis apparently throughout the animal kingdom (Bishop, 1967). As a constituent of germinal epithelium of both invertebrate and vertebrate species, of forms which breed by either external or internal fertilization, and of species with either flagellated, motile sperm or nonflagellated, immotile gametes, there is good reason to conclude that SDH bears a significant relation to germ-cell differentiation itself. As an index of spermatogenic activity, it constitutes a reliable, sensitive, and quantitative assay system; as a fingerprint for differentiation, its activity profile indicates that the primary spermatocytes are particularly reactive (Bishop et al., 1967). These generalizations are supported by a variety of recently accumulated evidence, which is briefly summarized in the paragraphs below.

Prompted by the demonstration of SDH in ram sperm by King and Mann (1958, 1959) and the suggestion by Williams-Ashman (1963) that biochemical assay of the enzyme might serve to monitor germinal epithelial changes in cryptorchid rat testes, work was initiated in the writer's laboratory to investigate the distribution, localization, and role of testicular SDH and to extract, purify, and characterize the enzyme from mammalian sources.

Distribution of testicular SDH. The general significance of testicular SDH, as well as its value as a spermatogenic fingerprint, would seem to be enhanced by the finding that the enzyme is present in testicular homogenates of very many, diversified types of mature animals. The range in enzyme activity (Table 2) reflects species

Table 2

Sorbitol Dehydrogenase Activity in Testicular Homogenates
of a Variety of Mature Animals

Species	ΔO.D./min_{340} [a]
Grasshopper	0.052
Guinea pig	0.031
Mouse	0.024
Macaque	0.019
Rat	0.015
Rooster	0.014
Frog	0.007
Starfish	0.005
Man	0.004
Rabbit	0.004
Sand dollar	0.004
Horseshoe crab	0.004
Spider crab	0.002

[a] Absorption at 340 mμ by homogenate supernates of tissue equivalents on a wet-weight basis; sorbitol 0.1 M, NAD 5×10^{-4} M, enzyme extract 6.6 percent v/v, tris-HCl buffer 0.5 M, pH 8.2, determined or calculated at 23°C.

variation, on the one hand, and state of active spermatogenesis at the time of sampling, on the other hand. The data presented in Table 2 are representative, but not necessarily maximal, values for those species listed. Among mammals, for example, mature guinea pig testis consistently shows the greatest activity, while that of the rabbit testis is characteristically low; moreover, the source material for the human determination was histopathologically abnormal, and this value is probably unusually reduced. Enzyme activity is here expressed as change in optical density ($\triangle$O.D.) with time, as determined spectrophotometrically at 340 mμ in the usual way and with adequate controls; the change in absorption is directly related to the reduction of coenzyme, NAD, to NADH$_2$, while sorbitol is oxidized to fructose.

When attention was turned to submammalian and invertebrate animals, several surprising findings were divulged. The testis of the frog, as well as those of certain invertebrates which also indulge in external fertilization, showed significant SDH activity (Table 2). These spermatozoa, where tested cytochemically, showed SDH in the mitochondria-bearing midpiece, and yet it is unlikely that, in these forms, the gametes could rely on an exogenous substrate for metabolic activity after spawning. Certain invertebrates show very intense testicular SDH activity; indeed, the value for the mature insect, *Melanoplus,* is the highest we have recorded. In this connection it is noteworthy that no LDH activity could be demonstrated in the testis of this grasshopper, suggesting that SDH may here replace LDH in the regulation of the $NAD/NADH_2$ ratio.

The discovery of significant SDH activity in the testes of both decapod crustacea, e.g., *Libinia,* the spider crab, and the horseshoe crab, *Limulus,* is intriguing and provocative. The former produce nonflagellated, immotile spermatozoa, but, nevertheless, the testes give positive SDH determinations. *Limulus,* on the other hand, produces SDH-bearing sperm of the usual flagellated type; here the interest lies in the extremely ancient phylogenetic origin of this "living fossil," which indicates that sorbitol dehydrogenase arose as a germ-cell enzyme several hundred million years ago! The presence of SDH in the testes of echinoderms and insects supports this evolutionary history of the enzyme and certainly enhances its biological significance as something other than a mere transitory aid to sperm metabolism in present-day homoiothermic animals.

It is to be emphasized that SDH is not testis-specific or testis-limited in the sense that these appellations apply to the hexokinase and LDH isozymic reactions noted above. Sorbitol dehydrogenase is characteristic of a variety of fructose-elaborating tissues (seminal vesicles, placenta, eye lens) and occurs in the liver ("xylitol dehydrogenase") as part of the glucuronate–xylulose metabolic pathway (Touster and Shaw, 1962). Nevertheless, the enzyme is sufficiently unique physiologically, and limited in its distribution and function, to facilitate its use as a marker or indicator of spermatogenic activity. Furthermore, although SDH does not display an exciting isozymic configuration (Fig. 2), it offers considerable biological advantage by virtue of its spectrum of substrate specificities, reactivity with NAD analogues, and extractability in highly purified form (see below).

Localization of Testicular SDH

Several approaches have been followed to localize SDH with respect to stage of germ-cell differentiation. Developmental studies demonstrate quite clearly that activity in testes of both the guinea pig and fowl increases with age and state of germinal epithelial maturation. In spectrophotometric determinations on guinea pig testicular homogenates, the low, prenatal level of activity continues on until about 4 weeks of age, at which time a marked increase occurs,

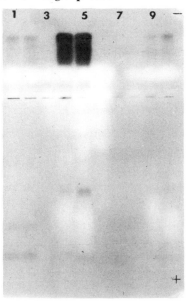

Fig. 2 Electrophoretic patterns of sorbitol dehydrogenase from guinea pig tissues; sorbitol substrate. Samples from left to right as follows: (1, 2, 3) testis preincubated 15 minutes at 4, 55, and 80°C, respectively; (4, 5, 6) liver preincubated 15 minutes at 4, 55, and 80°C; (7) blank; (8, 9, 10) placenta preincubated 15 minutes at 80, 55 and 4°C, respectively. Significant band migrates toward cathode; minor bands below correspond in position to LDH bands 1, 2, and 3.

coincident (in these Hartley strain animals) with the appearance in the testes of primary spermatocytes (Fig. 3). Enzyme titers, expressed on either a wet weight or specific activity basis, level off at a maximal value characteristic of the species and then remain fairly constant during the reproductive career of the animal. Suspensions of epididymal sperm of the guinea pig display SDH activity, detectable by both spectrophotometric and cytochemical methods, but at a lower level than that of crude enzyme extract from testicular homogenate, cleared by centrifugation.

From quite an unexpected source, confirmatory evidence for this rough demonstration that the more mature germ cells, but not necessarily spermatozoa, constitute the major source of SDH activity was supplied by studies on the sea urchin, *Arbacia*. Both males and females of this marine invertebrate are induced to spawn by stimulation with either mild electric shock or injection of KCl. Shedding of male gametes is immediately followed by a wave of active spermato-

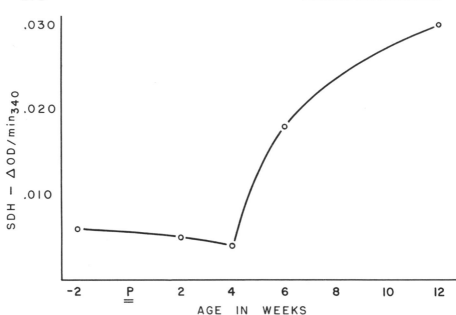

Fig. 3 Abrupt increase in SDH activity in guinea pig testes between 4 and 5
         weeks of age, at time primary spermatocytes first appear.

genesis which persists for 6 or 7 days and gives rise to a new batch
of ripe gametes. If testes are harvested from spawned sea urchins at
daily intervals after stimulation and assayed spectrophotometrically
for SDH, a significant increase in activity promptly occurs, reaches
a peak at about 4 days, and then rapidly subsides to the low, barely
detectable level of the mature gonad as spermatogenic activity ceases
(Fig. 4).

Cytochemical demonstrations of SDH activity also indicate that
the more mature germ cells, in contrast to the spermatogonia, are
highly reactive. By means of a modified tetrazolium-reduction procedure, enzyme activity can be visualized in fast-frozen ($-80°C$),
unfixed, prerinsed sections of guinea pig testis (Fig. 5). Control
sections, incubated in the absence of substrate, and neonatal testes
fail to show activity. Despite intrinsic limitations in the histochemical
procedure, the results have aided in the cellular localization of SDH
and also yield crude quantitative data relative to the general amount
of activity in various generations of germ cell.

The enzyme has now been labeled more precisely in germ cells
of the guinea pig seminiferous tubule by means of fluorescent-antibody
labeling. Spermatocytes, spermatids, and mature spermatozoa selec-

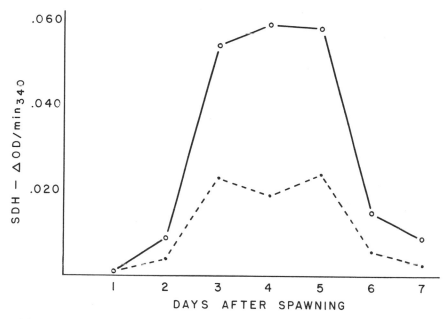

Fig. 4 Increase in SDH activity during spermatogenic wave induced in the sea urchin by KCl-stimulated spawning; solid line, relative, and dashed line, specific activities plotted against time.

tively accept the label and indicate that SDH, as antigen, is located in these stages, again in contrast to negligible amounts in spermatogonia. No immunochemical reaction is displayed by either the Sertoli cells or elements in the interstitium. For these labeling procedures, rabbit antiserum was prepared against guinea pig testicular SDH, extracted and purified as noted below, and employed in a sandwich technique involving antirabbit globulin sheep serum. Visualized in the UV microscope, the spermatozoa are brightly fluorescent (Fig. 6a); the entire flagellum would appear to contain SDH throughout its length. Of particular interest is the labeling of large, discrete, and brightly fluorescent cells which have been tentatively identified as primary spermatocytes at the so-called resting or growth stage of premeiotic differentiation (Fig. 6c). This may indeed be the last period for active protein synthesis on a large scale before the nuclear and cytoplasmic changes ensue which are characteristic of meiosis and spermiogenesis.

Changes induced, by whatever means, in the germinal epithelial content of the mature testis result in alterations in SDH activity and can therefore be monitored by this relatively simple enzymic assay.

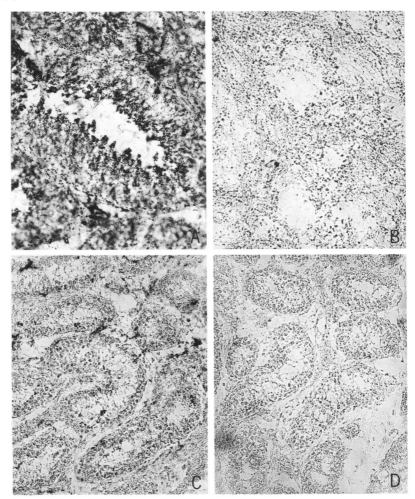

Fig. 5 Cytochemical demonstration of SDH in guinea pig testis; (A) mature seminiferous tubule, (B) control, incubated without substrate, (C) immature testis, and (D) control for (C). Tissues were rapidly frozen in 2-methylbutane at $-80°$C, sectioned, unfixed, and prerinsed in buffer before incubation in reaction mixture for tetrazolium-reduction test.

Cadmium-treated or X-irradiated testes of the guinea pig show serious depletions in activity. Both immunologically (autoallergic) damaged and surgically cryptorchidized animals display enzymic changes in the impaired testes which accompany, and perhaps precede, cytological injury (Bishop and Carlson, 1965; Bishop et al., 1967). The decrease in testicular SDH which follows experimental cryptorchidism of the adult guinea pig is prompt and dramatic (Table 3); in young animals the response is reversible after orchiopexy. Immunologically induced aspermatogenesis in the guinea pig is most

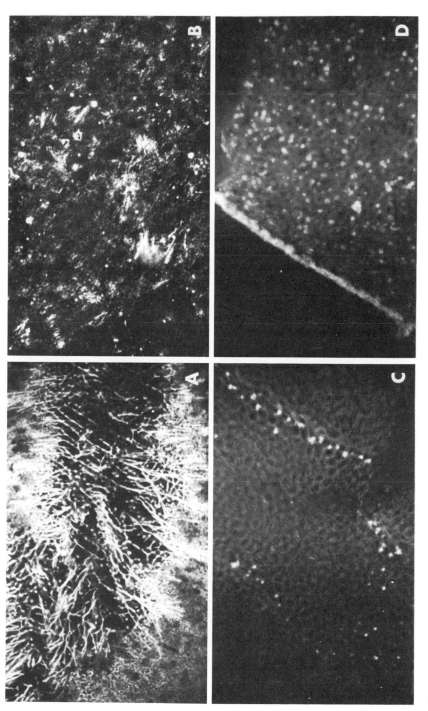

Fig. 6 Immunofluorescent labeling of guinea pig tissue with anti-SDH serum by means of the sandwich technique. (A) Dark-field fluorescence of spermatozoa in seminiferous tubule; (B) dark-field control with normal serum; (C) phase fluorescence of tubule showing labeled germ cells tentatively identified as primary spermatocytes; (D) phase fluorescence in liver showing widespread distribution of SDH antigen cross-reactive with testicular SDH antiserum.

Table 3

Decrease in Sorbitol Dehydrogenase in Cryptorchid Guinea Pig Testes

Days cryptorchid	ΔO.D./min$_{340}$	% of control
0	0.032	100
3	0.030	93
6	0.024	74
9	0.016	50
12	0.011	33
15	0.008	25

Table 4

Testicular Sorbitol Dehydrogenase Levels during Induced Aspermatogenesis

Days after sensitization	ΔO.D./min$_{340}$	% of control
1	0.033	100
14	0.028	85
21	0.021	64
28	0.008	24
56	0.004	12

marked some 6 to 8 weeks after sensitization; by means of the SDH assay a series of animals can be monitored during the early, incipient stages of the syndrome (Table 4). Since in the guinea pig neither induced cryptorchidism nor aspermatogenesis results in impairment of Leydig cell function, at least during the course of such experimentation, these data serve as additional evidence that testicular SDH is a component of the germinal epithelium, and its estimation reflects changes therein. As an assay system, per se, the determination of testicular SDH would seem to have great value in a variety of studies by the addition of that needed note of quantitation to an otherwise unwieldy and subjective method of analysis. Lord Kelvin may have had the germ-cell cytologist in mind when he noted that ". . . when you can measure what you are speaking about, and express it in numbers, you know something about it . . . !"

Extracted and Purified Testicular SDH

This is not the time or the occasion to dwell extensively on highly successful efforts to extract SDH from mammalian testes or to characterize it in terms of purity, tissue specificity, and enzyme kinetics. Much of this has been accomplished (Bishop et al., 1967), is undergoing further study, and will be reported elsewhere. We do hasten to acknowledge here, however, the work of Libby (1962), who, together with Williams-Ashman, extracted the ketose reductase from rat liver, and whose procedure we have followed, with considerable modification, owing to the peculiar behavior and relative scarcity of testicular SDH. The enzyme extract, as eluted from the final CM-cellulose column (Fig. 7), is highly active, is purified about 500-fold over the initial crude testicular preparation, presents a peak specific activity of 12 to 15 μmoles of $NADH_2$ produced/min/mg of protein, and is stable upon careful lyophilization or storage at $-70°C$ in 50 percent glycerol or dimethyl sulfoxide (DMSO). Certain characteristics of the extracted guinea pig preparation are presented in Table 5.

The very fact that testicular SDH can be extracted and utilized in relatively pure form goes a long way toward accomplishing the main objectives initially set forth in this survey. To serve as a meaningful and operational marker or index, the biochemical function of a "fingerprint" should be appreciated, and the best way to understand its activity is to isolate it and characterize its behavior.

A significant advantage of SDH isolation is its use in serological

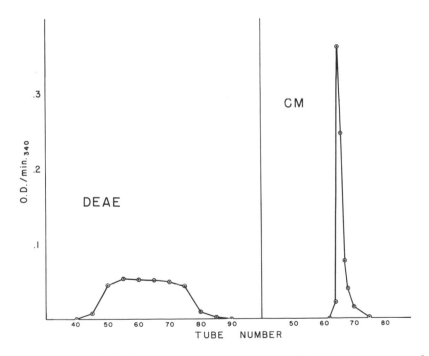

Fig. 7 Sorbitol deyhydrogenase activity in successive (5-ml) fractions separated by column chromatography after previous partial purification; DEAE- and CM-cellulose columns.

and immunochemical analysis. This has consisted of four kinds of studies which need not be elaborated further here: (1) serological analysis of enzyme purity in accordance with immunodiffusion and immunoelectrophoretic principles, (2) tissue- and species-specificity of testicular SDH, (3) immunofluorescent analysis as noted above, and (4) enzyme inhibition by specific antibody.

One additional finding, however, should be included which grew out of attempts to inhibit testicular SDH activity and/or elaboration in vivo by treatment with enzyme or antienzyme serum. Over the

Table 5

Characteristics of Extracted Guinea Pig Testicular Ketose Reductase
(Specific activity = 15 μmoles of $NADH_2$/min/mg of protein, 23° C; 500 $\times$ purified; 29 μg protein/ml)

Relative substrate specificity		Temperature inactivation (½ hr incubation)	Storage stability	Contaminants	SDH–anti-SDH immuno-diffusion bands	
Sorbitol	— 100%	23°C—100%	Glycerol, 1:1 −70°C—100%	MDH, +	Unabs.	1–3
Ribitol	— 74%	50°C— 87%	DMSO, 1:1 −70°C—100%	LDH, −	Heart-abs.	1
Xylitol	— 33%	55°C— 73%	Buffer −70°—0	SucDH, −	Testis-abs.	0
Mannitol	— 26%	60°C— 73%	Lyophilization 50–70%	AlcDH, −	Liver-abs.	0
L-Arabitol	— 22%	65°C— 53%		GlyDH, −		
D-Arabitol	— 0	70°C— 30%		GluDH, −		
Inositol	— 0					
Lactate	— 0					

short range, treatment of healthy adult guinea pigs with either purified SDH or ammonium sulfate–fractionated anti-SDH serum, produced in the rabbit, did not lead to any apparent disorder. On the other hand, purified SDH extract proved to be an effective long-range aspermatogenic agent in guinea pigs when administered in adjuvant by intracutaneous injection. After sensitization, the germ-cell response is less severe and less prompt to occur than when the well-known polysaccharide–polypeptide aspermatogenic antigen of Jules Freund is injected (see Bishop and Carlson, 1965), but the ultimate result involving germinal epithelial damage, is, in the guinea pig, very much the same (Fig. 8). It is a difficult way to induce male infertility, and one with species limitations, but it adds another tool to the ever-broadening study of spermatogenesis and reproductive behavior.

We have found, for example, that aspermatogenic guinea pigs, whose interstitial tissue is functionally intact, tend to be sexually inactive as judged by copulatory interest in the female. This finding would seem to bear on the early observation of Stone (1924) and the more recent demonstration of Webster and Young (1951) that the normal awakening of sexual arousal, possibly associated with adolescent sterility in the rat and the guinea pig, correlates roughly, if not directly, with the differentiation of advanced stages of germ cells in the seminiferous tubules.

Conclusions

This, we feel, is more a time for a beginning than for a conclusion. Time will tell whether testicular enzymes, used as fingerprints, will prove a fruitful approach to the study of spermatogenesis. And the future may reveal other, more useful tools in such a method of analysis, for example, malic dehydrogenase (Ford and Huggins, 1963; Goldberg, 1963) or α-glycerophosphate dehydrogenase (Schenkman et al., 1965). The most rewarding discovery would be the identification and association of enzyme systems with early, key phases of spermatogenesis, e.g., the determination of the proliferative

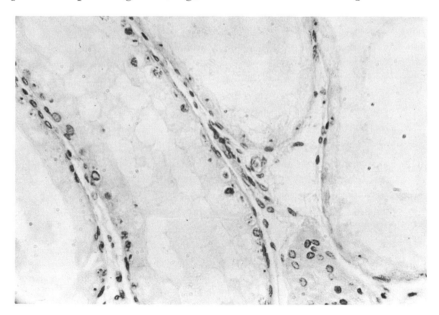

Fig. 8 Immunologically induced aspermatogenesis in guinea pig brought about by sensitization with purified testicular SDH extract administered in complete adjuvant.

spermatogonium as distinct from the stem cell. Whatever relation might be established between a structural feature of spermatogenesis and its biochemical individuality would seem worthy of pursuit. And the process seems sufficiently complex and dynamic that there must be much from which to choose. It seems appropriate for this discussion and for this volume to quote from a recent review of William Young (1964) concerning another system of physiological regulation at the cellular level: "The variability is a means by which the maturity or immaturity of a pattern can be revealed; in male animals, for example, a variable in the form of an incomplete pattern is observed in prepuberal subjects. Familiarity with the variability displayed within a group of animals, and with the fact that many individuals tend to display the same pattern from cycle to cycle, led to an analysis of the role of tissue responsiveness in the action of gonadal hormones in bringing mating behavior to expression."

Acknowledgments

Many thanks and much gratitude are due Arlyne D. Musselman for her continued effort, cooperation, and initiative throughout the course of the experimentation which underlies this contribution. Appreciation is also gratefully acknowledged to William H. Duncan for much histological and cytochemical aid, and to W. W. Schrank, E. C. Muecke, and R. L. Shoger, whose collaboration in various aspects of the SDH program have made this work more enjoyable. I am indebted to the staff of the Marine Biological Laboratory, Woods Hole, for help and facilities in the studies of marine invertebrates, and especially to numerous colleagues at Cornell University for their cooperation and stimulation, which have made the preparation of this manuscript possible.

References

Allen, J. M. 1961. Multiple forms of lactic dehydrogenase in tissues of the mouse: Their specificity, cellular localization, and response to altered physiological conditions. *Ann. N.Y. Acad. Sci.*, **94**: 937–951.

Ambadkar, P. M., and J. C. George. 1964. Histochemical localization of certain oxidative enzymes in the rat testis. *J. Histochem. Cytochem.*, **12**: 587–590.

Balogh, K., and R. B. Cohen. 1964. A cytochemical technique for studying oxidative enzyme systems of mammalian spermatozoa in semen smears. *Fertil. Steril.*, **15**: 35–39.

Basu, S. L., J. Nandi, and S. Nandi. 1966. Effects of hormones on adult frog (*Rana pipiens*) testes in organ culture. *J. Exptl. Zool.*, **162**: 245–255.

Bishop, D. W. 1961. Biology of spermatozoa. In *Sex and Internal Secretions*, 3rd ed. (W. C. Young, ed.). Williams & Wilkins, Baltimore, pp. 707–796.

Bishop, D. W. 1967. Significance of testicular sorbitol dehydrogenase (SDH). *J. Gen. Physiol.*, **50**: 2504.

Bishop, D. W., and G. L. Carlson. 1965. Immunologically induced aspermatogenesis in guinea pigs. *Ann. N.Y. Acad. Sci.*, **124**: 247–266.

Bishop, D. W., W. W. Schrank, A. D. Musselman, and E. C. Muecke. 1967.

Testis sorbitol dehydrogenase (SDH) and activity changes during induced aspermatogenesis and cryptorchidism. *Federation Proc.*, 26: 646 (Abstr.).

Blackshaw, A. W., and J. I. Samisoni. 1967. Histochemical localization of some dehydrogenase enzymes in the bull testis and epididymis. *J. Dairy Sci.*, 50: 747–752.

Blanco, A., and W. H. Zinkham. 1963. Lactate dehydrogenase in human testes. *Science*, 139: 601–602.

Blanco, A., W. H. Zinkham, and L. Kupchyk. 1964. Genetic control and ontogeny of lactate dehydrogenase in pigeon testes. *J. Exptl. Zool.*, 156: 137–152.

Burgos, M. H. 1955. Histochemistry of the testis in normal experimentally treated frogs (*Rana pipiens*). *J. Morphol.*, 96: 283–299.

Cahn, R. D., N. O. Kaplan, L. Levine, and E. Zwilling. 1962. Nature and development of lactic dehydrogenases. *Science*, 136: 962–969.

Champy, C. 1920. De la méthode de culture des tissus: VI. Le testicule. *Arch. Zool. Exptl. Gén.*, 60: 461–500.

Chandley, A. C., and A. J. Bateman. 1962. Timing of spermatogenesis in *Drosophila melanogaster* using tritiated thymidine. *Nature*, 193: 299–300.

Clermont, Y. 1960. Cycle of the seminiferous epithelium of the guinea pig. *Fertil. Steril.*, 11: 563–573.

Clermont, Y. 1962. Quantitative analysis of spermatogenesis of the rat: A revised model for the renewal of spermatogonia. *Am. J. Anat.*, 111: 116–129.

Clermont, Y. 1966. Spermatogenesis in man: A study of the spermatogonial population. *Fertil. Steril.*, 17: 705–721.

Clermont, Y., and B. Perey. 1957. The stages of the cycle of the seminiferous epithelium of the rat: Practical definitions in PA-Schiff-hematoxylin and hematoxylin-eosin stained sections. *Rev. Can. Biol.*, 16: 451–462.

Dan, J. C. 1967. Acrosome reaction and lysins. In *Fertilization*, Vol. I (C. B. Metz and A. Monroy, eds.), Academic Press, New York, pp. 237–293.

Dorfman, R. I., K. M. J. Menon, D. C. Sharma, S. Joshi, and E. Forchielli. 1967. Steroid hormone biosynthesis in rat, rabbit, and capuchine testis. In *Endocrinology of the Testis* (G. E. W. Wolstenholme and M. O'Conner, eds.) Little, Brown, Boston, pp. 91–101.

Drobeck, H. P., and F. Coulston. 1962. Inhibition and recovery of spermatogenesis in rats, monkeys, and dogs medicated with bis(dichloroacetyl)-diamines. *Exptl. Mol. Pathol.*, 1: 251–274.

Eik-Nes, K. B. 1964. Effects of gonadotrophins on secretion of steroids by the testis and ovary. *Physiol. Rev.*, 44: 609–630.

Ernster, L. 1959. Distribution and interaction of enzymes within animal cells. *Biochem. Soc. Symp.*, 16: 54–71.

Featherstone, R. M., W. O. Nelson, F. Weldon, E. Marberger, A. Boccabella, and R. Boccabella. 1955. Pyruvate oxidation in testicular tissues during Furadroxyl-induced spermatogenic arrest. *Endocrinology*, 56: 727–736.

Firlit, C. F., and J. R. Davis. 1966. Radio-autographic incorporation of L-lysine-^{3}H into protein of cells of the germinal epithelium in cryptorchidism. *J. Reprod. Fertil.*, 11: 125–131.

Ford, E., and C. Huggins. 1963. Selective destruction in testis induced by 7,12-dimethylbenz[a]anthracene. *J. Exptl. Med.*, 118: 27–40.

Fox, B. W., and M. Fox. 1967. Biochemical aspects of the actions of drugs on spermatogenesis. *Pharmacol. Rev.*, 19: 21–57.

Fox, B. W., and H. Jackson. 1965. In vivo effects of methylene dimethanesulphonate on proliferating cell systems. *Brit. J. Pharmacol.*, 24: 24–28.

Goldberg, E. 1963. Lactic and malic dehydrogenases in human spermatozoa. *Science*, **139:** 602–603.

Goldberg, E., and C. Hawtrey. 1967. The ontogeny of sperm specific lactate dehydrogenase in mice. *J. Exptl. Zool.*, **164:** 309–316.

Goldschmidt, R. 1915. Some experiments on spermatogenesis in vitro. *Proc. Natl. Acad. Sci.*, **1:** 220–222.

Grant, J. K., K. Griffiths, and C. G. Pierrepoint. 1967. Steroid biosynthesis in abnormal testes. In *Endocrinology of the Testis* (G. E. W. Wolstenholme and M. O'Conner, eds.), Little, Brown, Boston, pp. 280–295.

Gupta, B. L., and V. P. Kamboj. 1962. Histochemical localization of succinic dehydrogenase activity in the mitochondria of some invertebrate spermatozoa. *Nature*, **193:** 788–789.

Haffen, K. 1960. La culture in vitro de l'épithélium germinatif isolé des gonades mâles et femelles de l'ambryon de Canard: II. Influence de la médullaire sur la différenciation de l'épithélium germinatif. *J. Embryol. Exptl. Morphol.*, **8:** 414–424.

Heller, C. G., and Y. Clermont. 1964. Kinetics of the germinal epithelium in man. *Recent Progr. Hormone Res.*, **20:** 545–571.

Hrudka, F. 1965. Cytochemical demonstration of catabolic activity in spermatozoa by the formazan test. *J. Reprod. Fertil.*, **10:** 15–20.

Jirásek, J. E., and J. Raboch. 1963. Histochemical study of testicular material from patients with various disorders. *Fertil. Steril.*, **14:** 237–245.

Kaplan, N. O., and M. M. Ciotti. 1961. Evolution and differentiation of dehydrogenases. *Ann. N.Y. Acad. Sci.*, **94:** 701–722.

Katzen, H. M. 1967. The multiple forms of mammalian hexokinase and their significance to the action of insulin. *Advan. Enzyme Regulat.*, **5:** 335–356.

King, T. E., and T. Mann. 1958. Sorbitol dehydrogenase in spermatozoa. *Nature*, **182:** 868–869.

King, T. E., and T. Mann. 1959. Sorbitol metabolism in spermatozoa. *Proc. Roy. Soc. (London)*, **B151:** 226–243.

Koudstaal, J., E. L. Frensdorf, J. Kremer, J. M. Mudde, and M. J. Hardonk. 1967. The histochemical pattern of the human adult testis. *Acta Endocrinol.*, **55:** 415–426.

Leblond, C. P., and Y. Clermont. 1952. Spermiogenesis of rat, mouse, hamster and guinea pig as revealed by the "periodic acid-fuchsin sulfurous acid" technique. *Am. J. Anat.*, **90:** 167–215.

Lewis, M. R., and W. R. B. Robertson. 1916. The mitochondria and other structures observed by the tissue culture method in the male germ cells of *Chorthippus curtipennis* Scudd. *Biol. Bull.*, **30:** 99–125.

Libby, P. R. 1962. Studies on the enzymatic oxidation of polyhydric alcohols. University of Chicago dissertation, Chicago, Ill.

Lindsay, D. T. 1963. Isozymic patterns and properties of lactate dehydrogenase from developing tissues of the chicken. *J. Exptl. Zool.*, **152:** 75–89.

Mancini, R. E., J. Nolazco, and F. A. de la Balze. 1952. Histochemical study of normal adult human testis. *Anat. Rec.*, **114:** 127–147.

Mancini, R. E., A. Alonso, J. Barquet, B. Alvarez, and M. Nemirovsky. 1964. Histo-immunological localization of hyaluronidase in the bull testis. *J. Reprod. Fertil.*, **8:** 325–330.

Mann, T. 1964. *The Biochemistry of Semen and of the Male Reproductive Tract.* Methuen, London.

Mann, T. 1967. Sperm metabolism. In *Fertilization,* Vol. I (C. B. Metz and A. Monroy, eds.), Academic Press, New York, pp. 99–116.

Markert, C. L. 1963. Epigenetic control of specific protein synthesis in differentiating cells. In *Cytodifferential and Macromolecular Synthesis* (M. Locke, ed.), Academic Press, New York, pp. 65–84.

Markert, C. L. 1964. Cellular differentiation—an expression of differential gene function. *Second International Conference on Congenital Malformations.* International Medical Congress Ltd., New York, pp. 163–174.

Markert, C. L., and E. Appella. 1961. Physicochemical nature of isozymes. *Ann. N.Y. Acad. Sci.,* **94:** 678–690.

Markert, C. L., and E. Appella. 1963. Immunochemical properties of lactate dehydrogenase isozymes. *Ann. N.Y. Acad. Sci.,* **103:** 915–928.

Markert, C. L., and F. Møller. 1959. Multiple forms of enzymes: Tissue ontogenetic and species specific patterns. *Proc. Natl. Sci.,* **45:** 753–763.

Markert, C. L., and H. Ursprung. 1962. The ontogeny of isozyme patterns of lactate dehydrogenase in the mouse. *Develop. Biol.,* **5:** 363–381.

Meyer, J., and J. P. Weinmann. 1957. Phosphamidase activity during spermatogenesis in the rat. *Am. J. Anat.,* **101:** 461–476.

Mietkiewski, K., and A. Lukaszyk. 1966. Nachweis der α-Glycerophosphatdehydrogenaseaktivität während der Spermiogenese im Rattenhoden. *Histochemie,* **7:** 28–38.

Monesi, V. 1962. Autoradiographic study of DNA synthesis and the cell cycle in spermatogonia and spermatocytes of mouse testis using tritiated thymidine. *J. Cell Biol.,* **14:** 1–18.

Montagna, W. 1952. The distribution of lipids, glycogen, and phosphatases in the human testis. *Fertil. Steril.,* **3:** 27–32.

Moore, C. R. 1927. A qualitative indicator for the testis hormone. *Proc. Soc. Exptl. Biol. Med.,* **24:** 847–848.

Moree, R. 1947. The normal spermatogenic wave-cycle in Peromyscus. *Anat. Rec.,* **99:** 163–176.

Muckenthaler, F. A. 1964. Autoradiographic study of nucleic acid synthesis during spermatogenesis in the grasshopper, *Melanoplus differentialis. Exptl. Cell Res.,* **35:** 531–547.

Murray, R. F., and J. A. Ball. 1967. Testis-specific and sex-associated hexokinases in *Drosophila melanogaster. Science,* **156:** 81–82.

Nelson, L. 1967. Sperm motility. In *Fertilization,* Vol. I (C. B. Metz and A. Monroy, eds.), Academic Press, New York, pp. 27–97.

Niemi, M., and M. Kormano. 1964. Nucleoside diphosphatase activity of germ cells during the cycle of the seminiferous epithelium in the rat testis. *Exptl. Cell Res.,* **35:** 197–200.

Niemi, M., and M. Kormano. 1965. Cyclical changes in and significance of lipids and acid phosphatase activity in the seminiferous tubules of the rat testis. *Anat. Rec.,* **151:** 159–170.

Novikoff, A. B. 1960. Biochemical and staining reactions of cytoplasmic constituents. In *Developing Cell Systems and Their Control* (D. Rudnick, ed.), Ronald Press, New York, pp. 167–203.

Pósalaky, Z., A. Gyévai, and B. Bukulya. 1961. Contributions to the mechanism of spermatogenesis, on the basis of studies of the acid-fast staining, succinic dehydrogenase activity and histochemical examination of lipids. *Acta Morphol. Acad. Sci. Hung.,* **10:** 137–152.

Roosen-Runge, E. C., and F. D. Barlow. 1953. Quantitative studies on human spermatogenesis: I. Spermatogonia. *Am. J. Anat.*, **93**: 143–169.

Roosen-Runge, E. C., and L. O. Giesel, Jr. 1950. Quantitative studies on spermatogenesis in the albino rat. *Am. J. Anat.*, **87**: 1–30.

Schenkman, J. B., D. A. Richert, and W. W. Westerfeld. 1965. α-Glycerophosphate dehydrogenase activity in rat spermatozoa. *Endocrinology*, **76**: 1055–1061.

Schneiderman, H. A., M. Ketchel, and C. M. Williams. 1953. The physiology of insect diapause: VI. Effects of temperature, oxygen tension, and metabolic inhibitors on in vitro spermatogenesis in the Cecropia silkworm. *Biol. Bull.*, **105**: 188–199.

Stallcup, O. T., and J. D. Roussel. 1965. Development of the lactic dehydrogenase enzyme system in the testes and epididymis of young dairy bulls. *J. Dairy Sci.*, **48**: 1511–1516.

Stambaugh, R., and J. Buckley. 1967. The enzymic and molecular nature of the lactic dehydrogenase subbands and X_4 isozyme. *J. Biol. Chem.*, **242**: 4053–4059.

Steinberger, A., and E. Steinberger. 1967. Factors affecting spermatogenesis in organ cultures of mammalian testes. *J. Reprod. Fertil.*, (Suppl. 2) 117–123.

Steinberger, E. 1962. A quantitative study of the effect of an alkylating agent (triethylenemelamine) on the seminiferous epithelium of rats. *J. Reprod. Fertil.*, **3**: 250–259.

Stone, C. P. 1924. The awakening of copulatory ability in the male albino rat. *Am. J. Physiol.*, **68**: 407–424.

Tice, L. W., and R. J. Barrnett. 1963. The fine structural localization of some testicular phosphatases. *Anat. Rec.*, **147**: 43–63.

Touster, O., and D. R. D. Shaw. 1962. Biochemistry of the acyclic polyols. *Physiol. Rev.*, **42**: 181–225.

Walker, D. G., and A. M. Seligman. 1963. The use of formalin fixation in the cytochemical demonstrations of succinic and DPN- and TPN-dependent dehydrogenases in mitochondria. *J. Cell Biol.*, **16**: 455–469.

Webster, R. C., and W. C. Young. 1951. Adolescent sterility in the male guinea pig. *Fertil. Steril.*, **2**: 175–181.

Williams-Ashman, H. G. 1963. Personal communication.

Wislocki, G. B. 1949. Seasonal changes in the testes, epididymides and seminal vesicles of deer investigated by histochemical methods. *Endocrinology*, **44**: 167–189.

Wolff, E., and K. Haffen. 1965. Germ cells and gonads. In *Cells and Tissues in Culture*, Vol. II (E. N. Willmer, ed.), Academic Press, New York, pp. 697–743.

Yamane, J. 1956. The primary significance of testicular hyaluronidase for fertilization in mammals. *Proceedings of the Third International Congress on Animal Reproduction*, Cambridge University Press, New York, pp. 70–72.

Young, W. C. 1964. The hormones and behavior. In *Comparative Biochemistry*, Suppl. Vol. VII (M. Florkin and H. S. Mason, eds.), Academic Press, New York, pp. 203–251.

Zinkham, W. H., A. Blanco, and L. J. Clowry, Jr. 1964. An unusual isozyme of lactate dehydrogenase in mature testes: Localization, ontogeny, and kinetic properties. *Ann. N.Y. Acad. Sci.*, **121**: 571–588.

Zinkham, W. H., A. Blanco, and L. Kupchyk. 1966. Isozymes: Biological and clinical significance. *Pediatrics*, **37**: 120–131.

REPRODUCTION AND SEXUAL BEHAVIOR (M. Diamond ed.), 287–302, © Indiana University Press

19

Brain Investigation Techniques in the Study of Reproduction and Sex Behavior

Robert D. Lisk

Regulation is a function which occurs at all levels of organization. Specifically in reference to control of reproduction, one finds that throughout vertebrate history three classes of stimuli are of basic importance: (1) stimuli for induction of gamete development (usually a seasonal phenomenon); (2) stimuli to initiate appropriate behavior patterns between male and female, either to synchronize release of gametes or to effect internal fertilization; and (3) stimuli to induce care and feeding of the young.

All three classes of stimuli, whether between environment and animal or animal–animal interactions, require the central nervous system for specific recognition of the signal and for organization of a response. The question then becomes how one can determine which regions of the nervous system are necessary for the various aspects of reproduction.

A variety of techniques have been used to obtain information about localization of function in the central nervous system. Those which have proved most useful may be classified under three headings: lesioning, stimulation, and recording. Reference will be made to the major variations in each technique as presently employed. Whenever possible, discussion will include the question that was asked by the investigator who employed the technique. These questions may prove useful to a future investigator in evaluating the various techniques that might apply to new problems he has in mind.

Lesioning

Localized damage to the nervous system can be accomplished in a wide variety of ways. Some variation of this technique has been and still is, by far, the most popular approach to localization of function. For many years only the surface of the brain was available for mapping because no method was known for destroying deep structures while leaving the surface intact. Ablation of various-sized areas of the surface was usually accomplished by gentle suction. Studies of this type showed that the cortex was not essential for continuance of the reproductive cycle and mating behavior in the female [cat (Bard, 1939), rabbit (Brooks, 1937), rat (Davis, 1939)]. The early studies of Beach and his colleagues indicated that the cortex was important for expression of the copulatory pattern in the male (Beach, 1940). However, in the rat no specific area was found; it appeared to be a mass effect. Reexamination of this problem (again using suction for ablation) indicated the motor sensory and sensory motor areas were important (Larsson, 1962, 1964). A similar relationship holds in other species which have been investigated (Beach et al., 1955, 1956; Zitrin et al., 1956).

Accurate and systematic investigation of deep brain structures was frustrated until the development of the stereotaxic apparatus by Horsley and Clarke (1908). This has undoubtedly been the most important piece of instrumentation for brain research. The apparatus consists essentially of a head holder which allows rigid fixing of an animal's head in the same planes in space each time it is secured in the machine. The head holder is attached to a rigid framework which runs along both sides of the head. Micromanipulators can be placed on this framework and probes of various types attached to the end of the manipulators. An anterior–posterior scale on the framework plus horizontal and vertical scales on the micromanipulators allow one to place a probe in some known structure in the brain and to record its position using the readings on the three scales. By repeating this operation for various landmarks in the brain, one can prepare a map in stereotaxic coordinates for any animal of interest. Since the head of the animal is always held in the same way, a map once prepared should be accurate for all individuals of that species within a certain size range. In 1946 Krieg published details for a stereotaxic instrument plus an atlas for the rat's brain. Today there are a variety of these instruments commercially available. However, anyone with a little ingenuity can make his own instrument for use with small animals. An ingenious design to use the microscope as a stereotaxic instrument has been published by Barry et al. (1963).

Employing the stereotaxic instrument, probes of various types have been inserted to produce destruction of localized regions deep in the brain while producing minimum damage to surface structures. Destruction by electrolysis is probably the most common method. Direct current is passed through an electrode, usually constructed of stainless steel, which is insulated with varnish except at the tip, where the varnish is scraped off for about ½ mm. The circuit is completed by a large metal electrode placed outside the cranial cavity, usually in the anus. Destruction of brain tissue results from several factors—electrolysis, coagulation from the heat developed, and mechanically from the gas discharged during electrolysis. Repeated experience suggests that the electrode in the brain should be connected to the anode, since a smaller volume of gas seems to be produced and a narrower zone of edema occurs. This allows the production of smaller and more uniform lesions.

Use of this technique has provided important information on a series of questions concerning reproductive function. Does the brain regulate function in the pituitary–gonad axis in relation to maintenance of the reproductive tract and ovulation? Is sexual maturation regulated by the brain? What regions of the brain effect copulatory activity in the male and female?

As early as the 1920s reports appeared which suggested that lesions in the hypothalamus may produce genital atrophy (Bailey and Bremer, 1921; Smith, 1927). Fisher et al. (1938) observed that female cats suffering from diabetes insipidus as a result of lesions in the hypothalamus–hypophysial tract never bred in the laboratory. This observation led to a thorough investigation by Dey and his colleagues of the effects of various hypothalamic lesions on reproduction in the guinea pig (Dey, et al., 1940; Dey, 1941, 1943). Animals with lesions in the median eminence became acyclic and genital atrophy ensued. Animals with lesions at the caudal edge of the optic chiasma had hypertrophied genital organs and a permanently open vagina. Gonadal atrophy following lesions of the median eminence has been confirmed for many animals, i.e., in female rats (D'Angelo, 1959; Cook, 1959; Flerkó and Bárdos, 1959), in female cats (Laqueur et al., 1955), in female rabbits (Flerkó, 1953), in male rats (Mess, 1952; Bogdanove and Halmi, 1953), in dogs (Daily and Ganong, 1958; Davidson and Ganong, 1960), and in the duck (Benoit and Assenmacher, 1955).

The early work of Dey and co-workers (see above) plus experiments by Hillarp (1949) demonstrated that lesions in the anterior hypothalamus block ovulation and lead to a state of constant estrus. These findings have been confirmed by many laboratories (Greer 1953; Barrnett and Mayer, 1954; Alloiteau, 1954, among others).

Animals of species in which ovulation is a reflex event initiated by coitus, as in the rabbit, may also be blocked from ovulating by hypothalamic lesions (Sawyer, 1959).

A current question of interest is how the brain regulates sexual maturation. This question has been studied by a number of laboratories using the rat (Donovan and van der Werff ten Bosch, 1956, 1959a; Bogdanove and Schoen, 1959; Elwers and Critchlow, 1960; Corbin and Schottelius, 1960; Gellert and Ganong, 1960). All these experiments produced a syndrome that has been labeled precocious puberty. A related question which has received little attention is: What stimuli initiate the breeding season? The work of Rowan (1925) showed that in the junco the length of the photoperiod was a primary stimulus for gonad development. The generality of this observation was provided from observations on numerous birds and mammals (Hammond, 1954). In a brilliant series of experiments extending from the 1930s, Benoit and his colleagues showed that, in the drake, light exerts a direct action on the hypothalamus in regulating gonad growth (Benoit, 1961). These results need to be confirmed and extended to other species. Many seasonally breeding mammals employ light stimuli for initiation of the breeding season. The eye is thought to be essential for this purpose. However, in the ferret— also a seasonally breeding mammal—Donovan and van der Werff ten Bosch (1959b) found that lesions in the anterior hypothalamus would advance the annual breeding season.

Reduced levels of sex behavior or its complete disappearance has been observed following lesions in the anterior hypothalamus of both male and female. This was first observed in male guinea pigs by Brookhart and Dey (1941), in the male rat by Soulairac (1963) and Larsson and Heimer (1964), and in the male guinea pig by Phoenix (1961). Following such lesions the reproductive tract remains normal. One can give hormone treatment, yet mating does not occur. Recent studies indicated that lesions made at the ventral border of diencephalon and mesencephalon can result in an increased sex drive in the male rat (Heimer and Larsson, 1964; Lisk, 1966a, 1966b).

Lesions in the preoptic–anterior hypothalamic region of the female have also been reported to interfere with mating [cats (Fisher et al., 1938; Sawyer and Robison, 1956), guinea pig (Brookhart et al., 1940; Dey et al., 1942), rat (Clark, 1942), ewe (Clegg et al., 1958)]. In the rabbit lesions in the premammillary area suppress mating (Sawyer, 1959). Lesions in other parts of the midbrain limbic system have resulted in appearance of mating at times other than estrus, i.e., diestrus (Law and Meagher, 1958), during pregnancy (de Groot, 1962), and following castration (Goy and Phoenix, 1963).

Recently radiofrequencies have proved popular for production of brain lesions. This has been partially due to discrepancies in results following use of stainless-steel electrodes and electrolytic lesioning in various laboratories. These will be discussed under stimulation techniques. When radiofrequencies are employed, one must use a pair of electrodes placed close together. The radiofrequency produces a purely thermal lesion with the extent of damage being related to the total energy employed.

As an alternative to stainless-steel electrodes one can use 90 percent platinum–10 percent iridium wire which is insulated by glass capillary tubing. The lack of enthusiasm for this electrode is probably related both to its expense and fragility.

Focused ultrasound is now being employed in a number of laboratories for localized lesioning of deep structures. Its advantage is that no electrode tract extends through the brain. Theoretically damage occurs only where the two beams of ultrasound interact to destroy the tissue. At the present time a room full of equipment is required; thus until some technological breakthrough is achieved, this technique will only be available in the million dollar laboratory. For general review and application see Kelly (1957) and Young and Lebe (1964).

Lesions have been made following implantation of a trocar and extrusion from its end of some chemical causing necrosis, or by radon seeds which gradually destroy a region of tissue, the radius depending on the specific activity (Larsson et al., 1958; Leksell et al., 1960).

Microknives, which are inserted through a trocar, have been designed in a number of laboratories. These knives allow one to isolate an island of nervous tissue and leave it in situ or to sever specific sets of connections to a region of the brain (Halász and Pupp, 1965; de Groot, 1962).

The rationale of many investigators seems to imply that the hypothalamus is all-important for regulation of reproduction. Use of the microknife has allowed the investigator to ask: Will reproduction proceed normally if the hypothalamus is isolated from its connections with the rest of the brain? If reproduction does not proceed normally, where are the signals coming from which are essential to normal reproduction?

The experiments of Halász and co-workers have shown that the endocrine system appears relatively normal when the hypothalamus is isolated, but ovulation does not occur. Further experiments indicated that the signals essential for ovulation entered the hypothalamus only from the anterior end (Halász and Pupp, 1965; Halász and Gorski, 1966).

Stimulation

It was early recognized that the nervous system produced electrical discharges. Furthermore, the nerve impulse was identifiable as an electrical change. This fact probably accounts for the popularity of using electrical stimulation to decipher function of various regions in the brain. Although the technique appeared to have great promise, it has proved very difficult to repeatedly elicit any complex response from an organism as a result of electrical stimulation.

The stimulus parameters are exceedingly important, as responses are usually obtained within rather narrow ranges of current strength, repetition rate, and duration of the stimulus.

An early interest was shown in the mechanism of reflex ovulation. This is peculiar to the rabbit and members of the cat family plus a few other species. In these animals ovulation normally only occurs as a consequence of copulation. If this could be produced by localized electrical stimulation to the brain, it might be possible to isolate the neural mechanism involved.

Harris (1937) reported the first success at eliciting ovulation in the rabbit from localized electrical stimulation. Similar findings were reported by Haterius and Derbyshire (1937) and Markee et al. (1946). Recent studies from Sawyer's laboratory indicate that sites throughout the basal diencephalon from medial preoptic to the tuberal region will result in ovulation both in rabbit and cat (Sawyer, 1959) (see Chapter 3).

Following blockage of spontaneous ovulation in the rat, using pentobarbital, Critchlow (1958) reported induction of ovulation by electrical stimulation to the hypothalamus. Everett and co-workers have made careful studies concerning the effects of electrical stimulation on ovulation in the rat. They found that the electrical stimulation they had been applying to the preoptic anterior hypothalamic region only produced ovulation when electrodes made with ferrous metals were employed. Close examination showed that during stimulation metallic ions were being deposited and a lesion formed. Production of a similar-sized lesion by electrolysis using platinum electrodes or by radiofrequency did not result in ovulation. Subsequently, it was found that microinjection of 5 percent ferric chloride alone, into this brain region, would produce ovulation (Everett and Radford, 1961; Everett et al., 1964; Everett, 1964) (see Chapter 4).

The iron electrode is thought to be effective by production of an irritative zone around the edge of the lesion, which results in continued nervous activity perhaps for hours. Investigations of feeding behavior by Reynolds (1963) appear to confirm this view. Electrolytic destruction of the ventromedial nuclei in rats using ferrous metals and electrolysis led to viciousness and hyperphagia. Lesions of similar size produced by radiofrequency did not produce these results.

These experiments suggest that observations made on animals bearing lesions produced by iron electrodes, used with direct current stimulators, may be in need of reinterpretation. Findings may be the result of a destruction of tissue or due to an irritative focus at the periphery of destruction.

Recent studies with the rat, using platinum electrodes, indicate that when the appropriate stimulus parameters are employed ovulation can be evoked from electrical stimulation to preoptic and anterior hypothalamus (Everett, 1965).

A number of workers have attempted to map brain regions involved in sexual functions by use of electrical stimulation. MacLean and co-workers at the National Institutes of Health have been able to trace pathways both for penile erection and for ejaculation in the squirrel monkey (MacLean and Ploog, 1962; MacLean, 1962; MacLean et al., 1963). Working with the rat Vaughan and Fisher (1962) had three subjects which showed complete male copulatory patterns following electrical stimulation to the anterior hypothalamus. However, 30 other animals showed no response. Herberg (1963) found that electrical programmed stimulation or self-stimulation in the area of the lateral mammillary nucleus in the male rat would produce ejaculation. Caggiula and Hoebel (1966) have confirmed this and further find they can get stimulus bound copulation from this region. For a general review of self-stimulation as a technique for unraveling brain function, see Olds (1962).

A lesion is irreparable, since nervous tissue has little or no power for regeneration. One can, however, block the functioning of a region by suitable chemical application. As soon as the chemical is removed or its effect has worn off, normal activity is again possible. A favored recipe for suppression of surface structures is application of 25 percent KCl by placing a pledget of cotton soaked with this solution on the area of interest. Larsson has used this technique to study the relevance of various areas of the cortex to mating behavior in both male and female rats (Larsson, 1962).

Localized application of neural depressants or anesthetizing agents does not appear to have been applied to deep structures in the brain in order to map circuits related to sex behavior. However, this technique has been used quite successfully for tracing circuitry involved in eating and drinking behavior (Epstein, 1960). Another promising approach is local application of neural transmitters or substances known to antagonize these transmitters. Using such techniques circuits related to eating and drinking have been traced (Grossman, 1960; Fisher and Coury, 1962; Levitt and Fisher, 1966). Since some of these agents come in crystalline form, it is a relatively simple experiment to make local application of a test substance. One needs only to stereotaxically implant a concentric double-barreled cannula in which the outer barrel is fastened to the skull. The inner barrel can then be removed and a few crystals of the test substance tamped into its end. It can be lowered into place once again and the behavior of the animal observed. This approach may prove particularly fruitful in tracing circuits which appear to act in an inhibitory manner to control the level of sex drive in the male or, in the female, to lock receptivity to the estrous phase of the cycle.

Implantation of fine capillary tubes bearing at their tips some crystalline sex steroids has proved an effective technique for determining neural areas involved in detection of hormone levels in relation to regulation of both the pituitary–gonad axis and sex behavior. In all species studied, two separate hormone sensitive systems have been detected. The one regulating the pituitary–gonad axis appears localized in the median eminence region [rat (Lisk, 1960, 1962a), dog (Davidson and Sawyer, 1961a), rabbit (Davidson and Sawyer, 1961b), lizard (Lisk, 1967a)]. Sex behavior appears to operate through a hormone-sensitive neural link localized in the preoptic–anterior hypothalamus in the rat (Lisk, 1962b, 1966c; 1967b; Lisk and Suydam, 1967; Davidson, 1966), cat (Sawyer, 1963; Harris and Michael, 1964; Michael, 1965a), and bird (Barfield, 1964, 1965), while the premammillary region is implicated in the rabbit (Palka and Sawyer, 1966). The results from hormone implant studies have been in remarkable agreement with the earlier observations from the lesion work.

Recording

The female sexual response is a passive presentation, and no one seems to have attempted to produce this posture by electrical stimulation. Rather the questions asked are: Do specific changes in brain activity occur which are associated with estrus or copulation? Do sex hormones influence the activity in any neural pathways? The first question has been explored by implantation of gross electrodes in various regions of the brain. These may be unipolar, in which case they resemble a probe used for lesioning. A reference electrode must be placed somewhere outside the brain. More often they are concentric, bipolar electrodes which only monitor the potential difference between the two tips. Such electrodes may be implanted chronically. The two poles of the bipolar electrode must be made of similar metal to avoid setting up a battery. The output from these electrodes is fed into sensitive galvanometers which are attached to pens resting on a roll of moving paper. The ever-changing electrical potentials in the brain result in the pens tracing squiggly lines on the paper. This is the electroencephalograph (EEG).

Using this technique Porter et al. (1957) showed that in the female cat real or simulated copulation resulted in a characteristic EEG recording from electrodes in the anterior lateral hypothalamus. Similarly, changes were found in the anterior hypothalamus of the rabbit (Green, 1954) and rat (Barraclough, 1960) in relation to mating. An ingenious series of experiments by Kawakami and Sawyer (1959) indicated that hormones probably produce complex changes in many regions of the brain. Furthermore, the effects are time-related. The same material may produce a biphasic response, the particular pattern observed being dependent upon time elapsed since hormone treatment.

Circuitry within the nervous system may be traced plus changes in the circuit evaluated by use of the evoked potential technique. In this case a signal of known parameters is inserted at one point in the circuit while the activity resulting at a further point, due to the signal, is monitored. Since random activity is occurring at all times, one requires averaging equipment such as the computer of average transients for this type of study. This technique is useful for study of conduction time and volume of conduction over a particular pathway. Modification of these parameters by hormones, light cycles, or time of day would aid our understanding of neuroendocrine regulation. So far, few studies of relevance to reproduction have been attempted. For general background see reviews by John et al. (1964) and Uttal (1965).

Following detection of regions of importance for endocrine regulation, a few workers have begun the search for neural units within these regions which show specific responses to hormones or environmental influences (see Cross and Silver, 1966, for review).

The brain is assuredly our most complex and least understood organ. If the same result can be produced by a number of different experimental manipulations, one can feel much more confidence in the validity of a finding. Thus whenever possible double-checking by different techniques is certainly desirable. It is possible to design multiple purpose probes for use both in electrical and chemical stimulation (Hoebel, 1964).

There are certainly few techniques which have led to more controversy than that found in the vast literature based on variations of lesioning. This does not mean the technique is of no value today. Certainly all the techniques mentioned here have great value for the future. Although the evidence is only as strong as the tools used for gathering it, still, the most exciting evidence will be produced only by the investigator who makes the effort to construct the best hypothesis in the light of what appears to be known and then attempts to verify his hypothesis by utilizing the variety of techniques at his disposal.

One further technique seems very promising and that is the uptake of substances by specific neurons. The trick here is to have some method of visualizing the substance so that localization is possible. One chemical, gold thioglucose, appears to have a selective affinity for certain cell groups in the hypothalamus and certain other regions of the brain. Depending on the quantity given, this material destroys the cells and one finds lesions at autopsy (Liebelt and Perry, 1957; Perry and Liebelt, 1961; Deter and Liebelt, 1964).

When it became evident that hormones were exerting many of their regulatory influences at the level of the brain, injection of steroids containing a ^{14}C or ^{3}H label were made. Autoradiographs were prepared from the sectioned brain tissue to determine whether the hormone did indeed get into the brain, its distribution, and the time course of appearance and removal. The work of Michael (1962, 1965b) has helped clarify which cells accumulate estrogen and the time course of this accumulation in relation to the appearance of estrous behavior.

Such techniques hold great promise for the problem of unraveling the sites of the specific neurons which react with, and therefore are probably important in monitoring hormones. Time-course studies make it theoretically possible to study interrelationships between time of hormone application and appearance of measurable physiological or behavioral responses.

At the outset I listed three fundamental classes of stimuli basic to regulation of reproduction in the vertebrates. No mention was made of the class "parent–young interactions" during the discussion and very little of the "environment–animal" class. What little information we have deals almost entirely with the internal regulatory system of a single animal except for some data on interactions with respect to sex behavior. Furthermore, most of this information concerns the laboratory rat, cat, or rabbit. The tools are available; with a little imagination many exciting discoveries might be made if only the horizons are expanded to include a bit more of the animal kingdom.

References

Alloiteau, J. J. 1954. Effets de doses minimes de progestérone sur l'oestrus permanent consécutif à des lésions hypothalamiques chez la ratte. *Compt. Rend. Soc. Biol.*, **148**: 223–226.

Bailey, P., and F. Bremer. 1921. Experimental diabetes insipidus. *Arch. Internal Med.*, **28**: 773–803.

Bard, P. 1939. Central nervous mechanisms for emotional behavior patterns in animals. *Res. Publ. Assoc. Res. Nervous Mental Disease*, **19**: 190–218.

Barfield, R. J. 1964. Induction of copulatory behavior by intracranial placement of androgen in capons. *Am. Zoologist*, **4**: 301.

Barfield, R. J. 1965. Induction of aggressive and courtship behavior by intra-cerebral implants of androgen in capons. *Am. Zoologist*, **5**: 203.

Barraclough, C. A. 1900. Hypothalamic activation associated with stimulation of the vaginal cervix of proestrus rats. *Anat. Rec.*, **136**: 159.

Barrnett, R. J., and J. Mayer. 1954. Endocrine effects of hypothalamic lesions. *Anat. Rec.*, **118**: 374–375.

Barry, T. J., W. D. Hagamen, and J. E. Sherlock. 1963. Microscope as a stereotaxic instrument for the rat. *J. Appl. Physiol.*, **18**: 445–446.

Beach, F. A. 1940. Effects of cortical lesions upon the copulatory behavior of male rats. *J. Comp. Psychol.*, **29**: 193–239.

Beach, F. A., A. Zitrin, and J. Jaynes. 1955. Neural mediation of mating behavior in male cats II. Contribution of the frontal cortex. *J. Exptl. Zool.*, **130**: 381–401.

Beach, F. A., A. Zitrin, and J. Jaynes. 1956. Neural mediation of mating in male cats. I. Effects of unilateral and bilateral removal of the neocortex. *J. Comp. Physiol. Psychol.*, **49**: 321–327.

Benoit, J. 1961. Opto-sexual reflex in the duck: Physiological and histological aspects. *Yale J. Biol. Med.*, **34**: 97–116.

Benoit, J., and I. Assenmacher. 1955. Le contrôle hypothalamique de l'activité préhypophysaire gonadotrope. *J. Physiol. (Paris)*, **47**: 527–567.

Bogdanove, E. M., and N. S. Halmi. 1953. Effects of hypothalamic lesions and subsequent propylthiouracil treatment on pituitary structure and function in the rat. *Endocrinology,* **53:** 274–292.

Bogdanove, E. M., and H. C. Schoen. 1959. Precocious sexual development in female rats with hypothalamic lesions. *Proc. Soc. Exptl. Biol.,* **100:** 664–669.

Brookhart, J. M., and F. L. Dey. 1941. Reduction of sexual behavior in male guinea pigs by hypothalamic lesions. *Am. J. Physiol.,* **133:** 551–554.

Brookhart, J. M., F. L. Dey, and S. W. Ranson. 1940. Failure of ovarian hormones to cause mating reactions in spayed guinea pigs with hypothalamic lesions. *Proc. Soc. Exptl. Biol. Med.,* **44:** 61–64.

Brooks, C. M. 1937. The role of the central cortex and of various sense organs in the excitation and execution of mating activity in the rabbit. *Am. J. Physiol.,* **120:** 544–553.

Caggiula, A. R., and B. G. Hoebel. 1966. "Copulation-Reward Site" in the posterior hypothalamus. *Science,* **153:** 1284–1285.

Clark, G. 1942. Sexual behavior in rats with lesions in the anterior hypothalamus. *Am. J. Physiol.,* **137:** 746–749.

Clegg, M. T., J. A. Santolucito, J. D. Smith, and W. F. Ganong. 1958. The effect of hypothalamic lesions on sexual behavior and estrous cycles in the ewe. *Endocrinology,* **62:** 790–797.

Cook, A. R. 1959. Effects of hypothalamic lesions on endocrine activity in female rats. *Texas Rept. Biol. Med.,* **17:** 512–536.

Corbin, A., and B. A. Schottelius. 1960. Effects of posterior hypothalamic lesions on sexual maturation of immature female albino rats. *Proc. Soc. Exptl. Biol.,* **103:** 208–210.

Critchlow, B. V. 1958. Ovulation induced by hypothalamic stimulation in the anaesthetized rat. *Am. J. Physiol.,* **195:** 171–174.

Cross, B. A., and I. A. Silver. 1966. Electrophysiological studies on hypothalamus. *Brit. Med. Bull.,* **22:** 254–260.

Daily, W. J. R., and W. F. Ganong. 1958. The effect of ventral hypothalamic lesions on sodium and potassium metabolism in the dog. *Endocrinology,* **62:** 442–454.

D'Angelo, S. A. 1959. Thyroid hormone administration and ovarian and adrenal activity in rats bearing hypothalamic lesions. *Endocrinology,* **64:** 685–702.

Davidson, J. M. 1966. Activation of the male rat's sexual behavior by intracerebral implantation of androgen. *Endocrinology,* **79:** 783–794.

Davidson, J. M., and W. F. Ganong. 1960. The effect of hypothalamic lesions on the testes and prostate of male dogs. *Endocrinology,* **66:** 480–488.

Davidson, J. M., and C. H. Sawyer. 1961a. Evidence for an hypothalamic focus of inhibition of gonadotropin by androgen in the male. *Proc. Soc. Exptl. Biol.,* **107:** 4–7.

Davidson, J. M., and C. H. Sawyer. 1961b. Effects of localized intracerebral implantation of oestrogen on reproductive function in the female rabbit. *Acta Endocrinol.,* **37:** 385–393.

Davis, D. C. 1939. The effects of ablations of neocortex on mating, maternal behavior and the production of pseudopregnancy in the female rat and on copulation activity in the male. *Am. J. Physiol.,* **127:** 374–380.

de Groot, J. 1962. The influence of limbic brain structures on reproductive functions of female rats. *Excerpta Med. Intern. Congr. Ser.,* **48.**

Deter, R. L., and R. A. Liebelt. 1964. Goldthioglucose as an experimental tool. *Texas Rept. Biol. Med.,* **22:** 229–243.

Dey, F. L. 1941. Changes in ovaries and uteri in guinea pigs with hypothalamic lesions. *Am. J. Anat.*, **69:** 61–87.

Dey, F. L. 1943. Evidence of hypothalamic control of hypophyseal gonadotropic function in the female guinea pig. *Endocrinology*, **33:** 75–82.

Dey, F. L., C. Fisher, C. M. Berry, and S. W. Ranson. 1940. Disturbances in reproductive functions caused by hypothalamic lesions in female guinea pigs. *Am. J. Physiol.*, **129:** 39–46.

Dey, F. L., C. R. Leininger, and S. W. Ranson. 1942. The effects of hypothalamic lesions on mating behavior in female guinea pigs. *Endocrinology*, **30:** 323–326.

Donovan, B. R., and J. J. van der Werff ten Bosch. 1956. Precocious puberty in rats with hypothalamic lesions. *Nature*, **178:** 745.

Donovan, B. R., and J. J. van der Werff ten Bosch. 1959a. The hypothalamus and sexual maturation in the rat. *J. Physiol. (London)*, **147:** 78–92.

Donovan, B. R., and J. J. van der Werff ten Bosch. 1959b. The relationship of the hypothalamus to oestrus in the ferret. *J. Physiol. (London)*, **147:** 93–108.

Elwers, M., and B. V. Critchlow. 1960. Precocious ovarian stimulation following hypothalamic and amygdaloid lesions in rats. *Am. J. Physiol.*, **198:** 381–385.

Epstein, A. N. 1960. Reciprocal changes in feeding behavior produced by intra-hypothalamic chemical injections. *Am. J. Physiol.*, **199:** 969–974.

Everett, J. W. 1964. Preoptic stimulative lesions and ovulation in the rat: "Thresholds" and LH-release time in late diestrus and proestrus. In *Major Problems in Neuroendocrinology* (E. Bajusz and G. Jasmin, eds.). Karger, Basel, pp. 346–366.

Everett, J. W. 1965. Ovulation in rats from preoptic stimulation through platinum electrodes. Importance of duration and spread of stimulus. *Endocrinology*, **76:** 1195–1201.

Everett, J. W., and H. M. Radford. 1961. Irritative deposits from stainless steel electrodes in the preoptic rat brain causing release of pituitary gonadotropin. *Proc. Soc. Exptl. Biol. Med.*, **108:** 604–609.

Everett, J. W., H. M. Radford, and J. Holsinger. 1964. Electrolytic irritative lesions in the hypothalamus and other forebrain areas: Effects on luteinizing hormone release and the ovarian cycle. In *Hormonal Steroids*, Vol. I (L. Martini and A. Pecile, eds.). Academic Press, New York, pp. 235–246.

Fisher, A. E., and J. N. Coury. 1962. Cholinergic tracing of a central neural circuit underlying the thirst drive. *Science*, **138:** 691–693.

Fisher, C., H. W. Magoun, and S. W. Ranson. 1938. Dystocia in diabetes insipidus. The relation of pituitary oxytocin to parturition. *Am. J. Obstet. Gynecol.*, **36:** 1–9.

Flerkó, B. 1953. Einfluss experimenteller Hypothalamusläsionen auf die Funktionen des Sekretion-apparatus im Weiblichen Genitaltrakt. *Acta Morphol. Acad. Sci. Hung.*, **3:** 65–86.

Flerkó, B., and V. Bárdos. 1959. Zwei verschiedene Effekte experimenteller Läsion des Hypothalamus auf die Gonaden. *Acta Neuroveget. (Vienna)*, **20:** 248–262.

Gellert, R. J., and W. F. Ganong. 1960. Precocious puberty in rats with hypothalamic lesions. *Acta Endocrinol.*, **33:** 569–576.

Green, J. D. 1954. Electrical activity in hypothalamus and hippocampus of conscious rabbits. *Anat. Rec.*, **118:** 304 (Abstr.).

Greer, M. A. 1953. The effect of progesterone on persistent vaginal estrus produced by hypothalamic lesions in the rat. *Endocrinology*, 53: 380–390.

Grossman, S. P. 1960. Eating or drinking elicited by direct adrenergic or cholinergic stimulation of hypothalamus. *Science*, 132: 301–302.

Goy, R. W., and C. H. Phoenix. 1963. Hypothalamic regulation of female sexual behavior: Establishment of behavioral oestrus in spayed guinea pigs following hypothalamic lesions. *J. Reprod. Fertility*, 5: 23–40.

Halász, B., and R. A. Gorski. 1966. Neural pathways required for ovulation in rats. *Exercpta Med. Intern. Congr. Ser.*, 111: 194 (Abstr.).

Halász, B., and L. Pupp. 1965. Hormone secretion of the anterior pituitary gland after physical interruption of all nervous pathways to the hypophysiotrophic area. *Endocrinology*, 77: 553–562.

Hammond, J., Jr. 1954. Light regulation of hormone secretion. *Vitamine Hormone*, 12: 157–206.

Harris, G. W. 1937. The induction of ovulation in the rabbit by electrical stimulation of the hypothalamo-hypophysial mechanism. *Proc. Roy. Soc. (London)*, **B122**: 374–394.

Harris, G. W., and R. P. Michael. 1964. The activation of sexual behavior by hypothalamic implants of oestrogen. *J. Physiol. (London)*, 171: 275–301.

Haterius, H. O., and A. J. Derbyshire, Jr. 1937. Ovulation in the rabbit following upon stimulation of the hypothalamus. *Am. J. Physiol.*, 119: 329–330.

Heimer, L., and K. Larsson. 1964. Drastic changes in mating behavior of male rats following lesions in the junction of diencephalon and mesencephalon. *Experientia*, 20: 1–4.

Herberg, L. J. 1963. Seminal ejaculation following positively reinforcing electrical stimulation of the rat hypothalamus. *J. Comp. Physiol. Psychol.*, 56: 679–685.

Hillarp, N.-Ä. 1949. Studies on the localisation of hypothalamic centres controlling the gonadotropic function of the hypophysis. *Acta Endocrinol.*, 2: 11–23.

Hoebel, B. G. 1964. Electrode-cannulas for electrical or chemical treatment of multiple brain sites. *Electroenceph. Clin. Neurophysiol.*, 16: 399–402.

Horsley, V., and R. H. Clarke. 1908. The structure and functions of the cerebellum examined by a new method. *Brain*, 31: 45–124.

John, E. R., B. S. Ruchkin, and J. Villegas. 1964. I. Experimental background: Signal analysis and behavior correlates of evoked potential configurations in cats. *Ann. N.Y. Acad. Sci.*, 112: 362–420.

Kawakami, M., and C. H. Sawyer, 1959. Induction of behavioral and electroencephalographic changes in the rabbit by hormone administration or brain stimulation. *Endocrinology*, 65: 631–643.

Kelly, E. (ed.). 1957. *Ultrasound in Biology and Medicine*. AIBS, Washington, D.C., p. 243.

Krieg, W. J. S. 1946. Accurate placement of minute lesions in the brain of the albino rat. *Quart. Bull. Northwestern Univ. Med. School*, 20: 199–208.

Laqueur, C. L., S. M. McCann, L. H. Schreiner, E. Rosemberg, D. McK. Rioch, and E. Anderson. 1955. Alterations of adrenal cortical and ovarian activity following hypothalamic lesions. *Endocrinology*, 57: 44–54.

Larsson, K. 1962. Mating behavior in male rats after cerebral cortex ablation. I. Effects of lesions in the dorsolateral and the median cortex. *J. Exptl. Zool.*, 151: 167–176.

Larsson, K. 1964. Mating behavior in male rats after cerebral cortex ablation. II. Effects of lesions in the frontal lobes compared to lesions in the posterior half of the hemispheres. *J. Exptl. Zool.,* **155:** 203–224.

Larsson, K., and L. Heimer. 1964. Mating behavior of male rats after lesions in the preoptic area. *Nature,* **202:** 413–414.

Larsson, B. L. Leksell, B. Rexed, P. Sourander, W. Mair, and B. Andersson. 1958. The high energy proton beam as a neurosurgical tool. *Nature,* **182:** 1222.

Law, T., and W. Meagher. 1958. Hypothalamic lesions and sexual behavior in the female rat. *Science,* **128:** 1626–1627.

Leksell, L., B. Larsson, B. Andersson, B. Rexed, P. Sourander, and W. Mair. 1960. Lesions in the depth of the brain produced by a beam of high energy protons. *Acta Radiol.,* **54:** 251–264.

Levitt, R. A., and A. E. Fisher. 1966. Anticholinergic blockade of centrally induced thirst. *Science,* **154:**520–521.

Liebelt, R. A., and J. H. Perry. 1957. Hypothalamic lesions associated with gold-thioglucose-induced obesity. *Proc. Soc. Exptl. Biol. Med.,* **95:** 774–777.

Lisk, R. D. 1960. Estrogen sensitive centers in the hypothalamus of the rat. *J. Exptl. Zool.,* **145:** 197–208.

Lisk, R. D. 1962a. Testosterone-sensitive centers in the hypothalamus of the rat. *Acta Endocrinol.,* **41:** 195–204.

Lisk, R. D. 1962b. Diencephalic placement of estradiol and sexual receptivity in the female rat. *Am. J. Physiol.,* **203:** 493–496.

Lisk, R. D. 1966a. Inhibitory centers in sexual behavior in the male rat. *Science,* **152:** 669–670.

Lisk, R. D. 1966b. Increased sexual behavior in the male rat following lesions in the mammillary region. *J. Exptl. Zool.,* **161:** 129–136.

Lisk, R. D. 1966c. Hormonal implants in the central nervous system and behavioral receptivity in the female rat. In *The Brain and Gonadal Function* (R. A. Gorski and R. E. Whalen, eds.). Univ. California Press, Berkeley, pp. 98–117.

Lisk, R. D. 1967a. Neural control of gonad size by hormone feedback in the desert iguana *Dipsosaurus dorsalis dorsalis. J. Gen. Comp. Endocrinol.,* **8:** 258–266.

Lisk, R. D. 1967b. Neural localization for androgen activation of copulatory behavior in the male rat. *Endocrinology,* **80:** 754–761.

Lisk, R. D., and A. J. Suydam. 1967. Sexual behavior patterns in the prepubertally castrate rat. *Anat. Rec.,* **157:** 181–189.

MacLean, P. D. 1962. New findings relevant to the evolution of psychosexual functions of the brain. *J. Nervous Mental Diseases,* **135:** 289–301.

MacLean, P. D., and D. W. Ploog. 1962. Cerebral representation of penile erection. *J. Neurophysiol.,* **25:** 29–55.

MacLean, P. D., D. Sushil, and R. H. Denniston. 1963. Cerebral localization for scratching and seminal discharge. *Arch. Neurol.,* **9:** 485–497.

Markee, J. E., C. H. Sawyer, and W. H. Hollinshead. 1946. Activation of the anterior hypophysis by electrical stimulation in the rabbit. *Endocrinology,* **38:** 345–357.

Mess, B. 1952. Influence of hypothalamic injury on spermatogenesis in albino rats. *Acta Morphol. Acad. Sci. Hung.,* **2:** 275–285.

Michael, R. P. 1962. Estrogen-sensitive neurons and sexual behavior in female cats. *Science,* **136:** 322–323.

Michael, R. P. 1965a. Oestrogens in the central nervous system. *Brit. Med. Bull.*, **21**: 87–90.

Michael, R. P. 1965b. The selective accumulation of estrogens in the neural and genital tissues of the cat. *Proc. 1st Intern. Congr. Hormonal Steroids, Milan, 1962*, Vol. 2 (L. Martini and A. Pecile, eds.). Academic Press, New York, pp. 469–481.

Olds, J. 1962. Hypothalamic substrates of reward. *Physiol. Rev.*, **42**: 554–604.

Palka, Y. S., and C. H. Sawyer. 1966. The effects of hypothalamic implants of ovarian steroids on oestrous behavior in rabbits. *J. Physiol. (London)*, **185**: 251–269.

Perry, J. H., and R. A. Liebelt. 1961. Extra-hypothalamic lesions associated with gold-thioglucose induced obesity. *Proc. Soc. Exptl. Med.*, **106**: 55–57.

Phoenix, C. H. 1961. Hypothalamic regulation of sexual behavior in male guinea pigs. *J. Comp. Physiol. Psychol.*, **54**: 72–77.

Porter, R. W., E. B. Cavanaugh, B. V. Critchlow, and C. H. Sawyer. 1957. Localized changes in electrical activity of the hypothalamus in estrous cats following vaginal stimulation. *Am. J. Physiol.*, **189**: 145–151.

Reynolds, R. W. 1963. Ventromedial hypothalamic lesions without hyperphagia. *Am. J. Physiol.*, **204**: 60–62.

Rowan, W. 1925. Relation of light to bird migration and developmental changes. *Nature*, **115**: 494–495.

Rowan, W. 1938. London starlings and seasonal reproduction in birds. *Proc. Zool. Soc. London*, **A108**: 51–77.

Sawyer, C. H. 1959. Effects of brain lesions on estrous behavior and reflexogenous ovulation in the rabbit. *J. Exptl. Zool.*, **142**: 227–246.

Sawyer, C. H. 1963. Induction of estrus in the ovariectomized cat by local hypothalamic treatment with estrogen. *Anat. Rec.*, **145**: 280 (Abstr.).

Sawyer, C. H., and B. Robison. 1956. Separate hypothalamic areas controlling pituitary gonadotropic function and mating behavior in female cats and rabbits. *J. Clin. Endocrinol.*, **16**: 914–915.

Smith, P. E. 1927. The disabilities caused by hypophysectomy and their repair. The tuberal (hypothalamic) syndrome in the rat. *J. Am. Med. Assoc.*, **88**: 158–161.

Soulairac, M. L. 1963. Étude expérimentale des régulations hormono-nerveuses du comportement sexuel du rat male. *Ann. Endocrinol. (Paris)*, **24**(Suppl.) 1–94.

Uttal, R. W. 1965. Do compound evoked potentials reflect psychological codes? *Psychol. Bull.*, **64**: 377–392.

Vaughan, E., and A. E. Fisher. 1962. Male sexual behavior induced by electrical stimulation. *Science*, **137**: 758–760.

Young, G. F., and P. P. Lebe. 1964. Focal lesions in the brain of growing rabbits produced by focused ultrasound. *Exptl. Neurol.*, **9**: 502–511.

Zitrin, A., J. Jaynes, and F. A. Beach. 1956. Neural mediation of mating in male cats. III. Contribution of the occipital, parietal and temporal cortex. *J. Comp. Neurol.*, **105**: 111–125.

REPRODUCTION AND SEXUAL BEHAVIOR (M. Diamond ed.), 303–340, © Indiana University Press

20

Differentiation of the Neural Mechanisms Which Control Gonadotropin Secretion and Sexual Behavior

Richard E. Whalen

Males are different—they differ from females, as females differ from males. Male–female differences are apparent in structure and function, in individual and social behavior. We find these sex differences in chromosome pattern, gonadal structure and hormonal function, in genital morphology and accessory reproductive structure, in gender role and libido, and in courtship and parental activities. The causes of these differences are complex. There is little doubt that sex differences in structure, function, and behavior are reflections of sex differences in genetic constitution. Yet there is equally little doubt that the expression of any genotype is critically dependent upon the environment in which that genotype "matures." Males look, function, and behave as males and not as females because their genotype develops in a hormonal and social environment which is different from that experienced by genotypic females.

This paper will review classical and contemporary research relevant to one small component of the psychobiology of sexual differentiation. This paper will deal only with that research which has led to our modern concept that sex differences in reproductive physiology and behavior are influenced by hormonally determined differences in brain function.

One of the most striking differences between male and female lies in the sequence of events which constitute the reproductive process. Most females exhibit cyclic follicular growth and ovulation, mating, pregnancy, and parturition, while males exhibit relatively constant spermatogenesis and acyclic mating. It is generally believed today that these cyclic–tonic differences in reproductive function and behavior between females and males are the result of differences in brain functioning. The notion that sex differences in gonadal activity and mating are the result of brain differences between male and female is a modern concept, the result of a very few revealing studies conducted in an atmosphere which compelled investigators to realize that reproduction is under neural control. There is little doubt that Harris' monograph, *Neural Control of the Pituitary Gland* (1955), played a major role in creating the atmosphere which generated the experimental and theoretical advances which have been made in the past decade. Harris' review made it very clear that the adenohypophysis is modulated by the brain. This conclusion immediately implies that gonadotropin secretion, gonadal hormone secretion, and ultimately sexual behavior are all under neural control. It was but a short step to the inference that sex differences in the pattern of gonadotropin secretion, gonadal hormone secretion, and mating also represent sex differences in neural control. In fact, Harris (1955) suggested this hypothesis in his statement ". . . it seems likely that some neural structure in the male animal becomes differentiated and fixed in its function under the influence of androgens in early life."

While there were certainly supporting studies, three particular experiments must be considered the foundation for our current ideas of the sexual differentiation of the brain. The first of these studies was Barraclough's demonstration (1961) that a single subcutaneous injection of testosterone in the neonatal female rat results in permanent anovulatory sterility if the testosterone is administered prior to 10 days of age. Rats treated at 20 days of age develop normally, ovulate, mate, and produce offspring. In interpreting his data Barraclough remarked ". . . this hypothesis would mean that it is not the pituitary which is undifferentiated at birth, but rather the regions of the hypothalamus controlling gonadotropin secretion." The second study which helped to generate our current concept of sexual differentiation dealt with behavior. In 1959 Phoenix et al. reported that the female offspring of guinea pigs treated with testosterone during pregnancy fail to display feminine mating responses when administered estrogen and progesterone, and exhibit more frequent male-like mounting responses when administered testosterone than normal females. Phoenix et al. concluded from their data: ". . . for the neural tissues mediating mating behavior corresponding relationships seem to exist. The embryonic and fetal periods are periods of organization or differentiation in the direction of masculinization or feminization." The third important study in the series was carried out by Harris and Levine (1962). These workers injected 5-day-old female rats with testosterone and examined both ovulatory and behavioral processes in adulthood. They found that the androgen-treated females fail to mate when placed with vigorous males, fail to mate when administered estrogen and progesterone, and exhibit male-like mounting responses when given testosterone. These females do not ovulate and do not become pregnant. Their ovaries contain follicles but no corpora lutea. With respect to their data, Harris and Levine remarked "there is evidence that the secretions of the fetal and immature gonads influence sexual differentiation in the central nervous system."

The important thing about these studies was that in each the data were interpreted to mean that male–female differences in reproductive functions are due to male–female differences in brain function. This conceptual development was extremely important. The postulation of this concept, however, need not have waited upon the completion of these experiments. In fact, ample evidence existed well before 1950 for the postulation that sexual differentiation of the brain underlies sex differences in gonadotropin secretion and sexual behavior.

The Control of Gonadotropin Secretion

Probably the single most important experimental contribution to the sexual differentiation literature prior to 1950 was Pfeiffer's 1936 paper, "Sexual Differences of the Hypophyses and Their Determination by the Gonads." In this work Pfeiffer castrated male and female rats at birth. Some of these animals received gonadal transplants in the neck region at the same time; others were untreated until adulthood. When these animals reached puberty an ovary was transplanted to the eye, and this ovary was examined for the presence of follicles and for the formation of corpora lutea. Table 1 shows the effects of these early treatments upon the ocular ovarian transplant. In this experiment corpora lutea developed in the transplanted ovaries only in those animals which developed with no postnatal hormonal stimulation.

Table 1

State of Ocular Ovarian Transplant in Adult Rats
Hormonally Manipulated at Birth [From Pfeiffer (1936)]

Genetic sex	Treatment at birth	State of transplant
Male	Orchidectomy	Follicles, corpora lutea
Male	Orchidectomy + testis transplant	Follicles
Female	Ovariectomy	Follicles, corpora lutea
Female	Ovariectomy + testis transplant	Follicles

These findings of Pfeiffer represent an extension of the earlier work of Goodman (1934), which demonstrated that ocular ovarian transplants in castrated adult female rats would exhibit follicles and corpora lutea and maintain vaginal cycles and that transplants in males, castrated when adult, would only maintain follicles.

Taken together these early studies showed that males and females differ in their potential to induce luteinization in transplanted ovaries and that this difference is due to testicular stimulation during development. Pfeiffer further demonstrated that the male pattern could be induced in females by testicular transplant at birth and that the female pattern could be induced in males by castration at birth. Modern research on sexual differentiation has not modified these findings. The interpretation of these findings, however, has changed. Pfeiffer concluded: "The hypophysis in the rat at birth is bipotential and capable of being differentiated as either male or female depending upon whether an ovary or a testis is present." Today we would substitute the term hypothalamus for the term hypophysis.

Two important aspects of sexual differentiation not dealt with by Pfeiffer were the time at which differentiation occurs and the nature of the differentiating stimulus. One could presume that the stimulus was testicular androgen, but this was not in fact demonstrated. One also knew from the data that differentiation occurred postnatally in the rat, but the limits of the sensitive period could not be determined in Pfeiffer's experiment because the testicular transplants remained in place from birth to maturity.

Bradbury presented evidence pertaining to these problems in 1941. He found that the administration of either antuitrin-S daily from day 6 to day 24 of age or testosterone propionate on alternate days from day 6 to day 38 of age would induce continuous vaginal estrus in female rats following the cessation of hormone treatment. These animals were found to be sterile and to possess ovaries without corpora lutea. Bradbury further demonstrated that if the ovaries are removed from the masculinized females and transplanted to a normal host, they would maintain normal estrous cycles and develop corpora lutea, thus indicating that the absence of luteinization in the neonatally hormone-treated female is not due to any altered capacity of the ovary.

Additional evidence on the sensitive period for masculinization was provided by Wilson et al. (1940, 1941). These workers reported that female rats treated with testosterone propionate postnatally from birth to 28 days after birth were permanently sterilized. However, some of their animals treated prenatally by injections to the pregnant mothers on days 14 to 16 of gestation escaped sterilization. These data suggested that the period of maximum sensitivity to androgen was probably after birth in the rat. In their second experiment Wilson et al., demonstrated that one must treat the female neonatal rat with androgen before the fifteenth postnatal day if the inhibition of corpora lutea formation is to be induced. Animals whose testosterone treatment was started on the fifth or tenth postnatal day were sterilized, while those whose treatment began on the fifteenth postnatal day escaped sterilization. In this important paper Wilson et al. also reported that sterilization could be induced in the rat by postnatal treatment with estrogen as well as with androgen, and that the abnormalities induced by estrogen are "in some instances more severe than those obtained with androgens." Again these studies were interpreted as support for Pfeiffer's hypothesis on the sexual differentiation of the hypophysis.

The older studies reviewed here represent only a sample of the many experiments which were published prior to 1950 which could have been interpreted in terms of hormone-induced sexual differentiation of the brain. These studies very clearly provided evidence supporting the hypothesis that males differ from females in the pattern of gonadotropin secretion because of differences in brain function. This evidence has been rediscovered in independent experiments conducted in the 1960s.

This brief review of some highlights of experimental neuroendocrinology provides us with another example of the importance of the tenor of the times upon experimentation. It would seem that the problem of sexual differentiation was not actively pursued throughout the 1940s because the theoretical concepts which were common at that time did not force investigators to continue. Pfeiffer's concept of the sexually differentiated adenohypophysis seemed to adequately account for the available data, and, as a result, experimenters were not led to brain research on this problem. The late 1940s were characterized, however, by the development of the concept of neural control of adenohypophyseal function. The research at this time culminated in the formulation of the "hypothalamo-hypophyseal chemotransmitter" hypothesis and forced upon the field the notion that adenohypophyseal function is directly controlled by the brain (Harris, 1955).

One experiment which resulted from the ferment generated by these new theoretical ideas forever destroyed Pfeiffer's hypotheses of the sexually differentiated pituitary. Harris and Jacobsohn (1952) extended the earlier work of Greep (1936) and showed that male pituitaries transplanted under the hypothalamus of hypophysectomized female recipients would become functional and support estrous cycles, ovulation, mating, pregnancy, and parturition. One could no longer claim that the adenohypophysis of the male is functionally different from that of the female. The differences in male–female pituitary function must be the result of differences in brain function.

Contemporary Research

The development of the concept of neural control of the pituitary led to the rediscovery that sexual differentiation is under the control of gonadal hormone stimulation during a sensitive period of maturation. These experiments did not stop with the simple demonstration of male–female differences in gonadal function. They have been carried forward to reveal the nature and locus of the neural control of sex differences in gonadotropin secretion. Because of the volume of research which has been done on problems of the neural control of gonadotropin secretion and on sex differences in the control mechanisms, it is not possible to present a complete review here. Only selected articles will be discussed which give the flavor of the research and concepts which have developed in the past decade. Recent scholarly reviews of this research are available (Bogdanove, 1964; Everett, 1964; Gorski, 1966; Harris, 1964).

Contemporary research has very clearly defined the conditions which result in the development of the male and female patterns of gonadotropin secretion in the rat. (Little research has been devoted to animals other than the rat. We still know next to nothing about sexual differentiation in seasonal animals.) The normal female is characterized by the cyclic secretion of FSH and LH, while the male exhibits relatively constant or tonic secretion of these hormones. The cyclicity or tonicity of gonadotropin release is typically evaluated by observing changes in the vaginal smear pattern and the formation of corpora lutea in the ovary. These characteristics of vaginal and ovarian tissue may be evaluated in both males and females with the use of the appropriate tissue transplants. In a normal female the vagina undergoes cyclic changes, while in the male the transplanted vagina shows constant cornification when stimulated by a transplanted ovary (Yazaki, 1959, 1960). In a normal female the ovary contains follicles and corpora lutea, while in the normal male the transplanted ovary contains follicles but no corpora lutea (Yazaki, 1959; Harris, 1964; Gorski and Wagner, 1965).

The male pattern of gonadotropin secretion can be permanently induced in the female by stimulating the female with either androgenic or estrogenic steroids at the appropriate point during development (Barraclough, 1961; Harris, 1964; Harris and Levine, 1962, 1965; Gorski, 1963; Whalen and Nadler, 1965). The critical period for the induction of the male pattern in the female rat runs from birth to the tenth postnatal day (Barraclough, 1961; Swanson and van der Werff ten Bosch, 1964). There is some interaction between dose of steroid and time of administration. Sterility may be induced with as little as 10 μg of testosterone when administered 96 hours after birth; a larger dose of the steroid may be required to sterilize the 10-day-old animal.

The female pattern of gonadotropin secretion may be induced in the male by castration at the appropriate developmental stage. Takewaki (1962), Harris (1964), and Gorski and Wagner (1965) agree that the sensitive period is short-lived in the male. The testes must be removed from the male within 3 to 4 days of birth if the male rat is to develop the potential to cause ovulation in a transplanted ovary.

These and several studies are consistent with the notion that sexual differentiation is the result of androgenic stimulation during a sensitive developmental period, and that the locus for sexual differentiation is the brain. All these studies, however, deal with the sexual differentiation of the brain only by inference. None of these studies provides evidence about changes in neural responsiveness under various conditions of sexual differentiation. The first report to clearly demonstrate alterations in brain function resulting from early androgen treatment appeared in 1961. At that time, Barraclough and Gorski reported that the neonatally androgenized female rat would not ovulate, even following electrical stimulation of the median eminence region of the hypothalamus; stimulation which will induce ovulation in normal females. These workers further showed that the adenohypophysis of the sterilized rat is capable of releasing sufficient LH to induce ovulation. If the androgen-sterilized rat is treated with progesterone, electrical stimulation of the ventral medial-arcuate region, but not stimulation of the preoptic region, will induce ovulation.

In the study mentioned above, the rats had been treated with 1.25 mg of testosterone 5 days after birth. In a subsequent study Gorski and Barraclough (1963) showed that the degree of neural refractoriness induced by early androgen treatment is a function of the dose of testosterone administered. In this latter study sterility was induced by 10 μg of testosterone. In these animals electrical stimulation of the median eminence did induce ovulation, and did so without progesterone pretreatment. Stimulation of the preoptic-superchiasmatic region of these animals did not cause ovulation, however, unless the animals were pretreated with progesterone.

Barraclough and Gorski (1961, 1962) and Gorski (1966) have taken these data and data from related experiments to indicate that two neural systems are involved in the control of ovulation, a posterior system which regulates the tonic discharge of gonadotropin, and an anterior system which acts as the focus for the neurogenic stimuli which time ovulation. The anterior region is seen to integrate stimuli provided by hormone levels and by the environment, and to control the posterior tonic system which in turn directly regulates the adenohypophysis. Additional evidence for the validity of this hypothesis is currently being provided by Halász and Gorski using surgical techniques for the neural isolation of these regions (see Gorski, 1966).

Gorski (1966) postulates that the primary alteration in brain function produced by androgen stimulation during the sensitive period is localized in the preoptic-superchiasmatic control system. Gorski further feels that the changes in brain function revealed by studies of the androgen-sterilized female rat adequately represent the natural changes which occur in the male. The several available studies of the effect of neonatal castration in the male on the development of the potential to cause ovulation in a transplanted ovary would seem to support this contention (Gorski and Wagner, 1965; Harris, 1964; Pfeiffer, 1936). It is very clear that the male castrated as an adult, the male castrated and administered androgen at birth, and the female administered androgen at birth act the same with respect to a transplanted ovary; all fail to induce ovulation and corpora lutea formation. Similarly, the male castrated at birth and the normal female appear equal, and both can cause ovulation and corpora lutea formation. These notions about the locus and sexual differentiation of the gonadotropin control systems are depicted in Fig. 1. Extensive validation of these hypotheses can be expected in the next few years.

The Barraclough–Gorski experiments illustrate one approach to the study of the nature and locus of sexual differentiation of the brain. A second important approach, which is just now gaining favor, involves the direct hormonal manipulation of the brain. Working in this reviewer's laboratory on a thesis problem, R. D. Nadler developed a

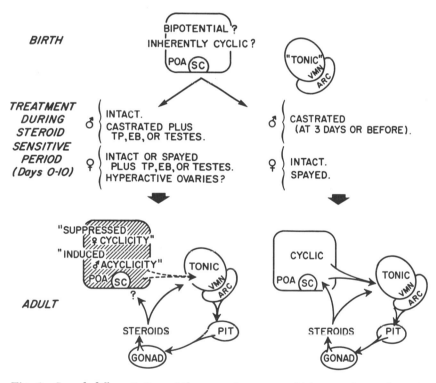

Fig. 1 Sexual differentiation of the neural systems which control gonadotropin secretion. Anterior and posterior GTH control systems are depicted. The possibly bipotential or inherently cyclic preoptic-superchiasmatic system is seen to be suppressed by androgenic or estrogenic stimulation in the early postnatal period in the rat. ARC, arcuate nucleus; EB, estradiol benzoate; POA, preoptic area; SC, superchiasmatic nucleus; TP, testosterone propionate; VMN, ventromedial nucleus. [From Gorski and Wagner (1965).]

technique for implanting minute amounts of hormone into the brain of neonatal (5-day-old) rats (Nadler, 1965). Nadler demonstrated that it was possible to induce anovulatory sterility and persistent vaginal cornification in over 90 percent of his animals with 2.5 μg of testosterone propionate implanted in the brain. Significant sterility (32 percent) was induced with as little as 1.25 μg, and 13 percent of a group implanted with 0.25 μg of testosterone were sterilized. The effective dose levels here are appreciably lower than those which will induce sterility by the systemic route, suggesting that the androgen does work at the level of the brain to induce sexual differentiation.

Nadler also sought to determine the neural locus for the induction of sterility using animals implanted with 1.25 or 1.67 μg of testosterone propionate. Figure 2 is a composite parasagittal reconstruction of the rat brain illustrating implant loci 0 to 1.5 mm lateral to the midline. It can be seen that the effective loci tend to cluster in diencephalic structures while negative loci were consistently in dorsal structures. This relationship was even more evident in implants located 1.6 to 5.00 mm lateral to the midline (Nadler, 1965).

Wagner et al. (1966) have recently published a report of their experiments using a similar technique. They also found that doses of testosterone propionate which would be ineffective if administered systemically produced sterility when placed in the brain. Like Nadler, they found that positive points were distributed throughout the basal hypothalamus.

The results of both of these implant experiments strongly implicate hypothalamic structures in the sexual differentiation process and thus support the findings obtained using brain-stimulation techniques. Neither of these experiments, however, is able to specify whether or not the preoptic-superchiasmatic region is crucially involved in differentiation, as suggested by Gorski. It is to be expected that technical refinements will ultimately facilitate the acquisition of this information.

A third approach which has provided and will continue to provide information about the nature of the sexual differentiation process involves the use of the recently synthesized antiandrogenic substances. Neumann and co-workers have published an extensive series of papers on the effects of one of these compounds, cyproterone acetate (Neumann and Elger, 1965a, 1965b). This steroid at appropriate doses will inhibit the effect of endogenous or exogenous testosterone on peripheral androgen-sensitive structures such as the seminal vesicles and prostate. In our laboratory, for example, (Whalen and Edwards, unpublished) adult male rats were castrated and treated with (1) 150

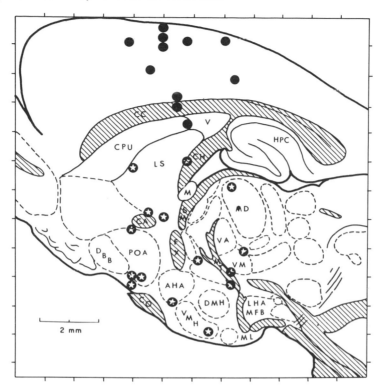

Fig. 2 Composite parasagittal reconstruction of the rat brain illustrating loci 0 to 1.5 mm lateral to midline where the implantation of testosterone in 5-day-old female rats induced persistent estrous sterility. Starred circles, persistent estrus; filled circles, cyclic; AHA, anterior hypothalamic area; C, anterior commissure; LS, lateral septum; MT, mamillothalamic tract; POA, preoptic area; VM, nucleus ventralis of the thalamus; VMH, ventromedial nucleus of the hypothalamus. [From Nadler (1965).]

μg/day testosterone propionate, (2) 150 μg/day testosterone propionate plus 10 mg/day cyproterone acetate, or (3) oil. After 2 weeks of treatment the seminal vesicles were removed and wet weights of the expressed organs taken. The mean weights for these groups were as follows: (1) 307 mg, (2) 170 mg, and (3) 148 mg. These differences, which were highly significant statistically, indicated that the cyproterone acetate prevented the maintenance of seminal vesicle weight normally produced by testosterone propionate.

When this compound is administered to pregnant rats during the latter half of gestation and to the young during the first 3 postnatal weeks, vaginal development is induced in the male offspring (Neumann et al., 1966). In these animals the scrotum is incompletely developed, the phallus resembles a clitoris, and there is nipple development which is uncharacteristic of normal males. Vaginal smears taken from these males are of the diestrous character until the animal is treated with estrogen. Estrogen treatment results in the cornification of the male vagina.

If such feminized males are castrated and implanted with an ovary from an infantile rat, the vagina will start to exhibit cyclic changes as revealed by the smear pattern (Neumann and Kramer, 1966). Later histological analysis of the transplanted ovaries indicates that they contain corpora lutea.

A worthwhile next step in this series will be the implantation of antiandrogenic substances into limited hypothalamic regions using the techniques developed by Nadler (1965) and Wagner et al. (1966). That such an approach is feasible is indicated by Bloch and Davidson's recent demonstration of enhanced testicular secretion in male rats resulting from the implantation of cyproterone acetate in the median eminence negative feedback region (1967). Studies using antiandrogen implants in neonatal male animals can be expected to reveal whether such "protection" of a limited hypothalamic area will prevent differentiation induced by endogenous testicular secretion.

Finally, the use of radioactively labeled hormones can be expected to provide information about the neural locus and temporal course of sexual differentiation. Such research is exemplified by the recent findings of Diamond and Dale (1967). These workers treated neonatal rats with labeled testosterone on the day of birth, 2, 3, 5, 10, or 20 days after birth and examined the neural and nonneural uptake of the hormone. They found that the hormone was localized primarily in the hypothalamus, except in those animals treated on day 10 or on day 20. These data suggest that the hypothalamus is selectively sensitive to androgen and that this sensitivity diminishes as the animal matures. More work of this nature can be expected in the future. Of course, one must interpret these and similar findings with caution, since the mere uptake of hormone by the hypothalamus does not, by itself, prove that the hypothalamus is the site of action of the hormone.

Summary

The evidence available today indicates that gonadotropic secretion is controlled by hypothalamic neurons. This control system seems to exist in both males and females, but functions differently in the adults of each sex. Only in the female does the system exert cyclic control over gonadotropin secretion. This sex difference in function seems to be the result of brain differentiation induced in the male by endogenously secreted androgen acting during a critical period of development. Normally in the male rat this neural differentiation is complete by the end of the fourth postnatal day. However, it can be shown that the affected system remains sensitive to androgens at least until the tenth postnatal day as long as differentiation has not already occurred. If differentiation is prevented for 15 days, even high doses of androgen will not permanently alter those neurons which control the cyclic release of gonadotropins. The evidence is quite strong that basal diencephalic structures comprise the gonadotropin control system. Increasing evidence suggests that the system is composed of two components: one in the region of the ventral medial arcuate nuclei which exerts tonic control over gonadotropin secretion and one in the region of the preoptic-superchiasmatic nuclei, which exerts cyclic control over adenohypophyseal function. It seems quite clear at this point that the nature and location of these control systems will be elucidated in the next few years.

The Control of Sexual Behavior

The development of our current concepts of differentiation and sexual behavior to a great extent parallels the development of our modern concepts of differentiation and gonadotropin secretion. In each area a few important experiments have provided the impetus for extensive research, and in each case modern concepts could have been generated on the basis of evidence which existed prior to 1950.

Before we examine the historical aspects of the differentiation of behavior, a few comments about the nature of sexual behavior are in order. Mating behavior differs strikingly from ovulation along several dimensions. Ovulation is a discrete event—it can either occur or not occur under a particular hormonal condition. It does not occur to a greater or lesser degree. Mating, on the other hand, can occur in varying degrees. It can be more or less intense. In a given animal, ovulation cannot occur in both the male pattern and in the female pattern simultaneously or closely linked in time. Mating in a given animal, however, can occur in both the male and female pattern within a single relatively limited observation period. The genetic and hormonal female can exhibit female and male behavior patterns alternately. For these reasons adequate analysis of the sexual behavior of an organism requires an analysis of the intensity of the display of both male and female patterns. The analysis of the potential to display *both* male and female patterns becomes critical in the study of sexual differentiation; the analysis of the intensity of sexual responding is critical in all studies on sexual behavior. Any analysis of mating which does not consider the frequency and/or probability of responding must be considered inadequate today.

Another important consideration in the study of mating is the nature of the responses which are shown under a particular hormone condition. The male rat, for example, has at least three distinct components in his mating pattern: mounts without intromission, mounts with intromission, and mounts with ejaculation. The frequencies with which these responses occur are not independent; that is, the occurrence of one of these responses, for example, ejaculation, influences the probability of occurrence of another one of these responses, for example, intromission (Beach and Whalen, 1959a, 1959b). Further, these responses are differentially influenced by hormonal state. Low-level androgenic stimulation may result in the elimination of ejaculation responses and the continued display of mounts with intromission (Beach and Holz-Tucker, 1949). Because of these dependencies it is very important that the different mating responses be distinguished and measured separately.

The sexual behavior of the female rat also consists of various components, e.g., lordosis, ear wiggling, and hopping. It is both reasonable and customary to use the lordosis reflex as an index of receptivity. The simple presence or absence of the lordosis reflex, however, does not provide an accurate measure of receptivity. The probability that a mount by a male will induce lordosis in the female varies with the stage of the female's estrous cycle (Kuehn and Beach, 1963) and with the nature of the hormones administered. An estrogen–progesterone combination produces a higher level of receptivity than does estrogen alone (Beach, 1942a; Edwards et al., 1968). If the animal is a guinea pig, rather than a rat, the timing and temporal sequence of the estrogen–progesterone combination critically determines the receptivity level induced (Zucker, 1966). Thus receptivity is not an all or none response; it does vary in intensity. For these reasons one must assess the probability of lordosis to obtain an adequate measure of receptivity.

These details of the analysis of mating become quite important in the study of sexual differentiation. It is one thing to note that the female rat treated with androgen in infancy exhibits mounting responses; it is quite another thing to note that these responses resemble the intromission pattern of the male. Similarly, it is one thing to note the presence of sperm in a vaginal lavage and another to note that the female exhibits lordosis each time she is mounted by the male.

As with the analysis of gonadotropin secretion, experimentation on behavioral sexual differentiation has a long history. As noted by Young et al. (1964), Dantchakoff reported in 1938 that the female offspring of guinea pigs treated with testosterone during pregnancy exhibit reduced feminine behavior and show masculine behavior when treated with testosterone in adulthood. Unfortunately, this important research lacked the appropriate controls needed for one to conclude that the early hormone treatment permanently altered these animals in the masculine direction. Normal female guinea pigs do exhibit male-like mounting responses as part of their normal estrous pattern.

It was also shown many years ago that the early treatment of the female rat with hormones would cause inhibition of adult mating behavior. Wilson et al. (1940) administered testosterone propionate to female rats both postnatally (to day 28) and prenatally by injections to the pregnant mother. When mature these females did not exhibit mating responses spontaneosuly. When they were treated with 100 RU of estradiol benzoate, none of the animals treated with androgen postnatally mated. Sixty percent of the prenatally treated animals, however, did mate. These data suggest that the rat is more sensitive to androgen in the postnatal than in the prenatal period. The intensity of receptivity induced in these animals was not specified, unfortunately.

A later paper (Wilson et al., 1941) examined the relationship between the time of initiation of early androgen treatment and the inhibition of later behavior. In none of the animals for whom androgen treatment began at 5 or 10 days of age was normal spontaneous estrous behavior found; all animals whose treatment started at 15 days of age or later exhibited normal receptivity in adulthood. When administered estrogen and progesterone in adulthood the animals treated with androgen prior to 15 days of age were found to be less responsive to exogenous hormone than control animals spayed in adulthood. It is interesting to note that the authors concluded that "the tissues of the uterus and the mechanism responsible for estrous behavior were not responsive to the quantity of estrogen which is usually effective in untreated animals." They did not, however, go on to hypothesize that the brain is in fact the mechanism responsible for estrous behavior.

In 1943 Wilson demonstrated that it is possible to induce permanent inhibition of sexual responsiveness with estrogenic as well as androgenic substances. Wilson treated rats for 28 days with estradiol dipropionate starting at birth, 5, 10, 15, 20, 30, or 40 days after birth. He found that animals whose treatment started before the fifteenth postnatal day failed to exhibit spontaneous mating behavior and failed to mate even when treated with relatively high doses of exogenous estrogen and progesterone.

Finally, in a somewhat confusing paper, Koster (1943) reported on the masculine behavior of female rats treated with either testosterone or estrogen from birth to maturity. He noted that the testosterone-treated females would mount normal receptive females (as would untreated virgin females) and that these females would not permit copulation by normal males. Koster further reported that the females treated with estrogen in infancy would also exhibit masculine behavior toward receptive females, and that this behavior was more persistent and intense than that displayed by the androgenized females. Some of the estrogen-treated females even displayed what Koster termed "the spasm," the female's equivalent of the male's intromission pattern. (Koster felt that the "spasm" of the female was equivalent to the ejaculation pattern of the male. However, Koster's lucid description of the behavior he observed makes it clear that the spasm is similar to the male's intromission pattern.)

One of the interesting features of this last study was the interpretation of the results. Koster said "in sex-reversal the hormones upset the established organization of behavior and stimulate the functioning of other sensory-motor routes which are normally suppressed. In this reorganization of behavior patterns the pituitary is probably not involved and the sex hormones probably act directly on some part of the central nervous system." By today's standards this interpretation is certainly reasonable, but it seemed to have little impact upon the research of the time.

In all these studies we can find problems which prevent clear conclusions about the hormonal basis of sexual differentiation. In some, appropriate control groups were absent; in others, the intensity of the behavior was not measured. At the time of this early work on sex differentiation and behavior the potential of the normal male and female to display the behavior of the opposite sex had not been clearly defined. Koster (1943) had stated that "the female rat is genetically endowed with a nervous and muscular organization for both male and female behavior and these two systems can function concurrently in the same individual," but his data certainly could not validate that conclusion.

In a series of papers published in the 1940s Beach described the spontaneous occurrence of opposite sex behavior in both sexes of rat (1938, 1942b, 1945; Beach and Rasquin, 1942), and he described the induction of opposite sex behavior in castrated male and female rats by the application of homotypical and heterotypical hormones (1941, 1942d, 1942e, 1945). These papers are particularly noteworthy because they present quantified data on the intensity of each of the component mating responses. Beach's reports show quite clearly that female rats often exhibit male-like mounting responses but rarely mounts with intromission or with ejaculation. In the normal female the frequency of these mounts is independent of the stage of the estrous cycle or even of the presence of the ovaries (Beach, 1942b, 1942d; Beach and Rasquin, 1942). The administration of testosterone increases the frequency of mounting and increases the probability that these mounts will resemble the intromission pattern of the male. Male rats treated with testosterone were shown to exhibit lordosis when mounted by other males (Beach, 1941), although these responses were sluggish. Further, one male which spontaneously exhibited both masculine and feminine responses was castrated and administered estrogen and progesterone. This animal then exhibited clear lordosis responses when mounted by another male (Beach, 1945).

These studies indicate that both male and female rats do possess the neuromuscular apparatus for the display of both masculine and feminine responses. Beach favored such an hypothesis and felt that the two sexes differed in their threshold for response to androgenic and estrogenic substances.

Beach's work on the spontaneous occurrence and hormonal induction of behavior normally characteristic of the opposite sex suggests that the nature of the sexual differentiation of behavioral control mechanisms is different, at least in degree, from the sexual differentiation of gonadotropin secretion. Both males and females can, and do, seem to possess the potential to show both masculine and feminine behavior patterns. They do, however, exhibit these patterns with different probabilities and at different intensities. These facts must be kept in mind in any study of the sexual differentiation process (see Chapter 7).

Contemporary Research

Owing to the publication of the papers by Phoenix et al. (1959) and Harris and Levine (1962), active research on behaviorial differentiation has been carried out in several laboratories for the past 9 years. No attempt will be made to review all these studies; rather, this reviewer will describe the particularly pertinent studies from the growing literature and some of the research from his own laboratory. For a different selection of studies and a different emphasis, the reader should consult the reviews by Young et al. (1964), Young (1965), and Goy (1966) (see also Chapters 5 and 25).

The Development of the Feminine Behavior Control System— Facilitation. The normally developing female rodent will display the lordosis response indicative of receptivity after puberty and the onset of ovarian cyclicity and vaginal opening. Lordosis responses occur periodically when the animal is stimulated by endogenous estrogen and progesterone. In the rat the intensity of receptivity increases to a peak at about the second fifth of the total receptive period and then declines progressively until the female fails to exhibit lordosis when mounted by a male (Kuehn and Beach, 1963). Artificial receptivity, which mimics natural receptivity in its qualitative and quantitative aspects, can be induced by the administration of estrogen and progesterone. The administration of estrogen alone induces low-level receptivity (e.g., Edwards et al., 1968), which differs from estrogen–progesterone induced receptivity only in intensity.

Endogenous hormonal stimulation during maturation is not necessary for the female rat to develop the potential to show lordosis. Females which are ovariectomized at birth and administered estrogen and progesterone in adulthood display lordosis when mounted by males. Figure 3, taken from our own research (Whalen and Edwards, 1967), illustrates this point and shows that the neonatally ovariectomized female is neither more nor less receptive than the female ovariectomized in adulthood when both are treated with estrogen and progesterone. The ovary, therefore, seems to play no role in the feminization process.

Neonatal steroid stimulation in the female rat may result in an altered mating pattern. Barraclough and Gorski (1962) reported that females treated with 10 μg of testosterone propionate at 5 days of age would show persistent receptivity (Fig. 5). Some of these animals would accept the male for as many as 9 consecutive days. Nadler (1965) has replicated this finding in rats in which 1.67 μg of testosterone propionate had been implanted in the brain at 5 days of age. In one set of Nadler's animals all mated repeatedly and they mated on an average of 9.2 of 10 successive test days. It should be noted that the animals which mated repeatedly in both of these experiments also exhibited persistent vaginal cornification indicating a relatively constant secretion of estrogen. This same phenomenon may be induced in the adult castrate female by the daily administration of estrogen (Edwards et al., 1968). Since there is no evidence that the

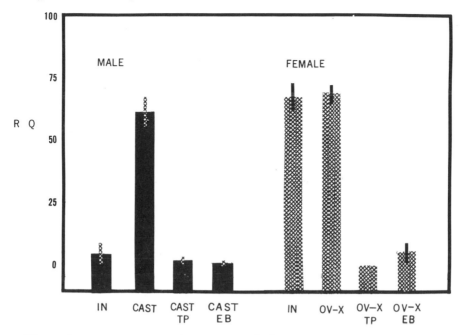

Fig. 3 Receptivity quotient (mounts with lordosis/total mounts) of adult male and female rats treated with estrogen and progesterone following hormonal manipulation at birth. IN, incision controls castrated when adult; **Cast,** castrated at birth; **Cast TP,** castrated and administered testosterone propionate at birth; **Cast EB,** castrated and administered estradiol benzoate at birth; OV-X, overiectomized at birth; OV-X-TP, ovariectomized and administered testosterone propionate at birth; OV-X-EB, ovariectomized and administered estradiol benzoate at birth.
[From Whalen and Edwards (1967).]

repeatedly mating females exhibit more intense receptivity than normal receptive females, repeated mating by itself cannot be considered an indication of "hypersexuality."

The normal male rat differs from the female in the frequency with which lordosis occurs spontaneously or following estrogen–progesterone priming. Normal males rarely exhibit lordosis (Beach, 1945; Feder and Whalen, 1965; Grady et al., 1965; Whalen and Edwards, 1967). The male will, however, develop a potential to display intense receptivity if he is castrated shortly after birth (Feder and Whalen, 1965; Grady et al., 1965; Harris, 1964; Whalen and Edwards, 1966, 1967). Concurrent castration and stimulation by exogenous estrogen does not facilitate, but rather inhibits, the development of this potential (Feder and Whalen, 1965; Whalen and Edwards, 1967). Figure 3 illustrates these effects and shows that males cas-

trated within 24 hours of birth can display lordosis in adulthood.
It is particularly interesting to note that the neonatally castrated
males do not differ from females ovariectomized at birth or in adulthood in their potential to show feminine behavior.

For the potential to display lordosis to develop in the male rat,
he must be castrated shortly after birth. Grady et al. (1965) determined the Receptivity Quotient (mounts with lordosis/total mounts)
of male rats castrated at various times after birth. The RQs of these
animals following adult treatment with estrogen and progesterone are
shown in Fig. 4. It can be seen that castration must occur before
the tenth postnatal day if the male is to show significant levels of
lordosis in adulthood.

Chemical as well as surgical castration of the male allows for the
development of the potential to show female behavior. Neumann and
Elger (1965a, 1965b) treated male rats pre- and postnatally with
antiandrogenic agents. When these animals were mature they received
a transplanted ovary and were tested with sexually active males. The

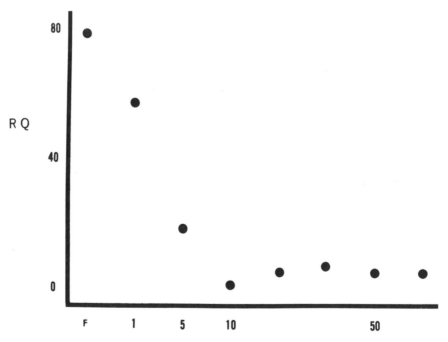

Fig. 4   Receptivity quotient of adult male rats treated with estrogen and progesterone following postnatal castration. The abscissa represents the postnatal day
of castration. "F" indicates the performance of control females. [From Grady et
al. (1965).]

treated animals exhibited the lordosis reflex when mounted and were considered by Neumann and Elger to resemble normal female rats. Unfortunately, these authors presented no data on the intensity of the mating responses of these animals.

The neonatally castrated male rat is *permanently* different from the normal male. Neither testosterone stimulation in adulthood nor the combination of testosterone stimulation and masculine sexual experience will alter the potential of the neonatally castrated male rat to show lordosis (Whalen and Edwards, 1966).

At present there are no definitive data on the development of feminine behavior in the male in species other than the rat. The major reason for this is that sexual differentiation appears to be completed before birth in the other animal whose sexual behavior has been studied extensively, the guinea pig. It is to be expected, however, that studies using the antiandrogenic chemicals will yield information on the hormonal determinants of the development of feminine behavior in the guinea pig in the near future.

Preliminary data from our own laboratory indicate that, like rats, male cats castrated at birth develop the potential to display feminine sexual responses in adulthood. These males exhibit lordosis, hind-leg treading, and tail deviation when mounted. However, some males castrated when adult will also show these signs of receptivity following estrogen treatment (Whalen and Hardy, unpublished). Unfortunately, sufficient data have not yet been collected to draw any firm conclusions about the comparability of the sexual differentiation processes in the rat and cat.

The Development of the Female Behavior Control System—Inhibition. The data reviewed above reveal that the female behaviorial control system develops endogenously when the animal, whether male or female, is not stimulated by hormones during the early maturational period. Data from several laboratories indicate that this female control system can be suppressed in rats and guinea pigs by exogenous androgenic or estrogenic stimulation or by endogeneous androgenic stimulation during the critical developmental period (Barraclough and Gorski, 1962; Feder and Whalen, 1965; Grady et al., 1965; Harris and Levine, 1962, 1965; Levine and Mullins, 1964; Phoenix et al., 1959; Whalen and Edwards, 1967; Whalen and Nadler, 1963, 1965). Figure 5 presents data from the work of Harris and Levine and Barraclough and Gorski which illustrate this suppression effect.

In the female rat the critical period for the suppression of the development of the female system begins at birth and continues until approximately 10 days of age (Goy et al., 1962). Female rats treated

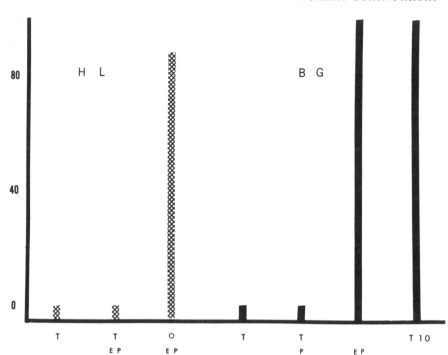

Fig. 5 Percentage of adult female rats displaying lordosis following hormonal treatment 5 days after birth. HL data taken from Harris and Levine (1965); BG data taken from Barraclough and Gorski (1962). **T,** testosterone treatment in infancy (500 µg to 1.25 mg); **T 10,** 10µ of testosterone treatment in infancy; O, oil treatment in infancy; EP, estrogen and progesterone treatment in adulthood; P, progesterone treatment in adulthood.

with testosterone prenatally (Revesz et al., 1963) or after 10 days of age can exhibit the lordosis response at high intensity levels in adulthood. In our laboratory we have found receptive behavior in adult female rats with grossly masculinized genital systems (Whalen et al., 1966). These animals were administered an androgenic artificial progestin prenatally and were tested for receptivity in adulthood. As can be seen in Fig. 6, as the dose of progestin was increased, the degree of genital virilization was increased. In fact, the female rats treated with the highest progestin dose in this experiment never developed an external vaginal orifice. This treatment, however, had no inhibitory effect upon adult mating behavior.

In the guinea pig the development of the female system is inhibited when the animal is hormonally stimulated prior to birth (Phoenix et al., 1959; Young, 1965). The period of maximum suscepti-

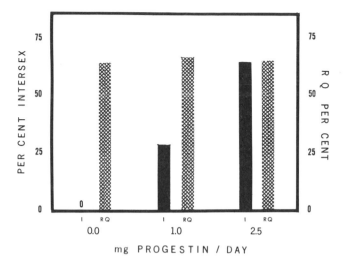

Fig. 6 Solid bars indicate percentage of newborn female rats genitally virilized by prenatally administered androgenic progestin. Intersexes had an anogenital distance at birth of 2.1 to 2.9 mm. Hatched bars indicate the receptivity quotient of the virilized rats following estrogen and progesterone treatment. The abscissa shows the prenatal dose of progestin. [From Whalen et al. (1966).]

bility to androgenic stimulation is between 30 and 35 days postconception (Goy et al., 1964). It is interesting to note that this critical period is similar to that found for the rat if the two species are compared in terms of "days postconception" rather than in terms of "days after birth" (Young, 1965).

It is certainly to be presumed that the inhibition of a female system observed in these studies reflects hormone-induced changes in brain function. However, in none of these studies was the brain directly manipulated. In his thesis project Nadler (1965) accomplished this manipulation by implanting testosterone into the brain of 5-day-old female rats. Nadler found that such treatment could suppress the female system. Females implanted with 12.5 μg of testosterone propionate exhibited only low-intensity receptivity when administered estrogen and progesterone in adulthood. These data support the general assumption that neonatal androgen treatment does alter behavior by its action on the brain.

The inhibition of the female system is not specific to androgenic stimulation. Female rats treated with estrogen shortly after birth also fail to mate spontaneously or in response to estrogen and progesterone treatment in adulthood (Harris and Levine, 1962, 1965; Levine and Mullins, 1964; Whalen and Nadler, 1963, 1965; Whalen and Edwards,

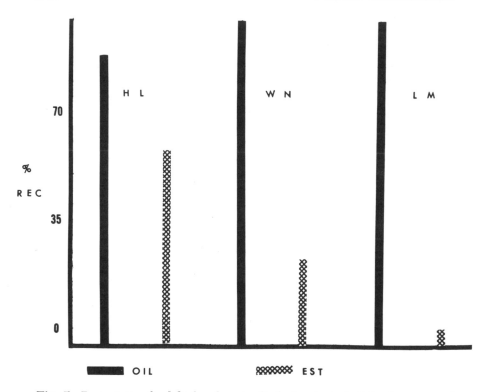

Fig. 7 Percentage of adult female rats displaying lordosis following neonatal treatment with estrogen or oil. HL data taken from Harris and Levine (1965); WN data taken from Whalen and Nadler (1963); LM data taken from Levine and Mullins (1964).

1967). This effect is illustrated in Figs. 3 and 7 by data from three different laboratories. The degree of inhibition produced by estrogen is a function of the dose of estrogen administered the neonate (Whalen and Nadler, 1965).

These studies indicate that rats and guinea pigs of both sexes become male-like in their responsiveness to estrogen and progesterone when stimulated by androgenic and estrogenic steroids in infancy. Presumably these effects mimic the natural suppression of feminine responsiveness which occurs when males are stimulated by endogenously secreted testicular androgen.

The Development of the Masculine Control System—Facilitation. Most normally developing postpuberal male rodents will attempt to mount other animals of the same species. If the mounted animal is a sexually receptive female intromission and ultimately ejaculation may occur. The male rat will continue to copulate until several ejaculations have been achieved (Beach and Jordan, 1956). Male guinea pigs usually achieve only a single ejaculation in a 24-hour period (Grunt and Young, 1952). Adult rodents will cease mating when castrated and will resume mating when treated with the appropriate dose of testosterone. With the rat, but not the guinea pig, the neuromotor control system for this behavior is fully developed well before puberty (Beach, 1942c; Gerall, 1963).

Endogenous hormonal stimulation during postnatal maturation is *not* necessary for the male rat to exhibit masculine mating responses in adulthood. Male rats castrated at birth and administered testosterone in adulthood do exhibit mounting responses (Beach and Holz, 1946; Grady et al., 1965; Whalen and Edwards, 1966, 1967). However, the adult androgen treatment induces behavior qualitatively and quantitatively different from that induced in normal males castrated in adulthood and given exogenous testosterone. Males castrated at birth are less likely to achieve intromission and ejaculation than males castrated in adulthood. Figure 8 illustrates this rela-

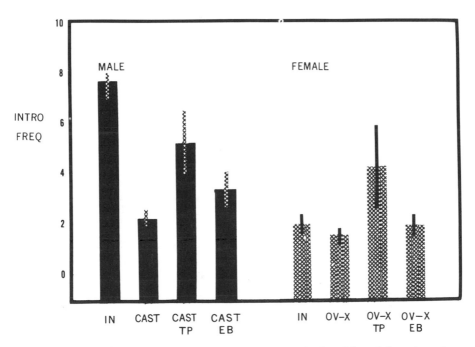

Fig. 8 Mean frequency of the intromission pattern displayed by adult male and female rats treated with testosterone following hormonal manipulation at birth. Group code as in Fig. 3. [From Whalen and Edwards (1967).]

tive reduction in intromission frequency of males castrated at birth.

It is possible to interpret this reduction in masculine behavior as an indication of incomplete sexual differentiation. Grady et al. (1965) seemed to favor this hypothesis but did allow for alternative interpretations. The neonatally castrated male rat not only exhibits incomplete mating in adulthood, but also exhibits incomplete penile development (Beach and Holz, 1946; Grady et al., 1965). The length of the penile shaft is greatly reduced even in animals administered androgen in adulthood. Table 2 contains data obtained in our own

Table 2

Penis Size in Adult Male Rats Hormonally Manipulated at Birth
(From Whalen and Edwards, unpublished)

| | Treatment in adulthood | | | | | |
| | Nothing | | | Testosterone propionate | | |
Treatment at birth	Shaft, mm	Glans, mm	Total, mg	Shaft, mm	Glans, mm	Total, mg
Castration N = 7	9.0	4.3	30.3	10.6	5.9	124.1
Castration + 1.25 mg TP on day 1 N = 8	10.2	5.0	66.4	14.7	6.7	235.8
Castration + 1.25 mg TP on day 4 N = 7	7.1	5.7	55.5	13.4	6.9	218.6

laboratory (Whalen and Edwards, unpublished) from rats castrated at birth and treated with androgen at birth and/or in adulthood. It can be seen that males castrated at birth show reduced penile development even if they were treated with testosterone propionate in infancy. Stimulation with testosterone in adulthood causes an increase in shaft and glans length and an increase in phallic weight. However, this increase is striking only for animals which were androgen-treated in infancy. Apparently the phallus also goes through a critical period of differentiation.

The important question here is whether incomplete penile development can entirely account for the failure of the neonatally castrated animal to achieve intromission and ejaculation or whether this effect is due also to incomplete neural differentiation. Grady et al. (1965) concluded "even now the choice between alternatives is difficult to make." This author favors the hypothesis that the reduced intromission frequency of the neonatally castrated male is due to inadequate penile development. Some of the evidence which has led to this hypothesis is outlined below.

1. Beach and Holz (1946) selected sexually active male rats and in each removed 5 mm of bone from the shaft of the penis. When tested after operation the surviving animals displayed no ejaculations and infrequent mounts with intromission. These animals did exhibit a high frequency of mounts without intromission, indicating that the operation did not alter their basic sexual responsiveness.

2. In our laboratory we took a small set of male rats which did display intromission responses and surgically removed the glans of the penis. Following surgery, these males mounted receptive females repeatedly, but did not achieve intromission.

3. Carlsson and Larsson (1964) took 14 sexually active male rats and bathed the glans penis of 7 of these animals in 2 percent tetracaine, a local anesthetic, shortly before mating tests. The penis of the control animals was bathed in saline. When tested, all the control animals achieved intromission and ejaculated. Among the experimental animals only one intromission and no ejaculations were observed. The tetracaine-treated animals did, however, exhibit vigorous mounting responses.

4. Adler and Bermant (1966) applied either the local anesthetic lidocaine or Vaseline to the penis of male rats. The anesthetic treatment reduced the probability of intromission and ejaculation, but not mounting without intromission.

These data indicate that various manipulations which alter the sensitivity of the penis reduce the probability of intromission and ejaculation. It is very likely that neonatal castration is another treatment which reduces penile sensitivity and, thereby, intromission and ejaculation behavior.

Part of our argument rests on the assumption that mounting behavior is the appropriate index of the presence or absence of a masculine control system. One could contend that the occurrence of intromission or ejaculation is the proper index of masculine behavior. However, since these latter behaviors depend so much upon the state of the phallus for their occurrence, we have come to accept mounting with or without intromission as indicative of masculinity. In essence, we are distinguishing here between masculine "motivation" and masculine sexual "performance." Sexual motivation is seen to be composed of two components, "arousal," a transient state of sexual excitement, and "arousability" the propensity to become aroused by sexual stimuli (Whalen, 1966). Sexual performance, on the other hand, is simply the execution of the discrete component mating responses. Since the neonatally castrated male rat does respond to the female and does display mating responses, we have concluded that this animal is sexually arousable and therefore possesses a functioning masculine motivational control system.

Given our assumption that mounting reflects the state of the masculine control system, there is one other source of evidence which leads us to believe that endogenous androgenic stimulation during the postnatal period in the rat is not necessary for the development of masculine behavior. We have argued that if gonadal hormones are not necessary for the development of the masculine system, both male and female rats should exhibit equivalent levels of masculine behavior when treated with testosterone in adulthood. Further, we felt that if testosterone is necessary in infancy for the development of the system, gonadectomy plus testosterone treatment at birth should result in equivalent facilitation of the masculine system in both male and female despite difference in genital apparatus (Whalen and Edwards, 1967). To test these hypotheses male and female rats were gonadectomized at birth. Some of these animals were also treated with androgen or estrogen at birth; others were sham operated at birth and castrated when mature. When adult all animals were administered testosterone and tested for male behavior. The results of this experiment are shown in Figs. 8 and 9. It is clear that neonatal steroid treatment did not facilitate the display of mounting responses in either males or females, but it did have a dramatic effect upon the display of mounts with intromissions. If we accept the conclusion that the differential intromission frequencies are due to differential phallic development in these animals, we are lead to conclude that the development of the substrate for masculine behavior is independent of hormonal stimulation after birth in the rat, since hormone treatment at birth did not facilitate the tendency to execute mounting responses.*

Figure 9 does indicate that regardless of early postnatal hormonal stimulation, genetic males exhibit mounting behavior more frequently than genetic females. This differential response to androgen in adulthood may indicate that hormone-induced differentiation does occur in the rat but occurs prenatally rather than postnatally. Experiments

---

* Compare the role of the genitalia presented here with its "signal" function stressed by Diamond in Chapter 25. Here the peripheral effects on the genitalia are presented as possibly structuring the behavior. In Diamond's presentation regarding humans, the genitalia primarily serve to orient upbringing, give some indication as to the prenatal and pubertal endocrine environment, and hint at what type of sexual behavior might be anticipated.

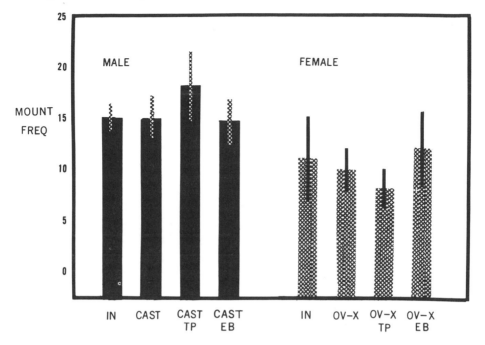

Fig. 9 Mean frequency of mounting responses displayed by adult male and female rats treated with testosterone following hormonal manipulation at birth. Group code as in Fig. 3. [From Whalen and Edwards (1967).]

using prenatal androgenic stimulation or prenatal antiandrogen treatment will help to resolve this problem.

In opposition to the view expressed above, there *is* some evidence which indicates that steroid stimulation during the critical period does facilitate the display of masculine behavior in adulthood: (1) Phoenix et al. (1959) demonstrated that the prenatally androgen-treated female guinea pig exhibits more frequent male-like mounting responses than control females; (2) Harris and Levine (1965) indicated that their neonatally androgen-treated female rats exhibited more frequent mounts than control females; (3) Nadler (1965) reported that his female rats, with neonatal brain implants of testosterone, mounted more frequently than control animals; (4) Levine and Mullins (1964) noted that their female rats treated with estrogen in infancy exhibited more frequent mounts, intromission, and ejaculation patterns than control females following adult treatment with testosterone. All these studies provide some evidence that hormone stimulation during the neonatal period is important for the development of the masculine control system. However, as is evident in Fig. 9, we have not been able to replicate these findings of enhanced mounting activity in neonatally androgen- or estrogen-treated rats.

It should be apparent that our major unanswered question about the role of gonadal hormones in the development of masculine behavior concerns the relative effect of hormone on the differentiation of the central and of the peripheral systems which mediate mating performance. Until we can clearly determine the effect of early hormone stimulation on each of these systems we will not truly understand the differentiation process.

The Development of the Masculine Control System—Inhibition. Early androgen treatment, which leads to the suppression of the female control system, has little or no effect upon the development of masculine behavior in males. Prenatally treated male guinea pigs (Phoenix et al., 1959) and postnatally treated male rats (Harris and Levine, 1965; Whalen, 1964) will exhibit spontaneous and hormone-induced copulatory responses in adulthood. Male rats treated with estrogen in infancy, however, do not exhibit normal masculine behavior in adulthood (Harris and Levine, 1965; Levine and Mullins, 1964; Whalen, 1964). This suppression effect is illustrated in Fig. 10.

At some dose levels, early estrogen treatment completely inhibits spontaneous and hormone-induced mating in adulthood. At other dose levels odd effects are induced. For example, Levine and Mullins (1964) found that male rats treated with 100 μg of estradiol benzoate 96 hours after birth would spontaneously mount receptive females but would not achieve intromission. The mounts which did occur were inappropriately directed at the female. Many of these mounts were directed at the head, side, or high on the back of the female. Whalen (1964) found that early estrogenized males did not spontaneously mate, but when administered testosterone these males directed their thrusting toward the back and not toward the vagina of the female. During four tests during which these males mounted there were 301 mounts without intromission and only one mount with intromission. The nature of this phenomenon is not at all understood. The fact that the deviant pattern has never been observed in neonatally castrated males would seem to indicate that it is not simply due to reduced penile development. To this reviewer's knowledge the inhibition of masculine behavior by early estrogen treatment has not been observed in species other than the rat. Furthermore, the implications of these findings for our understanding of the role of hormones in the ontogeny of masculine behavior are still unclear. The observed effects of early estrogen treatment, nonetheless, are unusual and should not be dismissed as a pharmacological oddity.

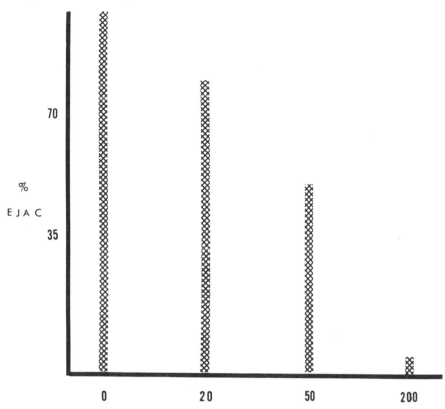

Fig. 10 Percentage of adult male rats displaying the ejaculation response following treatment with 0, 20, 50, or 200 µg of estradiol benzoate 96 hours after birth. [From Whalen (1964).]

Summary

Recent experimentation has demonstrated that the neuro behaviorial control system which underlies female behavior develops endogenously in both males and females if this neural system is not stimulated by gonadal steroids during a critical maturational period. Once this system has developed it cannot be inhibited by androgen or masculine sexual experience. Estrogenic stimulation in the critical period inhibits and does not facilitate the development of this system.

Males and females not stimulated by gonadal hormones during the critical period develop the potential to display some components of the masculine behavioral pattern. Mounting responses, occasional intromission responses, but not ejaculation responses may be induced in these animals. This finding may indicate that androgenic stimulation is needed during development for the complete differentiation of the masculine neurobehavioral control mechanism. However, other evidence supports the hypothesis that androgenic hormones are not critical for masculine differentiation, except as they influence the genital structures which determine sexual performance.

Retrospect and Prospect

Like the ovary, the study of the sexual differentiation of gonadal activity and sexual behavior undergoes cyclic periods of production and quiescence. Unlike the ovary, our knowledge of sexual differentiation does not fluctuate between stable maxima and minima. Each surge of research has had a permanent effect upon later research and upon the total body of information which we possess. In the 1930s and early 1940s we moved from a state of relatively little understanding of differentiation to a state in which we understood many of the relevant parameters of this process. For example, during this period we learned of the characteristics of hormone-induced changes in ovulatory potential and mating, and we learned that the inhibitory effects of early hormone treatment are restricted to a limited period of development. We did not, however, learn that the sexual differentiation of gonadotropin secretion and of sexual behavior is a reflection of the hormone-induced sexual differentiation of the brain. This was a later development.

The late 1940s and early 1950s were periods of very active research on sexuality. In the physiological realm, the work of Harris, Green, Everett, Sawyer, and many others revealed that the adenohypophysis and thereby gonadotropin secretion is neurally controlled. In behavioral studies, Beach, Young, and others outlined the genetic, experiential, and hormonal determinants of mating activity. During this time there was scant study of the sexual differentiation process. The advances made during this period, however, provided the basic conceptual and experimental tools for the work on sexual differentiation which has had its impact in the 1960s.

The past 9 years have seen the development of a new understanding of the nature and parameters of sexual differentiation. This information has been outlined in the present paper.

What of the future? This reviewer foresees two developments in the study of sexual differentiation. First, there will be a progressive decline over the next decade in the amount of effort devoted to the study of sexual differentiation. This should be more evident in the physiological area than in the behavioral area because we already have a better understanding of the factors which control adenohypophyseal-gonadal relationships than of the factors which control sexual behavior. This is not to imply that there will be no major advances in our understanding of the brain–pituitary–gonadal system. We can expect to learn better what components of the nervous system control pituitary function and sex differences in pituitary function. We can expect to learn about brain differentiation and its control over the secretion of the releasing factors of the median eminence. These will be important contributions toward our understanding of sexual differentiation, but these advances should be made within a decade.

In behavioral research, there will also be a decline in the study of sexual differentiation. The characteristics of the process have already been well defined in rats and guinea pigs, and there is relatively little work left to do on this aspect of the problem. Again, research in the next decade should reveal which neural components are involved in differentiation. Some of Nadler's work (1965) hints that the neural components involved in behavior may be different from those which control sex differences in gonadotropin secretion. The validity of this difference should become evident in a very few years.

One area of the study of behaviorial sexual differentiation will probably become more, rather than less, active during the next decade. This is the study of differentiation in primates. Since the early 1960s Young et al. (1964) have been studying the influence of pre-natal androgen stimulation on the postnatal development of sex and sex-related behaviors in the rhesus monkey. They have found that such treatment produces pseudohermaphroditic female monkeys which exhibit male-like behaviors in group situations. Their latest evidence (Goy, 1966) indicates that these females also exhibit fewer female-type presentation responses and more male-type mounting responses than normal intact females. These findings must be considered important. However, because of the complexity of the social situation characteristic of monkey colonies, and because of the major role of experiential factors in monkey behavior, research in this area must expand before we can adequately interpret these findings. It is to be expected that this expansion will occur in the next decade and that we will learn much about the hormonal determinants of primate behavior and about the interactions between the hormonal and experiential determinants of behavior in primates (see Chapter 5).

In spite of the continuing analysis of primate sexuality, we can expect to see increasing disinterest in the study of differentiation. However, after a quiescent era, we can expect a third cycle of activity in this area. This reviewer expects that the third cycle will mimic the second in that it will be characterized by initial replications of the findings generated in the 1960s followed by an extension of these findings. The extension of our present findings will be into the realm of the *neurochemical* control systems which underlie the differences between male and female neuronal functioning.

Today we know relatively little about the relationships between brain chemistry and brain function. In a decade we can expect to know quite a bit more. A cursory examination of the biological sciences today reveals the beginnings of this trend. When the time comes that we have a solid foundation in brain neurochemistry, interest will develop in the neurochemical aspects of sexual differentiation.

Research being published today indicates that this development will be fruitful. One step toward a complete neurochemical analysis of the systems controlling sexual function is represented by the work of Zolovick et al. (1966). These investigators analyzed monamine oxidase (MAO) activity levels in the hypothalamus, amygdala, and frontal cortex throughout the estrous cycle in rats and found that MAO levels fluctuate with this cycle. During diestrus MAO levels are relatively low and they increase to a peak during proestrus and estrus, the absolute levels doubling during this period. The highest absolute levels of MAO during both diestrus and estrus are found in the hypothalamus. The interpretation of these findings presents a problem, however. The authors realize that in this type of study it is impossible to separate cause and effect. Nonetheless, the data do show systematic relationships between brain chemistry and gonadotropin secretion, and for this reason alone these data are valuable.

Meyerson (1964a, 1964b, 1964c, 1966) has shown that central monoamine levels may also be important in behavior. Using pharmacological techniques to selectively alter brain serotonin, noradrenaline, and dopamine levels, he has shown that estrogen-progesterone–induced receptive behavior is inhibited by agents which increase serotonin levels. Further, he has found that agents such as reserpine, which reduce serotonin levels, may be substituted for progesterone in the hormonal induction of receptivity.

These two sets of studies implicate central monoamine systems in the control of gonadotropin secretion and sexual behavior. The neurochemical control of gonadotropin secretion and behavior is not likely to be limited to monoamine systems alone, however. Lindstrom and Meyerson (1966) have recently reported data which also implicate central cholinergic mechanisms in the control of sexual behavior. Until we know much more about neurochemistry it is unlikely that we will be able to interpret these recent findings and develop a new understanding of the central determinants of sexuality. We can, nonetheless, expect to see the development during the next decade of a basic neurochemistry which will allow us to determine the neurochemical basis of sexuality and of sexual differentiation. This will be the future.

Acknowledgment

The research from the author's laboratory described in this review was supported by Grant HD-00893 from the National Institute of Child Health and Human Development of the U.S. Public Health Service.

References

Adler, N., and G. Bermant. 1966. Sexual behavior of male rats: Effects of reduced sensory feedback. *J. Comp. Physiol. Psychol.,* **61:** 240–243.

Barraclough, C. A. 1961. Production of anovulatory, sterile rats by single injections of testosterone propionate. *Endocrinology,* **68:** 62–67.

Barraclough, C. A., and R. A. Gorski. 1961. Evidence that the hypothalamus is responsible for androgen-induced sterility in the female rat. *Endocrinology,* **68:** 68–79.

Barraclough, C. A., and R. A. Gorski. 1962. Studies on mating behaviour in the androgen-sterilized female rat in relation to the hypothalamic regulation of sexual behaviour. *J. Endocrinol.,* **25:** 175–182.

Beach, F. A. 1938. Sex reversals in the mating pattern of the rat. *J. Genet. Psychol.,* **53:** 329–334.

Beach, F. A. 1941. Female mating behavior shown by male rats after administration of testosterone propionate. *Endocrinology,* **29:** 409–412.

Beach, F. A. 1942a. Importance of progesterone to induction of sexual receptivity in spayed female rats. *Proc. Soc. Exptl. Biol. Med.,* **51:** 369–371.

Beach, F. A. 1942b. Execution of the complete masculine copulatory pattern by sexually receptive female rats. *J. Genet. Psychol.,* **60:** 137–142.

Beach, F. A. 1942c. Sexual behavior of prepuberal male and female rats treated with gonadal hormones. *J. Comp. Psychol.,* **34:** 285–292.

Beach, F. A. 1942d. Male and female mating behavior in prepuberally castrated female rats treated with androgens. *Endocrinology,* **31:** 673–678.

Beach, F. A. 1942e. Copulatory behavior in prepuberally castrated male rats and its modification by estrogen administration. *Endocrinology,* **31:** 679–683.

Beach, F. A. 1945. Bisexual mating behavior in the male rat: Effects of castration and hormone administration. *Physiol. Zool.,* **18:** 390–402.

Beach, F. A., and A. M. Holz. 1946. Mating behavior in male rats castrated at various ages and injected with androgen. *J. Exptl. Zool.,* **101:** 91–142.

Beach, F. A., and A. M. Holz-Tucker. 1949. Effects of different concentrations of androgen upon sexual behavior in castrated male rats. *J. Comp. Physiol. Psychol.,* **42:** 433–453.

Beach, F. A., and L. Jordan. 1956. Sexual exhaustion and recovery in the male rat. *Quart. J. Exptl. Psychol.,* **8:** 121–133.

Beach, F. A., and P. Rasquin. 1942. Masculine copulatory behavior in intact and castrated female rats. *Endocrinology,* **31:** 393–409.

Beach, F. A., and R. E. Whalen, 1959a. Effects of ejaculation on sexual behavior in the male rat. *J. Comp. Physiol. Psychol.,* **52:** 249–254.

Beach, F. A., and R. E. Whalen. 1959b. Effects of intromission without ejaculation upon sexual behavior in male rats. *J. Comp. Physiol. Psychol.,* **52:** 476–481.

Bloch, G. J., and J. M. Davidson. 1967. Antiandrogen implanted in brain stimulates male reproductive system. *Science,* 155: 593–594.

Bogdanove, E. M. 1964. The role of the brain in the regulation of pituitary gonadotropin secretion. *Vitamin Hormone,* 22: 205–260.

Bradbury, J. T. 1941. Permanent after-effects following masculinization of the infantile female rat. *Endocrinology,* 28: 101–106.

Carlsson, S. G., and K. Larsson. 1964. Mating in male rats after local anesthetization of the glans penis. *Z. Tierpsychol.,* 21: 854–856.

Diamond, M., and E. Dale. 1967. Distribution of radiolabeled steroid after administration to the neonatal rat. *Anat. Rec.,* 157: 234 (Abstr.).

Edwards, D. A., R. E. Whalen, and R. D. Nadler. 1968. The induction of estrus: Estrogen-progesterone interactions. *Physiol. Behavior,* 3: 29–33.

Everett, J. W. 1964. Central neural control of reproductive functions of the adenohypophysis. *Physiol. Rev.,* 44: 373–431.

Feder, H. H., and R. E. Whalen. 1965. Feminine behavior in neonatally castrated and estrogen-treated male rats. *Science,* 147: 306–307.

Gerall, A. A. 1963. The effect of prenatal and postnatal injections of testosterone propionate on prepuberal male guinea pig sexual behavior. *J. Comp. Physiol. Psychol.,* 56: 92–95.

Goodman, L. 1934. Observations on transplanted immature ovaries in the eyes of adult male and female rats. *Anat. Rec.,* 59: 223–252.

Gorski, R. A. 1963. Modification of ovulatory mechanisms by postnatal administration of estrogen to the rat. *Am. J. Physiol.,* 205: 842–844.

Gorski, R. A. 1966. Localization and sexual differentiation of the nervous structures which regulate ovulation. *J. Reprod. Fertility* (Suppl. 1): 67–88.

Gorski, R. A., and C. A. Barraclough. 1963. Effects of low dosages of androgen on the differentiation of hypothalamic regulatory control of ovulation in the rat. *Endocrinology,* 73: 210–216.

Gorski, R. A., and J. W. Wagner. 1965. Gonadal activity and sexual differentiation of the hypothalamus. *Endocrinology,* 76: 226–239.

Goy, R. W. 1966. Role of androgens in the establishment and regulation of behavioral sex differences in mammals. *J. Animal Sci.,* 25: 21–31.

Goy, R. W., C. H. Phoenix, and W. C. Young. 1962. A critical period for the suppression of behavioral receptivity in adult female rats by early treatment with androgen. *Anat. Rec.,* 142: 307 (Abstr.).

Goy, R. W., W. E. Bridson, and W. C. Young. 1964. Period of maximum susceptibility of the prenatal female guinea pig to masculinizing actions of testosterone propionate. *J. Comp. Physiol. Psychol.,* 57: 166–174.

Grady, K. L., C. H. Phoenix, and W. C. Young. 1965. Role of the developing rat testis in differentiation of the neural tissues mediating mating behavior. *J. Comp. Physiol. Psychol.,* 59: 176–182.

Greep, R. O. 1936. Functional pituitary grafts in rat. *Proc. Soc. Exptl. Biol. Med.,* 34: 754–755.

Grunt, J. A., and W. C. Young. 1952. Psychological modification of fatigue following orgasm (ejaculation) in the male guinea pig. *J. Comp. Physiol Psychol,* 45: 508–510.

Harris, G. W. 1955. *Neural Control of the Pituitary Gland.* Arnold, London.

Harris, G. W. 1964. Sex hormones, brain development and brain function. *Endocrinology,* 75: 627–648.

Harris, G. W., and D. Jacobsohn. 1952. Functional grafts of the anterior pituitary gland. *Proc. Roy. Soc. London,* B139: 263–276.

Harris, G. W., and S. Levine. 1962. Sexual differentiation of the brain and its experimental control. *J. Physiol.* (*London*), 163: 42P–43P.

Harris, G. W., and S. Levine. 1965. Sexual differentiation of the brain and its experimental control. *J. Physiol.* (*London*), 181: 379–400.

Koster, R. 1943. Hormone factors in male behavior of the female rat. *Endocrinology*, 33: 337–348.

Kuehn, R. E., and F. A. Beach. 1963. Quantitative measurement of sexual receptivity in female rats. *Behaviour*, 21: 282–299.

Levine, S., and R. F. Mullins, Jr. 1964. Estrogen administered neonatally affects adult sexual behavior in male and female rats. *Science*, 144: 185–187.

Lindstrom, L., and B. J. Meyerson. 1966. Effects of cholinergic and anticholinergic agents on estrogen-progesterone activated estrus behaviour in ovariectomized rats. *Acta Physiol. Scand.*, 68 (*Suppl. 277*): 121.

Meyerson, B. J. 1964a. Central nervous monoamines and hormone induced estrus behaviour in the spayed rat. *Acta Physiol. Scand.*, 63 (*Suppl. 241*): 1–32.

Meyerson, B. J. 1964b. The effect of neuropharmacological agents on hormone-activated estrus behaviour in ovariectomized rats. *Arch. Intern. Pharmacodyn.*, 150: 4–33.

Meyerson, B. J. 1964c. Estrus behaviour in spayed rats after estrogen or progesterone treatment in combination with reserpine or tetrabenazine. *Psychopharmacologica*, 6: 210–218.

Meyerson, B. J. 1966. The effect of imipramine and related antidepressive drugs on estrus behaviour in ovariectomized rats activated by progesterone, reserpine or tetrabenazine in combination with estrogen. *Acta Physiol. Scand.*, 67: 411–422.

Nadler, R. D. 1965. Masculinization of the female rat by intracranial implantation of androgen in infancy. Unpublished Doctoral dissertation, University of California, Los Angeles.

Neumann, F., and W. Elger. 1965a. Proof of the activity of androgenic agents on the differentiation of the external genitalia, the mammary gland and the hypothalamic-pituitary system in rats. In *Androgens in normal and pathological conditions. Excerpta Med. Intern. Congr. Ser.*, 101: 168–185.

Neumann, F., and W. Elger. 1965b. Physiological and psychical intersexuality of male rats by early treatment with an anti-androgenic agent (1,2 α-methylene-6-chloro-Δ^6-hydroxyprogesterone acetate). *Acta Endocrinol. Suppl.*, 100: 174.

Neumann, F., and M. Kramer. 1966. Female "brain" differentiation of male rats as a result of early treatment with an androgen antagonist. *Excerpta Med. Intern. Congr. Ser.*, 111 (Abstr.).

Neumann, F., W. Elger, and M. Kramer. 1966. Development of a vagina in male rats by inhibiting androgen receptors with an anti-androgen during the critical phase of organogenesis. *Endocrinology*, 78: 628–632.

Pfeiffer, C. A. 1936. Sexual differences of the hypophyses and their determination by the gonads. *Am. J. Anat.*, 58: 195–225.

Phoenix, C. H., R. W. Goy, A. A. Gerall, and W. C. Young. 1959. Organizing action of prenatally administered testosterone propionate on the tissues mediating mating behavior in the female guinea pig. *Endocrinology*, 65: 369–382.

Revesz, C., D. Kernaghan, and D. Bindra. 1963. Sexual drive of female rats "masculinized" by testosterone during gestation. *J. Endocrinol.*, 25: 549–550.

Swanson, H. E., and J. J. van der Werff ten Bosch. 1964. The "early-androgen" syndrome: Differences in response to prenatal and postnatal administration of various doses of testosterone propionate in female and male rats. *Acta Endocrinol.*, **47**: 37–50.

Takewaki, K. 1962. Some aspects of hormonal mechanism involved in persistent estrus in the rat. *Experientia*, **18**: 1–6.

Wagner, J. W., W. Erwin, and B. V. Critchlow. 1966. Androgen sterilization produced by intracerebral implants of testosterone in neonatal female rats. *Endocrinology*, **79**: 1135–1142.

Whalen, R. E. 1964. Hormone-induced changes in the organization of sexual behavior in the male rat. *J. Comp. Physiol. Psychol.*, **57**: 175–182.

Whalen, R. E. 1966. Sexual motivation. *Psychol. Rev.*, **73**: 151–163.

Whalen, R. E., and D. A. Edwards. 1966. Sexual reversibility in neonatally castrated male rats. *J. Comp. Physiol. Psychol.*, **62**: 307–310.

Whalen, R. E., and D. A. Edwards. 1967. Hormonal determinants of the development of masculine and feminine behavior in male and female rats. *Anat. Rec.*, **157**: 173–180.

Whalen, R. E., and R. D. Nadler. 1963. Suppression of the development of female mating behavior by estrogen administered in infancy. *Science*, **141**: 273–274.

Whalen, R. E., and R. D. Nadler. 1965. Modification of spontaneous and hormone-induced sexual behavior by estrogen administered to neonatal female rats. *J. Comp. Physiol. Psychol.*, **60**: 150–152.

Whalen, R. E., C. K. Peck, and J. Lo Piccolo. 1966. Virilization of female rats by prenatally administered progestin. *Endocrinology*, **78**: 965–970.

Wilson, J. G. 1943. Reproductive capacity of adult female rats treated prepuberally with estrogenic hormone. *Anat. Rec.*, **86**: 341–359.

Wilson, J. G., W. C. Young, and J. B. Hamilton. 1940. A technic suppressing development of reproductive function and sensitivity to estrogen in the female rat. *Yale J. Biol. Med.*, **13**: 189–202.

Wilson, J. G., J. B. Hamilton, and W. C. Young. 1941. Influence of age and presence of the ovaries on reproductive function in rats injected with androgens. *Endocrinology*, **29**: 784–789.

Yazaki, I. 1959. Effects of adrenalectomy, injections of hormonic steroids or gonadotrophins and subjection to stressful stimuli on subcutaneous ovarian grafts in castrated male rats as studied by daily examinations of vaginal smears. *Japan. J. Zool.*, **12**: 267–277.

Yazaki, I. 1960. Further studies on endocrine activity of subcutaneous ovarian grafts in male rats by daily examination of smears from vaginal grafts. *Annot. Zool. Japon.*, **33**: 217–225.

Young, W. C. 1965. The organization of sexual behavior by hormonal action during the prenatal and larval periods in vertebrates. In *Sex and Behavior* (F. A. Beach, ed.). Wiley, New York, pp. 89–107.

Young, W. C., R. W. Goy, and C. H. Phoenix. 1964. Hormones and sexual behavior. *Science*, **143**: 212–218.

Zolovick, A. J., R. Pearse, K. W. Boehlke, and B. E. Eleftheriou. 1966. Monoamine oxidase activity in various parts of the rat brain during the estrous cycle. *Science*, **154**: 649.

Zucker, I. 1966. Facilitatory and inhibitory effects of progesterone on sexual responses of spayed guinea pigs. *J. Comp. Physiol. Psychol.*, **62**: 376–381.

21

Pheromonal Influences on Mammalian Reproduction

F. H. Bronson

Investigations of specific sensory systems as mediators of environmental stimuli which regulate mammalian reproductive performance have concentrated heavily on light–optic–endocrine interactions. This is not surprising considering the importance of photoperiodicity as a regulator of seasonal and diurnal cycles. Olfaction, on the other hand, has often been conceptualized as playing a primary role only in the mediation of stimuli that support, but may not be essential to, sex and parental behavior. During the last few years a body of literature has developed which indicates that olfactory stimuli may also play a more central role. It is the intent of this paper to provide both a synthesis and an overview of our knowledge concerning both types of socio-olfactory stimuli and their effects on mammalian reproductive processes.

Both a model and a system of terminology for studying olfactory communication have already been provided by entomologists. The term "pheromone" denotes a chemical substance that is liberated by one animal and which results in relatively specific modification of the behavior of a recipient animal following its chemoreception or ingestion (Kalmus, 1964). Some degree of species specificity is usually implied but exceptions are known (Wilson and Bossert, 1963). A rich foundation of knowledge about the chemistry, modes of action, and functions of insect pheromones is available and, as an example of such phenomena, the process of sex attraction among certain moths has become a classic in biology. How far the concepts developed by entomologists may be generalized is uncertain. Initially, however, categorization of chemical stimuli into two types based on function appears as warranted in mammals as it does in insects. Wilson and Bossert (1963) have classified pheromones as being either "primer" or "releaser," depending upon how directly they act on the central nervous system to modify a recipient's behavior; a releaser acting rapidly and directly (e.g., a sex attractant) while a primer activates a longer series of physiological events (e.g., the inhibition of oogenesis). While a dichotomy of function is warranted. the term releaser probably should not be generalized to mammals, since it has been used to denote both an innateness and a degree of fixedness of response that is probably not applicable to many complex and modifiable mammalian behavior patterns. The term primer is probably acceptable as a descriptive modifier even though most or all such substances act following ingestion in insects, while these effects are probably brought about by olfactory (or accessory olfactory) mediation in mammals (Whitten, 1966). At the risk of confusion by proliferation of terms, the rest of this paper will categorize mammalian substances as either signaling (e.g., releasing) or priming pheromones.

Signaling Pheromones

A wealth of observational information supports the concept that olfactory stimuli often play a primary (but not necessarily an exclusive) role in intrapopulation communication and precopulatory behavior in mammals (Hediger, 1951; Bourliere, 1955; Schloeth, 1956; Wynne-Edwards, 1962). It is unfortunate that this area of behavioral research has attracted relatively little experimental endeavor, and hence solid evidence on which to base a discussion about olfactory signals is scanty. The situation is somewhat paradoxical since considerable information is already available concerning some of the substances themselves; i.e., specialized glands which probably have pheromonal functions have been studied physiologically and anatomically in a wide variety of species (see Parkes and Bruce, 1961) and, in addition, several pheromonal substances have been examined by chemists (e.g., civetone, muskone, and castoreum; Lederer, 1950;

Kingston, 1964). Almost never have chemists and mammalian behaviorists found themselves working on the same problems.

Because in so few instances is our information on the chemistry and modes of action of signaling pheromones correlated with behavioral responses, it seems premature to attempt categorization at any level other than that of four general communicative functions: identifying, attracting, repelling (and/or inhibiting), and arousing. It should be noted that one odorous substance could serve all these purposes and, furthermore, that the amount of overlap between such functions is obviously great. It should also be noted that no implication of stereotyped responses is intended by the use of entomological terms.

Information regarding several levels of identification may be transmitted by odorous substances: species, sex, state of sexual activity, and membership in a strange versus the home "colony" (Barnett, 1963). In addition, laboratory rats can even be trained to discriminate between two males of the same age, apparently utilizing olfactory stimuli as primary cues (Husted and McKenna, 1966). Identification of the signaling animal, once accomplished, may be followed by attraction, avoidance, or no response on the part of the recipient animal. Examples of olfactory attraction to a receptive female are reports for dogs (Beach and Gilmore, 1949), deer (Golley, 1957), and rats (LeMagnen, 1952). Sex attraction is a two-way process; for example, estrous ewes will successfully seek out a ram without the use of visual cues (Lindsay, 1966). A series of papers by Carr and his associates (Carr and Caul, 1962; Carr et al., 1965, 1966) has examined the relative roles of gonadal state and past sexual experience as modifiers of identification–attraction responses in rats. Ability of rats of either sex to detect odors of sexually active members of the opposite sex is independent of their own gonadal state. Attraction to that odor, on the other hand, requires that females be either sexually experienced or under the influence of estrogen while positive responses by males require both androgen and sexual experience. Of particular interest to future studies of identification–attraction phenomena is the report by Barraclough and Cross (1963), who found a threefold increase in the number of single units in the diencephalon that responded to smell (ethyl acetate) during proestrus when compared to estrus and metestrus.

Studies on the androgen-dependent chin gland of the Australian rabbit provide the best evidence for the existence of repelling or inhibiting signals (Myktowycz, 1962, 1965). Socially dominant males have large chin glands and spend a large proportion of their daily activities in chinning objects, including does and young. Subordinate males have smaller glands and chin less often while chinning by all males is inhibited to a great degree when in another buck's territory. The functions of this gland, then, as discerned by direct behavioral observation, are those of repelling or inhibiting certain behaviors of other males. The repellent action of the odor of one male upon another has been demonstrated for other species, e.g., mice (Chanel and Varnet-Maury, 1963).

Information of the type discussed above could undoubtedly be transmitted by other sensory modalities, and hence we must consider pheromones as often playing a primary but not necessarily an exclusive role in such communication. For example, a ram loses its normal preference for an estrous over a nonestrous ewe when rendered anosmic, yet rams which are thoroughly experienced in semen-collecting procedures (tethered ewe, artificial vagina) learn to ignore olfactory signals entirely and will even attempt to mount a tethered castrate male (Lindsay, 1965). The prime utility of olfactory signals, then, occurs at long range and under natural population conditions (the "broadcast" type of sexual stimuli of Schein and Hale, 1965). Unfortunately distance components have not been examined in mammalian pheromone studies. The documentation of a high degree of olfactory sensitivity for a few mammals, nevertheless, would indicate their potential importance. Carr et al. (1962) found some male rats still able to detect the smell of urine from an estrous female when air was drawn across a mixture containing as little as 1 part urine to 100,000 parts water and many workers have documented the olfactory sensitivity of dogs to biological odors (Kalmus, 1955; Kloek, 1961; King et al. 1964).

An arousal function for mammalian pheromones has been documented both electrically in the hypothalamus and by observation of overt behavior. Lissak (1962), for example, reported that the odor of valeric acid resulted in both estrus-like behavior and relatively specific changes in the electrical activity of the anterior hypothalamus in anestrus cats (no changes in the posterior hypothalamus, amygdala, or reticular systems). The characteristic changes in hypothalamic activity were enhanced by estrogen but unaltered by progesterone or testosterone. Lissak (1962) postulated that valeric acid mimicked a female-originating pheromone, since vaginal smears of estrous females elicited somewhat similar responses. Catnip may possibly mimic an arousal-type pheromone normally found in the urine of male cats, since an ether-extractable fraction of male (but not female) urine elicits a catnip-like response: head shaking and rolling (Todd, 1963). The catnip response resembles an aspect of estrous behavior but some degree of confusion exists relative to the pheromone's function, since the response is independent of either sex or gonadal state (Palen and Goddard, 1966). Signoret and du Mesnil du Buisson (1961) demonstrated that 90 percent of their estrous sows would assume a copulatory stance given the sound and smell of a boar and pressure of a handler's hand (compared to 51 percent for hand pressure only). Finally, it is probable that all identification–attraction type pheromones result in some degree of CNS arousal particularly in sexually experienced animals. How necessary pheromonal-induced arousal is to normal copulatory behavior in those species where it occurs, however, is not known.

An important area of pheromonal function that has received relatively little attention is in adult–young interactions. Retrieval of young rats by their mothers is definitely multisensorial but recognition of individual young seems to be primarily olfactory (Beach and Jaynes, 1956a, 1956b). Birth fluid of goats contains a potent, labile factor or factors which immediately mark newborn kids individually (Klopfer et al., 1964).

Priming Pheromones

Two recent and excellent reviews by Bruce (1966) and Whitten (1966) have extensively documented the existence of primer pheromones in mammals. Mediating sensory systems are thought to be olfactory, but accessory olfactory (e.g., vomeronasal) pathways cannot be ruled out (Whitten, 1963). No primer pheromones have been identified so far; however, at least three separate phenomena are known from studies of laboratory mice: (1) suppression of estrus by all-female grouping (van der Lee and Boot, 1955; Whitten, 1957); (2) a factor in male urine which accelerates the attainment of estrus (Whitten, 1956a); and (3) an olfactory discrimination on the part of a recently inseminated female that is made between the urines of stud and strange males and which leads to implantation failure (Bruce, 1959).

Suppression of the estrous cycle among all-female groups of mice apparently has two bases: an increase in the incidence of spontaneous pseudopregnancy and a prolongation of diestrus. All-female grouping may result in spontaneous pseudopregnancy rates as high as 61 percent of all cycles compared to 0 to 2 percent in isolates (Dewar, 1959). True pseudopregnancy has been confirmed by several techniques, including deciduoma formation (Caschera, 1960; van der Lee and Boot, 1955). Workers in three laboratories have shown that this response is alleviated by olfactory lobectomy, thereby implicating an odor passed from female to female as the causative agent (van der Lee and Boot, 1956; Biancifiori and Caschera, 1963; Mody, 1963). Of a somewhat different nature are reports where all-female grouping typically resulted in a condition of prolonged diestrus. Whitten (1959) reported anestrum of up to 40 days duration acompanied by decreased ovarian and uterine weight and, importantly, a rapid return to estrus when females were paired with a male—decidedly not characteristics of pseudopregnancy. Other investigators have reported similar findings (Lamond, 1958a; Mody and Christian, 1962). The olfactory mediation of such prolonged diestrum has not been critically confirmed, but Whitten (1959) demonstrated that such suppression was independent of vision, audition, and physical contact.

It has been assumed that differences in cage (population) density promote the appearance of the two types of cycle irregularities (Parkes and Bruce, 1961; Whitten, 1966). This is an intriguing possibility but an unsafe assumption since the evidence is based on different stocks of mice studied in different laboratories. Just as reasonable would be to look to differences in genetic background or an early experiential variable as possible causative factors. Strain differences in all-female grouping responses are known (Muhlbock and Boot, 1960; Krzanowska, 1964) and a variety of reports indicating altered hypothalamic–pituitary–target organ responses because of early experiential factors make it unsafe to dismiss this latter possibility. It is tempting, nevertheless, to look at the two types of aberrant cycles as merely different degrees of the same physiologic alteration; a relaxation of the normal tonic inhibition exerted by the hypothalamus on luteotropin release and an accompanying decrease in circulating gonadotropin.

The presence of another primer pheromone, having as its function the induction and acceleration of the estrous cycle, was first noted and has been most extensively examined by Whitten (1956a). The pheromone is found in male urine (Marsden and Bronson, 1964) and is either an androgen metabolite or the product of androgen-maintained tissues, since castration removes it from urine and testosterone therapy in castrates of either sex returns it (Bronson and Whitten, 1967). Strains of mice differ in their capacity to produce this urine factor; e.g., hybrid males apparently produce more than inbreds (Krzanowska, 1964) and males heterozygous for the lethal yellow gene are reportedly deficient in it (Bartke and

Wolff, 1966). The pheromone is apparently transmitted as a vapor and reception is (also apparently) either olfactory or accessory olfactory since (1) the acceleration of the female's estrous cycle does not require vision, audition, or physical contact with a male and will occur to some degree just in the presence of male-soiled bedding (Whitten, 1958); and (2) the presence of males in the same animal room with females is sufficiently stimulating to alter expected patterns of estrus (Chipman and Fox, 1966).

The action of the urine factor requires prolonged (24 to 48 hours) exposure while the female is in either a metestrus or diestrus condition (Whitten, 1957). For this reason its effects are most easily demonstrated among females whose cycles have been suppressed by grouping. Introduction of a male or his urine then simultaneously initiates cycling in many females and results in a synchronization of estrus 3 or 4 days later (Whitten, 1957, 1959; Lamond, 1959). There is no carryover of the pheromone's effect from one cycle to the next. Isolation of previously grouped females, because it releases them from the suppressive effects of grouping, will also act somewhat as a synchronizer of estrus (Marsden and Bronson, 1965a). Since the pathway of the urine factor undoubtedly involves hypothalamic mediation, the recent findings of a more rapid sexual maturity among females in the presence of an adult male is not unexpected (Vandenbergh, 1967; Castro, personal communication). Species specificity of the male urine factor has been confirmed in a very limited manner (Marsden and Bronson, 1965a), but a concurrent report of some degree of strain-specificity has not stood up to more intensive examination.

The development of knowledge about the two priming factors discussed so far, those associated with all-female grouping and the male urinary pheromone, actually forces us to reopen the question of what is to be considered the normal estrous cycle of mice. A series of data recently gathered on two inbred strains may be used as an illustration. Adult females of either the 129/J or C57BL/6J strains were grouped in a male-free room for 2 weeks to suppress their cycles. The females were then either isolated, regrouped seven or eight per cage, or regrouped and housed under drip cages containing 8 to 10 C57BL/6J males (i.e., the bottom of the males' cages terminated in tubes that entered the tops of females' cages, allowing urine to drip on them while fecal material was retained by screening; see Bronson and Whitten, 1968. Vaginal smears were obtained for 12 consecutive days beginning on the third day after the change in housing. The data (Fig. 1) show a strong interaction be-

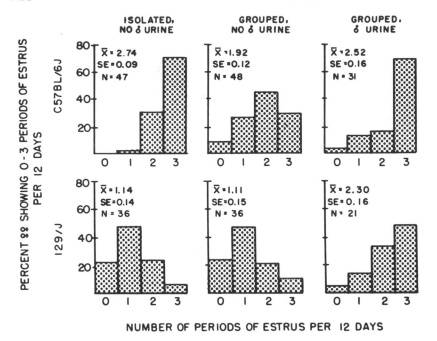

Fig. 1 Frequency of estrus in two strains of mice when either isolated or grouped (7 to 8 per cage) in a room free of male odor or grouped and exposed to male urine by housing them under drip cages containing males.

tween experimental condition and strain. The C57BL/6J strain showed a mode of three periods of estrus when maintained under either of two conditions: isolated in a male-free room or exposed to male urine. This strain showed a mode of only two periods per 12 days when grouped in a male-free room, thus illustrating the suppressive effects of grouping in the absence of male odor. The 129/J strain, on the other hand, showed a slower cycle in the absence of male odor averaging only one period of estrus in 12 days regardless of whether isolated or grouped, but exposure to male urine accelerated the cycle to a mode of three periods in 12 days. These data on frequency of estrus may be used to infer cycle length, and hence three classes of cycle lengths were observed (modes of 1, 2, or 3 periods of estrus per 12 days)—all "normal," depending upon what genetic background and olfactory environment were studied. Significant differences between the two strains occurred only in the absence of male odor, while a suppression of estrus due to all-female grouping occurred only in one of the two strains under consideration. The 4 to 5-day cycle usually recorded as average for the mouse, therefore, probably reflects, to a large degree, a considerable amount of data obtained in poorly ventilated animal rooms. The fact that both strains responded in a marked manner to male urine supports this concept.

A third primer effect to be considered is that in which exposure of a recently inseminated female mouse to any male other than her stud results in implantation failure and a rapid return to estrus (during which she will mate with the second male; Bruce, 1959, 1961a, 1966). Experimentally induced pseudopregnancy may be altered in a similar manner (Dominic, 1966a). The effectiveness of the strange male definitely depends upon his genetic relationship with the stud; up to 80 percent of the pregnancies being blocked if the two males are of different strains and considerably lower if the two are of the same strain (Parkes and Bruce, 1961). Interestingly enough, exposure to a single strange male is as stimulating as exposure to many (Bruce, 1963). Like the accelerating factor discussed previously, the presence of the male may be duplicated using urine pooled from strange males (Dominic, 1964; 1966b) and is entirely androgen-dependent; castration inhibiting the effectiveness of male urine, and androgen therapy in castrates of either sex returning it (Bruce, 1965; Dominic, 1965). Strain differences in the ability of a male to produce the pheromonal substances are known (Bruce, 1963). Transmission to the female is probably as a vapor and olfactory- or accessory olfactory-mediated, since the effect can be reproduced using dirty cages (Parkes and Bruce, 1962) and olfactory lobectomy abolishes the response (Bruce and Parrott, 1960). Volatility of the pheromonal component(s) can prove troublesome (Parkes and Bruce, 1962; Dominic, 1966b). The first 4 days following insemination are about equally susceptible to the blocking stimulus in laboratory mice; 12 hours of exposure resulting in some blocking but maximal effects requiring 48 hours of exposure to the strange male (Bruce, 1961b). Chipman et al. (1966), using wild house mouse males, obtained significant effects with only three 15-minute exposures per day for 4 days.

The obvious effect of the pheromonal discrimination by the inseminated female is to inhibit luteotropin release and hence block implantation because of the failure of functional development of the corpora lutea. Our information on this point is conclusive: The effect of a strange male or his urine can be abolished by either endogenous prolactin (Bruce and Parkes, 1960; Dominic, 1966c) or large doses of progesterone (Dominic, 1966d) and does not occur in either lactating females (Bruce and Parkes, 1960) or in females bearing ectopic pituitary implants (Dominic, 1966c). Ovarian histology in blocked females also supports this concept (Bruce, 1960; Dominic, 1966c). Reserpine inhibits the response to a strange male, reportedly because of its hypothalamic action on prolactin release (Dominic, 1966e) but possibly also because of a depression of stimulus transmission along higher pathways.

Whitten (1966) has invoked the concept of a reciprocal relationship between luteotropin and FSH release (Everett, 1963) to postulate that the estrus-accelerating and implantation-blocking effects of male urine are actually due to the same pheromone. Whitten (1966) has also mentioned the possibility of more individual "identifier" pheromones to account for the fact that the blocking response has its basis in a discrimination between two males, while, apparently, any male urine (of the correct species) will accelerate estrus. Establishing the validity of this thesis will undoubtedly await not only more definitive (chemical) isolation of the odors involved but also further clarification of the relationships between the various releasing factors in the hypothalamus. On the surface, however, what appears to be the more demanding role played by the CNS in the blocking response may not be sufficiently explained by postulating the presence of identifiers. For example, the female's blocking response is strongly modified by beforehand exposure to many males or by simultaneous exposure to many females (Parkes and Bruce, 1961). In addition, many highly inbred strains of mice have lost the blocking phenomenon, probably due to the high levels of unintentional selection which normally accompany inbreeding (Marsden and Bronson, 1965b), yet the estrus-accelerating pheromone is common among these strains. These findings do not negate Whitten's hypothesis; they do indicate that considerable more information is needed and that the picture is far from complete at this time.

The possible importance of such primer pheromones in the reproduction of mammalian species other than house mice is still unclear. Indirect indications exist for sheep (see Hulet, 1966), pigs (Signoret and du Buisson, 1961), goats (Shelton, 1960), and possibly voles (Chitty and Austin, 1957). In one species, the prairie deermouse, it has been established that all-female grouping will suppress estrus and that exposure to male urine will both accelerate estrus and block implantation (Bronson and Eleftheriou, 1963; Bronson and Marsden, 1964; unpublished). Pseudopregnancy rate may be influenced by social conditions in rats (Alloiteau, 1962; Everett, 1963), but the pregnancy blocking response could not be demonstrated (Davis and de Groot, 1964). Considering the effects of inbreeding and strain variability reported for various stocks of mice, the negative pregnancy blocking results obtained in one stock of rats should not be generalized at this time. Of particular interest would be pheromonal studies involving wild rats.

Indirect physiological evidence for the possible importance of primer pheromones occurs in a variety of studies involving olfactory insult or anosmia. For example, irrigation of the nasal mucosa with either ammonia (Takewaki, 1949) or silver nitrate (Rosen et al., 1940) induces pseudopregnancy in rats. David et al. (1952) report modification of the vaginal cycle of cats following electrical stimulation of the olfactory bulb, and Lissak (1962) found some follicle growth after 24-hour exposure to valeric acid in the same species. Olfactory lobectomy is followed by anestrus in guinea pigs (Magnotti, 1936) and by relatively specific inhibition of FSH release in pigs (Signoret and Mauleon, 1962). Sawyer (1955) prevented histamine activation of the pituitary in nembutalized female rabbits by ablation of their olfactory bulbs. Reports dealing with anosmia in rabbits show conflicting results (Brooks, 1937; Franck, 1966a, 1966b). With respect to mice, Whitten (1956b) reported the reduction of genital tracts to an immature or castrate condition following bulbectomy in females, Lamond (1958b) reported similar but more variable findings, but several workers have utilized anosmic females in reproductive experiments with no apparent difficulty (van der Lee and Boot, 1956; Bruce and Parrott, 1960; Biancifiori and Caschera, 1963). Ablation of the olfactory lobes was followed by no demonstrable gonadal changes in either rats (Rosen et al., 1940) or ewes (Signoret, 1964). The relationship between olfactory integrity and gonadal function, then, is highly specific for species and, apparently, even for strain. Conflicting variables such as age, type of measurement used, and possible interaction with food intake make generalization of the direct relationships between anosmia and reproduction even more hazardous.

A final area of primer function which deserves strong attention is in the effects of odors of adult animals on the developing nervous systems of their preweaning offspring, i.e., to alter or imprint later responses to signaling pheromones. Mainardi (1963a), for example, found that the normal sexual preferences of one subspecies of *Mus* for males of the same subspecies was eliminated if no adult males were present during the preweaning period. Mainardi et al. (1965) also showed that perfuming the mother altered later expected patterns of mating preferences of the females in her litter but not of the males. Marr and Gardner (1965) reported somewhat similar findings in an experiment with rats.

Discussion

Some generalities have emerged regarding the potential role of pheromones in mammalian reproduction. Most sex pheromones, of either the signaling or priming type, are thought to be transmitted as vapors and their effects mediated by olfactory or accessory olfactory systems. Figure 2, an attempt to summarize the state of our knowl-

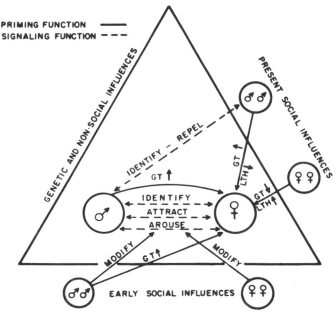

Fig. 2 Schematic representation of socio-olfactory functions known to occur in mammals; LTH, luteotropin; GT, gonadotropin.

edge, is, therefore, conceptualized on the basis of olfactory function rather than dealing with specific pheromones. Known primer factors which may impinge upon a postweaning female consist of stimuli which accelerate her sexual maturity and, once she is mature, either suppress or induce an estrous cycle, the latter occurring even if she is preimplantationally pregnant. These functions are mediated via releasing factors in the hypothalamus, and chemical isolation of even one such odor could yield a valuable tool for the experimental study of higher brain mechanisms and hypothalamic function. While chemical identification of the odorous substances and their interaction with limbic and, specifically, hypothalamic factors constitute the two biggest challenges facing this field of research, a third necessity is a more thorough search to establish the generality of these functions among other species. Our knowledge of these potentially important substances is, at present, limited to data collected on two species of rodents, house mice and deermice, with indirect indications from a few other species. In addition, a primer function that has received only the barest investigation is that which modifies, early in the life of young animals, the neural pathways for later response to signaling pheromones. How exclusively this is an olfactory function remains to be seen; however, it is probable that species-imprinting functions in general would usually be mediated by more than one sensory system. Figure 2 also illustrates an effect of a mature male on the developing direct-acting pheromonal processes. Such effects are known to occur even though it has not been verified that olfaction plays a primary role in producing them.

Observational evidence documents the occurrence of signaling pheromones in most mammals. These are thought to be usually vapors acting as olfactory signals. Tentative categorization has given us four general functions served by such pheromones: identification at several levels including that of the individual, attraction (given compatibility of the identification), repelling or inhibiting (given incompatibility of the identification), and arousal (Fig. 2). It is probable that a single compound or mixture of compounds could have all these functions. It is also probable that these direct-acting pheromones could play primary roles in promoting reproductive behavior in some species and be of considerably less importance in others, e.g., nocturnal versus diurnal species. Short-range effects such as identification, attraction, and arousal are functions which, undoubtedly, could be mediated by other stimuli and sensory systems. Beach (1947) has stated that probably no single sensory modality is indispensable for successful copulatory behavior among mammals. Such a statement is generally true and particularly so when dealing with the typical situation in which sex behavior is usually assessed, i.e., pairs of animals that are confined in small quarters and often belonging to a laboratory or domestic stock that is the product of intensive selection for maximum reproduction. Any degree of departure from this "normal" situation, however, must just as certainly interact with the loss of a sensory system to the detriment of reproductive efficiency (see also Beach, 1951). As an example, we might consider a natural population of nocturnal rodents. The members of such a population normally live in a relatively dispersed fashion. They must distribute their activities in such a manner that the use of their environment will be optimal and, during their nightly activity periods, they must survive, explore, forage, and interact sexually or aggressively with their neighbors. It is in such a situation that signaling pheromones must play a large role in intrapopulation communication and, as such, promote efficiency of the population's reproductive activities. Olfactory signals have one advantage over other types of communication in natural environments: all that is required for communication to occur is that the spatial activities of two animals overlap some time during the time limit imposed by the life of the pheromone. Long-range and latent communication, then, is probably the one really important function of signaling pheromones in mammals, although CNS-arousing functions are possibly of real importance in some species.

The most pressing problems facing research in the field of signaling pheromones are largely within the realm of the behavioral scientist. Anatomists and chemists have produced considerable information regarding some potentially direct-acting substances; information either in the form of description and physiology of specialized glands or in the form of actual chemical isolation. Behavioral work in this field, on the other hand, has been limited in too many cases to the uncritical collection of observational data.

The concepts of species specificity and the utility of mammalian sex pheromones as isolating mechanisms have only been cursorily examined. The situation is probably relatively simple regarding the signaling substances. These involve a form of communication that may be the primary means in some species, of less importance in others, but could probably be dispensed with entirely in most with a loss only in terms of efficiency. Therefore it seems reasonable that, in general, such substances would not serve as sole means of ensuring reproductive isolation. Selection pressures, nevertheless, should have worked to ensure species specificity in those species in which this is a prime means of communication even when operating in conjunction with other isolation mechanisms that are effective at short range. For example, Moore (1962) studied two species of *Peromyscus*, one occurring as a geographical isolate in its natural environment, while the other occurred sympatrically with other species of the same genus. The geographically isolated species, when tested in the laboratory, responded to the odors of its own and the second species in an indiscriminate manner, while the normally sympatric species discriminated between odors of the two species to a high degree. Godfrey (1958) found that male voles discriminated to some degree between the odor of two species of estrous voles.

Whether or not primer pheromones are species specific should be considered as second-order questions, since we still do not know how widely occurring these substances are among mammals. Specificity has been experimentally demonstrated in only one case; Marsden and Bronson (1965b) found estrous characteristics of laboratory mice to be altered by urine from male laboratory mice but not by urine from male deermice. With respect to the pregnancy blocking response, Bronson et al. (1964) found that both males and females of one subspecies of deermouse blocked implantation in a second subspecies, probably indicating more than one mechanism in operation rather than a lack of specificity. The question of adaptive significance of such potent sociophysiological responses poses intriguing problems. It is easy to visualize a relationship between selective pressures and primer pheromone(s) from males. Ability to promote earlier estrus in terms of age or seaeson as well as the ability to block another male's insemination and return the female to estrus (and then reinseminate her) would certainly be a selective advantage. Selection to promote the ability of one female to suppress the estrous cycle of another is a more dubious process, although this might possibly be advantageous in a seasonably breeding animal, since it may result in a real degree of synchrony. Bruce and Parrott (1960) have discussed the possibility that one function of the blocking phenomenon is to promote heterozygosity. Worthy of note in this respect are reports by Mainardi (1963b, 1963c) indicating that female mice show some degree of sexual preference for different strains but not for different subspecies.

Finally, we might attempt to put the potential relationships between olfaction, pheromones, and reproduction into a proper perspective. Pheromones serve obvious and important functions in lower animals. Wilson and Bossert (1963) have estimated that as few as 10 pheromones could answer the needs for total social organization in an ant colony. Responses to pheromones among insects are immediate and stereotyped. Primers are also utilized among insects as efficient means to accomplish physiological ends (e.g., caste determination). Pheromonal function, on the other hand, apparently remains only vestigially in humans. LeMagnen's (1950) "exaltolide phenomena," where the perception of this substance is almost entirely dependent upon circulating estrogens, is one of several examples that indicate such vestigial function (see also Kloek, 1961, and Kalogerakis, 1963). The role played by olfactory pheromones in infrahuman mammals falls in between these two extremes. Signaling pheromones are heavily utilized as primary modes of communication in many species but are of little importance in others (e.g., dairy bulls under the conditions studied by Hale, 1966). Responses to signaling pheromones are usually not as stereotyped as those seen in lower animals; rather, such responses are modifiable by stimuli encountered during preweaning life and by adult social experiences. Finally, the use of primers as a means of controlling reproductive processes in mammals undoubtedly defies generalization to all mammals in the same manner that relationships between olfactory integrity and reproduction are highly species specific. The use of primers and the presence of direct olfactory–hypothalamic relationships probably reflects a large variety of selective factors that have operated during the evolution of each species and probably is closely paralled by species differences in organization of the CNS, particularly the limbic system (see de Groot, 1965).

Acknowledgment

This investigation was supported by U.S. Public Health Service Grant HD-00767 from the National Institute of Child Health and Human Development.

References

Alloiteau, J. J. 1961. Le controle hypothalamique de l'adenohypophyse. III. Regulation de la fonction gonadotrope, femelle. Activite LTH. *Biol. Med. (Paris)*, **51**: 250.

Barnett, S. A. 1963. *The Rat, A Study in Behavior*. Aldine Press, Chicago.

Barraclough, C. A., and B. A. Cross. 1963. Unit activity in the hypothalamus of the cyclic female rat: Effect of genital stimuli and progesterone. *J. Endocrinol.*, **26**: 339–359.

Bartke, A., and G. L. Wolff. 1966. Influence of the lethal yellow (A^y) gene on estrous synchrony in mice. *Science,* **153**: 79–80.

Beach, F. A. 1947. A review of physiological and psychological studies of sexual behavior in mammals. *Physiol. Rev.*, **27**: 240–307.

Beach, F. A. 1951. Instinctive behavior: Reproductive activities. In *Handbook of Experimental Psychology* (S. S. Stevens, ed.). Wiley, New York.

Beach, F. A., and R. Gilmore. 1949. Response of male dogs to urine from females in heat. *J. Mammal.*, **30**: 391–392.

Beach, F. A., and J. Jaynes. 1956a. Studies of maternal retrieving in rats. I. Recognition of young. *J. Mammal.*, **37**: 177–180.

Beach, F. A., and J. Jaynes. 1956b. Studies on maternal retrieving in rats. III. Sensory cues involved in the lactating female's response to her young. *Behaviour*, **10**: 104–125.

Biancifiori, C., and F. Caschera. 1963. The effect of olfactory lobectomy and induced pseudo-pregnancy on the incidence of methyl-cholanthrene-induced mammary and ovarian tumours in C3Hb mice. *Brit. J. Cancer*, **17**: 116–118.

Bourliere, F. 1955. *The Natural History of Mammals*. Harrap, London.

Bronson, F. H., and B. E. Eleftheriou. 1963. Influence of strange males on implantation in the deermouse. *Gen. Comp. Endocrinol.*, **3**: 515–518.

Bronson, F. H., and H. M. Marsden. 1964. Male-induced synchrony of estrus in deermice. *Gen. Comp. Endocrinol.*, **4**: 634–637.

Bronson, F. H., B. E. Eleftheriou, and E. I. Garick. 1964. Effects of intra- and inter-specific social stimulation on implantation in deermice. *J. Reprod. Fertility,* 8: 23–27.

Bronson, F. H., and W. K. Whitten. 1968. Oestrus-accelerating pheromone of mice: assay, androgen-dependency and presence in bladder urine. *J. Reprod. Fertil.,* 15: 131–134.

Brooks, C. McC. 1937. The role of the cerebral cortex and of various sense organs in the excitation and execution of mating activity in the rabbit. *Am. J. Physiol.,* 120: 544–553.

Bruce, H. M. 1959. An exteroceptive block to pregnancy in the mouse. *Nature,* 184: 105.

Bruce, H. M. 1960. A block to pregnancy in the mouse caused by the proximity of strange males. *J. Reprod. Fertility,* 1: 96.

Bruce, H. M. 1961a. An olfactory block to pregnancy in mice. I. Characteristics of the block. Proc. IVth Intern. Congr. Animal Reprod., The Hague, pp. 159–162.

Bruce, H. M. 1961b. Time relations in the pregnancy-block induced in mice by strange males. *J. Reprod. Fertility,* 2: 138–142.

Bruce, H. M. 1963. Olfactory block to pregnancy among grouped mice. *J. Reprod. Fertility,* 6: 451–460.

Bruce, H. M. 1965. The effect of castration on the reproductive pheromones of male mice. *J. Reprod. Fertility,* 10: 141–143.

Bruce, H. M. 1966. Smell as an exteroceptive factor. *J. Animal Sci.,* 25 (*Suppl.*): 83–89.

Bruce, H. M., and A. S. Parkes. 1960. Hormonal factors in exteroceptive block to pregnancy in mice. *J. Endocrinol.,* 20: xxix–xxx.

Bruce, H. M., and D. M. V. Parrott. 1960. Role of olfactory sense in pregnancy block by strange males. *Science,* 131: 1526.

Carr, W. J., and W. F. Caul. 1962. The effect of castration in the rat upon the discrimination of sex odours. *Animal Behavior,* 10: 20–27.

Carr, W. J., B. Solberg, and C. Pfaffman. 1962. The olfactory threshold for estrous female urine in normal and castrated male rats. *J. Comp. Physiol. Psychol.,* 55: 415–417.

Carr, W. J., L. S. Loeb, and M. L. Dissinger. 1965. Responses of rats to sex odors. *J. Comp. Physiol. Psychol.,* 59: 370–377.

Carr, W. J., L. S. Loeb, and N. R. Wylie. 1966. Responses to feminine odors in normal and castrated male rats. *J. Comp. Physiol. Psychol.,* 62: 336–338.

Caschera, F. 1960. La "pseudogravidanza spontanea" in topi femmine vergini, isolate e coabitanti, del BALB/cf substrain. *Lav. Inst. Anat. Univ. Perugia,* 20: 17–30.

Castro, B. Magalhaes. 1966. Personal communication.

Chanel, J., and E. Vernet-Maury. 1963. Détermination par un test olfactif des inter-attractions chez la souris. *J. Physiol. (Paris)* 55: 121–122.

Chipman, R. K., and K. A. Fox. 1966. Oestrous synchronization and pregnancy blocking in wild house mice (*Mus musculus*). *J. Reprod. Fertility,* 12: 233–236.

Chipman, R. K., J. A. Holt, and K. A. Fox. 1966. Pregnancy failure in laboratory mice after multiple short-term exposure to strange males. *Nature,* 210: 653.

Chitty, H., and C. R. Austin. 1957. Environmental modification of oestrus in the vole. *Nature,* 179: 592–593.

David, R., G. Thiery, M. Bonvallet, and P. Dell. 1952. Effets de la stimulation des bulbes olfactifs sur le cycle sexuel de la chatte. *Compt. Rend. Soc. Biol.,* **146:** 670–672.

Davis, D. L., and J. de Groot. 1964. Failure to demonstrate olfactory inhibition of pregnancy ("Bruce effect") in the rat. *Anat. Rec.,* **148:** 366 (Abstr.).

de Groot, J. 1965. The influence of limbic structures on pituitary functions related to reproduction. In *Sex and Behavior* (F. Beach, ed.). Wiley, New York.

Dewar, A. D. 1959. Observations on pseudopregnancy in the mouse. *J. Endocrinol.,* **18:** 186–190.

Dominic, C. J. 1964. Source of the male odour causing pregnancy-block in mice. *J. Reprod. Fertility,* **8:** 265 (Abstr.).

Dominic, C. J. 1965. The origin of the pheromones causing pregnancy block in mice. *J. Reprod. Fertility,* **10:** 469–472.

Dominic, C. J. 1966a. Block to pseudopregnancy in mice caused by exposure to male urine. *Experientia,* **22:** 534.

Dominic, C. J. 1966b. Observations on the reproductive pheromones of mice. I. Source. *J. Reprod. Fertility,* **11:** 407–414.

Dominic, C. J. 1966c. Observations on the reproductive pheromones of mice. II. Neuro-endocrine mechanisms involved in the olfactory block to pregnancy. *J. Reprod. Fertility,* **11:** 415–421.

Dominic, C. J. 1966d. The inhibition of the olfactory block to pregnancy in mice by the administration of exogenous progesterone. *Z. Naturwiss.,* **12:** 310–311.

Dominic, C. J. 1966e. Reserpine: Inhibition of olfactory blockage of pregnancy in mice. *Science,* 152: 1764–1765.

Everett, J. W. 1963. Pseudopregnancy in the rat from brief treatment with progesterone: Effect of isolation. *Nature,* **198:** 694.

Franck, H. 1966a. Effets de l'ablation des bulbes olfactifs sur la physiologie genitale chez la lapine adulte. *Compt. Rend. Soc. Biol.,* **160:** 863–865.

Franck, H. 1966b. Ablation des bulbes olfactifs chez la lapine impubere. Repercussions sur la tractus genital et le comportement sexuel. *Compt. Rend. Soc. Biol.,* **160:** 863–865.

Godfrey, J. 1958. The origin of sexual isolation between bank voles. *Proc. Roy. Phys. Soc. Edinburgh,* **27:** 47–55.

Golley, F. B. 1957. Gestation period, breeding and fawning of Columbian black-tailed deer. *J. Mammal.,* **38:** 116–120.

Hale, E. B. 1966. Visual stimuli and reproductive behavior in bulls. *J. Animal Sci.,* **25**(*Suppl.*): 36–48.

Hediger, H. 1951. Observations sur la psychologie animale dans les Parcs Nationaux du Congo Belge. Institut des Parcs Nationaux du Congo Belge, Brussels.

Hulet, C. V. 1966. Behavioral, social and psychological factors affecting mating time and breeding efficiency in sheep. *J. Animal Sci.,* **25:** (*Suppl.*): 5–20.

Husted, J. R., and F. S. McKenna. 1966. The use of rats as discriminative stimuli. *J. Exptl. Analysis Behavior,* **9:** 677–679.

Kalmus, H. 1955. The discrimination by the nose of the dog of individual human odours and in particular of the odours of twins. *Brit. J. Animal Behaviour,* **3:** 25.

Kalmus, H. 1964. Some potentialities and constraints of chemical telecommunication. Paper presented at the 2nd Intern. Congr. Endocrinol., London.

Kalogerakis, M. G. 1963. The role of olfaction in sexual development. *Psychosomat. Med.*, **25**: 420.

King, J. F., R. F. Becker, and J. E. Markee. 1964. Studies on olfactory discrimination in dogs: (3) Ability to detect human odour trace. *Animal Behavior*, **12**: 311–315.

Kingston, B. H. 1964. The chemistry and olfactory properties of musk, civet, and castoreum. *Proc. 2nd Intern. Congr. Endocrinol.*, London.

Kloek, J. 1961. The smell of some steroid sex hormones and their metabolites. Reflections and experiments concerning the significance of smell for the mutual relation of the sexes. *Psychiat. Neurol. Neurochir.*, **64**: 309.

Klopfer, P., D. K. Adams, and M. S. Klopfer. 1964. Maternal imprinting in goats. *Proc. Natl. Acad. Sci.*, **52**: 911–914.

Krzanowska, H. 1964. Studies on heterosis. III. The course of the sexual cycle and the establishment of pregnancy in mice, as affected by the type of mating. *Folia Biol. (Warsaw)*, **12**: 415–426.

Lamond, D. R. 1958a. Spontaneous anoestrus in mice. *Proc. Australian Soc. Animal Prod.*, **2**: 97–101.

Lamond, D. R. 1958b. Infertility associated with extirpation of the olfactory bulbs in female albino mice. *Australian J. Exptl. Biol. Med. Sci.*, **36**: 103–108.

Lamond, D. R. 1959. Effect of stimulation derived from other animals of the same species on oestrus cycles in mice. *J. Endocrinol.*, **18**: 343–349.

Lederer, E. 1950. Odeurs et parfums des animaux. *Fortschr. Chem. Org. Naturstoffe*, **6**: 87–153.

LeMagnen, J. 1950. Physiology of sensations. New facts on the exaltolide phenomenon. *Compt. Rend. Soc. Biol.*, **230**: 1103.

LeMagnen, J. 1952. Les Phenomenes olfacto-sexuels chez le rat blanc. *Arch. Sci. Physiol.*, **6**: 295–332.

Lindsay, D. R. 1965. The importance of olfactory stimuli in the mating behavior of the ram. *Animal Behavior*, **13**: 75.

Lindsay, D. R. 1966. Mating behaviour of ewes and its effect on mating efficiency. *Animal Behavior*, **14**: 419–424.

Lissak, L. 1962. Olfactory-induced sexual behavior in female cats. Symposium XIV. *Excerpta Med. Intern. Congr. Ser. 47*, **1**: 653–656.

Magnotti, T. 1936. L'importanza dell'olfatto sullo sviluppo e funzione degli organi genitali. *Boll. Mal. Orecch. Gola Naso*, **54**: 281.

Mainardi, D. 1963a. Eliminazione della barriera etologica all'isolamento reproduttino tra *Mus musculus domesticus e M. m. bactrianus* mediante axione sull'apprendimento infantile. *Inst. Lombardo (Rend. Sci.)* **B97**: 291–299.

Mainardi, D. 1963b. Un Esperimento sulla parte attira svolta dalla femmina nella selezione sussuale in *Mus musculus*. *Arch. Sci. Biol. (Bologna)*, **47**: 227–237.

Mainardi, D. 1963c. Speciazone nel topo fattori etologici determinanti barriere reproduttive tua *Mus musculus domesticus e M. m. bactrianus*. *Inst. Lombardo (Rend. Sci.)* **B97**: 135–142.

Mainardi, D., M. Marsan, and A. Pasquali. 1965. Causation of sexual preferences of the house mouse. The behavior of mice reared by parents whose odour was artificially altered. *Atti Soc. Ital. Sci. Nat. Museo Civico Storia Nat. Milano*, **104**: 325–338.

Marr, J. N., and L. E. Gardner, Jr. 1965. Early olfactory experience and later social behavior in the rat: Preference, sexual responsiveness, and care of young. *J. Genet. Psychol.*, **107**: 167–174.

Marsden, H. M., and F. H. Bronson. 1964. Estrous synchrony in mice: Alteration by exposure to male urine. *Science*, **144**: 3625.

Marsden, H. M., and F. H. Bronson. 1965a. The synchrony of oestrus in mice: Relative roles of the male and female environments. *J. Endocrinol.*, **32**: 313–319.

Marsden, H. M., and F. H. Bronson. 1965b. Strange male block to pregnancy: Its absence in inbred mouse strains. *Nature*, **207**: 878.

Mody, J. K. 1963. Structural changes in the ovaries of IF mice due to age and various other states: Demonstration of spontaneous pseudopregnancy in grouped virgins. *Anat. Rec.*, **145**: 439–447.

Mody, J. K., and J. J. Christian. 1962. Adrenals and reproductive organs of female mice kept singly, grouped or grouped with a vasectomized male. *J. Endocrinol.*, **24**: 1–6.

Moore, R. E. 1962. Olfactory discrimination as an isolating mechanism between *Peromyscus maniculatus rufinus* and *Peromyscus polionotus leucocephalus*. Unpublished doctoral dissertation, University of Texas, Austin.

Muhlbock, O., and L. M. Boot. 1960. Symposium: Phenomena of tumor viruses, New York.

Myktowycz, R. 1962. Territorial function of chin gland secretion in the rabbit, *Oryctolagus cuniculus* (L.). *Nature*, **193**: 799.

Myktowycz, R. 1965. Further observations on the territorial function and histology of the submandibular cutaneous (chin) glands in the rabbit, *Oryctolagus cuniculus* (L.). *Animal Behavior*, **13**: 400–412.

Palen, G. F., and G. V. Goddard. 1966. Catnip and oestrus behaviour in the cat. *Animal Behavior*, **14**: 372–377.

Parkes, A. S., and H. M. Bruce. 1961. Olfactory stimuli in mammalian reproduction. *Science*, **134**: 1049–1054.

Parkes, A. S., and H. M. Bruce. 1962. Pregnancy-block in female mice placed in boxes soiled by males. *J. Reprod. Fertility*, **4**: 303–308.

Rosen, S., M. C. Shelesnyak, and L. R. Zacharias. 1940. Nasogenital relationship. II. Pseudopregnancy following extirpation of the spenopalatine ganglion in the rat. *Endocrinology*, **27**: 463–468.

Sawyer, C. H. 1955. Rhinencephalic involvement in pituitary activation by intraventricular histamine in the rabbit under nembutal anesthesia. *Am. J. Physiol.*, **180**: 37–46.

Schein, M. W., and E. B. Hale. 1965. Stimuli eliciting sexual behavior. In *Sex and Behavior* (F. Beach, ed.). Wiley, New York, pp. 440–482.

Schloeth, R. 1956. Zur Psychologie der Begegnung zwischentieren. *Behaviour*, **10**(11/2): 1–80.

Shelton, M. 1960. Influence of the presence of a male goat on the initiation of oestrous cycling and ovulation of angora does. *J. Animal Sci.*, **19**: 368–375.

Signoret, J. P. 1964. Action de l'ablation des bulbes olfactifs sur les mecanismes de la reproduction. *Proc. 2nd Intern. Congr. Endocrinol.*, London.

Signoret, J. P., and F. du Mesnil du Buisson. 1961. Etude du comportement de la truie en oestrus. *Fourth Intern. Congr. Animal Reprod. Artif. Insem.*, The Hague.

Signoret, J. P., and P. Mauleon. 1962. Action de l'ablation des bulbes olfactifs sur les mecanismes de la reproduction chez la truie. *Ann. Biol. Animale Biochim. Biophys.,* **2:** 167–174.

Takewaki, K. 1949. Occurrence of pscudopregnancy in rats placed in vapor of ammonia. *Proc. Japan Acad.,* **25:** 38–39.

Todd, N. B. 1963. The catnip response. Doctoral dissertation, Harvard University.

Vandenbergh, J. G. 1967. Effect of the presence of a male on the sexual maturation of female mice. *Endocrinology,* **81:** 345–349.

van der Lee, S., and L. M. Boot. 1955. Spontaneous pseudo-pregnancy in mice. *Acta Physiol. Pharmacol. Neerl.,* **4:** 442–443 (Abstr.).

van der Lee, S., and L. M. Boot. 1956. Spontaneous pseudopregnancy in Mia. II. *Acta Physiol. Pharmacol. Neerl.* **5:** 213–214.

Whitten, W. K.1956a. Modifications of the oestrous cycle of the mouse by external stimuli associated with the male. *J. Endocrinol.,* **13:** 399–404.

Whitten, W. K. 1965b. The effect of removal of the olfactory bulbs on the gonads of mice. *J. Endocrinol.,* **14:** 160–163.

Whitten, W. K. 1957. Effect of exteroceptive factors on the oestrous cycle of mice. *Nature,* **180:** 1436.

Whitten, W. K. 1958. Modification of the oestrous cycle of the mouse by external stimuli associated with the male. Changes in the oestrous cycle determined by vaginal smears. *J. Endocrinol.,* **17:** 307–313.

Whitten, W. K. 1959. Occurrence of anoestrus in mice caged in groups. *J. Endocrinol.,* **18:** 102–107.

Whitten, W. K. 1963. Is the vomeronasal organ a sex chemoreceptor in mice? Second Asia and Oceania Congr. Endocrinol., Sydney.

Whitten, W. K. 1966. Pheromones and mammalian reproduction. In *Advances in Reproductive Physiology,* Vol. 1 (A. McLaren, ed.). Academic Press, New York, pp. 155–177.

Wilson, E. O., and W. H. Bossert. 1963. Chemical communication among animals. *Recent Prog. Hormone Res.,* **19:** 673–716.

Wynne-Edwards, V. C. 1962. *Animal Dispersion in Relation to Social Behaviour.* Oliver & Boyd, London.

22

The Role of Progesterone in Behavior

M. X. Zarrow, P. N. Brody, and V. H. Denenberg

Much has been written on the role of the ovarian steroids in sexual and maternal behavior in the female, and the subject has been reviewed extensively in the past decade (Young, 1961; Lehrman, 1961; Beach, 1961, Hamburg, 1966). These reviews clearly demonstrate the synergistic action between the estrogens and progestogens and confirm the classical findings in endocrinology that pretreatment or conditioning with estradiol is necessary before the action of progesterone is manifested. Indeed it is most interesting that the behavioral studies amply bear out the original findings involving morphogenetic and histologic changes. Courrier (1950) reviewed the question of estrogen–progesterone interactions involving such classical end points as uterine weight, vagina mucosa, decidual formation, implantation, progestational type of uterus, lactation, etc. He concluded that both the absolute level of progesterone and the estrogen–progesterone ratio were of significance in determining the specific action of progesterone.

The present review is concerned primarily with the role of progesterone in the manifestation of certain behavioral characteristics. We have made no effort to make a complete survey of the literature but concentrated on the current developments and some of the data from our own laboratory. It is obvious that a paucity of data still exists on this subject but some tentative generalizations can be made.

Aves

The Presence of Progestin in the Avian Species

The role of progesterone in the reproductive behavior of birds has been systematically investigated only in doves (Lehrman, 1965), although studies of the reproductive cycle in canaries (Hinde and Steel, 1966) and domestic fowl (van Tienhoven, 1961) have produced relevant information. In addition to a paucity of data concerning the effect of progesterone on other avian species, there is no clear indication of the tissue source of progestin in birds. The overt behavioral patterns obtained following progesterone are limited to incubation behavior, aggressive behavior, and suppression of male courtship behavior. These activities can be obtained with other hormones and raises the question of specificity. That progesterone is a normal biologically active substance in birds is inferred mainly from observations of its ability, upon administration, to elicit the appearance of several naturally occurring physiological and behavioral events.

Progesterone or progestins have been found in the ovary of the laying and nonlaying chicken (Layne et al., 1957), the ovaries and testes of Wilson's phalarope, red-winged blackbird, mallard, and killdeer and in the testes of the pigeon (Höhn and Cheng, 1967). Progestins have also been demonstrated in the blood of hens and roosters (Fraps et al., 1948, 1949; Lytle and Lorenz, 1958) but not in that of capons (Fraps et al., 1949). Lofts and Marshall (1959) detected progestins in the blood and testes of hypophysectomized male pigeons but not in intact birds and concluded that since the sequence of gonadal changes following hypophysectomy is apparently identical with the postnuptial tubular steatogenesis seen in the testes of wild birds (Marshall, 1949, 1950; Marshall and Serventy, 1956), this activity is functionally homologous with the formation of the mammalian corpus luteum. Histological observations have indicated that both pre- and postovulatory ovarian follicles contain active secreting cells (Deol, 1964).

The bulk of the information relating progesterone to reproductive processes in birds is concerned with the preovulatory development of the oviduct, brood-patch development, ovulation, and incubation behavior. It is well known that progesterone or LH can induce premature ovulation in intact laying hens (Fraps, 1955), but in hypophysectomized hens (van Tienhoven et al., 1954), hens with lesions in the ventromedian portion of preoptic nucleus (Ralph and Fraps, 1959), or animals treated with adrenergic blocking agents (van Tienhoven, 1961, for review) progesterone can no longer produce this response. That progesterone has its effect on ovulation by way of an action on the CNS is further supported by Ralph and Fraps (1960), who reported that levels of progesterone inadequate to induce ovulation when injected systematically or directly into the anterior pituitary did induce ovulation when injected into the preoptic nucleus and caudal parts of the forebrain. Desoxycorticosterone acetate (DCA) was just as effective as progesterone in inducing premature ovulation and was also blocked by pharmocologic blocking agents (Fraps, 1955). Both DCA and progesterone at higher doses inhibited ovulation in the pigeon and the chicken (Dunham and Riddle, 1942; Höhn, 1960; van Tienhoven, 1961). It is highly possible that this progesterone-like action of desoxycorticosterone is due to its conversion to progesterone in the body (Zarrow et al., 1950). The findings that removal of the most recently ruptured follicle delays the oviposition of the just ovulated egg (Rothchild and Fraps, 1944) and disrupts the nesting behavior associated with oviposition suggested to Wood-Gush and Gilbert (1964) that this tissue is associated with progesterone secretion. However, the inability of Gilbert and Wood-Gush (1964) to induce nesting behavior by treatment with progesterone indicates the possibility of some other humoral substance being involved and lends support to van Tienhoven's (1961) view that the ruptured follicle contains negligible amounts of progesterone.

Development of the oviduct to a full secretory condition can be induced in the chicken by the synergistic action of progesterone or testosterone and estrogen (Brant and Nalbandov, 1956). In the ring dove progesterone and estrogen are the effective agents in the development of the secretory oviduct (Lehrman and Brody, 1957), whereas in the canary either progesterone or prolactin will synergize with estrogen (Steel and Hinde, 1963). In the capon, prolactin is just as effective as progesterone in inducing a molt, and it has been suggested that prolactin may be the immediate effective agent in stimulating feather regeneration (Juhn and Harris, 1955). No all-inclusive statement can be made here as to whether prolactin is acting directly on such end points as incubation and correlated physiologic events such as changes in the oviduct, brood patch, molting, etc.

The available data on molting alone are confusing and difficult to interpret, and the possibility of species differences adds to the confusion. Kobayashi (1958) reported that 17α-hydroxyprogesterone caproate was ineffective on the induction of molting in seasonal breeders such as the canary but was active in nonseasonal breeders such as the Bengalees finch. A suggestion that prolactin may possibly exert its effect in the canary via a "luteotropic" action is seen in the findings that while either progesterone or prolactin can augment the estrogen-induced increase in tactile sensitivity of the brood patch in the intact animal, only progesterone has this effect in the ovariectomized bird (Hinde and Steel, 1964). Some confirmation of this concept is seen in the report that prolactin can produce a steatogenesis in the testes of the pigeon and that this is also seen after hypophysectomy. Such a testis is characterized by a high progesterone content (Lofts and Marshall, 1956, 1959). However, this important question is still unsolved and requires direct experimentation.

It has been shown in the ring dove that preventing the birds from nest building delays the development of the oviduct, ovulation, and the readiness of the birds to incubate. This suggests that this behavior may well be involved in the regulation of progesterone secretion (Lehrman et al., 1961).

Incubation Behavior

It has been clearly demonstrated that systematic injection of progesterone can efficiently induce ring doves to incubate eggs (Riddle and Lahr, 1944; Lehrman, 1958). However, there is considerable evidence to indicate that only prolactin can induce incubation behavior in broody strains of domestic hens (Riddle et al., 1935; Lehrman, 1961). van Tienhoven (1958) interrupted broodiness in turkeys by treatment with progesterone. It was found in the ring dove that prolactin is not nearly as effective as progesterone in initiating incubation behavior but is very effective in maintaining the "willingness" of the ring dove to incubate once incubation has started (Lehrman and Brody, 1961). The relationship between progesterone and prolactin with regard to incubation behavior in doves is interesting in that in addition to the above findings it has also been shown that the act of incubation is involved in promoting the secretion of prolactin. The sight of the female incubating is a sufficient stimulus for the secretion of prolactin from the pituitary gland of the male ring dove as long as the pair had not been separated before the completion of egg laying (Patel, 1936) and that castration of the male during

incubation interferes with neither his incubation behavior nor prolactin secretion (Riddle and Dykshorn, 1932; Patel, 1936). In subsequent cycles (the females lay in spite of the males' loss of courtship
activity) the castrated males continue to incubate, although the
behavior is not completely normal, and they do not secrete prolactin
as a result of their sitting (Patel, 1936). Patel also observed this in
males castrated prior to pairing. It would be interesting to know
if progesterone treatment of such castrated, incubating males would
result in the secretion of prolactin and if castration of either male
or female ring doves would interfere with the effect of prolactin on
maintaining the incubation "mood." It is already known that castration of the male ring dove severely reduces the induction of incubation behavior by progesterone (Stern, 1966), and preliminary experiments indicate that concurrent treatment of the castrates with
testosterone restores their ability to respond to the progesterone
(Stern, 1967).

Komisaruk (1967) has observed both the induction of incubation
behavior and the suppression of courtship by the male following
intramuscular injection or implantation in the central nervous system
of progesterone. The preoptic nuclei and the tracts which connect
these nuclei to the forebrain basal ganglia were found to be the sites
from which progesterone implants could elicit incubation behavior.

Just as there are morphological concomitants of incubation behavior such as the development and maintenance of the brood patch,
so are there behavioral elements that have been observed to accompany incubation and broodiness. That these ancillary behavioral
changes might be controlled by hormones associated with incubation
has been suggested by Breitenbach et al. (1965), who propose that
the increased levels of pituitary prolactin in the broody pheasant
might be related to the increased aggressiveness seen in this animal.
Vowles and Harwood (1966) have shown that aggressive and defensive behavior increases in both male and female ring doves at the
time of onset of incubation and is maintained until the young are
about 10 days old. They have also shown that chronic treatment of
female doves with progesterone, progesterone and estrogen, or prolactin increases the defensive behavior of these birds toward another
dove. Progesterone (with and without estrogen), but not prolactin, increases the aggressive and defensive behavior of the males toward
other doves. Single injections of these hormones show that the latency
to the onset of these changes in behavior differ with the different
hormonal treatments. Whereas progesterone and estrogen or prolactin
elicit a response in the females within 30 minutes following the in-

jection (as does progesterone and estrogen in the males), the response to progesterone alone does not appear until 14 hours after injection in the females and 5 hours in the males. This would seem to indicate that the progesterone acts in some less direct manner than does the combined estrogen–progesterone or prolactin.

The extensive and elegant studies of the interaction of interoceptive and exteroceptive factors involved in reproductive behavior of the canary have been reviewed (Hinde, 1965; Hinde and Steel, 1966). Although these studies have demonstrated that progesterone (and prolactin) can interact with estrogen in the development of the brood patch, its changes in tactile sensitivity, and the development of the oviduct, there has been no indication that progesterone (or prolactin) has any clear-cut effect on any of the behaviors exhibited by canaries during the course of the reproductive cycle. It is highly unlikely that the brood patch plays no role at all, since Hinde and Steel (1966) report a direct correlation between the incidence of incubation and the amount of increase in tactile sensitivity of the brood patch, a condition which is probably a function of estrogen and progesterone secretion. These investigators conclude that the hormonal interaction is between estrogen and progesterone, since progesterone effectively augments the action of estrogen on the sensitivity of the brood patch in the ovariectomized as well as the intact canary, while prolactin is effective only in the intact bird. Whether prolactin acts directly or via the release of progesterone is still unanswered. If the action of prolactin is via the release of progesterone, then the assumption that defeathering in the canary is due to an interplay of estrogen and an extragonadal hormone would not be valid. The evidence presented by Steel and Hinde (1963, 1964) for an extragonadal factor is inadequate, since they failed to obtain maximal defeathering with estrogen alone in the intact bird and also failed to use hypophysectomized canaries. Bailey (1952) obtained complete defeathering in the hypophysectomized bird treated with estrogen and prolactin, but he failed to use the above treatment with ovariectomized birds. Hence the question of prolactin acting via the release of a gonadal hormone is still a moot point.

The above reports plus the recent findings of increased levels of prolactin in the pituitary of nesting male phalaropes (Nicoll et al., 1967) point to a role for prolactin in nesting behavior but does not settle the issue of whether prolactin is acting directly or indirectly via the gonad or indeed whether the prolactin levels are a function of the nesting behavior (Lehrman, 1963; Riddle, 1963). The argument concerning the question as to whether prolactin is the hormone of nesting behavior in the bird is not realistic at this time. The question of species differences in the bird has not been fully explored. Doves respond to progesterone and broody strains of chickens respond to prolactin. It is also important to distinguish between the factors involved in the onset of nesting behavior as well as the maintenance of this phenomenon. It may be that prolactin in some birds is not concerned with the onset but is involved in the maintenance. In other species the hormone might conceivably be involved in both aspects.

Sexual Behavior

Although there is now a considerable amount of evidence indicating that estrogen and progesterone interact to produce sexual receptivity in female mammals, practically no work has been done in this area with birds. Adams and Herrick (1955), working with young chicks, found that progesterone augmented estrogen-induced squatting, and a few observations have been made on ovariectomized hens in which rather high doses of estrogen permitted some retention of sexual receptivity (Allee and Collias, 1940; Davis and Domm, 1941).

Progesterone may also play a role in the regulation of male courtship behavior. It is possible to inhibit this behavior in ring doves by systemic injection of progesterone or by implants of crystalline progesterone in any of several hypothalamic nuclei and the tracts which connect these nuclei to the forebrain basal ganglia (Komisaruk, 1967). Electrical stimulation of the pigeon brain (Åkerman, 1966) and androgen implants in the capon brain (Barfield, 1965) elicit courtship behavior when the loci of the treatments are the same as those at which progesterone inhibits this behavior in ring doves. Sexual behavior can be fully maintained in castrated male ring doves by treatment with testosterone propionate, but concurrent administration of progesterone completely suppresses the androgen-supported behavior. These data strongly suggest an antagonistic interaction between these hormones at a neural level (Erickson et al., 1967).

In conclusion we should like to quote the following statement from Young (1964) as a caveat against making easy generalizations about hormonal and behavioral relationships in birds: "Variation in the relationships of the gonadal hormones to behavior is seen in birds which may be greater than that in any other phylum. The significance of these deviant patterns is that all occur within a hormonal framework that is essentially similar—the same steroid substances produced by tissues that are homologous with the tissues which secrete these hormones in males and females in the other phyla. A survey of the relationship between hormones and behavior in birds reveals additional evidence for the view that the locus of change as animals have evolved resides more in the tissues on which the hormones act than in the endocrine organs producing the hormones."

Mammals

Mating Behavior

In 1936 Dempsey et al. first demonstrated that the display of the full copulatory response in the ovariectomized guinea pig required treatment with estrogen followed by progesterone. This has been amply confirmed (Boling, et al. (1938) and extended to many other species: rat (Boling and Blandau, 1939), mouse (Ring, 1944), hamster (Frank and Fraps, 1945), cow (Melampy et al., 1957), the rabbit (Sawyer and Everett, 1959), and the ewe (Robinson, 1954, 1955).

Except for the ewe, the above animals display the normal mating behavior pattern following treatment in which estrogen precedes the progesterone. This follows the normal physiologic events in that the animal is exposed to increasing levels of estrogen during proestrus followed by progesterone prior to ovulation. This has been suggested as a possibility for many years and has only recently been confirmed by direct measurement in the rabbit (Hilliard et al., 1963) and in the rat (Grota and Eik-Nes, 1967). In the case of the ovariectomized ewe, the induction of mating behavior requires pretreatment with progesterone for 3 days followed by 2 days of estrogen. No explanation can be offered at this time for this anomalous situation. It would be most valuable to have some simultaneous measurements of both total estrogens and progestin levels in the ewe throughout the estrous cycle and in relation to estrus.

Inhibition of sexual behavior in the female is another aspect of the action of progesterone. This is not too surprising in view of the well-known antagonistic action of progesterone. Indeed recent work in ovulation indicates that progesterone can either facilitate or inhibit ovulation (Sawyer and Everett, 1959; Zeilmaker, 1966; Zarrow and Hurlbut, 1967; and also see recent reviews by Everett, 1961; Rothchild, 1965). This has also been confirmed with sexual behavior as the end point. Goy et al. (1966) have reported that the induction of estrous behavior in the guinea pig is dependent on the stage of the cycle at which treatment is given. Only a few animals responded with estrous behavior following treatment with estrogen and progesterone during the first 11 days of the cycle, whereas in the later stages of the cycle from 70 to 100 percent responded positively. From this and other experiments they argue that the corpus luteum, by means of its hormonal secretion, progesterone, regulates the responsiveness of the neural tissue.

Somewhat comparable experiments by Zucker (1966) also indicate a facilatory and inhibitory effect by progesterone on the sexual response of the guinea pig. The investigator noted that estrous behavior was facilitated by progesterone in the estrogen-primed ovariectomized animal, but these animals were then refractory to either progesterone or the combination of estrogen and progesterone for an extended period. He also noted that the facilatory effect of progesterone occurred only following a pretreatment period with estrogen. If the progesterone is given prior to the completion of the estrogen period, the effect of the progesterone is inhibitory. Studies on the action of progestogens in sexual receptivity have, however, indicated that the occurrence of behavioral estrus in the guinea pig is not necessarily followed by sexual refractoriness (Zucker and Goy, 1967). Thus it is concluded that the facilitation and inhibition of sexual behavior by progesterone can be attributed to two separate actions of the hormone. The same authors reported that 20a-OH progesterone facilitated behavioral estrus but had no inhibitory effect. Inhibition of normal sexual behavior has also been reported following treatment with progesterone of the normal male guinea pig or the testosterone-treated orchidectomized guinea pig (Diamond, 1966). Progesterone has also been shown capable of inhibiting androgen-induced mounting behavior in the female guinea pig (Diamond and Young, 1963; Diamond, 1967).

The action of progesterone, however, appears to differ in the rat as compared to the guinea pig. Zucker (1967) reports that ovariectomized rats brought into estrus by treatment with estrogen and progesterone were not refractory to progesterone at the termination of estrus. He also showed that progesterone given prior to the completion of estrogen treatment was not inhibitory in the rat. Feder et al. (1967) reported a marked increase in plasma progesterone levels in the rat during the early stages of sexual receptivity. From this they concluded that progesterone plays a significant role.

Maternal Behavior

Maternal behavior involves a complex series of interrelated events which begin shortly after conception and continue through parturition and the weaning of the young. These events are known to be controlled in a complicated fashion both by hormones and the prior experiences (i.e., the central nervous system) of the female. In this section we shall be concerned with describing some of the maternal behaviors of rabbits and rodents which are under the control of progesterone.

One of the first behavioral expressions of pregnancy in the rabbit is nest building. This is generally presented in a two-phase sequence. The animal first builds a straw nest followed 1 to 5 days later by what we have called the "maternal nest" (Zarrow et al., 1962). The maternal nest differs from the straw nest in that the doe actively pulls hair from her body and incorporates this hair with the straw or other nesting materials. The straw is usually hollowed out first and then lined with the body hair, and after the young are born the nest is frequently covered over with the hair. Thus a large, well-insulated nest within which to deposit the young is fabricated by the mother. The maternal nest appears to be unique to pregnancy and pseudopregnancy. The straw nest has been observed to be built by nonpregnant females and by males. However, there has never been a report of a maternal nest built except under conditions of pregnancy, pseudopregnancy, or experimental manipulation involving the hormones of pregnancy. Correlated with the construction of the maternal nest is an actual loosening of the rabbit's body hair so that it is easier for the doe to pull out the hair (Sawin et al., 1960).

In attempting to relate endocrine manipulations to subsequent behavior, it is convenient and almost necessary to have unequivocal behavioral end points. We have selected for measurement the occurrence of the maternal nest (an all or none event) and the degree of loosening of the hair (a continuous event) as our two end points to study with respect to hormone manipulation.

Before discussing these more fully, however, some other characteristics of maternal behavior in the rabbit should be noted. One can roughly quantify the maternal nest by rating its quality (Sawin and Crary, 1953). The rating scale ranges from a flat nest with no hollowed-out area in which to place the young to a nest which is well hollowed out and completely covered over, thus offering maximum warmth and protection for the young (Sawin and Crary, 1953; Ross et al., 1956). Other behavioral patterns occurring during pregnancy and continuing after the young are born have been described by Sawin and Curran (1952) as involving "maternal protection" and "maternal interest." The former describes the doe's behavior toward an attendant who inspects the cage and nest box of the female. Rabbits range in their behavior from a high degree of timidity when approached by the attendant to vigorous, aggressive attacks upon the attendant. After the young are born, the degree of "maternal interest" may be rated on a five-point scale ranging from zero (no interest in the young) to four plus (interest in the young to the point of aggressively fighting off any attempt to approach the nest or manipulate the young). This measure differs from maternal protection in that the latter refers to the behavior of the doe when approached by the attendant. The interest ratings specifically refer to the response to manipulation of the nest or young. Sawin and Curran (1952) presented evidence that these two characteristics are relatively independent.

Another characteristic of maternal behavior is that of nursing the young. This can be simply scored by examining a neonate to see if the belly is distended and if the milk can be seen through the skin. It is thus possible to obtain a score based on the percentage of a litter which a mother nurses.

Two significant negative features of maternal behavior are scattering and cannibalism. Scattering is defined as the finding of one or more of the young outside the nest or nest box rather than in the nest. Cannibalism is defined as eating of part or all of one or more young (Denenberg et al., 1959).

Systematic analyses have been made of these various measures. An analysis of changes in nest quality over four litters has been reported by Ross et al. (1956). Relationships between nest quality, maternal interest, nursing, aggression, scattering, and cannibalism have been described by Denenberg et al. (1959). Any or all of these behaviors could have been used as end points against which to assess hormonal manipulation, but we chose not to use them because it would have been necessary to follow the mother and her litter through a number of postparturient days to obtain the necessary data. In planning our research strategy we felt it more advisable to be able to terminate all observations at the time of parturition using two unequivocal end points. Ultimately, however, it will be necessary to relate the hormonal status of the organism to the other behaviors which we have described above.

A common observation has been that the hair of rabbits becomes relatively loose around the time of parturition, particularly in specific areas of the body. This observation has been quantified by means of a combing technique. Two selected areas of the body were used for combing: the flank, which is defined as the area of the thigh located over the femur, and the back, which is defined as the area from the base of the neck to the tail. The comb was held at a 45-degree angle and passed over each flank area three times and over the back area six times. In each instance the hair from each pass was combined and weighed in total on a torsion balance to the nearest milligram.

The first experiment established that a significant degree of hair loosening occurred during gestation in the rabbit (Sawin et al., 1960). The peak of hair loosening occurred anywhere from 5 days prepartum to the day of parturition. In addition, one pseudopregnant rabbit also exhibited a significant increase in hair loosening on day 15 and on day 20 following the onset of pseudopregnancy. A control group of nonpregnant females failed to exhibit any increase in hair loosening over time.

Following the quantification of hair loosening and the demonstration that this is a phenomenon of pregnancy and pseudopregnancy, Farooq et al. (1963) investigated hair loosening as a function of endocrine factors. As found previously, normal pregnant females and pseudopregnant females both exhibited significant hair loosening. In another experiment progesterone was administered to animals from day 28 to 35 of pregnancy in order to inhibit parturition. With a daily dose of 4 mg of progesterone, parturition was duly inhibited at the normal time and none of these animals built a maternal nest. Although a percentage increase in hair weight was noted, this increase was significantly less than that of normal controls. In another experiment, pregnant animals were given 2 mg of progesterone. As with the 4-mg group, an increase in hair loosening occurred, but again the increase was still significantly less than that of normal controls. Unlike the 4-mg group, however, seven of the eight animals in this experiment did build a maternal nest.

Other experiments demonstrated that hair loosening could be induced in castrated females given a regimen of estradiol, progesterone, and prolactin for a period of 8 weeks. However, a similar regimen for 18 days failed to affect hair loosening. To determine whether hair loosening could be induced in the male, the same regimen which had been successful with castrated females was used with castrated males. No evidence of an increase in hair loosening was obtained.

The building of a maternal nest normally occurs during the end of pregnancy or pseudopregnancy (Tietz, 1933; Zarrow et al., 1961). The functional value of the nest has been shown by Zarrow et al. (1963) by clipping the entire hair coat of some females on day 28 or 29 of pregnancy. Some of these females and some nonclipped controls were given nesting material. Eighty-seven percent of young born to normal control mothers lived through weaning, while only 5.7 percent of the young reared with no nesting material survived.

An important question concerning maternal nest building is whether the hormones of pregnancy must act for a minimum period of time in order to initiate this behavior in the rabbit. One way to investigate this question is by castrating females at different times during pregnancy. This procedure was used since Zarrow et al. (1961) had previously demonstrated that nest building would occur consequent to castration late in pregnancy. Using the Dutch-belted strain, females were castrated 13, 14, 15, 16, or 17 days after the initiation of pregnancy. There is clear evidence of the presence of a critical period of exposure to hormones of pregnancy before nest building can occur. This is day 16 of gestation in this particular strain. Castration prior to day 14 of gestation resulted in a failure to build a maternal nest; essentially all rabbits built a maternal nest if castrated after day 16 of pregnancy. In all instances castration terminated pregnancy (Zarrow et al., 1962).

Not only will castration after a certain critical period induce nest building, but complete removal of the entire conceptus mass on days 22 to 27 of gestation will also do so (Zarrow et al., 1962). In addition, rabbits made pseudopregnant with human chorionic gonadotropin will also build maternal nests (Zarrow et al., 1961).

Following the above documentation that the hormones of pregnancy significantly control nest-building behavior, Zarrow et al. (1963) set out to determine whether maternal nest building could be induced in a nonpregnant female by the appropriate hormonal manipulations. Castrated females were given various regimens of hormones and the occurrence of maternal nest building was observed. Three regimes were found to induce nest building 100 percent of the time. The first treatment involved the daily injection of 5 μg of estradiol for a period of 56 days, 1 mg of progesterone during the second and third week, followed by 2 mg of progesterone for the remaining period, and 20 IU prolactin injected daily for the last 2 weeks. Within 3 or 4 days after the cessation of hormone treatment all 10 rabbits built maternal nests.

Since maternal nest building occurs in the rabbit during pregnancy, a period of exposure to the proper hormones for approximately

30 days should be sufficient to induce the phenomenon. Furthermore, maternal nest building, during either pregnancy or pseudopregnancy, is associated with a decline in the circulating level of progesterone. Accordingly, a regimen was set up in which the rabbit received 5 μg of estradiol for 31 days with 2 mg of progesterone on days 9 to 18 and 4 mg of progesterone on days 19 to 28. Under this regimen all rabbits built maternal nests. However, if both the estrogen and progesterone treatment were stopped simultaneously, nest building failed to occur.

In an attempt to reduce even further the length of treatment, 10 rabbits were injected with 5 μg of estradiol on days 1 to 18 and 4 mg of progesterone on days 2 to 15. All animals built maternal nests. Again, if treatment with estradiol and progesterone was maintained until day 18 and simultaneously stopped, nest building failed to occur.

Castrated males were subjected to the same treatments as the castrated females. In no instance was there any evidence of nest building on the part of the males.

It is apparent from the experiments described above that the onset of maternal nest building is always associated with a fall in progesterone levels (nest building occurs at parturition, near the end of pseudopregnancy, and after castration in the pregnant animal). If the fall in progesterone level triggers nest building, it then follows that the maintenance of high progesterone levels should prevent maternal nest building. Therefore, Zarrow et al. (1963) took 12 pregnant females and, starting on day 28, injected these females with 4 mg of progesterone until day 35 of gestation. Nest building was inhibited in all but one of these rabbits. Parturition was delayed in all animals and appeared only 3 to 4 days after the withdrawal of progesterone. A second group of 10 pregnant rabbits was treated in a similar fashion with a dose of 2 mg of progesterone. The delay as well as the subsequent onset of parturition was comparable to the former group, but 90 percent of these animals did build a maternal nest. The onset of nest building varied from normal to a slight delay of 1 or 2 days.

It is evident from the above result that the onset of maternal nest building may depend on a critical ratio between progesterone and estrogen. Therefore, either a decrease in progesterone or an increase in estrogen should result in maternal nest building. To test this hypothesis, 10 pregnant rabbits were given 10 μg of estradiol benzoate daily on days 20, 21, and 22 of pregnancy. Nine of these 10 animals built a maternal nest between days 22 and 24 of gestation.

In summary, a necessary aspect to the induction of maternal

nest building in the rabbit appears to be an exposure to a combination of the two steroids, estrogen and progesterone, with progesterone dominant followed by a withdrawal of the progesterone resulting in an estrogen dominance. Maternal nest building fails to occur if either steroid is given alone or if the progesterone level is maintained.

Maternal Behavior in the Rat. Taylor (1965) and Taylor et al. (1965) developed a technique to quantify maternal nest building in the rat and then utilized this to investigate the effects of hormone manipulations upon nest-building behavior. Nest building was quantified by giving each female a number of medium-grade hardwood dowels (⅜ inches in diameter, 2¼ inches in length). The rats would shred the dowels either by chewing the wood or else by holding the dowels in their paws and running their teeth along the long axis, thus stripping the wood. They would then take the shredded material and make a crude nest of it.

Each morning dowels, weighed to the nearest tenth of a gram, were placed in each cage. Twenty-four hours later the unshredded dowels and the shredded fragments were removed from each cage, and a new supply of dowels was provided. The unused dowels and the unshredded remains were weighed to the nearest tenth of a gram. The weight thus obtained was subtracted from the original dowel weight and was recorded as a daily nest material score.

Pregnant females exhibited a significant increase in shredding scores during pregnancy, with a peak either at the day of parturition or the day prior to parturition. Nonpregnant female controls did not exhibit a significant peak in performance when given equal exposure to dowel material. Also, males did not show a significant shredding score over an equivalent period of time. This pattern of a significant increase in scores for pregnant females at the time of parturition with a failure to find any significant changes in behavior for male and female controls may be taken as confirming the maternal aspects of this behavior pattern.

A series of experiments was then conducted involving estradiol, progesterone, or a combination of the two and attempting to relate these hormone manipulations to the dowel-shredding performance. However, in no instance was any relationship attained between hormone manipulation and the shredding score.

A second approach to the problem of the role of the endocrine system in maternal behavior has been the analysis of survival and growth of newborn rats placed with foster mothers. In one set of experiments mothers who had been lactating for 10 days had their natural young removed and replaced by newborn foster young. If the newborn young were fostered after their natural mother had cleaned them and eaten the placenta, then 26 percent of the fostered young survived until weaning. However, if the newborn young were fostered immediately after birth to the foster mother, so that she ate the placenta, then 67 percent of the young survived until weaning (Denenberg et al., 1963).

Since the placenta is eaten immediately upon fostering, it seemed likely that some substance (or substances) in this organ was implicated in the increase in survival. Another experiment was conducted in which newborn young were fostered after the natural mother had removed the placenta (a condition which results in 26 percent survival), but in this instance the foster mother had received one injection 4 μg of estradiol prior to being given the young. Under this condition, 66 percent of the young survived until weaning (Denenberg et al., 1963).

In still another experiment the procedure described above was repeated except that the foster mothers were given one injection of 2 mg of progesterone prior to being given the foster young. This resulted in a survival incidence of 50 percent, a significant increase over the base value of 26 percent.

The manner in which these hormones are producing their effect is not clear as yet, but it has been intimated that progesterone may be a key substance here. It has been known for some time that the placenta of the rat contains a luteotropic factor (Astwood and Greep, 1938) which behaves like prolactin. Recently, Grota and Eik-Nes (1967) reported a highly significant increase in plasma progesterone following consumption of placenta by the mother. This was reproducible in hypophysectomized rats. It might therefore be argued that the placental feeding is essentially supplying prolactin as well as both estrogen and progesterone and that the former is acting via increased release of endogenous progesterone. The hormones could then be producing their effects on maternal behavior via the central nervous system and on the mammary gland by direct action.

The early work on maternal behavior in the mouse made no attempt to evaluate the role of specific hormones but was concerned primarily with behavioral patterns such as retrieval of young, care of the young a nest, etc. (Leblond and Nelson, 1937; Leblond, 1938).

Koller (1952, 1955) describes the presence of a brood nest in pregnant mice as distinguished from a sleeping nest. The brood nest is much larger than the sleeping nest and appears only during pregnancy or treatment with progesterone. This nest is physically distinguished from the normal nest only on the basis of size and time of appearance. He noted that the appearance of the brood nest in the pregnant mouse coincided with the appearance of the corpora lutea of pregnancy. Treatment of intact or castrated female mice with either prolactin or estrone gave negative results, but progesterone at levels of 1.5 to 3 IU caused the appearance of a brood nest. Progesterone was ineffective in the intact or castrated male. Koller concluded that the regular or sleeping nest of the male and the nonpregnant female is built as a protection against the cold and that the brood nest is a part of the maternal complex stimulated during gestation by the increasing levels of progesterone available at that time. Thus it might be inferred that the regular nest is a response to ambient temperature, whereas the brood nest is the result of progesterone in a genetic female.

In the hamster Richards (1965) has reported an increase in time spent in nest building during pregnancy as well as an increase in nest weight. He also reports that an increase, comparable to that seen in pregnancy, was obtained in nonpregnant females by the injection of progesterone.

20α-OH-Progesterone

The findings that high levels of 20α-OH-progesterone are present in the rabbit (Hilliard et al., 1963), rat (Telegdy and Endröczi, 1963) and monkey (Hayward et al., 1963) and that the highest ratios of the 20α-OH-progesterone to progesterone occur during proestrus and estrus led to a study of this hormone in the induction of mating behavior in the female rat (Langford and Hilliard, 1967). Adult female rats were castrated, primed with a single injection of estradiol benzoate, and given the test dose of 20α-AH-progesterone 48 hours later. The presence of the lordosis reflex in the female following exposure to the male was considered a positive response. Comparison of the response indicated that 20α-OH-progesterone has approximately one half the potency of progesterone. This compares favorably with the findings that the 20α-OH-progesterone possesses one half to one third of the progestational activity of progesterone in the Clauberg test (Zander et al., 1958). Zucker (1967) reports that he and Goy have data indicating that 20α-OH-progesterone and pregnenolone, in addition to progesterone, can facilitate the expression of sexual receptivity in the estrogen-primed, spayed guinea pig. Although the 20α form of progesterone is less active than progesterone, its physiological significance cannot be discounted. Actually the amount present is of such magnitude, i.e., from two to four times more than progesterone, as to make the 20α-OH-progesterone as significant, if not more so, than progesterone. Recently, Hilliard et al (1967) reported the maintenance of LH levels in the blood of rabbits following treatment with 20α-OH-progesterone. They concluded that this progestin acts as a positive feedback agent to prolong and heighten LH discharge following mating in the rabbit.

Progesterone and the CNS

Preferential uptake of progesterone by the brain has been demonstrated in the rat (Loumas and Farooq, 1966). Within 2 minutes following the injection of tritiated progesterone, maximum uptake was obtained in a portion of the CNS containing hypothalamic tissue. The uptake of progesterone by the brain differs markedly from the uptake of estradiol in the speed with which it is taken up, the small amounts taken up, and the speed with which it is lost. Approximately 30 percent of the peak value seen at 2 minutes is left in the brain at 10 minutes and only 10 percent or less remains at 60 minutes. It would appear that the retention of progesterone by the brain cells is not necessary for the effect of this hormone on behavior. Nonetheless, although the uptake of progesterone by the brain is of extreme rapidity and short duration, it is highly significant and does lead to significant behavioral events after a lapse of hours or days. However, the rapid onset of behavioral changes has been reported for the rat and hamster. Lisk (1960) observed lordosis in the rats as short as 2.5 minutes following intravenous injection of progesterone; Kent and Liberman (1949) observed lordosis in the hamster as early as 10 minutes after injection of progesterone into the lateral ventricle.

Hamburg (1966) quotes some unpublished observations of M. Dallman which describe the uptake of tritium-labeled progesterone as indicated by autoradiography. He noted a significant uptake by the brain within 5 minutes and thereafter a steady decline. However, the rate of loss of the labeled hormone from the hypothalamus was much slower than that seen in other parts of the brain.

Other indications of a specific action of progesterone on the brain involve the anesthetic action of the hormone. Although large doses are necessary, progesterone is the most potent anesthetic of the naturally occurring hormones (Selye, 1941) and has been shown to be effective in rats, mice, guinea pigs, rabbits, cats, and human beings. Kawakami and Sawyer (1959, 1967) have shown that progesterone has a biphasic effect on the threshold of the response of the rabbit brain to electrical stimulation. In the estrous rat, Barra-clough and Cross (1963) have observed a decreased responsiveness of neurones in the lateral hypothalamus to stimuli such as cold, pain, and mechanical probing of the uterine cervix. They also showed that intravenous injection of 400 μg of progesterone to rats in proestrus and diestrus diminished the responsiveness of these cells to the cervical probing but not to the cold or pain stimuli. Injection of 800 μg of progesterone reduced the response to all the stimuli but did not produce any signs of generalized anesthesia. Cross and Silver (1965) found that the number of hypothalamic cells excited by cervical probing observed in pseudopregnant rats was only one fourth that of the number observed in cycling animals. Ovariectomy of pseudopregnant animals resulted in a fourfold increase in the number of responsive cells, but progesterone injection abolished this increase. The activity of these neurones in response to cold and pain was unaffected by pseudopregnancy, ovariectomy, or progesterone.

Single-cell and multiunit activity in the hypothalamus have been recorded simultaneously along with EEG in progesterone-treated rats (Ramirez et al., 1967; Komisaruk et al., 1967). These authors question the specificity of the influence of progesterone on the response of hypothalamic neurons to peripheral stimulation as has been suggested by Barraclough and Cross (1963) and Cross and Silver (1965). They suggest that light urethane anesthesia potentiates the anesthetic effects of progesterone on the EEG and that progesterone blocks the response of lateral hypothalamic units to vaginal stimulation but not to pain or thermal stimuli because the former is a weaker altering stimulus. They also conclude that effects of progesterone on hypothalamic activity may reflect cortical responses to changes in peripheral blood pressure as well as the direct action of the hormone on the central nervous system.

General Comments

Aves

Investigation in several broad areas is needed to clarify the role of progesterone in behavior of birds.

Interaction of progesterone with estrogen and testosterone has been shown under several experimental conditions (Vowles and Harwood, 1966; Stern, 1966, 1967; Erickson et al., 1967). Whether these experimental conditions reliably reflect naturally occurring physio-

logical and behavioral events must be determined by measurements
of levels of the hormones in the circulation and at presumptive sites
of action. The interaction may be inhibitory, as in the case of progesterone blocking the maintenance of courtship activity by testosterone in castrated male doves (Erickson et al., 1967). The manner
in which progesterone does this is unknown but might be due to an
inhibitory competition for the neural site at which the androgen acts.
It also might be due to a modification of the responsiveness of the
neural elements to testosterone. These suggested modes of action of
progesterone need not be mutually exclusive. Interaction of progesterone and estrogen has not been explored sufficiently especially
as concerns sexual receptivity of female birds. In light of current
knowledge about this behavior in mammals it is an area of some
interest. Possible interaction of progesterone and prolactin as a
means of modifying avian behavior has not been explored at all.

Several studies (Lofts and Marshall, 1959; Lehrman and Brody,
1964; Hinde and Steel, 1966) provide information which suggests
that prolactin might be involved in causing the release of progesterone. Findings that prolactin has a luteotropic action in some
mammals lend credence to this possibility. To elucidate this possible
explanation of the action of prolactin, measurements of the ability
of prolactin to modify behavior should be made in gonadectomized
animals as well as intact ones. In those case where prolactin does
elicit responses similar to those elicited by progesterone, it would be
informative to know if the rate of secretion of progesterone is increased. Whether progesterone can regulate the release of prolactin
is another area that is subject to careful investigation.

Mammals

Some of the questions raised in the previous section on aves hold
for the mammals also. Specific questions such as what normal
behavioral patterns are regulated, in part at least, by progesterone
remain only partially answered.

That progesterone influences the central nervous system is well
established. The evidence includes (1) the localization of the hormone in the CNS, (2) direct measurements of electrical activity in the
brain following progesterone treatment, and (3) the involvement
of progesterone in sexual and maternal behavior. This still leaves us
with the question of what progesterone is doing to influence behavior
and CNS activity: What is the mechanism of action? It would appear
that progesterone needs an estrogenized substrate on which to act

and that it influences electrical activity. This still leaves much to be answered.

Another area in need of much immediate attention is an analysis of the various aspects of maternal behavior and determination of which ones are regulated by progesterone. Not too much information is available on this point. Indeed it is most difficult to generalize due to lack of adequate data, especially on different species.

Finally, we need to know when the basic pattern for maternal behavior is laid down embryologically and whether hormones are involved at this time as they are for sexual behavior (Harris and Levine, 1965). We do know that maternal nest building is limited to the female in the rabbit. Hence the situation may be comparable. Along these lines it has been suggested that progesterone is crucial during pregnancy to prevent steroid related abnormal neural and genital development and differentiation (Diamond, 1967; Dorfman, 1967). Thus it may be concerned with both the development of the individual and with adult behavior. There is ample evidence the hormone is concerned in both a positive and negative fashion with sexual behavior, but we would raise the question of whether it is involved during embryogenesis.

In conclusion we would like to point out that there has been a tendency to regard progesterone as a synergist reacting with estrogen to induce sexual activity, maternal behavior, etc. We hope that this review, if it does anything, will influence the reader to think of progesterone not only as a synergist to estrogen but a hormone that must be considered as possessing specific physiologic and behavioral activities of its own. The fact that many of the activities ascribable to progesterone depend on an estrogenized substrate does not decrease the importance of progesterone to the regulation of physiological and behavioral events.

Acknowledgment

This paper was written during the tenure of Grant HD-02068, National Institutes of Health.

References

Adams, J. L., and R. B. Herrick. 1955. Interaction of the gonadal hormones in the chicken. *Poultry Sci.,* 34: 117–121.

Åkerman, B. 1966. Behavioural effects of stimulation in the forebrain of the pigeon. I. Reproductive behaviour. *Behaviour,* 26: 323–338.

Allee, W. C., and N. Collias. 1940. The influence of estradiol on the social organization of flocks of hens. *Endocrinology,* 27: 87–94.

Astwood, E. B., and R. O. Greep. 1938. A corpus luteum-stimulating substance in the rat placenta. *Proc. Soc. Exptl. Biol. Med.*, **38:** 713–716.

Bailey, R. E. 1952. The incubation patch of passerine birds. *Condor*, **54:** 121–136.

Barfield, R. J. 1965. Induction of aggressive and courtship behavior by intracerebral implants of androgen in capons. *Am. Zoologist*, **5:** 203.

Barraclough, C. A., and B. A. Cross. 1963. Unit activity in the hypothalamus of the cyclic female rat: Effect of genital stimuli and progesterone. *J. Endocrinol.*, **26:** 339–359.

Bates, R. W., E. L. Lahr, and O. Riddle. 1935. The gross action of prolactin and follicle-stimulating hormone on the mature ovary and sex accessories of fowl. *Am. J. Physiol.*, **111:** 361–368.

Beach, F. 1961. *Hormones and Behavior*. Cooper Square Publishers, New York, p. 368.

Boling, J. L., and R. J. Blandau. 1939. The estrogen-progesterone induction of mating responses in the spayed female rat. *Endocrinology*, **25:** 359–364.

Boling, J. L., W. C. Young, and E. W. Dempsey. 1938. Miscellaneous experiments on the estrogen-progesterone induction of heat in the spayed guinea pig. *Endocrinology*, **23:** 182–187.

Brant, J. W. A., and A. V. Nalbandov. 1956. Role of sex hormones in albumin secretion by the oviduct of chickens. *Poultry Sci.*, **35:** 692–700.

Breitenbach, R. P., C. L. Nagra, and R. K. Meyer. 1965. Studies of incubation and broody behavior in the pheasant (*Phasianus colchicus*). *Animal Behavior*, **13:** 143–148.

Courrier, R. 1950. Interactions between estrogens and progesterone. In *Vitamins and Hormones* (R. S. Harris and K. V. Thimann, eds.). Academic Press, New York, pp. 179–214.

Cross, B. A., and I. A. Silver. 1965. Effect of luteal hormone on the behaviour of hypothalamic neurones in pseudopregnant rats. *J. Endocrinol.*, **31:** 251–263.

Davis, D. E., and L. V. Domm. 1941. The sexual behavior of hormonally treated domestic fowl. *Proc. Soc. Exptl. Biol. Med.*, **48:** 667–669.

Dempsey, E. W., R. Hertz, and W. C. Young. 1936. The experimental induction of oestrus (sexual receptivity) in the normal and ovariectomized guinea pig. *Am. J. Physiol.*, **116:** 201–209.

Denenberg, V. H., S. F. Petropoulus, P. B. Sawin, and S. Ross. 1959. Genetic, physiological and behavioral background of reproduction in the rabbit. VI. Maternal behavior with reference to scattered and cannibalized newborn and mortality. *Behaviour*, **15:** 71–76.

Denenberg, V. H., L. J. Grota, and M. X. Zarrow, 1963. Maternal behavior in the rat: Analysis of cross-fostering. *J. Reprod. Fertility*, **5:** 133–141.

Deol, G. S. 1964. Studies in the structure and function of the ovary of the domestic fowl. Ph.D. thesis, Edinburgh.

Diamond, M. 1966. Progestagen inhibition of normal sexual behavior in the male guinea pig. *Nature*, **209:** 1322–1324.

Diamond, M. 1967. Androgen-induced masculinization in the ovariectomized and guinea pig. *Anat. Rec.*, **157:** 47–52.

Diamond, M., and W. C. Young. 1963. Differential responsiveness of pregnant and nonpregnant guinea pigs to the masculinizing action of testosterone propionate. *Endocrinology*, **72:** 429–438.

Dorfman, R. I. 1967. The antiestrogenic and antiandrogenic activities of progesterone in the defense of a normal fetus. *Anat. Rec.*, **157:** 547–558.

Dunham, H. H., and O. Riddle. 1942. Effects of a series of steroids on ovulation and reproduction in pigeons. *Physiol. Zool.*, 15: 383–394.

Erickson, C. J., R. H. Bruder, B. R. Komisaruk, and D. S. Lehrman. 1967. Selective blocking by progesterone of behavioral effects of androgen in the ring dove. *Endocrinology*. In press.

Everett, J. W. 1961. The mammalian female reproductive system and its controlling mechanisms. In *Sex and Internal Secretions* (W. C. Young, ed.). Williams & Wilkins, Baltimore, 3rd ed., pp. 497–553.

Farooq, A., V. H. Denenberg, S. Ross., P. B. Sawin, and M. X. Zarrow. 1963. Maternal behavior in the rabbit: Endocrine factors involved in hair loosening. *Am. J. Physiol.*, 204: 271–274.

Feder, H. H., R. W. Goy, and J. A. Resko. 1967. Progesterone concentrations in the peripheral plasma of cyclic rats. *J. Physiol.*, 191: 136P–137P.

Frank, A. H., and R. M. Fraps. 1945. Induction of estrus in the ovariectomized golden hamster. *Endocrinology*, 37: 357–361.

Fraps, R. M. 1955. Egg production and fertility in poultry. In *Progress in the Physiology of Farm Animals* (J. Hammond, ed.). Butterworth, London.

Fraps, R. M., C. W. Hooker, and T. R. Forbes. 1949. Progesterone in blood plasma of the ovulating hen. *Science*, 108: 86–87.

Fraps, R. M., C. W. Hooker, and T. R. Forbes. 1948. Progesterone in the blood plasma of cocks and non-ovulating hens. *Science*, 109: 493.

Gilbert, A. B., and D. G. M. Wood-Gush. 1964. Progesterone and nesting behavior in the domestic fowl. *Proc. 5th Intern. Congr. Animal Reproduction and Artificial Insemination.*

Goy, R. W., C. H. Phoenix, and W. C. Young. 1966. Inhibitory action of the corpus luteum on the hormonal induction of estrous behavior in the guinea pig. *Gen. Comp. Endocrinol.*, 6: 267–275.

Grota, L. J., and K. B. Eik-Nes. 1967. Plasma progesterone concentrations during pregnancy and lactation in the rat. *J. Reprod. Fertility*, 13: 83–91.

Hamburg, D. 1966. Effects of progesterone on behavior. In *Endocrines and the Central Nervous System* (R. Levine, ed.). Williams & Wilkins, Baltimore, pp. 251–265.

Harris, G. W., and S. Levine. 1965. Sexual differentiation of the brain and its experimental control. *J. Physiol. (London)*, 181: 379–400.

Hayward, J. N., J. Hilliard, and C. H. Sawyer. 1963. Preovulatory and postovulatory progestins in the monkey ovary and ovarian vein blood. *Proc. Soc. Exptl. Biol. Med.*, 113: 256–259.

Hilliard, J., D. Archibald, and C. H. Sawyer. 1963. Gonadotropic activation of preovulatory synthesis and release of progestin in the rabbit. *Endocrinology*, 72: 59–66.

Hilliard, J., R. Penardi, and C. H. Sawyer. 1967. A functional role for 20α-hydroxypregn-4-en-3-one in the rabbit. *Endocrinology*, 80: 901–909.

Hinde, R. A. 1965. Interaction of internal and external factors in integration of canary reproduction. In *Sex and Behavior* (F. A. Beach, ed.). Wiley, New York.

Hinde, R. A., and E. Steel. 1964. Effect of exogenous hormones on the tactile sensitivity of the canary brood patch. *J. Endocrinol.*, 30: 355–359.

Hinde, R. A., and E. Steel. 1966. Integration of the reproductive behaviour of female canaries. In *S.E.B. Symposia XX, Nervous and Hormonal Control of Integration*. Academic Press, New York, pp. 407–426.

Höhn, E. O. 1960. Action of certain hormones on the thymus of the domestic hen. *J. Endocrinol.*, 19: 282–287.

Höhn, E. O., and S. C. Cheng. 1967. Gonadal hormones in Wilson's phalarope (*Steganopis tricolor*) and other birds in relation to plumage and sex behavior. *Gen. Comp. Endocrinol.*, 8: 1–11.

Juhn, M., and P. C. Harris. 1955. Molt of capon feathering with prolactin. *Proc. Soc. Exptl. Biol. Med.*, 98: 669–672.

Kawakami, M., and C. H. Sawyer. 1959. Neuroendocrine correlates of changes in brain activity thresholds by sex steroids and pituitary hormones. *Endocrinology*, 65: 652–668.

Kawakami, M., and C. H. Sawyer. 1967. Effects of sex hormones and antifertility steroids on brain thresholds in the rabbit. *Endocrinology*, 80: 857–871.

Kent, G. C., Jr., and M. J. Liberman. 1949. Induction of psychic estrus in the hamster with progesterone administered via the lateral brain ventricle. *Endocrinology*, 45: 29–32.

Kobayashi, H. 1958. On the induction of molt in bids of 17α-oxyprogesterone-17-caproate. *Endocrinology*, 63: 420–430.

Koller, G. 1952. Der Nestbau der weissen Maus und seine hormonale Auslösung. *Zool. Anz. Suppl.*, 17: 160–168.

Koller, G. 1955. Hormonale und psychische Steurung beim Nestbau weiser Mause *Zool. Anz. Suppl.*, 19: 123–132.

Komisaruk, B. R. 1967. Effects of local brain implants of progesterone on reproductive behavior in ring doves. *J. Comp. Physiol Psychol.*, 64: 219–224.

Komisaruk, B. R., P. G. McDonald, D. I. Whitmoyer, and C. H. Sawyer. 1967. Effects of progesterone and sensory stimulation on EEG and neuronal activity in the rat. *Exptl. Neurol.*, 19: 494–507.

Langford, J., and J. Hilliard. 1967. Effect of 20α-hydroxypregn-4-en-3-one on mating behavior in spayed female rats. *Endocrinology*, 80: 381–383.

Layne, D. S., R. H. Common, W. A. Maw, and R. M. Fraps. 1957. Presence of progesterone in extracts of ovaries of laying hens. *Proc. Soc. Exptl. Biol. Med.*, 94: 528–529.

Leblond, C. P. 1938. Extra-hormonal factors in maternal behavior. *Proc. Soc. Exptl. Biol. Med.*, 38: 66–70.

Leblond, C. P., and W. D. Nelson. 1937. Maternal behavior in hypophysectomized male and female mice. *Am. J. Physiol.*, 120: 167–172.

Lehrman, D. S. 1958. Effect of female sex hormones on incubation behavior in the ring dove (*Streptopelia risoria*). *J. Comp. Physiol. Psychol.*, 51: 142–145.

Lehrman, D. S. 1961. Hormonal regulation of parental behavior in birds and infrahuman mammals. In *Sex and Internal Secretions* (W. C. Young, ed.). Williams & Wilkins, Baltimore, 3rd ed., pp. 1268–1382.

Lehrman, D. S. 1963. On the initiation of incubation behaviour in doves. *Animal Behavior*, 11: 433–438.

Lehrman, D. S. 1965. Interaction between internal and external environments in the regulation of the reproductive cycle of the ring dove. In *Sex and Behavior* (F. A. Beach, ed.). Wiley, New York, pp. 355–380.

Lehrman, D. S., and P. Brody. 1957. Oviduct response to estrogen and progesterone in the ring dove (*Streptopelia risoria*). *Proc. Soc. Exptl. Biol. Med.*, 95: 373–375.

Lehrman, D. S., and P. Brody. 1961. Does prolactin induce incubation behavior in the ring dove? *J. Endocrinol.*, 22: 269–275.

Lehrman, D. S., and P. Brody. 1964. Effect of prolactin on established incubation behavior in the ring dove. *J. Comp. Physiol. Psychol.*, 57: 161–165.

Lehrman, D. S., P. Brody, and R. P. Wortis. 1961. The presence of the mate and nesting material as stimuli for the development of incubation behavior and for gonadotropin secretion in the ring dove (*Streptopelia risoria*). *Endocrinology*, 68: 507–516.

Lisk, R. D. 1960. A comparison of the effectiveness of intravenous, as opposed to subcutaneous injection of progesterone for the induction of estrous behavior in the rat. *Can. J. Biochem. Physiol.*, 38: 1381–1383.

Lofts, B., and A. J. Marshall. 1956. The effects of prolactin administration on the internal rhythm of reproduction in male birds. *J. Endocrinol.*, 13: 101–106.

Lofts, B., and A. J. Marshall. 1959. The post-nuptial occurrence of progestins in the seminiferous tubules of birds. *J. Endocrinol.*, 19: 16–21.

Loumas, K. R., and A. Farooq. 1966. The uptake in vivo of [1, 2-3 H]- progesterone by the brain and genital tract of the rat. *J. Endocrinol.*, 36: 95–96.

Lytle, I. M., and F. W. Lorenz. 1958. Progesterone in the blood of the laying hen. *Nature*, 182: 1681.

Marshall, A. J. 1949. On the function of the interstitium of the testis. The sexual cycle of a wild bird, *Fulmaris glacialis* (L.). *Quart. J. Microscop. Sci.*, 90: 265–280.

Marshall, A. J. 1950. Mechanism and significance of the "Refractory Period" in the avian testis cycle. *Nature*, 166: 1034.

Marshall, A. J., and D. L. Serventy. 1956. The breeding cycle of the short-tailed shearwater, *Puffinus tenuirostris* (Temminck) in relation to trans-equatorial migration and its environment. *Proc. Zool. Soc. London*, 127: 489–510.

Melampy, R. M., M. A. Emerson, J. M. Rakes, L. J. Hanka, and P. G. Eness. 1957. The effect of progesterone on the estrous response of estrogen-conditioned ovariectomized cows. *J. Animal Sci.*, 16: 967–975.

Nicoll, C. S., E. W. Pfeiffer, and H. R. Fevold. 1967. Prolactin and nest behavior in phalaropes. *Gen. Comp. Endocrinol.*, 8: 61–65.

Patel, M. D. 1936. The physiology of the formation of "pigeon's milk." *Physiol. Zool.*, 9: 129–152.

Ralph, C. L., and R. M. Fraps. 1959. Effect of hypothalamic lesions on progesterone-induced ovulation in the hen. *Endocrinology*, 65: 819–824.

Ralph, C. L., and R. M. Fraps. 1960. Induction of ovulation in the hen by injection of progesterone into the brain. *Endocrinology*, 66: 269–272.

Ramirez, V. D., B. R. Komisaruk, D. I. Whitmoyer, and C. H. Sawyer. 1967. Effects of hormones and vaginal stimulation on the EEG and hypothalamic units in rats. *Am. J. Physiol.* 212: 1376–1381.

Richards, M. P. 1965. The behaviour of the pregnant golden hamster. *J. Reprod. Fertility*, 10: 285–286.

Riddle, O. 1963. Prolactin or progesterone as key to parental behaviour: A review. *Animal Behavior*, 11: 419–432.

Riddle, O., and S. W. Dykshorn. 1932. Secretion of crop-milk in the castrate male pigeon. *Proc. Soc. Exptl. Biol. Med.*, 29: 1213–1215.

Riddle, O., and E. L. Lahr. 1944. On broodiness of ring doves following implants of certain steroid hormones. *Endocrinology*, 35: 255–260.

Riddle, O., R. W. Bates, and E. L. Lahr. 1935. Prolactin induces broodiness in fowl. *Am. J. Physiol.*, 111: 352–360.

Ring, J. R. 1944. The estrogen-progesterone induction of sexual receptivity in the spayed female mouse. *Endocrinology,* **34:** 269–275.

Robinson, T. J. 1954. The necessity for progesterone with estrogen for the induction of recurrent estrus in the ovariectomized ewe. *Endocrinology,* **55:** 403–408.

Robinson, T. J. 1955. Quantitative studies on the hormonal induction of oestrus in spayed ewes. *J. Endocrinol.,* **12:** 163–173.

Ross, S., V. H. Denenberg, P. B. Sawin, and P. Meyer. 1956. Changes in nest building behaviour in multiparous rabbits. *Brit. J. Animal Behaviour,* **4:** 69–74.

Rothchild, I. 1965. Interrelations between progesterone and the ovary, pituitary and central nervous system in the control of ovulation and the regulation of progesterone secretion. In *Vitamins and Hormones,* Vol. 23, (H. S. Harris, I. G. Wood, and J. A. Loraine, eds.). Academic Press, New York, pp. 210–327.

Rothchild, I., and R. M. Fraps. 1944. On the function of the ruptured ovarian follicle of the domestic fowl. *Proc. Soc. Exptl. Biol. Med.,* **56:** 79–86.

Sawin, P. B., and D. D. Crary. 1953. Genetic and physiological background of reproduction in the rabbit. II. Some racial differences in the pattern of maternal behavior. *Behaviour,* **6:** 128–146.

Sawin, P. B., and R. H. Curran. 1952. Genetic and physiological background of reproduction in the rabbit. I. The problem and its biological significance. *J. Exptl. Zool.,* **120:** 165–201.

Sawin, P. B., V. H. Denenberg, S. Ross, E. Hafter, and M. X. Zarrow. 1960. Maternal behavior in the rabbit: Hair loosening during gestation. *Am. J. Physiol.,* **198:** 1099–1102.

Sawyer, C. H., and J. W. Everett. 1959. Stimulatory and inhibitory effects of progesterone on the release of pituitary ovulating hormone in the rabbit. *Endocrinology,* **65:** 644–651.

Selye, H. 1941. Studies concerning the anesthetic action of steroid hormones. *J. Pharmacol. Exptl. Therap.,* **73:** 127–141.

Steel, E., and R. A. Hinde. 1963. Hormonal control of brood patch and oviduct development in domesticated canaries. *J. Endocrinol.,* **26:** 11–24.

Steel, E., and R. A. Hinde. 1964. Effect of exogenous oestrogen on brood patch development of intact and ovariectomized canaries. *Nature,* **202:** 718–719.

Stern, J. M. 1966. The role of the testis in progesterone-induced incubation behavior in ring doves (*Streptopelia risoria*). *Am. Zoologist,* **6:** 536 (Abstr.).

Stern, J. M. 1967. Personal communication.

Taylor, R. L. E. 1965. Hormones and maternal behavior in the rat. Ph.D. thesis, Purdue University, Lafayette, Indiana.

Taylor, R. L. E., V. H. Denenberg, and M. X. Zarrow. 1965. Quantification of maternal nest building in the rat. *Am. Zoologist,* **5:** 676–677.

Telegdy, G., and E. Endröczi. 1963. The ovarian secretion of progesterone and 20α-hydroxypregn-4-en-3-one in rats during the estrous cycle. *Steroids,* **2:** 119–123.

Tietz, E. G. 1933. The humoral excitation of the nesting instincts in rabbits. *Science,* **78:** 316.

van Tienhoven, A. 1958. Effect of progesterone on broodiness and egg production of turkeys. *Poultry Sci.,* **37:** 428–433.

van Tienhoven, A. 1961. Endocrinology of reproduction in birds. In *Sex and*

Internal Secretions (W. C. Young, ed.). Williams & Wilkins, Baltimore, pp. 1088–1169.

van Tienhoven, A., A. V. Nalbandov, and H. W. Norton. 1954. Effect of dibenamine on progesterone induced and "spontaneous" ovulation in the hen. *Endocrinology*, **54:** 605–611.

Vowles, D., and D. Harwood. 1966. The effect of exogenous hormones on aggressive behavior in the ring dove (*Streptopelia risoria*). *J. Endocrinol.*, **36:** 35–51.

Wood-Gush, D. G. M., and A. B. Gilbert. 1964. The control of nesting behaviour of the domestic hen. II. The role of the ovary. *Animal Behavior*, **12:** 451–453.

Young, W. C. 1961. The hormones and mating behavior. In *Sex and Internal Secretions* (W. C. Young, ed.). Williams & Wilkins, Baltimore, 3rd ed., pp. 1173–1239.

Young, W. C. 1964. The hormones and behavior. *Comp. Biochem.*, **7:** 203–249.

Zander, J., T. R. Forbes, A. M. V. Munstermann, and R. Neher. 1958. Two naturally occurring metabolites of progesterone. Isolation, identification, biologic activity and concentration in human tissues. *J. Clin. Endocrinol.*, **18:** 337–353.

Zarrow, M. X., and E. C. Hurlbut. 1967. Inhibition and facilitation of PMS-induced ovulation in the immature rat following treatment with progesterone. *Endocrinology*, **80:** 735–740.

Zarrow, M. X., F. L. Hisaw, and F. Bryans. 1950. Conversion of desoxycorticosterone acetate to progesterone in vivo. *Endocrinology*, **46:** 403–404.

Zarrow, M. X., P. B. Sawin, S. Ross, V. H. Denenberg, D. D. Crary, and E. D. Wilson. 1961. Maternal behavior in the rabbit: Evidence for an endocrine basis of maternal-nest building and additional data on maternal-nest building in the Dutch-belted race. *J. Reprod. Fertility*, **2:** 152–162.

Zarrow, M. X., P. B. Sawin, S. Ross, and V. H. Denenberg. 1962. Maternal behavior and its endocrine basis in the rabbit. In *Roots of Behavior* (E. L. Bliss, ed.). Hoeber, New York, pp. 187–197.

Zarrow, M. X., A. Farooq, V. H. Denenberg, P. B. Sawin, and S. Ross. 1963. Maternal behavior in the rabbit: Endocrine control of maternal-nest building. *J. Reprod. Fertility*, **6:** 375–383.

Zarrow, M. X., L. J. Grota, and V. H. Denenberg. 1967. Maternal behavior in the rat: Survival of newborn fostered young after hormonal treatment of the foster mother. *Anat. Rec.*, **157:** 13–18.

Zeilmaker, G. H. 1966. The biphasic effect of progesterone on ovulation in the rat. *Acta Endocrinol.*, **51:** 461–468.

Zucker, I. 1966. Facilitatory and inhibitory effects of progesterone on sexual responses of spayed guinea pigs. *J. Comp. Physiol. Psychol.*, **62:** 376–381.

Zucker, I. 1967. Actions of progesterone in the control of sexual receptivity of the spayed female rat. *J. Comp. Physiol. Psychol.*, **63:** 213–216.

Zucker, I., and R. W. Goy. 1967. Sexual receptivity in the guinea pig: inhibitory and facilitatory actions of progesterone and related compounds. *J. Comp. Physiol. Psychol.*, **64:** 378–383.

REPRODUCTION AND SEXUAL BEHAVIOR (M. Diamond ed.), 391–410, © Indiana University Press

23

Human Sex Behavior Research

Paul H. Gebhard

It is impossible within the confines of a book chapter to outline human sex behavior research in more than the most general and necessarily incomplete terms. The subject is not a well-defined unit, but ramifies into numerous disciplines. This is, of course, what one would anticipate with such a pervasive and essential element of human life. In an attempt to deal with the subject coherently and reasonably succinctly, I propose to give a brief historical perspective of human sex research, then delineate its major fields, next describe the more recent developments in these fields, and finally discuss the future of such research.

This proposal, in addition to being embarrassingly ambitious, will inevitably suffer from my personal bias and limitation of knowledge. With this *caveat* in mind, I hope the readers will temper their judgments with mercy.

Historical Perspective

Prior to World War II relatively few individuals had studied human sexuality in any substantial way. Some of these persons had been drawn into sex research through related studies, notable examples being Freud (psychiatry), Robert L. Dickinson (gynecology), and Katherine Davis (social work). Others entered the field directly because of personal motivations: This was true of Magnus Hirschfeld, Havelock Ellis, and undoubtedly a considerable number of others. In addition to those who made major contributions, many individuals, chiefly medical men, wrote extensively. Men have always had a predisposition to think and talk about sex and, under the protective aegis of medicine or law, it was possible to write about sex with relative impunity. Too few withstood this titillating temptation, and the literature was burdened by inconsequential dramatic case histories, collections of medical and anthropological exotica, and dogmatic speculation. In this chaff there are occasional worthwhile grains, but student winnowers were more often misinformed than enlightened. It is this sort of writing that still sells in many bookshops, including those specializing in pornography, and it is this writing that has made the word "sexologist" largely disreputable in the United States. The courage of the bona fide scientists and scholars who did do sex research should not be underestimated for they risked both their professional and private reputations. The occasional use of pseudonyms by the authors of scientific publications indicated the appreciation of this risk. The stigma attached to sex research not only dissuaded some scholars, but on occasion prevented the publication of work already undertaken. There was, if I am correctly informed, a study of Harvard students which never saw print; a similar study of western college students by K. M. Peterson (1938) remains in manuscript form in the University of Colorado; and studies of postrevolution Russian college students were only partially reported. In a few even more unfortunate instances, destruction rather than suppression was employed. This was the fate of many of Sir Richard Burton's anthropological notes and observations on sexual behavior. There are other reports of censorship, most often of publications concerning contraception, but it is difficult to authenticate these since sex research lends itself readily to apocryphal rumors.

Despite the difficulties, sex research advanced as more persons of proved merit entered the field. Men such as Wilhelm Stekel, H. Rohleder, and Albert Moll could not be lightly dismissed as prurient cranks. In the realm of anthropology the names of Bronislaw Malinowski, Felix Bryk, and Margaret Mead lent respectability. The gradual acceptance of psychiatry and psychoanalysis did much to make the way easier for researchers such as Carney Landis and others too numerous to list here.

In the United States an organization of crucial importance in the ultimate "breakthrough" of sex research was the National Research Council Committee for Research in Problems of Sex. Powered by men of impeccable status, in particular Alan Gregg, George Corner, and Robert Yerkes, this group backed the marriage studies by George Hamilton (1929) and L. Terman (1938), the college student survey by M. Peck and F. Wells (1923–1925), and the research of Alfred Kinsey (1941ff.), as well as others. Animal studies were also encouraged and supported, providing an essential element in comprehensive sex research.

With this committee as a focal point, a small but select band of sex researchers developed. Most of them knew one another on a first-name basis, and at the formal and informal meetings there was a pioneering enthusiasm and directness of communication the likes of which we shall not see again. At such a gathering one would find, for example, Frank Beach in disputation with Lester Aronson in one corner, while in another Kinsey and Edward Dempsey conversed with Karl Lashley. And omnipresent was Bill Young with a retinue of students, many of whom went on to fulfill the high expectations he had of them. The discussions ranged widely, were often heated, and always profitable. The dedication of the group was not of a solemn sort; these were men who after a lengthy day of presentations and comments chose to relax after supper over coffee or drinks by continuing the subject.

The impetus provided by this group and carried on by their junior colleagues and students propelled sex research in the United States into recognition as a legitimate, if not wholly respectable, field of science. There has followed a burgeoning of research and publication which parallels, albeit on a smaller scale, the information explosion of the sciences in general. Indeed, we have reached the point where even specialists in the field are often chagrined to learn of consequential pieces of research which have begun, or even been completed, without their knowledge.

The financial fuel necessary for such growth came originally from large foundations, the Rockefeller Foundation being especially important in this regard, but of late these have been overshadowed by the National Institutes of Health. The Committee for Research on Problems of Sex realized its solicitations for support of research were no longer necessary and, its primary aim achieved, voluntarily disbanded.

The above brief sketch of sex research in the United States would be incomplete without mention of another organization, the American Association of Marriage Counselors. This group, whose membership was a curious mixture of professions, encouraged sex research, and a number of its constituents have contributed importantly.

The felicitous growth of sex research in the United States has not, unfortunately, been mirrored elsewhere in the world. While one could not hope for much from impoverished nations, Europe has not lived up to expectations. Totalitarian governments are not tolerant of sex research and the ravages of war naturally had a powerful adverse effect. Nevertheless, a revival is in evidence and nearly every European nation has a handful of individuals devoting an appreciable amount of their time to sex research. This renaissance is clinical in orientation because of financial considerations; one has the impression that if grant monies were more available, other forms of sex research would quickly blossom.

Fields of Sex Research

A major difficulty in delineating sex research today lies in the fact that many people are involved in only an indirect or temporary fashion. For example, a urologist may write one paper on some of his cases of impotence; a marriage counselor may write on the lack of orgasm in some wives; an attorney will discuss a particular sex offense case; and a sociologist may devote a chapter in his book to prostitution. While all of this is concerned with the study of sex, none of these people could fairly be called sex researchers if they are not specializing in that area of study. While one must not underestimate the significance of these sporadic contributions, the individuals are too numerous to name. The names mentioned hereafter will for the most part be those of persons who specialize in the study of human sexuality.

Sex research today consists primarily of five fields:

1. The clinical or medical field, where the research centers on problems and pathologies.

2. The legal or forensic field, which is concerned with the laws governing sexual behavior and with censorship.

3. The reproductive or population field concerned with fertility and contraception.

4. The sex education field, where the emphasis is upon providing knowledge and attempting to govern behavior through teaching.

5. The basic research field. Here the concern is with the parameters and variables that influence and mold sexual behavior per se as well as with attitudes toward sex in a broad sense. There is no trend toward social policy as in the legal and sex education fields, no concern with altering behavior as in the clinical field, and reproduction is regarded as a by-product of sex rather than a central issue.

I shall speak briefly of the first four fields of sex research, and devote the bulk of the chapter to basic research—my own interest.

Clinical Field

In this field there is still the old division between mind and body. A large number of psychiatrists, psychologists, and psychoanalysis are confronted with the sexual problems of patients, and hence some of these clinicians undertake sex research. Unfortunately a great deal of this consists solely of reporting upon a few, or even one, case histories with a comment or speculation thrown in for good measure. There are some happy exceptions to this generalization; for example, Bernard Glueck published on a substantial number of sex offenders and Irving Bieber assembled a large body of data on homosexuality. For many years the clinicians trying to modify sexual behavior or attitudes functioned chiefly within a conventional psychiatric-psycho-analytic framework, but more recently a number of innovations have appeared. Aversion therapy using electric shock or apomorphine is being tried to discourage undesirable behavior, hormones suppressing the sexual drive are being given to sex offenders, and experimental treatment of female frigidity with LSD has begun. The most effective treatment of male impotence and lack of orgasm in the female seems to be the straightforward teaching and training program of Dr. William Masters and Virginia Johnson in St. Louis. In essence these clinicians simultaneously instruct their patients how to behave and destroy restrictive inhibitions (see Chapter 24).

The clinical field is faced with a problem which nearly everyone prefers not to mention: that is, in making people emotionally healthy the clinician often must encourage attitudes and behavior contrary to conventional morality and law. For example, our sexual morality is a matter of age: virginity in a 17-year old is regarded as a virtue, but virginity in a forty-year old is generally regarded as ipso facto evidence of a pathological emotional immaturity, and a good clinician would look upon loss of virginity as a hopeful symptom. A more dramatic example is the recent decision of several reputable hospitals, including Johns Hopkins, to perform transsexual-type operations on those few cases where it is deemed necessary for mental health. A lawyer or clergyman could complain that these operations are promoting homosexual relationships, since only the external appearance is changed while the person still retains his original gender.

Legal Field

In recent years there has been great controversy over the right of society to determine the sexual behavior of its members. Laws which were sacrosanct are being openly questioned. The famous Wolfenden Committee in England proposed liberalizing the laws on homosexuality and prostitution, and the Anglican church amazed the world by agreeing. The Quakers and Unitarians have called for reevaluation of sexual attitudes and laws and the Episcopal Bishop Pike added his voice. In the United States two very prestigeful organizations—the Group for the Advancement of Psychiatry and the American Law Institute—have called for extensive revision and liberalization of sex laws. One state, Illinois, has already largely acted on this suggestion. Very recently several organizations have been established to promote more liberal laws concerning abortion.

All of this hue and cry has involved relatively little sex research. Perhaps the research most often used in this legal struggle is that of the Institute for Sex Research, the so-called Kinsey Institute. Certainly its data testify to the ineffectuality of laws which run counter to basic human sexuality. Studies of sex laws have been published by Ralph Slovenko and Robert Sherwin, among others.

The general consensus of research opinion is that there are only three instances in which society has a rational reason for bringing legal sanctions to bear on sexual behavior: (1) where force or duress is involved, (2) where there is sexual contact between children and adults, and, (3) where the sexual behavior constitutes a public nuisance.

Another aspect of the legal field is censorship. Here astonishing changes have been made and society is in a state of confusion. A few years ago people were being haled before court for selling Joyce's *Ulysses* or Cabell's *Jurgen,* and now one can go to the friendly local drugstore and buy *Fanny Hill, Candy,* and the *Naked Lunch.* Yet in various localities people are being arrested for selling *Playboy,* and there are powerful national organizations such as the Citizens for Decent Literature and the Legion of Decency striving for great censorship powers.

The irony is that the whole censorship battle is being fought without either side having any worthwhile research to back it up. There has been essentially no scientific demonstration that erotica or even outright pornography has any correlation with antisocial behavior

—J. Edgar Hoover notwithstanding. The need for research in this area is especially pressing since judicial and social policies are being made in sublime ignorance.

Reproduction Field

In contrast to the legal field, here an enormous amount of research is being done and huge sums of money expended. Recently the Ford Foundation alone gave something like 12 million dollars for reproductive research. Much of this research is centered on contraception, since overpopulation is indisputably one of the most serious problems confronting mankind. The so-called "pill" which prevents ovulation is not the answer, since the cost is prohibitive in poor countries and the uneducated and irresponsible cannot be expected to use it regularly. The most promising answer is the intrauterine device: a plastic loop or bow inserted in the uterus which prevents pregnancy as long as it remains there. Evidently such devices can be retained for years without ill effect. Research is also being carried out on pills to suppress sperm production in males and one such pill was formulated but had to be abandoned due to an unexpected and somewhat amusing side effect: the inability to tolerate even small amounts of alcohol. More importantly, work is being done on what can be called a "morning-after pill" (see Chapter 11).

The reproductive field has undergone marked changes in the past few decades. Originally it was dominated by dedicated individuals such as Margaret Sanger and a small following of courageous physicians, but now the field is shared with scientists making sophisticated demographic studies, as does Christopher Tietze, or extremely technical biochemical investigations such as those of John Rock and the late Warren Nelson and Gregory Pincus. After shying away from the subject despite its obvious importance, the U.S. government has now adopted an attitude of benevolence tempered by political fears toward contraceptive research.

Sex Education Field

This important field fosters very little research of its own and derives its data elsewhere. Nevertheless it produces an annual flood of literature ranging from countless marriage manuals and the ubiquitous books for young people to articles which fill not only professional journals but the pages of women's magazines. There are a number of organized sex education groups, the largest being S.I.E.C.U.S. (Sex Information and Education Council of the United States), recently founded by Mary Calderone.

The sex education field is divided into several warring camps bitterly divided over the issue of what to tell youth to do or not to do. One must add there is a complete disinterest in giving advice to the middle-aged. At one extreme is Evelyn Duvall, presenting conventional morality disguised as scientific knowledge, and at the other extreme is Albert Ellis, advocating nearly everything for everyone. The middle-ground people do much agonizing soul-searching and generally settle for weasel-worded compromises.

The brutal fact is that our society is not yet ready for rational effective sex education because it would in part clash with our religious mores and various cherished romantic myths.

Strange to say, no one has yet tested the effects of a sex education program. This is an omission we at the Institute for Sex Research hope to rectify.

Basic Research

Basic sex research is conspicuous by its absence in most of the world. While one can expect its absence in the poorer nations which are striving with more immediate problems, it is curious that many nations which could afford it, lack it. For example, I know of almost nothing recent worthy of the name of basic sex research in southeastern Europe, Belgium, Norway, and Finland. In all of Asia, research seems confined to Japan, and the same is true for Beirut and Israel in the Middle East. Sex research seems completely absent in all of Central and South America and very rare in Africa.

In essence, basic sex research is centered in Europe, England, and particularly in the United States. Outside the United States most of the research is very apt to be clinical or legal in its motivation, but since it includes much basic research I shall discuss it under this heading. For the sake of expediency the discussion will be by geographical area.

In Africa there are, or have recently been, a few anthropologists who gathered a substantial amount of sexual data along with the usual ethnographic information. These anthropologists are concerned only with Negro Africa; North Africa is an unfavorable place to work because of the attitudes about women and the Arabic sensitivity about the prevalence of homosexuality. In South Africa a few physicians have a bit of research underway. For example, M. Clark of Capetown has been studying 35 men who desire transsexual operations.

In the Middle East Samir Khalif has reported on students at the American University in Beirut and now has embarked on a study of prostitution. In Israel a study of students and kibbutz inhabitants has reportedly been made.

The only recent basic behavioral research in Asia was undertaken by Sin-iti Asayama, who studied Japanese young people. There is also a curious and ill-known Japanese sex study group founded by Tetsu Takahashi, but its membership seems largely to be of laymen rather than scientists. India has been mightily concerned with the by-product of sexual behavior, but since the death of A. Pillay no Indian sex researcher of comparable stature has emerged.

In the Pacific Islands and Australia, research is being done on native populations as a part of a general anthropological study. For example, Marshall and Suggs have published on Polynesia and the Berndts have described sexual life in aboriginal Australia. Davenport has written on sexual life in the Southwest Pacific.

Europe presents in a smaller version the same problems which make basic sex research in the United States difficult to discuss: There are numerous individuals who devote a portion of their time to such research. Moreover much of their work is clinical in motivation yet their discoveries are sufficiently fundamental to warrant labelling them as basic research. Lacking a detailed knowledge of the interests of many of these persons and hence being unable to group them by subject category, I am reduced to something perilously close to mere name dropping. Nevertheless in our present state of knowledge even this is better than nothing.

Russia, since the early Stalinist days, has had a rather puritanical attitude toward sexuality despite the fluctuations in policy concerning marriage, divorce, and abortion. The milieu has not been conducive toward sex research. I know—and only by surname—of only two qualified persons interested in sex research: Milman, a Leningrad urologist, and Vasilcenko, a Moscow psychiatrist. There is a rumor that a government-sponsored sex research center may be founded in Moscow, in part because of prestige competition with the Western world.

Spain, like Russia, has not been a good nation for sex research thanks to a combination of totalitarianism, economics, and state religion. Nevertheless. J. Lopez-Ibor, a prominent psychiatrist, plans a study of Madrid college students which will be directly comparable to the study conducted by Giese in Germany.

Italy has recently developed in Rome a sex institute, The Centro Italiano di Sessuologia, which published the journal *Sessuologia*. A study of male college students, again patterned on the Giese study, is planned by a Dr. Callera.

In France Jacques Remy and Robert Woog of the French Institute of Public Opinion surveyed slightly over one thousand women with a poll interview questionnaire and published their findings in 1960. This survey was primarily attitudinal rather than behavioral and in most respects is very similar to the mailed questionnaire survey of Belgian women conducted in the 1940s by Marc Lanval. These publications bring to mind a source of confusion concerning which the reader should be warned. Publishers in the United States occasionally translate a foreign book and issue it, sometimes years later, under a title completely unlike the original. Thus Lanval's report on his survey was published in 1946 as *L'Amour sous le masque* and was published five years later in New York as *An Inquiry into the Intimate Lives of Women*. In the French survey not only was the title changed in the U.S. edition, but the volume was attributed to the French Institute of Public Opinion and the names of Remy and Woog do not appear on the title page nor on the book spine. This sort of unnecessary and/or unexplained variation sometimes leaves the impression of two studies where in actuality only one exists.

Holland has a League for Sexual Reform with strong legal and clinical interests. Several physicians associated with it are pursuing some sex research. The leader of Netherland research is Conrad van Emde Boas, who in 1966 was completing a book on pornography.

England boasts a number of men who have done, or are currently engaged in, basic sex research. Recently Michael Schofield has published two studies: one on homosexuality and another on college students. Other scientists in the field include Alex Comfort, Geoffrey Gorer, and Eustace Chesser. Considering the Wolfenden Report, the liberal posture of the Church of England Moral Welfare Council, and other reform movements it is disappointing that more sex research has not been engendered.

East Germany is represented only by H. Rennert, who made a questionnaire survey of male and female students in 1963 and in 1966 was proposing a more general college student study. The long-standing predilection of Germans for writing about sex and compiling massive volumes of Sittengeschichte or treatise on aberrations seems to have been controlled by the German Democratic Republic.

West Germany, on the other hand, houses a very considerable amount of sex research. The Deutsche Gesellschaft für Sexualforschung is the focus for research and has a substantial membership of psychiatrists, physicians, and lawyers. This organization produces a journal, *Beiträge zur Sexualforschung*, and individual members also publish elsewhere. West German research owes a great deal to two men who provided the initial thrust: Hans Giese of Hamburg University and an influential Professor Ordinarius, Hans Bürger-Prinz, of the same institution. Giese, who recently completed a questionnaire survey of some 4000 college students, is also training a number of graduate students to follow in his steps, and those who assisted in his study are publishing portions of it. His chief assistant is Gunter Schmidt, who, among other duties, is in charge of the computer programming. Also among the Hamburg group are Werner Krause, Johann Burchardt, and Peter Fischer. No other group exists: Individual members of the Gesellschaft, too numerous to list, are scattered widely. A number of commercial presses are carrying on the old Germanic tradition of publishing books on sex which range widely in quality, some being suitable for sale in the waterfront area of St. Pauli, while others are worthwhile contributions. The volume of both is increasing.

Switzerland can boast of only a few persons actively involved in sex research, notably Hans Kunz and Theodor Bovet. The Jung Institute in Zurich has more than a peripheral interest and some of its members are studying sexuality.

Poland has a strong and partially government-subsidized Association for Family Planning which encourages research. The father of Polish sex research and the man who administers examinations in this field is Tadeusz Bilikiewcz, but the bulk of work is being carried on by a younger generation of men in Warsaw, chiefly Kazimierz Imielinski and Tadeuscz Zielinski. In Posnan sex research centers around Janusz Strzyzewski. One woman psychologist, Malawska, has also won some renown in the field. The Poles hope to establish an institution devoted to human sex research.

Sweden is quite receptive to sex research and two organizations are actively concerned. The nearly self-supporting Swedish Association for Sex Education is intensely interested in learning more of sexual attitudes and the effects of economic factors on sexuality. The government-sponsored Royal Commission on Sex Education, headed by Ragnar Lund, recently employed Hans Zetterburg, a sociologist, to do a random-sample study of 2000 men and women in which one hundred or so questions will be devoted to sexual behavior and attitudes. One of the moving spirits behind sex research in Sweden is the secretary of the Commission, a woman physician: Maj-Briht

Bergstrom-Walan. Two other women associated with the Commission's research are Brigitta Linner and Görel Alm. Uppsala University students have been studied by Gustav Jonsson, Gunnar Johnson, and Joachim Israel. B. Rundberg gave questionnaires to several hundred children in one town, and Nils Gustavsson had some sexual queries in his venereal disease study of 2000 men.

Denmark also is much indebted to an energetic woman, in this case the psychiatrist Kirsten Auken. In addition to her own research, she has urged and helped a number of her colleagues to enter the field with outstanding results. Owing to the size of the population and centralization of functions, the sampling done by many Danish researchers is superlative. I often found myself in an agony of envy. Preben Hertoft administered a questionnaire to 3000 draftees and interviewed 400. Knud Ekstrom, who rightly terms himself the greatest figure in world sex research (being over six and one-half feet tall), interviewed 200 female and 100 male teenage prostitutes in Copenhagen and also studied 500 teenage venereal disease patients. Lise Freundt interviewed 304 of the 305 women who came to the three major Copenhagen clinics in a given period of time for treatment for miscarriage or abortion. Anders Groth interviewed 800 randomly selected postpartum cases. Aagaard Olson similarly interviewed 800 men and women, chiefly unmarried, in Greenland using many of Hertoft's questions. There are, in addition, several interesting smaller studies, including Henrick Hoffmeyer's study of pregnant females under 18 and Christian Baastrup's long-time study of a group of transvestites and transsexuals.

Czechoslovakia has an Institute of Sexology in Praha connected with Karlovy University. It operates as a clinic, the research being done with the patients who funnel into it from the entire country, but unfortunately most of the research must be done on the clinicians' own time. The staff is headed by Josef Hynie and consists of Karel Nedoma (interested in male homosexuality), Vladimir Bartak (sex education and male sterility), Jar Pondelickova (female response), Iva Sipova (endocrine problems in children), Jiri Mellan (etiology of male sexual problems and personal interaction), and Jan Raboch (female sexuality and male problems). The latter is particularly enthusiastic in promulgating sex research and collaborating with scientists from other nations. Also in Czechoslovakia is Kurt Freund, who has published on homosexuality, and a mathematician, V. Pinkava, who is developing a mathematical model of human sexuality far beyond my powers of comprehension.

Canada has, considering its proximity to the United States, surprisingly few sex researchers. The most active is Stephen Neiger, who founded S.I.E.C. CAN. (Sex Information and Education Council of Canada)—the Canadian equivalent of the S.I.E.C.U.S. In Vancouver a psychiatrist, Douglas Alcorn, has been studying for some years the esoteric subject of bondage and masochism.

This brings us to the United States, where the proliferation of universities and the vast number of behavioral scientists and clinicians has resulted in so many persons being involved in sex research to varying degrees that it is possible to name here only a minority of them. However, one can see that there is a concentration of effort on certain subjects and hence discussion by subject category is feasible.

Young people and especially college students represent a particularly popular field of study. There is considerable social concern with these people, and they are generally intelligent, cooperative, and easy to collect. A dozen or more behavioral scientists have recently worked with youth. Some of the more noteworthy research has been, or is being done, by Ira Reiss, Lester Kirkendall, Winston Ehrmann, Harold Christenson, Marvin Freedman, Robert Bell, Nevitt Sanford, Eugene Kanin, and the Institute for Sex Research.

The family and the institution of marriage likewise receives much attention, chiefly in the form of small studies, and prominent names in this field include those of Robert Blood, Albert Ellis, Robert Hamblin, Lee Rainwater, and Jessie Bernard.

Homosexuality, particularly in the past decade, has been the subject of some intensive studies. Leading recent research has been done by Evelyn Hooker, Irving Bieber, Donald Cory, Albert Reiss, Franz Kallmann, and the Institute for Sex Research.

Despite their comparative rarity, the phenomena of pseudo-hermaphroditism, transvestism, and transsexualism have attracted a fair number of scientists because of the implications these deviations have for broader issues such as gender role. Harry Benjamin, for decades almost alone, now shares this exotic field with John Money, Wardell Pomeroy, Robert Sears, John Hampson, Ina Pauley, Robert Stoller, and Milton Diamond (see Chapter 25).

Sex offenders have in recent years been singled out for study to an unusual degree. The interest is in part an outgrowth of the spreading concept of crime as a symptom of illness or maladjustment rather than as simply an antisocial hedonism. Most of the sex-offender studies have been by psychiatrists and psychologists, notably Karl Bowman, Bernard Glueck, Albert Ellis, David Abrahamson, Benjamin Karpman, Manfred Guttmacher, and the Institute for Sex Research.

Aside from these popular fields sex research is sporadic. The topic of sexuality in children is largely left to a few such as Carlfred Broderick and William Reevy. William Masters and Virginia Johnson are nearly alone in physiological research. Paul Brady and Eugene Levitt have evaluated sexual response to visual stimuli, and Arthur Kling is doing similar work measuring pupillary response and adrenocortical hormone excretion. Clark Vincent has been investigating the subject of premarital pregnancy. Other examples of important but essentially isolated studies could be listed if space permitted. There is an increasing amount of sex research being undertaken by graduate students in sociology, anthropology, psychology, and law. Unfortunately many of these never see print and are for all practical purposes lost to the scientific community.

There are remarkably few organizations devoted to basic research and human sexuality. Harry Benjamin and William Masters have established institutions devoted to their particular specialties. Only two other organizations exist, and these have broad research interests. One is the Society for the Scientific Study of Sex, conceived by Albert Ellis, and now directed by a group of professional men who are themselves involved in sex research as their time permits: Hans Lehfeldt, Henry Guze, Hugo Beigel, Leo Chall, and Robert Sherwin. The Society, whose substantial membership includes the majority of U.S. sex researchers, now publishes a journal which will perhaps replace the defunct International Journal of Sexology. The second organization is the Institute for Sex Research, founded in 1947 by Alfred Kinsey and located at Indiana University. The Institute makes its library, archives, and much of its interview-derived data available to qualified scholars with research in progress. In cases where a scholar obtains most, or a large part, of his data from the Institute, he may be expected to publish in the Monograph Series recently inaugurated. Neither the Society for the Scientific Study of Sex nor the Institute for Sex Research are in a position to make grants or otherwise finance research other than their own.

The Institute for Sex Research is currently engaged in three research projects. One is a study of homosexual communities and how the male individuals cope socially and psychologically with the situations and stresses consequent upon their deviance. A second study, a random sample of college students, concentrates on the management of sexuality by youth only recently emancipated from direct parental control. A third study, small but of great potential, is an investigation of the effects of sex education.

The Future

Barring an atomic holocaust or an economic depression rivaling that of the 1930s, even the dullest clairvoyant can foresee more and better human sex research. It is one of the few major fields of behavioral science which is largely *terra incognita,* and this should attract many ambitious young men who hesitate to push into already crowded specialties. In addition, the subject has its intrinsic appeal which should not be underestimated even though it is rarely confessed. There is a new generation of scientists and scholars who were children when a journalist told Kinsey: "I don't see how I can say much about your book; no editor of a newspaper or family magazine would let a word like 'masturbation' be printed." While these younger men may lack some of the pioneering fervor, they also happily lack the impulse to always justify being in sex research.

Sex research will be better not only through ascertaining realities and gradually filling the multitudinous lacunae in our knowledge, but also through relating sexual behavior to other aspects of life. Counting noses and orgasms is necessary, but the resultant information gains most of its utility and importance when set in the broader context of human behavior. This development should make it easier to obtain grant monies. Foundation boards, often consisting of men of mature years and consequently conservative, may be unwilling to support bare-faced sex research, but would support sex research as a part of a study of learning, personality development, or socialization.

There is reason to anticipate that sexual studies will increasingly escape the confines of science and flourish in the fertile soil of the arts and letters. Following the first wave of writers and artists with explicitly sexual themes must come the inevitable flood of comments, critiques, term papers, and dissertations. Steven Marcus in his *Other Victorians* has shown how pornography may be mined for scholarly advantage, and his example will not pass unnoticed. With minimal effort one can conjure up future titles: "Folkloristic Themes in Pornographic Comic Books," "The Role of the Olympia Press in Twentieth-Century Literature," "Deviance and the Underground Film," "Sex and Pop Art."

One must also anticipate not only an increased scientific and scholarly publication, probably facilitated by several new organizations devoted to that end, but also a continued outpouring of pseudo-science and other exploitive commercial products—chiefly paperback books and magazines. Unabashed erotica or even erotica with unmerited artistic or literary pretensions (e.g., photographs of nudes for artists too impoverished to hire models) seemingly has no adverse social consequences, but pseudoscience can spread misinformation and reinforce existing error.

As research grows in Europe and as transportation becomes swifter and, hopefully, cheaper, we should see increasing international communication and collaboration. This will bring to the foreground a need already being felt, the need for some center or clearinghouse which will keep aware of what research is being undertaken where.

There should be an increase in experimentation with human subjects. The invaluable information resulting will undoubtedly be purchased dearly with adverse publicity, investigations, scandals, and lost grants. I have in mind not only neurophysiology, but since the subject lends itself so readily to the manipulation of variables, experimentation in its broadest sense. For example, a fetish object can be varied by small degrees—as animal experiments vary the size and coloration of eggs to see the effect upon the nesting birds. A male transvestite could be placed in a culture wherein female dress is quite unlike that of ours. A male hithertofore exclusively homosexual could be placed in a closed institution with females to see if "facultative heterosexuality" developed. Crippling inhibitions could be attacked with a combination of psychedelic drugs, cinema, and even demonstration. Last, of course, are important but less dramatic experiments such as timing recognition of stimuli, rank-ordering stimuli, and setting up contrived situations to test attitudes.

Human sex research, if not in its infancy, is scarcely adolescent. A few moments of reflection can produce enough questions to occupy years of research effort. Not only are there gaps in our substantive knowledge, but we are only partially cognizant of how sexual behavior and attitudes interrelate with other aspects of living. Last, we have only hints as to etiology. This important matter has long been almost a monopoly of the psychiatrist and psychoanalyst, and most of the vocabulary describing etiology is theirs. Other behavioral scientists should now make their contributions. We know from animal observation and experimentation that many rather elaborate patterns of behavior are not learned, and we should ascertain in what ways and to what degree human sexual behavior is similarly a phylogenetic heritage. Cross-cultural comparisons should prove crucial in such investigations, and one hopes that anthropologists will salvage as much data as possible from the vanishing preliterate societies. The role that cultural conditioning plays in etiology must be investigated by sociologists, anthropologists, and social psychologists using their particular philosophies and methods. A subject as richly complex as human sexuality necessitates the combined efforts of all the relevant disciplines, and now that sex research has attained sufficient respectability such vital collaboration is now a matter of expectation rather than hope.

Acknowledgment

The research upon which this paper is based was in part supported by National Institute of Mental Health Grant MH-12535-01.

Bibliography

It would be somehow unsuitable to enumerate, as I have, several score of individuals involved in human sex research and not mention the publications which represent their contributions to the field. I am therefore recording for each of most of the individuals named in this chapter a particularly important or a typical publication of theirs in sex research. Preference has been given to books, but since not all the persons have written relevant books, journal articles sometimes must suffice. Each individual is ordinarily allotted but one bibliographic citation; however, persons involved in coauthorship or in several areas of study may in consequence be mentioned more than once. A number of names are not represented in this bibliography despite their appearing in the preceding text; this is simply because I could not find a sufficiently complete citation or judged what I found not to adequately reflect the author's expertise or interest.

This bibliography should not be construed as a basic sex research bibliography. It is merely a list of books and articles illustrative of the publications of the persons prominent in the history of human sex research. Nevertheless any basic bibliography would include the majority of these publications.

Books

Abrahamsen, D. 1950. *Report on Study of 102 Sex Offenders at Sing Sing Prison.* State Hospitals Press, Utica, N.Y.

American Law Institute. 1955. *Model Penal Code.* American Law Institute, Philadelphia.

Asayama, S.-I. 1949. *Gendai Gakusei no Seikodo (Sex Behavior of Present Day Japanese Students)* Usui Shobo, Kyoto.

Auken, K. 1953. *Undersogelser over unge kvinders sexuelle adfaerd.* Rosenkilde & Bagger, Copenhagen.

Bell, R. 1966. *Premarital Sex in a Changing Society.* Prentice-Hall, Englewood Cliffs, N.J.

Benjamin, H. 1966. *The Transsexual Phenomenon.* Julian Press, New York.

Bernard, J., H. Buchanan, and W. Smith. 1958. *Dating, Mating and Marriage: A Documentary-Case Approach.* H. Allen, Cleveland.

Berndt, R., and C. Berndt. 1951. *Sexual Behavior in Western Arnhem Land.* Viking Fund, New York.

Bieber, I., et al. 1962. *Homosexuality: A Psychoanalytic Study*. Basic Books, New York.

Blood, R. 1962. *Marriage*. Free Press, New York.

Bowman, K. M. 1954. *Final Report on California Sexual Deviation Research*. Assembly of the State of California, Sacramento.

Bryk, F. 1928. *Neger-Eros*. A. Marcus & E. Weber, Berlin.

Burchardt, J. 1961. *Struktur und Soziologie des Transvestitismus und Transsexualismus*. Beiträge zur Sexualforschung: Heft 21, Enke, Stuttgart.

Chesser, E. 1956. *The Sexual, Marital and Family Relationships of the English Woman*. Hutchinson, London.

Christenson, H. 1950. *Marriage Analysis. Foundations for Successful Family Life*. Ronald Press, New York.

Church of England Moral Welfare Council. 1959. *The Street Offenses Bill: A Case for Its Amendment*. Church Information Board, London.

Comfort, A. 1950. *Sexual Behavior in Society*. Duckworth, London.

Cory, D. 1951. *The Homosexual in America. A Subjective Approach*. Greenberg, New York.

Davis, K. 1929. *Factors in the Sex Life of Twenty-two Hundred Women*. Harper & Row, New York.

Dickinson, R. L., and L. Beam. 1931. *A Thousand Marriages. A Medical Study of Sex Adjustment*. Williams & Wilkins, Baltimore.

Duvall, E. 1950. *Facts of Life and Love for Teenagers*. Association Press, New York.

Ehrmann, W. 1959. *Premarital Dating Behavior*. Holt, Rinehart and Winston, New York.

Ellis, A. 1963. *If This be Sexual Heresy . . .* Lyle Stuart, New York.

Ellis, A., and R. Brancale. 1956. *The Psychology of Sex Offenders*. Thomas, Springfield, Ill.

Ellis, H. 1905. *Studies in the Psychology of Sex*. Davis, Philadelphia.

Fischer, P. 1965. *Probleme des Sachverständigengutachtens bei der Pädophilie*. Beiträge zur Sexualforschung: Heft 34, Enke, Stuttgart.

Freund, K. 1963. *Die Homosexualität beim Mann*. S. Hirzel, Leipzig.

Gebhard, P. H., W. B. Pomeroy, C. E. Martin, and C. V. Christenson. 1953. *Pregnancy, Birth and Abortion*. Hoeber, New York.

Gebhard, P. H., J. H. Gagnon, W. B. Pomeroy, and C. V. Christenson. 1965. *Sex Offenders: An Analysis of Types*. Hoeber, New York.

Giese, H., and V. Gebsattel (eds.). 1962. *Psychopathologie der Sexuälitat*. Enke, Stuttgart.

Glueck, B. C., Jr. 1956. *Final Report, Research Project for the Study and Treatment of Persons Convicted of Crimes Involving Sexual Aberrations, June 1952 to June 1955*. State Department of Hygiene, New York.

Gorer, G. 1955. *Exploring English Character*. Criterion, New York.

Guttmacher, M. S. 1951. *Sex Offenses: The Problem, Causes and Prevention*. Norton, New York.

Hamilton, G. V. 1929. *A Research in Marriage*. Albert & Charles Boni, New York.

Hirschfeld, M. 1920. *Die Homosexualität des Mannes und des Weibes*. L. Marcus, Berlin.

Hynie, J. 1965. *Ked chlapec dospieva*. Obzor.

Imielinski, K. 1963. *Geneza homo-i biseksualizmu srodowiskowego. Panstwowy Zaklad Wydawnictu Lekarskich*, Warsaw.

Karpman, B. 1954. *The Sexual Offender and His Offenses: Etiology, Pathology, Psychodynamics and Treatment.* Julian Press, New York.

Khalaf, S. 1965. *Prostitution in a Changing Society.* Khayats, Beirut.

Kinsey, A. C., W. B. Pomeroy, and C. E. Martin. 1948. *Sexual Behavior in the Human Male.* Saunders, Philadelphia.

Kinsey, A. C., W. B. Pomeroy, C. E. Martin, and P. H. Gebhard. 1953. *Sexual Behavior in the Human Female.* Saunders, Philadelphia.

Kirkendall, L. 1961. *Premarital Intercourse and Interpersonal Relationships.* Julian Press, New York.

Kunz, H. 1946. *Die Aggressivität und die Zärtlichkeit. Zwei psychologische Studien.* A. Francke, Bern.

Lanval, M. 1946. *L'Amour sous le masque.* Le Laurier, Brussels.

Linner, B. 1965. *Society and Sex in Sweden.* Swedish Institute, Stockholm.

Malinowski, B. 1929. *The Sexual Life of Savages in Northwestern Melanesia.* Halcyon House, New York.

Marcus, S. 1965. *The Other Victorians. A Study of Sexuality and Pornography in Mid-Nineteenth-Century England.* Basic Books, New York.

Marshall, D. 1961. *Ra'ivava'e.* Doubleday, New York.

Masters, W. H., and V. E. Johnson. 1966. *Human Sexual Response.* Little, Brown, Boston.

Mead, M. 1939. *From the South Seas. Studies of Adolescence and Sex in Primitive Societies.* Morrow, New York.

Moll, A. (ed.). 1911. *Handbuch der Sexualwissenschaften.* . . . F. C. W. Vogel, Leipzig.

Rainwater, L. 1965. *Family Design, Marital Sexualty, Family Size and Contraception.* Aldine, Chicago.

Reiss, I. L., 1960. *Premarital Sexual Standards in America.* Free Press, New York.

Remy, J., and R. Woog. 1960. *La Francaise et l'amour.* Robert Laffont, Paris.

Report of the Committee on Homosexual Offenses and Prostitution (Wolfenden Report). 1957. H. M. Stationery Office, London.

Rohleder, H. 1907. *Vorlesungen über Geschlechtstrieb und gesamtes Geschlechtsleben des Menschen.* Fischer's Medicine, Berlin.

Sanford, N. 1962. *The American College.* J. Wiley, New York.

Schofield, M. 1965. *The Sexual Behavior of Young People.* Little, Brown, Boston.

Schofield, M. 1965. *Sociological Aspects of Homosexuality. A Comparative Study of Three Types of Homosexuals.* Little, Brown, Boston.

Sherwin, R. 1949. *Sex and Statutory Law.* Oceana, New York.

Slovenko, R. (ed.). 1965. *Sexual Behavior and the Law.* Thomas, Springfield, Ill.

Stekel, W. 1920. *Onanie und Homosexualität.* Urban & Schwarzenberg, Berlin.

Suggs, R. 1966. *Marquesan Sexual Behavior.* Harcourt, New York:

Terman, L. M. 1938. *Psychological Factors in Marital Happiness.* McGraw-Hill, New York.

Vincent, C. 1961. *Unmarried Mothers.* Free Press, New York.

Articles

Alcorn, D. 1960. Some experiences in sensory deprivation experiments. *Med. Serv. J.* (Can.), **16**: 955–962.

Brady, J. P., and E. Levitt. 1965. The relation of sexual preferences to sexual experiences. *Psychol. Rec.,* **15:** 377–384.

Diamond, M. 1965. A critical evaluation of the ontogeny of human sexual behavior. *Quart. Rev. Biol.,* **40:** 147–175.

Freedman, M. 1965. The sexual behavior of American college women: An empirical study and an historical survey. *Merrill-Palmer Quart.,* **11:** 33–48.

Hooker, E. (1958). Male homosexuality in the Rorschach. *J. Projective Tech.,* **22:** 33–54.

Kallmann, F. J. 1952. Comparative twin study on the genetic aspects of male homosexuality. *J. Nervous Mental Diseases,* **115:** 283–298.

Kanin, E. 1957. Male aggression in dating—courtship relations. *Am. J. Sociol.,* **63:** 197–204.

Levitt, E., and J. P. Brady. 1965. Sexual preferences in young adult males and some correlates. *J. Clin. Psychol.,* **21:** 347–354.

Neiger, S. 1966. Recent trends in sex research. Can. *Psychologist,* **7a:** 102–114.

Pauly, I. 1965. Male psychosexual inversion: Transsexualism. *Arch. Gen. Psychiat.,* **13:** 172–179.

Peck, M., and F. Wells. 1923. On the psycho-sexuality of college men. *Mental Hyg.,* **7:** 697–714.

Pinkava, V. 1963. On the coincidence of homosexuality in the human male with bisexual zoophilia and other related questions. *Cesk. Psychol.,* **7:** 259– 262.

Raboch, J. 1957. Thirty-one men with female sex chromatin. *J. Clin. Endocrinol. Metab.,* **17:** 1429–1439.

Reevy, W. 1959. Premarital petting behavior and marital happiness prediction. *Marriage and Family Living,* **21:** 349–355.

Reiss, A. J. 1961. Social integration of queers and peers. *Social Problems,* **8:** 103–120.

Rennert, H. 1966. Untersuchungen zur sexuellen Entwicklung der Jugend. *Z. ärztliche Fortbildung,* **60:** 140–152.

Schmidt, G. 1966. Homosexualitat und Vorurteil. *Studium Generale,* **19:** 346–355.

Stoller, R. 1964. A contribution to the study of gender identity. *Intern. J. Psychonal.,* **45:** 220–226.

Chapters

Davenport, W. 1965. Sexual patterns and their regulation in a society of the Southwest Pacific. In *Sex and Behavior* (F. A. Beach, ed.), Wiley, New York.

Hampson, J. L., and J. G. Hampson. 1961. The ontogenesis of sexual behavior in man. In *Sex and Internal Secretions* (W. C. Young, ed.), Williams & Wilkins, Baltimore, 3rd ed., pp. 1401–1432.

Jonsson, G. 1951. Sexualvanor hos svensk ungdom. In *Ungdomen Möter Samhället* (O. Wangson et al., eds.). Justitiedepartementet, Stockholm.

Money, J. 1961. Hermaphroditism. In *Encyclopedia of Sexual Behavior,* Vol. 1 A. Ellis and A. Abarbanel, eds.), pp. 472–485.

Sears, R. R. 1965. Development of gender role. In *Sex and Behavior* (F. A. Beach, ed.). Wiley, New York.

van Emde Boas, C. 1961. Sex Life in Europe. In *Encyclopedia of Sexual Behavior* (A. Ellis and A. Abarbanel, eds.). pp. 373–384.

Unpublished papers

Peterson, K. 1938. Early sex information and its influence on later sex concepts. Unpublished thesis. College of Education, University of Colorado, Boulder.

REPRODUCTION AND SEXUAL BEHAVIOR (M. Diamond ed.), 411–415, © Indiana University Press

24

Human Sexual Inadequacy and Some Parameters of Therapy

William H. Masters and Virginia E. Johnson

Biological or behavioral investigations of human sex and sexuality have little ultimate value unless the reported results embody material of potential clinical significance. Currently, research in this psychosocially threatening area is not only possible, but the probability of truly definitive work in the field certainly is eminent in the foreseeable future. Therefore, criteria established from years of basic science research and clinical performance in related fields of behavioral and biological investigation now can and should be applied without prejudice to research in human sexual response.

A multifaceted investigation of human sexual response was initiated in 1954 at the Washington University School of Medicine and continued in 1964 under the auspices of the Reproductive Biology Research Foundation. Initially oriented toward the unveiling of basic anatomic and physiologic data, the program was expanded in 1959 to include consideration of biologic and behavioral material developed in the laboratory which might have potential clinical application to treatment of human sexual inadequacy. In establishing this clinical facet of the research program, five specific criteria were selected for their potential contribution to the development of effective therapy techniques, programming for postgraduate training programs in human sexual response, and application to other sexually oriented areas of concern. These criteria are participation of both members of a marital unit in the therapy program, privilege and commitment to 5-year follow-up of therapy, representation of both sexes in all therapy teams, exposure to finite physical and laboratory checks, and a concentrated treatment period. These criteria are discussed in the following paragraphs together with detailed explanations of why the particular guide rules were established and controlled circumstances maintained in conducting the clinical research.

Subjects

Both laboratory and clinical experience have underscored the clinical concept that there is no such thing as an uninvolved partner existent in any marital relationship contending with the distresses of sexual inadequacy. The depths of psychosocial implications and complications that develop secondary to symptoms of sexual inadequacy have not previously been appreciated. Mutual fears of sexual performance and failure to verbalize material of sexual concern which result in secondary loss of partner confidence and esteem are as much, if not more, responsible for perpetuation of sexual inadequacy within the marital unit than are specific performance inadequacies of individual members of that unit. Failure to recognize the depth of partner involvement within the marital unit well may have been responsible for the previously high rate of failure to reverse such sexual inadequacies as impotence, frigidity, or premature ejaculation. Both partners of the sexual relationship are thus needed for the therapy program. Both are simultaneously evaluated and treated and their clinical progress is interrelated.

Commitment

The effectiveness of therapeutic programs designed to remove, reduce, or even reorient the symptoms of sexual inadequacy cannot be guaranteed or judged objectively at termination of the active stage of therapy. Just as one cannot judge effectiveness of specific surgical or definite radiation techniques or combinations of these two disciplines in concentrated attacks upon cancer immediately after termination of acute phases of treatment, neither can the effectiveness of any psychotherapeutic regime be evaluated objectively immediately after termination of active phases of therapy. Intensive radiation therapy for cancer, although never objectively considered a biological success, can be and is evaluated in terms of 5, 10, or more years of "cure." To establish basic security and full professional as well as patient acceptance for psychotherapeutic principles and techniques of treatment, the same objectivity of long-range evaluation of therapeutic results should be demanded of behavioral and psychosocial data. Exposure of accrued therapeutic results from the patients' viewpoint and the researchers' statistical evaluation over specific periods of time (5, 10, etc., years) following the active phases of therapy no longer can be avoided. The subjects and clinicians are thus obligated at onset of therapy for long-term programs.

Without question, therapy of the human psyche cannot be regimented or controlled with the exactness or integrity of a radiation or dose-response curve. Acknowledgment of the mercurial principle of variation for the human psyche enhances the obligation of the therapist to establish concepts of long-range-treatment evaluation. If this responsibility is assumed by clinical therapists, analytic, psychiatric, and behavioral techniques may be evaluated one against the other when specific clinical problems such as primary impotence are considered. The ultimate survival of specific professional concepts will thus be promulgated with statistical support. Regardless of professional orientation, psychotherapeutic programs for the treatment of human sexual inadequacy no longer can be reported as successful when arbitrary clinical determinations are made only at the termination of the active therapeutic effort. In brief, treatment of human sexual inadequacy, as with any other human behavioral problem, cannot be accepted as successful when an accounting of results is dependent upon the simple statement of fait accompli by the therapist immediately after discharge of the patient.

Therapy Team

The human male never can fully appreciate subjectively or comprehend objectively the total of female sexual response simply because he cannot undergo the experience. The opposite side of the coin obviously applies to the human female's consideration of male sexual performance. Therefore, there are obvious advantages in having both sexes represented actively in the diagnosis and treatment of sexual inadequacy. If both members of the sexually inadequate marital unit are to be subjected to interrogation, education, discussions in depth of symptom complexes, and reorientation to mutually effective sexual expression, professional representation from both sexes should be present to assume active roles in diagnosis and treatment in order to maintain therapeutic balance. The dual sexed team is of particular import in the interest of developing objectivity if the concept is accepted that there is no such thing as an uninvolved partner in a marital unit contending with sexual inadequacy.

Complete Examination

Impotence or frigidity usually have been considered symptoms of underlying chronic neurotic or, for that matter, acute psychotic behavior. However, in recent years work in the basic science laboratory supports the contention that major forms of human sexual inadequacy frequently may exist as primary clinical entities in themselves rather than only as symptoms of underlying psychopathology. While physical components rarely are of major etiologic concern in the sexual inadequacies, one should remain aware of the endocrinopathies that may lead to impotence and frigidity and to the high incidence of onset of sexual distress in association with excessive social indulgences. Many a male fails for the first time to achieve that quality of erection necessary for the mounting process, while attempting sexual connection during or immediately subsequent to episodes of acute alcoholic intoxication. Certainly some women have lost sexual tension and ultimately become nonorgasmic after 18 months to 3 years of exposure to contraceptive "pill" medication. It is for these and various other reasons that total physical examinations, extensive histories, and thorough and detailed laboratory checks have been established as an integral part of the investigation of human sexual inadequacy.

Concentrated Treatment

Recently, both laboratory and clinical experimentation have suggested major clinical consideration be directed toward a relatively unappreciated factor in human sexuality. Male and female response to sexual stimulation, i.e., visual, tactile, etc., has a marked positive cumulative effect from both physiologic and psychologic orientations. This factor of cumulative response has been of inestimable value when dealing with problems of sexual indadequacy. Repetitive exposure to sensual stimulation with deliberate reorientation to sexual anatomy are of major support when added to direct psychotherapeutic attack in the reversal of the symptomatology of sexual inadequacy. Therefore, the concept of rapid treatment in sexual inadequacy has been developed as an integral part of the research program. If symptoms of impotence, frigidity, or premature ejaculation cannot be reversed or major symptomatic improvement established during 10 days to 3 weeks of intensive therapeutic effort, the program is adjudged at fault and the immediate treatment result is recorded statistically as a failure.

Clinical experience in the last 9 years has confirmed the technique of orienting the sexually inadequate marital unit to basic psychophysiologic principles of sexual response while reeducating the unit to positive sexual response patterns and by negating both partners' fears of performance. These educational and orientational programs can be completed in a brief 10-day to 3-week period, presuming exposure of the marital unit to therapeutic regime on the basis of a 7-day week. Usually 20 to 40 hours are consumed by the diagnostic and therapeutic procedures before reversal of the specific sexual distress is accomplished, with an average time expenditure of 28 hours recorded to date.

Objective evaluation of the clinical phase of the investigative program in human sexual inadequacy will be available in 1970. This decade-long control period will provide not only statistics associated with immediate treatment success and failure during the acute therapeutic phases of the research program, but also will provide 5 years of follow-up of sexually inadequate marital units after the active treatment of their distress has been terminated. This program or concept of treatment of human sexual inadequacy can be considered to have reached clinical maturity only when fundamental principles of objective statistical evaluation are applied and the methods found successful.

No doubt the future will demand that laboratory and clinical findings which develop from application of established research criteria to sexually oriented questions and concerns are in turn applied to related social problems. Thereby we may replace superstition, fallacy, and lore with a scientific body of knowledge upon which society can depend. Basic research in sexual behavior then comes full circle and moves itself toward new demands for understanding of man and his reproductive functions.

REPRODUCTION AND SEXUAL BEHAVIOR (M. Diamond ed.), 417–443, © Indiana University Press

25

Genetic-Endocrine Interactions and Human Psychosexuality

Milton Diamond

In the study of human sexual behavior, aside from special ethical and social problems, we are faced with the same questions posed from any other arbitrary category of human behavior, be it aggression or schizophrenia. Such questions include: what are the origins of the behavior, what factors control it, and how can it best be modified?

In answering these questions for sexual behavior, however, we perhaps actually have an advantage not available for these other areas of behavior. Although the study of reproduction and sexuality has only been tolerated (if not fully respected) for the last 40 or so years, and many gaps still exist in our knowledge, there are available a remarkable wealth of clinical observations and animal research data in regard to the origins, control, and modification of sexual behavior. Some of these data pertaining to human genitosexual anomalies and accompanying psychosexuality, consolidated and analyzed here, are believed to exemplify this.

Support for the validity of studies in this area may be linked to successfully meeting the five general criteria for behavior–genetic studies enumerated by E. Anderson (1966), i.e., survival, intelligence, frequency, biochemistry, and treatment.

1. *Survival:* The genetic characters associated with sexual anomalies are usually not lethal and many carriers may reproduce and
live to old age.

2. *Intelligence:* The IQ range of individuals with sexual anomalies
falls within normal limits and is thus high enough to allow for
personal interview and a wide range of behavior patterns for study.

3. *Frequency:* Genitosexual anomalies are not rare and estimates
of their occurrence range from 1 in 200 to 500 (Overzier, 1963; Crew,
1965) to 2 to 3 per 100 (Overzier, 1967).

4. *Biochemistry:* The metabolic pathways and endocrinopathies
involved are well known in many instances.

5. *Treatment:* Medical and psychological treatment is often available to counteract the effects of the anomaly and allow observation
under the altered condition.

For many nonhuman species, including other anthropoids, the
evidence seems clear and the data well accepted that the prenatal
endocrine environment is crucial for determining adult patterns of
both gonadal cyclicity and sexual behavior (see Chapters 5 and 20).
In the case of the human, however, many clinicians and investigators
concerned with the question, while conceding that the gonads and
genitalia may be affected, usually still hold that sexual behavior and
psychosexual outlook is primarily a product of upbringing and environmental influences. The present paper will further examine this
question and attempt to show that sexual behavior in the human is
more dependent upon pre- and postnatal genetic–endocrine influences
than upon the postnatal environment. Some reasons for the opposite
appearance are presented.

Clinical Cases

The following two individuals will serve to present the problem:
The first patient (Fig. 1) came to Louisville General Hospital at the
age of 22 with a complaint of failure to menstruate. She was married
and wanted children. Physical examination revealed a generally
normal phenotypic female lacking, however, typical adult pubic or
axillary hair and possessing what appeared to be bilateral inguinal
hernias. This now-classical syndrome (Morris, 1953) suggested a
diagnosis of testicular feminization. Follow-up laparotomy sustained
this suspicion by revealing the herniating masses to be testes and
demonstrating the absence of ovaries or uterus. Subsequent karyotypes
of the patient showed typical male X and Y chromosomes. In manner
and expression the patient revealed "herself" psychologically as a

Fig. 1 XY individual with testes and external appearance of female.

typical anovulatory female concerned with her marriage, the prospect of bearing children, and other "womanly" interests. No indications of an ambivalent psychosexual status were seen. The patient considered herself a well-adjusted female and all interviewers agreed.

The second patient (Figs. 2 and 3) was originally seen as a probationary problem and was referred incidentally to the Louisville Children's Hospital for investigation of "his" pendulous breast development. Examination initially revealed a 12-year-old Negro boy with chief findings of enlarged breasts and hypospadias. Karyotyping seemed difficult to standardize, due to mosaicism in this case, but an eventful diagnosis of XX was confirmed by repeated cell smears and chromosome studies.

Shortly after admission to Children's Hospital, the patient began to menstruate. Psychiatric evaluation revealed the patient as a boy sensitive to the ambiguities of his condition yet fully convinced of his male status and place despite the development of pendulous breasts and the onset of menses. His discipline problem stemmed from his "playing hookey" to avoid the jibes and comments of his classmates. He was quite outspoken in his desire to have his breasts removed, the bleeding stopped, and that he be left alone to continue life as a male.

In short, two patients with two distinct problems have been presented. In the first case a genetic male is seen to be phenotypically and psychosexually a female. To the present he has never expressed doubt as to his status. In the second instance we see a genetic female, who until puberty was a phenotypic and psychosexual male. This masculine psychosexual orientation persists to the present day despite breast development, the onset of menstruation, and several attempts at psychological counseling. The problem, thus, is how to reconcile the psychosexual role with the apparently incongruent genetic status.

Developmental Review

The etiology of these conditions is best appreciated by an understanding of the general process of embryonic sexual differentiation. Sexual differentiation may be considered from three points of view: morphologic, endocrine, and behavioral. Once these general processes are reviewed the patients will be discussed in light of these data. The present review of morphological differentiation will be brief, since many excellent ones covering this area exist; among the latest are those of Grumbach and Barr (1958), Burns (1961), Jost (1961),

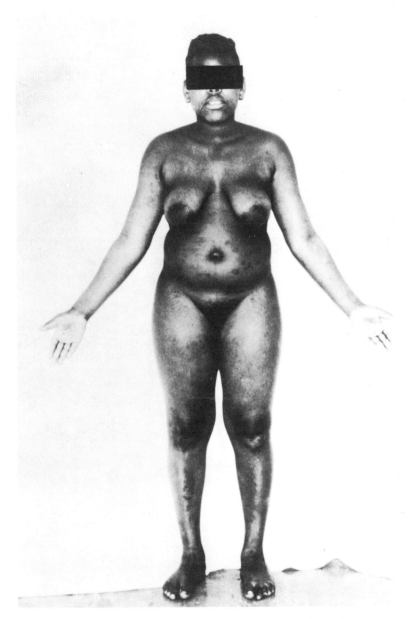

Fig. 2   XX individual with ovaries and pendulous breasts.

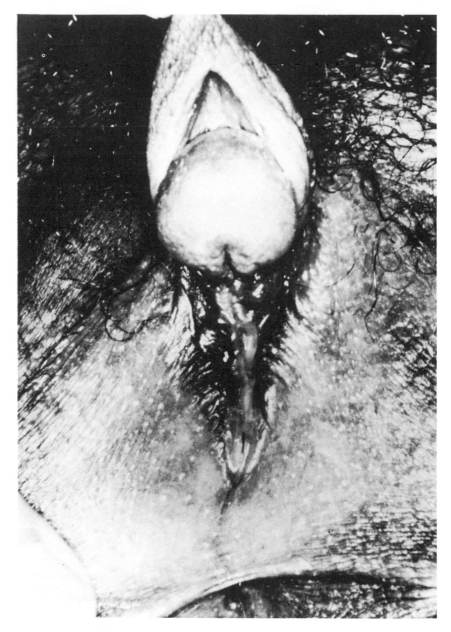

Fig. 3 "Hypospadic" condition giving genital appearance of male.

Sohval (1963), Watzka (1963), Bruner-Lorand (1964), Van Wyk (1965), and N. Anderson (1966).

It is well established that up to the sixth or seventh week the human fetus contains neither testes nor ovaries but only indifferent gonads (Fig. 4). At this time two systems of primitive ducts also exist in the fetus (Fig. 4). These are the Müllerian duct system, which can give rise to oviducts, uterus, and upper vagina, and the Wolffian duct system, which normally gives rise to the epididymides, vas deferens, and seminal vesicles.

Normally the individual's genotype will determine the direction of development for the primitive gonads. The gonads will normally develop into testes in individuals bearing a Y chromosome. Correspondingly, ovaries will normally develop in individuals with two X chromosomes. If only a single X chromosome is available, gonadal agenesis or dysgenesis will result. Once the gonad differentiates, it induces direction to the development of the two pairs of genital duct structures. An as-yet-unidentified fetal morphogenic testicular substance (F.M.T.S.) will not only induce masculine development of the Wolffian duct system but will simultaneously inhibit the development of the Müllerian duct system (Jost, 1947b, 1947c, 1955).*
On the other hand, the ovary does not elaborate a corresponding substance inducing development of the Müllerian duct system and regression of the Wolffian ducts; these phenomena have been shown to result from the *absence* of the F.M.T.S., since in animals of either sex, fetal castration or destruction of the gonads prior to sexual differentiation invariably leads to development along female lines (Jost, 1947a, 1947b, 1953; Raynaud, 1950; Raynaud and Frilley, 1947).

Similar, but not identical, processes are at work on the external genitalia. Prior to sexual differentiation, an indifferent genital tubercle exists and remains undifferentiated until about the end of the third month. Watzka (1963) considers this long interval prior to differentiation as an important factor accounting for the frequency and wide variety of sexual anomalies seen in man. For male or female differentiation of these external structures, however, F.M.T.S. does not seem too crucial. These sexually bipotential structures are differentiated as female genitalia unless stimulated by testicular, adrenal, maternal, or exogenous androgens (Fig. 5).

---

* The term fetal morphogenic testicular substance (F.M.T.S.) defines the period of activity and primary level of action as well as the tissues from which the substance originates. Although it is not clear whether, in actuality, only one substance is involved, the singular form will be used here.

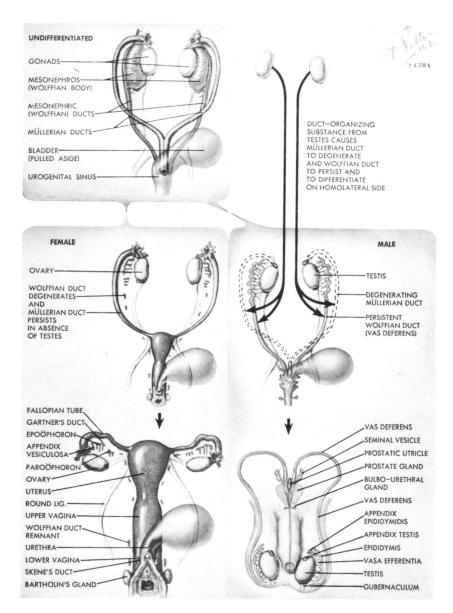

Fig. 4 Differentiation of genital ducts. (Copyright: *CIBA Collection of Medical Illustrations by Frank H. Netter, M.D.*)

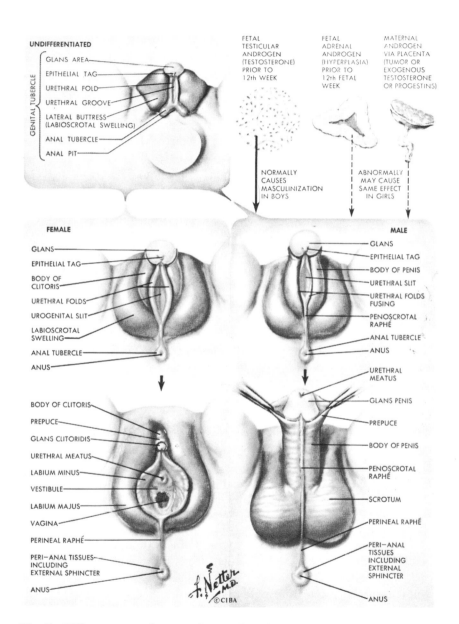

Fig. 5 Differentiation of external genitalia. (Copyright: *CIBA Collection of Medical Illustrations by Frank H. Netter, M.D.*)

As will be discussed below, the presence of circulating androgen, by itself, is not sufficient for virilization of tissues. The capability for proper end-organ response of pertinent tissues is required for masculinization. I consider this crucial and wish to emphasize it here and later demonstrate the significance of this.

This sexual differentiation of the soma discussed so far is known and accepted from many studies. Differentiation of a different type is also directly related to our interest: sexual differentiation of the neural–endocrine axis and the nervous tissues associated with reproduction and sexual behavior. This subject has been adequately reviewed previously (Diamond, 1965a; Phoenix et al., Chapter 5; Whalen, Chapter 20) and need not be repeated here. These references present evidence indicating that the same hormonal processes involved in genital differentiation are also active in differentiation of the neural tissues which mediate behavioral activities. In the adult this neural sexual differentiation affects reproductive behavior as well as gonadal cyclicity.

It is to be emphasized that the development of the genital tracts and external genitalia has its counterpart in the development of the endocrine and behavior mediating neural tissues. Moreover, the developing neural tissues show greater sensitivity than the developing genitalia to the prenatal–neonatal endocrine environment. This is evidenced by experiments in which low levels of androgens were seen to induce sexual differentiation of the hypothalamus while somatic effects were not seen in rodents (Phoenix et al., 1959) and primates (Goy, 1966). Admittedly, the behavioral evidence so far presented has been from nonhuman species. Clinical evidence of a sort is also available for this point, however. John Money and Anke A. Ehrhardt at the Johns Hopkins University have followed 10 normal appearing female children of mothers given androgenic progestins during gestation. They report that nine of the ten were tomboys according to their mothers and themselves. The chief symptom was abundant energy for outdoor athletic pursuits (although within limits acceptable for a female in today's upper middle class families) (Ehrhardt and Money, 1967). In summary, then, the presence of F.M.T.S. and androgens lead to masculine differentiation and bias, while the absence of these substances leads to feminine differentiation.

This may seem to imply a simple male versus female mechanism for setting the sexual thresholds within the nervous system. Actually no evidence exists for this extreme position. The absolute or relative amounts of F.M.T.S. and androgens present and biologically available, and the receptivity of the neural tissues at the various times of differentiation, will determine where, and to what extent, an individual's sexual range and bias will be established. As our methods of testing sexual behavior become refined, we may be able to distinguish, for various patterns, extensive gradations of behavior on a continuum with ends which for convenience we now call male to female; the center point need not be neuter but may reflect equipotential or ambivalent male/female behavior capacities. We may indeed find the sexual behavior repetories of males and females to be parallel and discontinuous rather than continuous.

One additional point needs to be made. Although postnatal sexual behavior is seen to be subject to prenatal endocrine organization, it must be emphasized that the magnitude of the effect is determined by time of onset, duration, and degree of endocrine exposure. This is seen clinically (Witschi et al., 1957) as well as experimentally (Goy et al., 1964; Swanson and van der Werff ten Bosch, 1964). The exact timing needed to produce the various sexual endocrinopathies in the human is only generally known. When more data are available we might see that these conditions actually reflect very limited and specific intervals in development. For humans, Lenz and Knapp (1962) and Lenz (1965) have reported that the intake of thalidomide between day 27 and day 30 of gestation will affect only the arms, whereas intake between days 30 and 35 will affect mainly the legs. Similarly, sexual biasing of the nervous system may occur during specific and short intervals for specific manifestations.

In a broad way testosterone has demonstrated the capacity to participate in time-critical sexual differentiation. If administered during adulthood, the behavioral effects of androgens are usually temporary. If administered during pregnancy, however, the hormones may be without effect on the mother, although the female fetuses being carried are permanently masculinized (Diamond and Young, 1963; Diamond, 1966). Considered in other terms, during fetal development hormones can act to organize the nervous system with a sexual bias for future sexual behavior. During adulthood, hormones act to instigate or "make manifest" this built-in bias (Phoenix et al., 1959; Harris, 1964; Diamond, 1965a; Young, 1961, 1965; Phoenix et al., Chapter 5). This built-in bias may be comparable to what Stoller refers to as a "biological force" (Stoller, 1964).

Discussion

The first patient, with testicular feminization, was an XY male with the appearance and psychosexual orientation of a female. Of six "sisters" at home, three have a similar problem. He has three normal brothers. In reviewing a large number of such cases, Morris and Mahesh (1963) consider the possibility that two classes of this disease exist and conclude that "this syndrome is either an X-linked recessive trait or a male-limited autosomal dominant inheritance." Boczkowski and Teter (1965) make a further distinction and consider this condition "a sex-controlled rather than a sex-limited trait."

Regardless of the mode of inheritance it is now fairly well established that the testes in these males may elaborate normal amounts of androgen as well as considerable amounts of estrogen (Simmer et al., 1965). However, it is both the lack of action of the androgen as well as the positive action of the estrogens which is responsible for this condition (Morris and Mahesh, 1963; David et al., 1965; Simmer et al., 1965). Wilkins (1950) has shown that administered androgens have repeatedly failed to masculinize individuals of these types and postulates that a defect exists in the responsiveness of the pertinent end-organ tissues. This theory is still applicable and has been consistent with subsequent findings. A recent study by Neuman and Elger (1965) supports this thesis. By administration of an antiandrogenic substance to fetal and neonatal rats, these investigators demonstrated that the general body build, external genitalia, mammary glands and sexual behavior of the growing pup develops along female, not male, lines, so that the resulting adult rat may be considered an experimental counterpart of the human "testicular female."

The lack of external somatic end-organ response to testicular androgens is in contrast to the response of the internal organs to F.M.T.S. Internally these patients show a male duct system and testes. Significantly, however, as discussed previously, the differentiation of the nervous tissues mediating the reproductive and sexual behavior patterns parallels the differentiation of the external genitalia and is androgen-dependent. In these patients with a demonstrated inability to respond to androgen, we may assume that the neural tissues which mediate sexual behavior were not primed toward maleness in utero, and as adults cannot be masculinized. Despite adequate circulating androgens, a "masculine" response of the nervous system is missing. These patients never have any doubt as to their female identity and role and never, on their own initiative, seek a change of sex.

The second patient during a subsequent panhysterectomy and chromosome study of the gonads was finally diagnosed as a true female. Despite extensive breast development and menstruation, this individual considered herself a male, refused repeated opportunities of change, and threatened suicide were she made to live as a girl. Either her gonads or adrenals may be assumed to have, at one time, secreted androgens, because the external genitalia have been masculinized (Figs. 3 and 5). Since experimental and clinical evidence indicate that the developing neural tissues usually have thresholds lower than the somatic tissues (Phoenix et al., 1959; Young et al., 1964; Ehrhardt and Money, 1967; Phoenix et al., Chapter 5), it may be concluded that not only did this modify her external genitalia but also affected (masculinized) her psychosexual bias as well.

It may be rightly argued that so far in this presentation I have ignored all the "environment" in favor of the "heredity" and all the "nurture" in favor of the "nature." In both cases presented, the bodily configuration determined the sex of upbringing and the respective female and male roles may be construed as derived from events and learning during this crucial early period of ontogeny. Many investigators (Money, 1961; Hampson and Hampson, 1961) and a preponderance of psychotherapists even have considered this the most crucial determinant of psychosexuality. It has even been claimed that change of sex status from male to female or vice versa may be psychiatrically traumatic and even disastrous after this initial "imprinting" even if the original sex assignment was in error (Hampson and Hampson, 1961; Money et al., 1955).

Two additional patients will be introduced at this point to clarify this issue. B.B. first came to Louisville Children's Hospital in 1952 at the age of 14 for an emergency appendectomy. Admitted as a female patient, it was noted during surgery that she had neither ovaries nor uterus. Closer investigations revealed the presence of a hypospadic penis, bifid scrotum, and cryptorchid testes. The family was informed of the nature of the findings and a change of sex role with appropriate surgery was recommended. The family and patient refused the offer. After surgery a note was made on the record and the patient was released.

Three years later this patient voluntarily presented himself for surgical repair and on his own volition requested a change of sex. He has since undergone over 25 surgical procedures in an attempt to rectify the anatomical problems but considers it worth the final outcome. In other words, despite the sex of rearing, an individual not only can, but may, switch voluntarily and without psychotic mishap to a sex role in which he feels best suited psychosexually. This is not an isolated case (Dewhurst and Gordon, 1963; Diamond, 1965a; Armstrong, 1966; Barton and Ware, 1966). These switches must, however, be preceded by appropriate biological "priming."

It has been indicated previously (Diamond, 1965a) that the desire for change of sex assignment, as in this case, usually occurs at or shortly after puberty. This is consistent with the emphasis on endocrine mediation of psychosexual orientation, since it is during this life stage that the nervous system is first beset with an adult endocrine physiology and the adult expression of the psychosexual basis is being goaded into action. Also, in cases, like this, the absence of normal female development probably contributes to self-doubt within a malassigned role.

The second additional patient, T.L.E., was born at Louisville General Hospital in 1960 and diagnosed at that time as having a salt-losing adrenogenital syndrome. In this condition a malfunctioning adrenal gland elaborates excessive amounts of androgen, leading, among other things, to masculinization. The child was placed on a medical-treatment schedule to arrest this condition and the mother told to return her periodically for outpatient care. Despite this advice to the mother, the patient was not seen again until she was brought back to Children's Hospital at the age of 5 years and 6 months. Phenotypically she displayed extensive virilization, i.e., stocky male somatotype, clitoral hypertrophy of 5 cm, and male hair distribution over her body, head, and pubis. She was replaced on an adequate drug-treatment schedule and a clitorectomy was performed 1 month later.

The initial interview with the child revealed an individual with interests and actions closer to those of a 6-year-old boy than of a girl and interview with the mother tended to confirm this impression. As the youngest sib with four older brothers and four older sisters. T. was considered by her mother to behave more like her brothers than her sisters. Her mother reported her as a "tomboy" in every respect. Observations in the hospital showed her to be quite aggressive, active, and to prefer boys' toys and games. She has volunteered to her mother that she is a "boy."*

In this case, as in the one before, the sex of rearing was female, yet the psychosexual-behavioral orientation seems inclined toward maleness.

These cases are not presented to imply that upbringing has nothing to do with psychosexual orientation, for both patients could

---

* Currently under cortisone and progestin therapy, she is considered to have "calmed down" considerably.

function within the sex in which they were reared and, in fact, one (T.L.E.) still does. This, however, should be considered a credit to human role flexibility and adaptability rather than an indelible feature of upbringing (Diamond, 1965a). It seems that the effect of the sex of rearing is strong when reinforcing the fetal and developmental endocrine predisposition but meets strong opposition when going counter to it. In fact, as seen in the case of B.B., a biological bias may be enough to overcome the upbringing if the bias is of the crucial endocrine-organizing type which occurs during differentiation of the nervous system, and the upbringing is such that the feelings of self-doubt may be entertained. This might even be predicted from a mathematical analysis of various psychosexual conditions and intersex states as formulated by Cappon et al. (1959). It is too early to predict the adult feelings of T.L.E. but some alteration from normal female role orientation and acceptance may be anticipated, even though basically overcome by the combination of endocrine therapy as well as rearing.

Normally the problem of a conflicting constitution and upbringing does not confront us. A normal male is brought up as a male and a normal female is brought up as a female. The various experiences during childhood, puberty, and adulthood tend to reinforce the biological predisposition. When due to some biological quirk, usually of genetic origin, and a conflict exists among the biological variables of sex, we may expect some concern as to the role of upbringing.

The numerous variables of sex may or may not be coincident with each other. As so often stated by many investigators, an individual's sex may be judged by the gonads, internal genitalia, external genitalia, hormone titers, chromosomal complement, or psychosexual orientation. For the normal individual, these are usually concordant. The genetic complement will induce proper gonadal development which, via the presence or absence of F.M.T.S., controls the differentiation of the internal genitalia and, via the presence or absence of androgens, controls differentiation of the external genitalia and the nervous system. With this involved process the human seems to be one of several species, along with the goat and pig, in which genitosexual anomalies are not uncommon.

Fortunately in pathologic as well as in normal cases, however, the presence or absence of androgens will usually determine differentiation of the external genitalia to male or female as well as affecting psychosexual differentiation of the nervous system. Therefore, regardless of incongruity, with the other variables of sex, rearing, usually based only on the appearance of the external genitalia, most often conforms to the sex of psychosexual bias. It is when these are in conflict that we may expect most instances of psychosexual problems.

Cappon et al. (1959) have concluded, after studying 17 intersexed patients, that to raise an individual contrary to his main physical nature would be to raise him "against the bulk of his psychosexual nature." Roth and Ball (1964), in a comprehensive review of this area have stated: "Even if it is accepted that most individuals with ambiguous sexuality accept the role conferred on them, whether biologically correct or otherwise, it can not be assumed until detailed comparisons along these lines have been conducted, that a more accurate assignment might not have yielded better psychological results." Or to put it another way: The acquiescence to a malassigned sex role by an individual does not by itself constitute "correctness" of assignment; a more correct assignment may (and should) be made when the error of assignment becomes apparent or is felt by the individual.

Among the common genitosexual anomalies are two others which are seen frequently enough to be considered here, i.e., Turner's and Klinefelter's syndromes. The Turner's individual usually has an XO choromosome complement, but mosaicism such as XO/XX and XO/XXX also occurs; an approximately equal ratio of chromatin-positive and chromatin-negative patients results (Hauser, 1963). This lack of an adequate second sex chromosome leads to gonadal agenesis and the subsequent absence of F.M.T.S. and androgen. As expected, this results in the development of female internal and external genitalia.

We may also thereby question whether in the chromatin negative as well as the chromatin positive individuals a female-biased nervous system does not also result. Witkin et al. (1966), based on verbal and performance IQ data collected by Shafer (1962), and Alexander et al. (1966), based on tests of visual-constructional ability, have indicated that patients with Turner's syndrome consistently score lower in tests of cognitive functions than normals. The possibility exists that these functions and analytic abilities (nervous system functions) are under the influence of sex chromosomes. The mediating mechanism may be hormonal. Landsdell (1961, 1962) had previously demonstrated sex differences in the cognitive processes of the nervous system.

These facts are concordant with the routine findings that men and women consistently differ in analytic (cognitive) abilities, females usually scoring lower. Since patients with Turner's syndrome are normally reared as females, no psychosexual problem should be anticipated despite possible incongruity with the sex-chromatin status, since their cognitive abilities are feminoid. Most investigators, as reviewed by Hauser (1963), find these patients to have sexual behavior reduced but heterosexual as a female. As long as no gonad is present, no F.M.T.S. or androgen secretion would be anticipated and we would predict the genitalia and rearing assignments to be female. No conflict should ensue, since neural organization would also have been female. As previously indicated by Dewhurst (1962) and Sohval (1964) for morphology, we can now also say for behavior that the clinical features demonstrated by these patients depend less upon the precise sex chromosome constitution and more upon the extent and nature of the fetal testicular failure.

The Klinefelter's syndrome usually results from a 47/XXY karyotype and is typified by a phenotypic male with small testes, gynecomastia, and female hair-distribution pattern. While testicular development occurs in these individuals it is not completely normal. Testicular biopsy during adulthood usually reveals hyalinized seminiferous tubules composed mainly of sustentacular cells with oligospermia. Adenomatous clumping of the interstitial (androgen-producing) cells is also seen. While F.M.T.S. secretion may be judged to have been normal on the basis of male differentiation of the Wolffian duct structures and regression of the Müllerian duct structures, these patients typically show androgen titers below normal and gonadotropin titers higher than normal. During embryonic periods of differentiation, the androgen supply may also have been deficient, leading to a less than complete sexual differentiation or nervous system bias. Concomitantly the same genetic process involved in the chromosomal anomaly also may be directly involved in a neural alteration of the psychosexual substrate. There is some indication that this is so, since these phenotypic males, reared as normal males, nevertheless are often found weakly heterosexual with low libido (Pasqualini et al., 1957; Money, 1963; Nielsen and Fischer, 1965) and suffer related marital difficulties (Sipova and Raboch, 1961). If only upbringing were involved, this could not be predicted, since these individuals are reared as normal males. The patients express and manifest difficulty in performing as normal males. They may occasionally be homosexual or transvestite (Money, 1963; Money and Pollitt, 1963; Roth and Ball, 1964; Benjamin, 1966). Schultz (1963) considers them close to an undifferentiated sex, and Crowley (1965) describes their sex role as ambivalent. It has been found clinically in many hospitals that these individuals are often passive or ambivalent toward their own androgen treatments.

As with the testicular feminization syndrome, androgen treatment of patients with Klinefelter's syndrome is not always successful in affecting libido. It is known that variability exists in the sexual orientation of these patients, as there is variability in masculine somatotypes and in elaboration of, and response to, androgen. It is possible that these differences reflect the different ways in which this condition may be brought about, e.g., by the union of a normal Y sperm with an abnormal XX ovum or the union of a normal X ovum with an abnormal XY sperm. When looked at critically, these circumstances may be expected to result in different syndromes. Despite the usually male upbringing, the nervous system seems to display a reduced capability for responding to sexual stimuli—as if the proper embryonic critical period priming were absent and the proper adult response lacking, even when adequate levels of androgens are present.

Some additional comments are warranted in regard to the adrenogenital syndrome. This condition has many subtypes, but basically involves either a congenital adrenal cortical hyperplasia with increased androgen secretion or a genetically determined enzymatic loss resulting in the production of abnormal quantities of androgen. The genetic condition has been determined to be due to a recurring autosomal recessive mutant gene (Childs et al., 1956; Grumbach and Barr, 1958). At birth a genetic male child usually appears normal, but, as seen for T.L.E., the affected genetic female appears masculinized. Occasionally, owing to the equivocal appearance of the genitalia, the sex of rearing is equivocal. However, even when the upbringing is normal, it is with these individuals that psychosexual conflicts may be anticipated.

If the female is reared as a boy and the disease not brought under control, the child's development will continue along male lines and she will present as a case of precocious puberty. If, at this time, a correct diagnosis is made (these patients usually seek treatment between 3 and 7 years of age), the disease can be arrested and the individual directed toward a female role. The difficulty involved in this switch may or may not be great and will depend upon the individual's self-evaluation, which in turn is related to the extent of androgenic differentiation of the somatic and neural tissues as well as age and the severity of rearing. Some evidence that the nervous system and end organs have been affected may be gleaned from reports from these patients, when adults, that when erotically excited their clitorides are subject to erection and occasional priapism (Money, 1965). This is a manifestation of excitement not usually seen in normal females (Masters and Johnson, 1966) but only in androgenized ones. If the individual's condition is not diagnosed she will develop phenotypically as a male with stunted growth, and a concomitant male sexual orientation.

When the individual is raised as a female, the virilization of her body type will usually prompt medical consultation and the problem will be treated from then on. Depending on when, how long, and how much androgen was present during her development, she will exhibit various degrees of psychosexual masculinization. As observed by Money (1965), this behavioral masculinization may be primarily manifest in a reduced threshold and increased frequency of sexual arousal and sexual initiative. However, as seen in the present patient, T.L.E., via such an alteration in thresholds, even object selection may have been affected, since her choice of toys, games, and identification are male despite female upbringing. More astute questioning of virilized adults may similarly reveal a male shift in goal orientation. Significantly, this reduced threshold to sexual stimuli may be seen in treated cases as well as untreated ones (Money, 1965)—again, an indication of a possible built-in sexual bias. In adults the androgenic bias seems to be manifest as an indiscriminate aphrodisiac, a feature it seems to possess for the normal male.* It will be interesting to watch the development of sexual behavior patterns and desires in those girls whose mothers were treated with androgens to see if they, too, are affected, as are the adrenogenital patients. It may be predicted that they will be. However, the inherent flexibility in sexual behavior expression for humans, and the loose definition of proper female behavior, may allow for their sexual performance to fall within the broad range of females in general (Diamond, 1965a).

---

* In an experimental study in female guinea pigs (Diamond, 1965b), an androgen, testosterone propionate, was compared with estrogen and progesterone for the ability to elicit sexual mounting behavior. During a 12-hour observation period the female hormones elicited significantly more mounts than did the androgen, but these were seen during a restricted estrus period of a few hours. The androgen initiated less mounting, but this pattern was observable during all hours of the test. Females normally will indulge in sexual behavior and mount only during estrus; males will indulge almost anytime.

Summary

Considering clinical and experimental data, human psychosexuality and derived sexual behavior are seen to be dependent upon genetic and endocrine factors present prior to birth. Normally the genetic factors structure the endocrine environment and this in turn affects the psychosexual bias of the nervous system.

The organization of these behavioral characters is seen most often to parallel the organization of the external genitalia. The totality of this sexual differentiation, coupled with the individual's somatotype, upbringing, and postnatal endocrine status, will determine to what extent his diasthetic bias develops and how the sexual world will be approached and reacted to. It is at this level that the sex of rearing is operating.

In genetic syndromes affecting the gonads or adrenals, it may be anticipated that some sort of psychosexual problem may need to be considered; the extent of concern should be related to the amount and type of hormonal imbalance thereby engendered and usually manifest by genital ambiguity.

When an individual is reared in the sex concordant with his prenatal endocrine heritage, psychosexually all will usually go well. When the prenatal influence is only moderate, the child still may adjust to his sex of rearing, owing to human behavioral flexibility, although he may have difficulty. But when the sex of rearing and the sex of the prenatal hormone environment are strongly conflicting, a situation unacceptable to the individual concerned may be anticipated. Thankfully, owing to the usual parallel differentiation of the external genitalia and the neural tissues which mediate sexual behavior, this last possibility is rare, since assignment of sex most often is based on the appearance of the genitalia.*

It should also be kept in mind that psychosexual problems may also arise, as in the Turner's or Klinefelter's syndrome, as the result of a genetic-endocrine defect despite apparently proper sex-role assignment. These are problems, however, only if we accept as "normal" that a human psychosexually must strongly be committed to a definite

---

* Compare the "signal" role seen for the genitalia here with the quite different concept presented by Whalen in Chapter 20. Here the genitalia primarily serve to orient upbringing, give some indication as to the prenatal and pubertal endocrine environment, and hint at what type of sexual behavior might be anticipated. In Whalen's presentation for rodents, the peripheral effects on the genitalia are presented as possibly structuring the behavior.

stereotyped male or female orientation and sexual behavior. It probably would be more correct biologically if we culturally accept a multiplicity of behavioral configurations concurrent with the many genetic and ontogenetic conditions which may lead to various levels of psychosexual bias within the nervous system.

The Future

As in the past, advances in our understanding of psychosexuality will depend upon multidisciplinary findings rather than data from any single source.

In the laboratory, efforts will be made toward uncovering the actual substances involved in the sex differentiating and activating processes, e.g., what is fetal morphogenic testicular substance (F.M.-T.S.), just which biochemical entities are involved in the organization and activation of psychosexuality, and how do these substances vary during the individual's life. A start has already been made in these directions (Diamond and Gennaro, 1967; Phoenix et al., Chapter 5). Further, since many processes differ in the developing and mature individual not only substances but mechanisms must be exposed, and studies will be directed to that end. For example, research will elucidate: the processes involved, during development, in the selective dominance of cortical (ovarian) versus medullary (testicular) areas of the indifferent gonad (see Burns, 1961); the persistence of one duct system and degeneration of the other (e.g., Price et al., 1967); the factors involved in protecting the pregnant adult female from genital and psychosexual alteration while leaving the fetal and nonpregnant adult female vulnerable (Diamond and Young, 1963; Diamond, 1967); and the means by which various maturational processes prod the latent, biased nervous system to manifest itself, e.g., via alteration in cognitive ability (Witkins et al., 1966). Of crucial importance will be developments in studies which demonstrate how endocrines affect genes within nervous tissues and thus provide a possible mechanism by which hormones would alter subsequent behavior. Here, too, a start has been made (see Karlson, 1963). We can equally envision compatible studies of drug, memory, and learning effects on human sexual behavior and psychosexuality.

From genetic studies per se, after extensive attempts, we should expect to see techniques developed which not only facilitate chromosome identification but allow mapping and analysis of genes as well. These techniques, once developed, would be used to compare behaviorally different individuals of a given phenotype and chromosome constitution as well as behaviorally similar individuals with similar constitutions. We must not, however, expect to find human sexual behavior the function of a single gene but rather a polygenic dependent variable. This simultaneously makes the original task of gene identity more difficult while facilitating theoretical interpretations. The difficulty arises from the need to locate many rather than a few gene loci. The facilitation accrues from the genetic concepts of multigenic penetrance, expressivity, and pleiotropism, which provide ample leeway for interpreting genetic-environmental interactions. These concepts parenthetically emphasize the contention that heredity and environment are interdependent in an individual's development. With these anticipated genetic methods in concert with additional research using classical twin-study techniques (e.g., Kallmann, 1952a, 1952b; Rainer et al., 1960), in addition to well conceived and competently executed long-term longitudinal studies of sexual developments, further inroads into the analysis of the involved nature–nurture controversy will be made.

Clinically most all psychotherapists, regardless of their own professional orientation, admit that psychosexual bias and sex-role identity of genetic-endocrine origin is usually refractory to extensive permanent change. Although, owing to personal flexibility, some individuals will accept a role outside their diasthetic predisposition (Diamond, 1965a), evidence, mainly from the Johns Hopkins Hospital in this country and from Scandinavia, Great Britain, and Morocco abroad, indicates that individuals with such problems may be best treated by surgery and acquiescence to their personal wishes rather than by extensive depth therapy. Regrettably, this course of action is not yet generally considered most appropriate. The future, however, will no doubt see this feeling change so that elective sexual surgery and sex role changes will fall into a category akin to other plastic surgery procedures or mode of life changes, with individualized treatment and compassion prevailing rather than a blank caveat (see Benjamin, 1966).

While much more conclusive evidence is needed to consider them as such it is appealing to speculate that homosexuality and transsexualism might fit into this category of genetic-endocrine psychosexual problems. This is probable since these behavior patterns are among the most firmly entrenched of psychosexual deviations and environmental influences seem of no, or only minor, importance in their etiology (Kallmann, 1952a, 1952b; Benjamin, 1966). If indeed these do prove of genetic-endocrine origin rather than environmentally determined, a far-reaching reappraisal of our clinical and social approach to these conditions may be anticipated.

From all of this we may expect to see develop an acceptable concept of sex and "proper" sexual behavior, as broad or narrow, dependent upon an individual's anatomic, physiologic, and psychologic constellation rather than on two arbitrarily arranged stereotypes of male or female. This realization, in itself, can have societal consequences far transcending biological or medical implications, since in this all-important sphere of sexuality in general and sexual behavior in particular, personal differences and desires will not be seen as abnormal or pathologic but as manifestations of a full continuum of human flexibility within a bimodal macrocosm.

Acknowledgments

Appreciation is extended to Drs. Warren N. Cox, Walton M. Edwards, Harold J. Kosasky, and Duncan R. MacMillen for cooperation in working with the patients presented and to Dr. Leonard E. Reisman for karyotype determinations.

Appreciation is also extended to Ciba Pharmaceutical Company for use of some of their illustrative material by Frank H. Netter, M.D.

This research was supported in part by U.S. Public Health Service Research Grants HD-02326 and HD-03394 from the National Institute of Child Health and Human Development.

References

Alexander, D., A. A. Ehrhardt, and J. Money. 1966. Defective figure drawing, geometric and human, in Turner's syndrome. *J. Nervous Mental Disease,* **142:** 161–167.

Anderson, E. 1966. Studies of behavior in genetically defined syndromes in man. Presented at Behavior Genetics, 2nd. Louisville Invitational Conference, S. Vandenberg (moderator).

Anderson, N. 1966. The influence of hormones on human development. In *Human Development* (F. Falkner, ed.) Saunders, Philadelphia, pp. 184–221.

Armstrong, C. N. 1966. Treatment of wrongly assigned sex. *Brit. Med. J.,* **1966:** 1255–1256.

Barton, D., and P. D. Ware. 1966. Incongruities in the development of the sexual system. *Arch. Gen. Psychiat.,* **14:** 614–623.

Benjamin, H. 1966. *The Transsexual Phenomenon.* Julian Press, New York.

Boczkowski, K., and J. Teter. 1965. Familial male pseudohermaphroditism. *Acta Endocrinol.,* **49:** 497–509.

Bruner-Lorand, J. 1964. Intersexuality in mammals. In *Intersexuality in Vertebrates Including Man* (C. N. Armstrong and A. J. Marshall eds.). Academic Press, New York, pp. 311–347.

Burns, R. K. 1961. Role of hormones in the differentiation of sex. In *Sex and*

Internal Secretions, 3rd ed. (W. C. Young, ed.). Williams & Wilkins, Baltimore, pp. 76–159.

Cappon, D., C. Ezrin, and P. Lynes. 1959. Psychosexual identification (psychogender) in the intersexed. *Can. Psychiat. Assoc. J.* 4: 90–106.

Childs, B., M. M. Grumbach, and J. J. Van Wyk. 1956. Virilizing adrenal hyperplagia: A genetic and hormonal study. *J. Clin. Invest.,* 35: 218–222.

Crew, F. A. E. 1965. *Sex-Determination.* Methuen, London.

Crowley, T. J. 1965. Klinefelter's syndrome and abnormal behavior: A case report. *Intern. J. Neuropsychiat.,* 1: 359–363.

David, R. R., M. Wiener, L. Ross, and R. L. Landau. 1965. Steroid metabolism in the syndrome of testicular feminization. *J. Clin. Endocrinol. Metab.,* 25: 1393–1402.

Dewhurst, C. J. 1962. XY/XO mosaicism. *Lancet,* 2: 783.

Dewhurst, C. J., and R. R. Gordon. 1963. Change of sex. *Lancet,* 2: 1213–1216.

Diamond, M. 1965a. A critical evaluation of the ontogony of human sexual behavior. *Quart. Rev. Biol.,* 40: 147–175.

Diamond, M. 1965b. The antagonistic actions of testosterone propionate and estrogens and progesterone on copulatory patterns of the female guinea pig. *Anat. Rec.,* 151: 449 (Abstr.).

Diamond, M. 1966. Discussion. In *Sex and Behavior* (F. A. Beach, ed.). Wiley, New York, pp. 101–102.

Diamond, M. 1967. Androgen-induced masculinization in the ovariectomized and hysterectomized guinea pig. *Anat. Rec.,* 157: 47–52.

Diamond, M., and J. Gennaro. 1967. Fetal testicular ultrastructure and sex differentiating substance(s). *Anat. Rec.,* 157: 354–355 (Abstr.).

Diamond, M., and W. C. Young. 1963. Differential responsiveness of pregnant and nonpregnant guinea pigs to the masculinizing action of testosterone propionate. *Endocrinology,* 72: 429–438.

Ehrhardt, A. A. and J. Money. 1967. Progestin-induced hermaphroditism: IQ and psychosexual identity in a study of ten girls. *J. Sex Res.,* 3: 83–100.

Goy, R. W. 1966. Role of androgens in the establishment and regulation of behavioral sex differences in mammals. *J. Animal Sci.,* 25: 21–35.

Goy, R. W., W. E. Bridson, and W. C. Young. 1964. Period of maximal susceptibility of the prenatal female guinea pig to masculinizing actions of testosterone propionate. *J. Comp. Physiol. Psychol.,* 57: 166–174.

Grumbach, M. M., and M. L. Barr. 1958. Cytologic tests of chromosomal sex in relation to sexual anomalies in man. *Recent Progr. Hormone Res.,* 14: 255–334.

Hampson, J. L., and J. G. Hampson. 1961. The ontogenesis of sexual behavior in man. In *Sex and Internal Secretions* (W. C. Young, ed.). Williams & Wilkins, Baltimore, 3rd ed. pp. 1401–1432.

Harris, G. W. 1964. Sex hormones, brain development and brain function. *Endocrinology,* 75: 627–648.

Hauser, G. A. 1963. Gonadal dysgenesis. In *Intersexuality* (C. Overzier, ed.). Academic Press, New York, pp. 298–339.

Jost, A. 1947a. Sur le rôle des gonades foetales dans le différenciation sexuelle somatique de l'embryon de lapin. *Compt. Rend. Assoc. Anat.,* 51: 255–263.

Jost, A. 1947b. Recherches sur la différenciation sexuel de l'embryon de lapin. 1. Introduction et embryologie génitale normale. *Arch. Anat. Microscop. Morphol. Exptl.,* 36: 151–200.

Jost, A. 1947c. Recherches sur la différenciation sexuelle de l'embryon de lapin. 2. Action des androgènes de synotrèse sur l'histogenèse génitale. *Arch. Anat. Miscroscop. Morphol. Exptl.,* **36:** 242–315.

Jost, A. 1953. Problems of fetal endocrinology. The gonadal and hypophyseal hormones. *Recent Progr. Hormone Res.,* **8:** 379–418.

Jost, A. 1955. Modalities in the action of gonadal and gonad-stimulating hormones in the foetus. *Mem. Soc. Endocrinol.,* **1:** 237–248.

Jost, A. 1961. The role of fetal hormones in prenatal development. *Harvey Lecture Ser.,* **55:** 201–226.

Kallmann, F. J. 1952a. Twin and sibship study of overt homosexuality. *Am. J. Human Genet.,* **4:** 136–146.

Kallmann, F. J. 1952b. Comparative twin study on the genetic aspects of male homosexuality. *J. Nervous Mental Disease,* **115:** 283–298.

Karlson, P. 1963. New concepts on the mode of action of hormones. *Prospect. Biol. Med.,* **6:** 203–214.

Lansdell, H. 1961. The effect of neurosurgery on a test of proverbs. *Am. Psychol.,* **16:** 448.

Lansdell, H. 1962. A sex difference in effect of temporal-lobe neurosurgery on design preference. *Nature,* **194:** 852–854.

Lenz, W. 1965. Epidemiology of congenital malformations. *Ann. N. Y. Acad. Sci.,* **123:** 228–236.

Lenz, W., and K. Knapp. 1962. Thalidomide embryopathy. *Arch. Environ. Health,* **5:** 100–105.

Masters, W. H., and V. E. Johnson, 1966. *Human Sexual Response.* Little, Brown, Boston.

Money, J. 1961. Sex hormones and other variables in human eroticism. In *Sex and Internal Secretions* (W. C. Young, ed.). Williams & Wilkins, Baltimore, 3rd ed., pp. 1383–1400.

Money, J. 1963. Cytogenetic and psychosexual incongruities with a note on space-form blindness. *Am. J. Psychiat.,* **119:** 820–827.

Money, J. 1965. Influence of hormones on sexual behavior. *Ann. Rev. Med.,* **16:** 67–82.

Money, J., J. G. Hampson, and J. L. Hampson. 1955. Hermaphroditism: Recommendations concerning assignment of sex, change of sex, and psychologic management. *Bull. Johns Hopkins Hosp.,* **97:** 284–300.

Money, J., and E. Pollitt. 1963. Cytogenic and psychosexual ambiguity; Klinefelter's syndrome and transvestism compared. *Arch. Gen. Psychiat.,* **11:** 589–595.

Morris, J. M. 1953. The syndrome of testicular feminization in male pseudo-hermaphrodites. *Am. J. Obstet. Gynecol.,* **65:** 1192–1211.

Morris, J. M., and V. B. Mahesh. 1963. Further observations on the syndrome "testicular feminization." *Am. J. Obstet. Gynecol.,* **87:** 731–748.

Neumann, F., and W. Elger. 1965. Proof of the activity of androgenic agents and the differentiation of the external genitalia, the mammary gland and the hypothalamic-pituitary system in rats. *Androgens in Normal and Pathologic Conditions, Excerpta Med. Intern. Cong. Ser.* **101:** 168–185.

Nielsen, J., and M. Fischer. 1965. Sex-chromatin and sex-chromosome abnormalities in male hypogonadal mental patients. *Brit. J. Psychiat.,* **111:** 641–647.

Overzier, C. 1963. In *Intersexuality* (C. Overzier, ed.). Academic Press, New York, p. 534.

Overzier, C. 1967. The classification of intersexuality. *Triangle,* 8: 32–41.

Pasqualini, R. W., G. Vidal, and G. E. Bur. 1957. Psychopathology of Kline-felter's syndrome: Review of 31 cases. *Lancet,* 2: 164–167.

Phoenix, C. H., R. W. Goy, A. A. Gerall, and W. C. Young. 1959. Organizing action of prenatally administered tesosterone propionate on the tissues mediating mating behavior in the female guinea pig. *Endocrinology,* 65: 369–382.

Price, D., E. Ortiz, and J. J. P. Zaaijer. 1967. Organ culture studies of hormone secretion in endocrine glands of fetal guinea pigs. III. The relation of testicular hormone to sex differentiation of the reproductive ducts. *Anat. Rec.,* 157: 27–42.

Rainer, J. D., A. Mesnikoff, L. C. Kolb, and A. Carr. 1960. Homosexuality and heterosexuality in identical twins. *Psychosom. Med.,* 22: 250–259.

Raynaud, A. 1950. Recherches expérimentales sur de développement de l'appareil génital et le foncitionnement des glandes endocrines des foetus de souris et de mulot. *Arch. Anat. Miscroscop. Morphol. Exptl.,* 39: 518–576.

Raynaud, A., and M. Frilley. 1947. Destruction des glandes génitales, de l'embryon de souris, par une irradiation au moyen des rayons X, a l'age de treize jours. *Ann. Endocrinol. (Paris),* 8: 400–419.

Roth, M., and J. R. B. Ball. 1964. Psychiatric aspects of intersexuality. In *Intersexuality in Vertebrates Including Man* (C. N. Armstrong and A. J. Marshall, eds.). Academic Press, New York, pp. 395–443.

Schultz, J. H. 1963. Intersexuality and transvestism. In *Intersexuality* (C. Overzier, ed.). Academic Press, New York, pp. 514–533.

Shafer, J. W. 1962. A specific cognitive deficit observed in gonadal aplasia (Turner's syndrome). *J. Clin. Psychol.,* 18: 403–406.

Simmer, H. H., R. J. Pion, and W. J. Dignam. 1965. *Testicular Feminization.* Thomas, Springfield, Ill.

Sipova, I., and J. Raboch. 1961. Significance of testoids for the sexual development and life of 51 men with female nuclear structure. *Cesk. Psychiat.,* 57: 22–28.

Sohval, A. R. 1963. Chromosomes and sex chromatin in normal and anomalous sex development. *Physiol. Rev.* 43: 306–356.

Sohval, A. R. 1964. Hermaphroditism with "atypical" or "mixed" gonadal dysgenesis. *Am. J. Med.,* 36: 281–292.

Stoller, R. J. 1964. A contribution to the study of gender identity. *Int. J. Psychoanal.,* 45: 220–226.

Swanson, H. E., and J. J. van der Werff ten Bosch. 1964. The "early-androgen" syndrome: Differences in response to pre-natal and post-natal administration of various doses of testosterone propionate in female and male rats. *Acta Endocrinol.,* 47: 37–50.

Van Wyk, J. J. 1965. In *Endocrine system and selected metabolic diseases,* Vol. 4 (P. H. Forsham, ed.). *Ciba Collection of Medical Illustration by F. H. Netter, M.D.,* pp. 113–115.

Watzka, M. 1963. The normal development of the gonads and the genital tract. In *Intersexuality* (C. Overzier, ed.). Academic Press, New York, pp. 1–15.

Wilkins, L. 1950. *The Diagnosis and Treatment of Endocrine Disorders in Childhood and Adolescence.* Thomas, Springfield, Ill.

Witkin, H. A., H. F. Faterson, D. R. Goodenough, and J. Birnbaum. 1966. Cognitive patterning in mildly retarded boys. *Child. Develop.,* 37: 301–316.

Witschi, E., W. O. Nelson, and S. J. Segal. 1957. Genetic, developmental and hormonal aspects of gonadal dysgenesis and sex inversion in man. *J. Clin. Endocrinol. Metab.*, **17**: 737–753.

Young, W. C. 1961. The hormones and mating behavior. In *Sex and Internal Secretions* (W. C. Young, ed.). Williams & Wilkins, Baltimore, 3rd ed., pp. 1173–1239.

Young, W. C. 1965. The organization of sexual behavior by hormonal action during the prenatal and larval periods in vertebrates. In *Sex and Behavior* (F. A. Beach, ed.). Wiley, New York, pp. 89–107.

Young, W. C., R. W. Goy, and C. H. Phoenix. 1964. Hormones and sexual behavior. *Science*, **143**: 212–218.

Dinner

REPRODUCTION AND SEXUAL BEHAVIOR (M. Diamond ed.), 447, © Indiana University Press

26

Dinner Introduction

Milton Diamond

To recapture some of Bill Young the person, two individuals who, over the years, probably knew him better than any others have been asked to speak. Dr. Edward Dempsey had been associated with Dr. Young during his earliest profesional years and Dr. Paul G. Roofe had been closely associated with him during his last years.

REPRODUCTION AND SEXUAL BEHAVIOR (M. Diamond ed.), 449–452, © Indiana University Press

27

William Caldwell Young

Paul G. Roofe

Dr. Diamond, Mrs. Young, friends of Dr. Young, guests, and I almost said fellow Kansans—I look around and I see that we have a goodly number here.

It is really an honor to be selected to pay tribute to my former esteemed colleague, Dr. Young. When Dr. Diamond asked me to speak I was convinced that I would be much out of place, not being a member of this illustrious fraternal order of endocrinologists, but since I am a Kansan and Bill was at Kansas for a long time, I felt that it was quite appropriate that I should say a few words.

Clement Attlee, the late prime minister of Great Britain, making a speech at the University of Kansas several years ago, remarked that his friends called him an elder statesman. Attlee replied that he was just an old politician. Tonight I am not a politician; I am just an old anatomist, a remnant of two departments. From Louisville, my former colleagues there are no longer with us. At Kansas, Professors Henry C. Tracy and Homer B. Latimer are no longer among us. In paying honor to Dr. William C. Young, I feel it is an obligation to mention these men who have preceded us and made it in a sense possible for Dr. Young to carry on so brilliantly and effectively at our institution. Dr. Tracy and especially Homer Latimer, worked very closely with our esteemed friend and colleague, Bill. Dr. Latimer was invited to come into the Endocrine Laboratory and

449

played a prominent role in Dr. Young's career at Kansas, especially aiding him in his analysis of statistical data.

I had known Bill for almost forty years. As a graduate student at the University of Chicago he was rooming at Meadville House at 57th and Woodlawn Avenue where I was enrolled as a theological student. I can now remember how intense an interest he took in his research work. This made a truly lasting impression on me.

I did not see Bill for 10 more years until I met him in Durham, North Carolina, when the Anatomists were meeting in 1937. It was almost another ten years before I personally made contact with him. This was shortly after the close of World War II. I was desperately seeking help to staff our department at Kansas. I wrote Bill at Cedar Crest College, Allentown, Pennsylvania, and asked him if he could recommend someone to come to Lawrence. Bill phoned me and said he himself was interested. This was a most fortunate turn of events. My association with him for 17 years was one of the most pleasant mutual relationships that I have had. He was anxious to establish a good guinea pig colony. He set up shop in an almost inaccessible spot in an old geology building which the Department of Anatomy occupied. However, this was not for long. Due to his intense drive and his persuasiveness he established two outstanding strains of guinea pigs in an old Army barracks which he had secured and moved from an Army post. Those of you who knew Dr. Young know that when he set his mind on something he went for it until he got it. The administration was slightly reluctant about moving an Army barracks to the campus of Kansas but Bill Young saw in it a wonderful opportunity and somehow, someway, the details of which I have forgotten, the barracks were erected and the Endocrine Laboratory was established. It was all due to the hard-working endeavor and insightful activity of Bill Young.

Most of you are aware of the outcome in truly epic-making papers derived from the sexually low and high drive strains which he established in this laboratory. It was the work of W. C. Young which, in a major way, permitted the Department of Anatomy to go forward in research and in good teaching. It was Dr. Young's ability to get good students, to some of whom I am now speaking, that made the Kansas scene in anatomy a success. One of Bill's outstanding attributes was his insistence on good scholarship.

Dr. Young established two outstanding courses at the University of Kansas. These he liked to teach. One he called, "The Endocrines and Behavior" and the other, "The Biology of the Endocrines." The former spearheaded a new discipline entitled "Animal Behavior," now supervised by many departments, including entomology, zoology, psychology, and anatomy.

In another area, it seems appropriate to quote a statement that Dr. Young made in paying tribute to a colleague and former scientist, Dr. Edgar Allen, editor of the first edition of *Sex and Internal Secretions.* Dr. Young wrote, "Understandably, this work is the most permanent and tangible memorial to him." It is with sincerity we can say that the third edition on which Bill worked for the greater part of two years also is a tangible memorial to its editor. He gave encouragement by letters and conferences to the 27 contributors which resulted in an outstanding book, and many of you here tonight are contributors to that book. It must be added that Dr. Young is the author of two chapters in this: "The Mammalian Ovary" and "Hormones and Mating Behavior."

His association of 17 years with the Department of Anatomy at the University of Kansas School of Medicine resulted in great productivity. Thirteen graduate students received the Doctor of Philosophy degree while he was there. During his years at Brown University he initiated new techniques of laboratory procedure relative to the study of sexual behavior in rat and guinea pigs. His students have contributed much to the field of biology and medicine as well as holding prominent positions in research and administration.

One cannot give an account of the work of Dr. Young in its entirety. It is impossible for us to do so but one can safely predict that many of his ideas will generate further investigation. His contributions to the histology of the reproductive tracts are basic. His electron microscopic study of the ductuli efferentes and the rete testis of the guinea pig with A. J. Ladman gives considerable evidence of his intense concern with basic problems. Of major significance are his studies, assisted by Drs. Robert Goy and Charles Phoenix, on induced hormonal effects during pregnancy in the guinea pig which have had a bearing on the sexual behavior of the offspring. We have already heard this afternoon that this particular study is being pursued with vigor on the primates at the Regional Primate Center in Oregon. The many scientific papers that composed his bibliography are evidence of the richness of his productive years. More than one half originated from the investigation carried on at the University of Kansas.

A brief personal biography reveals his intense interest in science. He was born September 8, 1899, in Chicago and received his A.B. in 1921 and his A.M. in 1925 at Amherst, in biology. He received his Ph.D. from the University of Chicago in 1927 with Dr. Carl Moore of the Department of Zoology. His thesis dealt with the environmental effect upon the testis of the guinea pig. Quite happily he combined teaching with research in several institutions. Beginning as an Assistant at the University of Chicago, 1927 to 1928, he accepted an Instructorship at Brown, from 1928 to 1931 and remained an Assistant Professor from 1932 to 1939. He was an Associate Professor of Primate Biology at Yale from 1939 to 1941. For a period of two years he was a Professor of Biology at Cedar Crest College at Allentown, Pennsylvania. In 1946 he was appointed Associate Professor of Anatomy at the University of Kansas. He gained the rank of full Professor in 1948.

Dr. Young gave freely of his time and talents. His interest in the scientific community is attested to by his membership in many professional organizations; naming only a few: American Association for Advancement of Science, American Association of Anatomists, American Society of Zoologists, and the Endocrine Society. The Jake Gimbel Lecture of the University of California and the Howard Crosby Warren Award offered by the Society of the Experimental Psychologists are representative of the professional honors he received. His son, Malcolm, told me that his father was probably as proud of this latter award as any he had ever received. Some fellowships that he held were the National Research Council Fellow, Frieburg, Germany, from 1931 to 1932; Yale University Honorary Fellow School of Medicine, 1937 to 1948; Population Council Fellow, 1956 to 1957.

Dr. Young had a wide range of interests outside his professional field. These included nature trips, camping, theater, and art in many forms. Plant ecology was an interest dominant in many of his hikes over the terrain of Kansas. Another hobby in which he had an extreme interest was railroading. It held a fascination for Bill. He had a large collection of time tables of railroads from very early times beautifully housed and catalogued.

In summing up his attitude toward life, I can say that his philosophy was one, not of being, but of becoming; not of life, but of living.

REPRODUCTION AND SEXUAL BEHAVIOR (M. Diamond ed.), 453–458, © Indiana University Press

28

William Caldwell Young
An Appreciation

Edward W. Dempsey

This is a bittersweet occasion. Tonight, as happens too often as one grows older, pleasure and pain are intermingled. It is a sorrowful time because Dr. Young is not here to share it with us as originally planned, but it is joyful too because we are gathered together to honor the man whose thoughts and actions have touched all our lives.

Dr. Young was born just as the nineteenth century was ending, and he lived during the fabulous era which began with the twentieth. Merely to survive intellectually has been a feat in itself, but to participate in leading the thoughts of the last several decades has been an achievement indeed.

A backward look, indeed only a glance, will show in high relief some of the changes which make today so different from yesterday. Dr. Young became, at birth, one of the 75 million people then living in the United States; today we have more than 196 million and will pass the 200 million mark before the end of this decade. In 1900 there were fewer than 14 million married women in the United States; today there are about 45 million, and more than half of them are of reproductive age. Can anyone doubt, considering these figures, that sex research is important?

With the increase in population there has occurred, *pari passu*, growth of our economy, improvement of our health, and enhancement of our expectations. In current prices, the gross national product was $17 million in the year Dr. Young was born; it was $90 million when he graduated from college and today is well over $700 million and growing rapidly. Life expectancy at birth was 47 years in 1900; today it is over 70. Dr. Young became one of 60,000 students who received an A.B. degree in 1921 and one of 1400 who earned a doctorate in 1927. According to the latest accounts, there are now about seven times as many baccalaureates and more than ten times as many doctorates awarded annually.

And so, along with our economy, our educational world has grown, too. With its new dimensions, it has become more diverse; with its increased numbers, new fields and subfields have yielded to intensive investigation. The obscurity of ignorance and the murk of prejudice have been replaced, at least in part, by a clarity of understanding resulting from dispassionate, objective study. Perhaps no field has undergone more recent and rapid changes than has sex research, particularly research on sex behavior.

In this brief moment tonight, I shall attempt to relate Dr. Young's life and activities to the times in which he lived; only from their beginning moments are events significant; only if reactions occur are actions effective; only as we were drawn into a common purpose did Dr. Young influence our lives; and only as the occasion permits can we, in turn, weave the woof of our attitudes into the warp of circumstances and so further the continuum.

Aberle and Corner, in their history of the National Research Council Committee for Research in Problems of Sex, call attention to the long-standing aversion in our culture to the open consideration of sex matters. They point out that the association of scholarship and theology, the tradition whereby education and research have been carried on largely in a celibate church, led to a view that sex should be viewed in reference to established codes, not as a natural phenomenon suitable for detached investigation. They go on to say that it may now seem incredible that a great deal of courage was required for a group of professional biologists to organize a committee for research on the problems of sex. But yet, it did, in the year 1921, the year Dr. Young graduated from Amherst.

A few American investigators, building on the work of European predecessors, were carrying on, successfully, studies related to reproduction. Franklin P. Mall, Leo Loeb, Charles Stockard, and Frank

Lillie were intellectually prepared to relate human sex behavior to the same chemical, physical, and psychological factors which influence other kinds of behavior and which control the actions of lower forms. They and others, after initial rebuffs, finally prevailed upon the National Research Council to set up the Committee on Sex; they secured the financial support on which the Committee functioned; and they launched, tentatively, the grant-in-aid program which was to become a model for the support of biological research. In the early years, among others who received support, were Edgar Allen, Herbert M. Evans, Frederick Hisaw, Karl Lashley, Frank R. Lillie, Adolph Meyer, Theophilus Painter, Philip E. Smith, and Calvin P. Stone. And in 1927, an indirect beneficiary of the grant to Lillie, Dr. Young received his Ph.D. from the University of Chicago.

The program outlined by F. R. Lillie as a guide for the Committee and the problems worked on by Dr. Young show many parallels. The Committee, understanding clearly the need to create a climate in which sex research could be prosecuted with dignity, undertook studies first in the basic biology of sex. Dr. Young's early work was upon factors influencing the maturation of spermatozoa in the testis, the ductuli efferentes, and in the epididymis. Later, the Committee undertook to support descriptive and experimental studies of sex behavior in laboratory animals. Dr. Young's descriptive account of estrus behavior in the guinea pig began in 1932 and was followed by the experimental induction of estrus in 1936. Once a sound and respectable basis had been established using laboratory animals, the Committee supported investigations of primate behavior; Dr. Young joined the Yerkes Laboratory in 1939, where chimpanzees and other primates were available. From then on he vacillated between his first love, the guinea pig, at Kansas and the alluring primate siren at the center in Oregon.

There were, then, parallels between Dr. Young's work and the principles guiding the Committee on Sex. But Young's laboratory was by no means imitative—it created its own methods and made major advances in its own right. By defining rigidly specified end points, it pioneered in teamwork so that several persons could collaborate, and so that sex behavior could be observed around the clock for months on end. Such observations established many degrees of variation in estrus behavior in the guinea pig; they led directly to the discovery that progesterone as well as estrogen was involved in sex behavior; they furnished the basis whereby it was possible to delay estrus and inhibit ovulation and so to set the stage for development of the contraceptive pill; and they launched an intensive search for the factors responsible for variations in length, intensity, and other qualities of normal and abnormal estrus.

In searching for a term to describe Dr. Young's most characteristic quality—the one making the greatest impact on all of us—I concluded finally that the word was persistence. The man never gave up—nor would he let any of us, his students, give up either! His congenital myopathy, whatever private griefs it may have caused him, never prevented his working as hard as any of us. His singlemindedness sustained him through the discomfort of radiation sickness— the only comment about it he ever voiced to me was that the heat of a Kansas summer made the drive home after a treatment difficult.

Two stories perhaps illustrate this quality of persistence, and of its undeviating impact on all of us. Once, at a critical time both in our experiments and in our application for funds, Dr. Young drove to Washington to attend the AAAS midwinter meeting. On the way back, he became ill, in a little town in New Jersey; he sought out a doctor and before he quite knew what had happened to him, he found himself in an isolation ward in an Elizabeth, N.J., hospital with a diagnosis of scarlet fever. He insisted that he should return to Providence; they insisted that he was a public health menace. He insisted that he must write instructions to Hugh Myers and me; they insisted that nothing could leave his room without its being sterilized. After what must have been an epic discussion, a solution was found—he could write on postcards, which would then be autoclaved. Whereupon, Myers and I began to get batches of serially numbered postcards. Some days the haul would be as many as 15 or 20, but not all would be from the same clutch. All of you have had experience with Dr. Young's handwriting, but have you ever tried to decipher it on wrinkled, water-stained postcards, each of which seemed out of context with all the others? Anyway, we tried, and in the middle of all this, Warren Weaver of the Rockefeller Foundation arrived to make what we would now call a project site visit. As a lowly graduate student, Weaver, to me, was a figure only imperceptibly less formidable than God. But, there was no ducking the problem, Weaver was there; what I had deciphered from the postcards made it unmistakable that I was expected to tell him what we were doing; another dimension of the problem was that if the grant were forthcoming, the part of it budgeted to pay me would permit my getting married (remember, this was in the midst of the depression!), and so, altogether, Dr. Young's persistence made quite an impression on me. Incidentally, I must have comprehended some of the hieroglyphics since we did get the grant!

The other story covers a longer period, is less dramatic, but much more consequential even than my getting married. Impressed with the variability of estrus behavior, we had thought originally that it might be correlated with the condition or number of ovarian follicles. After serially sectioning and studying literally hundreds of ovaries from animals with known behavioral records, it became clear that there was no correlation between the length or intensity of estrus and any observable condition of the ovaries. Hence it was postulated that an extraovarian factor must exist and must vary commensurately with the variation in behavior. At first we thought it likely this was a pituitary factor, and some evidence implicated the then poorly understood luteinizing hormone. However, this approach proved futile, whereas injections of estrogen and progesterone (Theelin and Proluton, in those days) unfailingly evoked estrus in ovariectomized females.

At this point I lost interest in the extraovarian factor. It seemed to me that the variations in behavior would likely find explanation in alterations of hormone metabolism or secretion. Moreover, with the implications of progesterone in causing estrus behavior, I thought we had possibly erred in thinking of an extraovarian factor; more probably, extrafollicular was a more exact term. At any rate, my own fortunes led me to Harvard, while Dr. Young and the rest of his group went first to Yale and then he to Orange Park. Years later, and after various excursions into primate studies, Dr. Young returned to the puzzling problem of why one animal consistently behaved differently from another, regardless of endocrine status. The solution finally emerged that both environmental isolation and deprivation as well as early endocrine exposures could modify an animal's later responsiveness to sexual stimuli. In the long run this work, carried on by many of you here tonight, may well provide the experimental basis for the socially most important sex research of our generation.

Merely to survive intellectually in this century has been a feat in itself; to participate actively in leading the thoughts of the last several decades has been an achievement indeed. Dr. Young *did* survive, against great handicaps. He *did* participate in discoveries which have altered all our attitudes. He *did* affect us all, by example and by precept. His influence continues in us, through the work we do and in the examples we set.

John Donne alluded to the indestructibility of ideas and concepts in his Sonnet on Death.

"Death be not proud, though some have called thee
Mighty and dreadful, for thou are not so;
For those whom thou think'st thou dost overthrow
Die not, poor Death; nor yet can'st thou kill me."

We are gathered together to honor Dr. Young—a man who has touched all our lives. And yet, we cannot bring honor to him by ceremony. His were achievements which brought honor to us all; we must so act that, in time and in turn, we will affect others as he affected us.

Hail and Farewell!

Afterword

REPRODUCTION AND SEXUAL BEHAVIOR (M. Diamond ed.), 461–479, © Indiana University Press

29

Perspectives in Reproduction and Sexual Behavior: An Afterword

Milton Diamond

There may be some value in a long gestation for a book as for an individual. First, the resulting offspring usually is more viable at birth and, second, the father has more time to contemplate the conception, morphogenesis, and future. While we will all judge this book's viability for ourselves, it may be fruitful to share some of my contemplations.

The selection of any set of contributors to a book or symposium, of necessity, involves a prejudicial process. My biases were admittedly multifaceted. Over all, an attempt was made to select investigators that would provide, first and foremost, work or an approach among the salient areas of development in reproduction and sexual behavior, and which could be considered significant in expanding horizons of study or serving as points of departure for future work. Further, the implicit intention was to present in addition to basic research data, material which would be projective or even speculative and thus not overly diminished by the time span of a few years. This selection wasn't simply a matter of choosing topics and then selecting suitable authors, or choosing the authors and leaving the topics open. An interplay of both was involved. For the program participants, also considered was the relationship of the investigator, or his work, to that of William C. Young, those considered closely aligned getting the first available spots. For the volume, however, no such restriction was imposed. To all these criteria of mine were added the predispositions and personal bent of each contributor. The resulting publication is thus, despite all initial resolve, the sum of all these parts. Dealing primarily with what we have rather than what we might have had, the following insight is offered.

Many of the investigators selected could equally as well have been requested (although they may not have been so willing) to write on other topics being handled in the volume. This capacity which at first seemed remarkable, turned out on closer consideration to be a matter of necessity for the researcher and is in itself testimony to the broad yet interwoven applicability of much herein. For the field of reproduction and sexual behavior an expert in one particular area is ever finding himself wed to developments and advancements in other areas of the overall field. Very narrow specialists are rare. Bibliographies to practically all the papers contain references to work by several of the volume's contributors and it should simultaneously be noted that more than half have themselves written or edited books covering many categories in this field. The import of this becomes more readily appreciated when it is realized that the organization of specialties within the study of reproduction are arbitrary and often encompass wide latitudes. For example, one who wishes to keep thoroughly abreast of developments and theories of ovulation and menstruation keeps abreast as well with related theories of estrogen and progesterone action. Similarly, one who tries to understand the influences of neonatal or prenatal endocrines on adult behavior must know about hypothalamic differentiation, and to fully appreciate brain–pituitary–gonad interactions, one must understand the basic parameters of brain investigation techniques. Many more cross-author (cross-chapter) links can be listed and are evidence of this overlapping interest. In this vein it is probably safe to say that each contribution interacts and has value and context with others presented, although the chapter titles may at first glance indicate otherwise. For the reader who approaches this volume via one particular chapter further reading is thus encouraged. This overall selection of papers should, it is hoped, signal increased breadth to the research encompassed by studies in reproduction and sexual behavior. Significantly, aspects of basic molecular endocrinology and enzymology are seen linked to features of molar behavior and physiological processes are inexorably related to entities as seemingly divergent as season, experience, and genetics. To researchers caught in the bind of already having too much to master in their immediate area, this may serve as a necessary stimulus (or threat) to at least maintain an acquaintance with developments in related peripheral areas.

Definitions

Included and considered not only appropriate but necessary for representative coverage are works related to themes which, to some, may appear quite diverse and unrelated or of little importance. Criticisms may occur for the choice of areas emphasized as well as those excluded. This is probably inevitable and perhaps warranted. What will be reemphasized thereby is that the borders used to delimit the area of "necessary" coverage are amorphous or nonexistent. (It also parenthetically reflects, to some extent, those fields which are getting the most encouragement, and those which have sufficient numbers of qualified investigators so that marked developments plus suitable *and available* authors could be found). On a most basic level, it may be easier to state that the fundamental themes of reproduction and sexual behavior are different entities than to find the dividing line between them or their conjoined boundaries. At one time refuge was sought by claiming that sexual behavior could occur without reproduction but not vice versa. The use of artificial insemination and ova transplants, however, quickly show this futile. In addition, one cannot fully argue against the "expressed desire to reproduce" by a woman, even via artificial insemination, being a manifestation of sexual behavior! I will defend the absence of a firm definition for these basic terms by claiming that this would limit our area of purview and be unduly restrictive; any loose definition would be too vague to be useful.

The difficulty in selecting acceptable definitions for the broad categories and areas exist as well for all operational terms. This is probably no more or less true for reproduction and sexual behavior than for any other discipline, but the remainder is timely. As is so often the case, frequent use of certain words lead to a sense of security with their meaning and the fact that they are being used as jargon is lost. Jargon has its place when terms are operationally defined and is defendable as being communicative to all those using the terms. Professional isolation or parochialism, however, perpetuates the use of idioms without their concomitant limits or awareness that serious issue might be taken with "basic assumptions." Words represent ideas and ideas per se can become jargon, meaning different things to different people. One investigator's basic assumptions and obvious axioms are not necessarily held true by other investigators. Exposure of these differences alone should initiate a valuable dialogue. It is noteworthy and a mark of experience that in the course of elaborating on concepts most of the authors have taken care to define the terms they use, probably having met other acceptable definitions which are thus routinely anticipated.

We might consider some definitions our authors have chosen or assumed. Everett defines the pseudopregnant situation for the rat and mouse as a progra120 state primarily under the control of prolactin synthesis and release and indicates this gonadotropin's relationships with a functionally maintained corpus luteum, decidual reaction, and vaginal condition. The necessity for this extensive definition is justifiable and reinforced by Nalbandov et al.'s caveat that prolactin may be without effect on the extended life span of corpora lutea in species other than laboratory rodents and that distinction should be made between luteotropic and steroidogenic effects. With examples of clinical cases with which we can all readily identify, Noyes goes to great lengths to define various reproductive conditions usually considered only on the black or white basis of fertility versus sterility. With a novel twist for a scientist, he suggests we include with our definition of eufertility a value judgment which may fluctuate depending upon whether it is society's or the individuals' values that are adhered to, and would "include the needs of the race as well as the individual."

Some terms, however, have not been defined but assumed understood by past repeated usage and general acceptance. Unfortunately, these words may have acquired connotations which are not universally accepted. For example, Masters and Johnson discuss the sexually "inadequate" couple. Impotence, frigidity, and premature ejaculation are considered as detrimental clinical conditions which the "inadequate" couple wants to change. While definitely advocating and agreeing with giving aid to those seeking help, we may simultaneously conceive that for some couples active sexual relations may be undesirable or harmful. Behavioral treatment processes for such individuals may beneficially *impose* impotence or frigidity. "Inadequacy" then, just as sterility, may be advantageous or desirable for some couples.

Intuitive assignments or normal and abnormal and natural and unnatural are ever with us; perhaps more so with sexual behavior studies than in others. For studying nonbehavioral reproductive processes and mechanisms investigators may proceed relatively unhindered by personal value commitments to the outcome of the work as well as its mode of investigation. Not only can all phases of contraception be examined but lately even abortificants for all stages of pregnancy are receiving attention and study. Although adverse pressure indeed comes from some quarters, e.g., religious, this too is rapidly changing. Encouragement for study, on the other hand, is heard from groups as divergent as farmers and breeders interested in the economic fall-out of such work, clinicians and patients faced with an undesirable situation, and demographers and eugenicists concerned with the future of mankind. This enviable situation is reflected in the comparative availability of funds for studies of even small links in the chain of reproduction. It must be said that the freedom was hard won transcending many taboos and cultural injunctions.

Studies of sexual behavior regrettably are still a long way from such free and open inquiry, not only among the laity but among professional personnel as well. Conditioned by society's injunctions or previous scientific training we may each have to watch the intuitions and taboos within ourselves. Consider the following: Beach has examined mounting phenomenon both as a male and as a female characteristic. In practically all species studied both sexes display the patterns not only heterosexually but homosexually. Yet many of our colleagues, academic as well as clinical, professional as well as lay, will persist in considering this behavior abnormal for a female, particularly in regard to analogous behaviors seen in the human. As suggested by Beach, Whalen, Phoenix et al., and myself in this volume, we might think of male–female behavior differences in terms of relative frequencies: i.e., males usually mount females more often than females mount females and females lordose more often than males, but females may mount females and males may lordose. Aronson and Cooper have reported how season and peripheral sensitivities may interact to effect male mating performance in the cat. Yet the claim is still often voiced that males are always "ever-ready." Undoubtedly, for the male as for the female, consideration must be given to multiple peripheral and external factors of which we are only slowly becoming aware. Bronson has indicated how urinary phermones effect estrous and nidation in the female mouse. Can we still persist in considering the estrous cycle or implantation as relatively inviolate? Whalen reviewed the effect of neonatal hormone treatment for rats; Phoenix, Goy, and Resko discussed prenatal endocrine effects on primates; and I presented some comparable material for humans. The reviews seem to leave no doubt that pre- or neonatal endocrine conditions can structure adult sexual behavior. Yet many will still deny the probability that humans too may be so effected. Obviously the more we learn the more we can, and probably should reexamine basic concepts, intuitions, and ideas long considered axiomatic.

Comparative Studies

One plea is repeatedly voiced or intimated by our authors, be they primarily biochemists, morphologists, endocrinologists, or behaviorists—more comparative information from diverse species is needed before generally applicable laws or axioms in reproduction or sexual behavior can be validly formulated. Comparisons are sought at every level of the reproductive process from biochemical to behavioral. From comparative data, Hafez probes the working of uterine enzyme systems while Villee and Williams-Ashman and Shimazaki study mechanisms of hormone action. From different species Cole asks how the gonadotropins function, Zarrow et al. study the role of progesterone in reproduction, and Nalbandov et al. question how corpora lutea are maintained. Bronson checks strain and specie differences in vaginal cycles and olfactory responses, and Beach looks at comparative mounting behavior. With increasing cross-specie comparisons, all preach caution in generalizing from species to species without adequate data. Mossman beautifully demonstrates diversity with such (who can yet really say extreme) examples as the elephant shrew, which ovulates an average of sixty eggs yet only implants two, and the human, which ovulates and implants only one. Which should we take as our model? Are we justified in taking the rat as our universal standard just because we probably know most about this species? Information being garnered from others indicates we may, with increased knowledge, select as a model species one with reproductive processes more consistent with different norms.

From various animal groups the distilled similarities and uniformities will provide us with the most applicable guides. The moral then is clear—we need more data from more species. The frequent repetition of this theme is a loud admission of ignorance from those best qualified to profess knowledge. Even more significant is the fact that this cry has repeatedly been voiced for some time now. Beach in 1950 (*American Psychologist,* **5:** 115–124) wrote a classical paper on this topic particularly pertinent to behavior and Mossman in 1945 with Hamilton and Boyd incorporated this thesis in the text *Human Embryology.* Why hasn't the cry been answered? Why the species gap? Somehow relative scientific values considered in terms of return for investment of time, effort, and funds seems to enter here. Interspecific differences are often seen as a deterrent to further research rather than a stimulus. Is it "better" to find out more about the reproductive process in one species or more about a particular phase in several species? Would a comparative study of ovulation in the mongoose, bat, and porpoise (all mammals), or the chicken, turtle, and camel (all vertebrates) return as much information as readily as an in-depth study of ovulation in any one species? Since most investigators do not do comparative work, the answer to these types of questions would appear to be negative. But this may be a function of lack of facilities, lack of peripherally related information, and general reluctance to run the gamut of non-problem-related complications which this type of study entails. It may also reflect the biases of funding agencies to "keep to proven paths."

Distilled from the pleas described above and the actual work of many of our authors, however, is the suggestion that compiling and working with comparative data rather than being scientific-dilettantism may actually lead to the core of some of the presently most vexing enigmas. Further, an intriguing set of additional problems are thus set for unveiling and interpretation, e.g., differences and similarities between reproduction in induced and spontaneous ovulators, short- and long-lived species, seasonal and perennial breeders, domestic and wild animals, nocturnal and diurnal species, and so forth.

A Model System

Several authors indicate that for their particular subjects much information but little knowledge exists. Simultaneously encyclopedic reviews or experiment oriented papers without extensive extrapolations or general statements are included in the volume. Nevertheless, the preceding chapters do record notable advances in our knowledge. This is especially obvious if we, for certain points, synthesize the enumerated factors to be considered for total appreciation and selectively incorporate negative information as well. In the main, optimism rather than pessimism should prevail. For example, a good deal of attention has been focused on the interplay of the hypothalamus, pituitary, gonads, and end organs as related to reproduction and sexual behavior. Consider how practically every author has presented some new insight or material pertinent to mechanisms which serve to regulate these physiological or behavioral processes. With primary emphasis on the role of the brain, Sawyer devotes his whole chapter to this problem of feedback mechanisms. The synthesis and release of pituitary gonadotropins is reviewed as controlled by the action of target-organ gonadal steroids working via direct influences on hypothalamic and hypophyseal centers. With experimental evidence from brain and pituitary steroid implants, electrical lesioning or recording, both positive and negative feedback influences are presented. In addition, indications are given that we must also consider an internal "short-loop" direct feedback action of LH on the hypothalamus which is independent of its influence on classical target organs.

Everett in his discussion of "delayed pseudopregnancy" characterizes many of the endocrine and neural interactions pertinent to this subject but significantly contributes to the overall picture of "feedback" by emphasizing what we can term a "long-loop" circuit. This is manifest by stimuli, copulatory or experimental, which are otherwise neutral in immediate endocrine effects but can set in motion reproductive events that lead to activation of corpora lutea at some later time.

Nalbandov, Keyes, and Niswender, without using the expression "feedback," discuss such factors in the regulation, function, and maintenance of corpora lutea. With particular emphasis on the gonadotropins, they show by comparative data that we need consider not only the biochemical nature of the tropic substance but its mode of and signal for release. They emphasize in this regard that special distinction need be given to whether the sex steroids themselves and the gonadotropins are acting as steroidogenic or luteotropic agents.

Scharrrer adds to our knowledge of feedback at the crucial linkage points of the nervous and endocrine systems. The separation of the systems may facilitate some studies, but the classical dichotomy is seen here as anachronistic. She places particular focus on dual-capacity neurons, i.e., those "cells that are capable of receiving nervous stimuli and of dispatching hormonal messages to endocrine centers." This type of integrative system is of significance not only in reproduction and reproductive behavior but is of concern to behaviorists of all stripes. (The interaction of the nervous and endocrine systems now taken so much for granted in endocrine studies is without a doubt among the most significant relationships crucial not only in understanding reproduction but in fully comprehending how an organism can respond to his environment. For all biologists and psychologists it provides a link for unifying external events with internal processes. For behaviorists the ramifications for understanding other physiologic-psychologic processes are rapidly becoming better appreciated.) Catecholamines are also discussed by Scharrer (and Whalen as well) as representing another category of neurosecretory hormones whose role in reproductive processes and control is yet to be fully realized and demands further study.

While the authors mentioned have probed what may be happening within the brain, Lisk contributes considerably to our knowledge on feedback systems by detailing the techniques available for further studying exactly where within the brain neural centers for the control of these phenomena may be localized.

"Control" at the target organ is stressed by such authors as Cole, Reynolds, and Mossman. These investigators provide data and questions pertinent to uterine and ovarian function and embryo–mother relations as well. Questions are posed in regard to the threshold levels of PMS needed to maintain pregnancy in the mare, the stimulus for estrogen on progesterone production by follicular cells, the functional relation of the uterine cervical ganglion to parturition, and the *absence* of feedback manifest by a nonallergic response between mother and embryo.

Pincus and Dorfman and Rooks are obviously concerned with feedback mechanisms, since the most promising contraceptive measures they mention other than via physical barriers work via alteration in one or another physiological control system. The various contraceptive pills and steroid preparations obviously fall in this category but the IUD too probably works by altering a normal feedback chain.

Hafez, Villee, Bishop, Williams-Ashman, and Shimazaki contribute to understanding control process from a molecular and biochemical viewpoint. Not only are the active moieties, be they enzymes or hormones, to be considered, but so too are the substrate or receptor sites, which themselves may be active or passive. These studies point up the very probable situation that at this ultramicroscopic level a multiplicity of feedback types may need be considered rather than an inclusive all-purpose control.

In contrast with the work and authors discussed above which may be considered to relate to feedback problems as more classically viewed in endocrinology, the following authors contribute insights on regulatory mechanisms from a behavioral perspective.

Aronson and Cooper review central mechanisms pertinent to arousal and sexual performance and bring special attention and stress to peripheral factors which mediate copulation. Not only are genital sensory stimuli per se seen to be crucial, but they are seen to interact with internal rhythms and seasons of the year. In this particular instance, however, the oddity is that the relation is more highly correlated in the desensitized males. In normal males the penile feedback is capable of overriding seasonal influences which tend to decrease sexual behavior.

Beach reviews various factors, internal and external, which are involved in mounting behavior by female mammals and stresses how species differences, even within the same order, are seen to be crucial considerations. Guinea pigs and rats, for instance, differ in their mounting responses to estrous and nonestrous stimuli females. Bronson shows that not only species but strains within a species may vary in sensitivity to various feedback factors. Witness his forceful demonstration that the innate estrous cycles of the C57 BL/6J and 129/J mice are mediated differently by male urine.

And it is now recognized from the work reviewed by Whalen, Phoenix et al., and myself that the various control systems involved both in reproduction and sexual behavior, at neural and endocrine responsive end-organ levels as well, may be organized pre- or neonatally to bias the feedback regulatory mechanisms seen in the adult and that this bias may be experimentally or naturally induced. With data from rodents, primates, and humans, we are in an enviable situation of having cross-species data which appears consistent in support of an endocrine-influenced developmental theory relative to the ontogeny of sexual phenotypes, mammalian sexual behavior, and reproductive conditions.

By amalgamating most of the above considerations, we came upon a view (Fig. 1) of the individual being subject to internal and external feedback factors which are responsive to stimuli at all levels. For some readers the figure may appear too general to be of use. To others, however, it will provide a clearer view of the complexities involved and possibly serve as a model for understanding other highly integrated disciplines. Certainly if nothing else, the figure emphasizes how an interdisciplinary view of a problem may indicate crucial factors for consideration. The total picture of this puzzle still lacks definition, but pieces are constantly being added and the outlines are being clarified.

We can repeat then that, for reproduction in general, optimism rather than pessimism is warranted. Basically we now know that in regard to physiologic as well as behavioral processes species may be expected to vary. These differences may exist in the biochemical and physiological mechanisms of related gonadotropin, steroid and enzyme actions. We now know that seasonal, situational, and peripheral conditions as well as tonic, genetic, and central phenomenon may influence reproductive and behavioral processes. Equally of importance we now have defined much of what we still need to know and

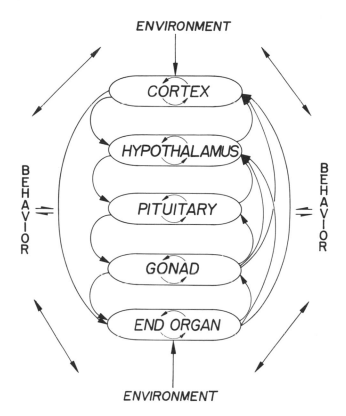

Fig. 1   Feedback paths in reproduction and sexual behavior. The arrows represent established routes of interaction.

most important we now know that the solution to problems in an area of physiology may provide the answers needed in an area of behavior and vice versa. Lest these be taken as inconsequential advances or banal truisms, reflect for a moment on the available data and relative status as a discipline of any other interacting biologic process and behavior pattern, e.g. the autonomic-adrenal system and aggression or the digestive system and feeding or drinking behavior. No other comparable discipline seems so well situated. (This may be an appropriate point to advocate the formation of a distinct discipline of Sexology and restore to good graces the title of avocation "sexologist.")

It is obvious that the hypothetical dichotomy between molar and molecular as bad versus good science is within a volume such as this more than amply dispelled for the study of reproduction. Discussions of mounting phenomena or mechanisms of sexual arousal or theories or molecular and enzyme action are equally scientific, basic, and valuable. Research on the degeneration and regeneration of the dorsal nerve of the penis is on a par with studies of seasonal variation in libido. And the comprehension of neurosecretory cell mechanisms is a challenge which only in technique and interest differs from the intellectual and scientific processes involved in analyzing problems in sex-role ontogeny or the methods by which homosexuals cope with their problems in society. The comprehension and appreciation of phermonal mechanisms requires equal parts of behavior study and biochemical procedures. The role of progesterone is analyzed as a behavior-mediating, physiology-mediating, or molecular-activity-mediating hormone, and the actual biochemical structure of the androgen involved in sexual differentiation is being sought by the same individuals observing the behavior. Not only then do behaviorists and biochemists work on the same problem, but both molar and molecular problems are often studied simultaneously by the same behaviorists or biochemists.

Similarly, the line between pure and clinical research as good versus bad science is seen to be arbitrary when we realize how often they are the same, how much they interrelate, and how much we can learn from each about basic mechanisms. A great deal is seen exposed and in need of further clarification from the "applied" studies by Masters and Johnson on techniques for altering sexual behavior patterns, the contraceptive methods discussed by Pincus or Dorfman and Rooks, the considerations on fertility enumerated by Noyes, or any of the many programs mentioned by Gebhard.

For example, Masters and Johnson claim rapid success in altering basic behavior patterns which no doubt in many cases developed over several years. Surely this brings to question the learning process, role of reinforcement, and status of "insight" in altering supposedly intractable human behavior. In addition, it calls to question those portions of sex play and copulatory methods which might be reversible and those which might be irreversible. The report of Dorfman and Rooks most probably reflects on some of the gonadotropin control mechanisms discussed by Sawyer, Everett, and Whalen, but the mysterious actions of the IUD reawaken us to the fact that we still lack a full understanding of egg transport, implantation, and uterine physiology. And Gebhard, probably because he covers so many types of studies, in progress or needed, certainly links pure and clinical research in a multitude of areas. Indeed, it seems a poor value judgment that condemns a study just because the results or methods do or do not apply primarily to humans. Consider, as an example, that it is not only animal behaviorists but human behaviorists as well which attempt to distinguish and separate those mechanisms that arouse individuals to sexual behavior from those mechanisms actually used in the performance of the behavior. This dichotomy has taken on new emphasis in the human, but the associated parameters have been an active area of research in animal studies for some time now. In the past it was generally assumed that an individual once "aroused" would "act." As indicated by Gebhard, however, we still lack data on the arousability of even items such as hard-core pornography, and statistical correlation of this arousability with behavior is nonexistent. Nevertheless, this material is condemned. On the other hand, we also have scant knowledge of the effects of sex education programs, but these are highly touted and increasing in number and scope. Understanding of these clinical and social questions regarding sex will give us better insight to the basic mechanisms sought in the laboratory and may likely reveal processes we don't yet know exist. In addition, the laboratory findings will no doubt help provide practical clinical and social approaches now unthought of. Both are mutually contributory and scientifically informative.

Technique and Approach

The criteria for good versus bad or pure versus applied science should rest on approach and rigor rather than techniques and goals. If a study or question is pursued using faulty technique, it is bad, regardless of whether it uses observational criteria or a spectrophotometer. If a study has proper controls and well-defined parameters, it may be scientifically good whether the outcome will satisfy only curiosity or satisfy a need. The techniques used do not per se determine scientific value or validity.

A further word is in order with regard to techniques. The general approaches to endocrine, physiological, and biochemical processes of interest are basically classic and standard. Much value is seen in the repetition of crucial studies in several laboratories and the repeated use of standardized methods. Much of value has also come from the judicial selection or design of new or seemingly bizarre methods. Along with classic surgical techniques which are well represented, Nalbandov et al. utilize X rays for the selective destruction of ovarian follicles without loss of the luteal or interstitial tissue. Along with the tissue culture techniques, biochemical and histochemical methods used by Hafez, Villee, Bishop, and Williams-Ashman and

Shimazaki, single-cell investigation methods are used by Scharrer. But noticeably missing from any of our authors' experimental reports is one of the least appreciated techniques, which may, however, be the most rewarding—constant observation. It is assumed that statistically sampled observations are as valid a source of data as constant observation. One wonders, nevertheless, if Young and co-workers had taken that course if the nuances of guinea pig behavior and associated endocrine conditions would have revealed themselves as graphically. Dempsey thinks not and I would tend to agree.

Owing to the significance and presently extensive use of brain investigative procedures, Lisk had been asked to discuss this methodology specifically. He reveals mutiple uses of the various techniques and relates them to the types of information thereby obtainable. Sawyer and Everett in their chapters amply demonstrate the types of data garnered by such methods.

Techniques should be considered not only as modes of operation but also as modes of approaching and thinking about a problem. This recent focus on the nervous system and shift away from the reproductive organs per se is a sign that as a result of a "new technique" and new approach, yet unchartered areas for exploration and means of studying reproduction have been opened.

Several chapters adequately demonstrate how biochemical techniques play a role in understanding reproduction and sexual behavior by providing solutions to immediate problems. For example, Bronson can seek and find the urinary components which serve as sexual attractants or pregnancy blocks and Nalbandov et al. can more definitively probe which portion of a gonadotropin complex acts as a luteotropic agent. Exposure to the more general and more abstract biochemical theories and mechanisms, however, once unraveled, could eventually be infinitely more valuable by providing a new conceptual dimension—possibly sufficient enough to usher in a shift away from the present emphasis on the nervous system in reproduction studies. Several examples will make my meaning clear. When Everett talks of a long-delayed response, will studies show us that cellular biochemical reactions are taking place which may require this time and thus account for the delay or will the delay be found in extensive reverberating neural circuits? When Beach talks of species differences in mounting behavior, what portion of these differences are to be accounted for by *intra*neural or membranous biochemical events and which to *inter*neuronal arrangement? Will Bishop's ideas and techniques of biochemical "fingerprinting" be of use in answering these types of questions?

The fact that animals differ in hormone levels, as graphically mentioned by Cole, may not be an index of what the animal needs for efficient reproduction, but may reflect enzyme systems which nullify the differences by having the same turnover rates, or presenting a common limiting number of appropriate receptor sites; manifestation of the differences may similarly be restricted by the amount of preformed proteins available for mobilization at any one time.

And if a good number of contraceptive agents seem to depend for their efficacy on estrogens, is this related to the hormones effect to stimulate growth rates, alter processes, or initiate new reactions otherwise dormant or absent? While Phoenix et al. are concerned with whether testosterone or another metabolite is active at the differentiating tissues or I am in a quandary regarding the nature of F.M.T.S., it basically may be more significant to know if the "organization" to which we refer is encoded within a genome, is the expression of genes encoded in the mitochondrial or nuclear DNA or both, and whether the mitochondria and nuclei are independently regulated by the hormones. Further, it is highly significant to know "whether the molecular processes which underlie expression of the 'organizational' actions . . . be recapitulated whenever the 'activational' effects of these hormones take place."

The investigator who mentally synthesizes the molar questions being asked throughout the book with the molecular concepts and data presented, or possible of being extrapolated from the chapters with biochemical orientations, cannot help but be impressed with the possible theoretical implications not only for understanding reproductive processes but much in biology at large.

Predictably, as a technique and mental approach, behavioral methods will continue to expand their influence in providing new insight into reproductive processes at all levels. The methods used for behavioral analysis may seem less standard than those used in classical biology and deserve some special comment. In few areas does imagination in the development of new measures seem so rewarding and so ever present. Zarrow, Brody, and Denenberg evaluate the weight of nesting material used by a rabbit and the amount of loose hair picked up by combing. They find that these measures not only correlate with pregnancy, but are interrelated with survival of young. Aronson and Cooper record direction and physical approach of a male cat and find this related to his copulatory success and capable of telling us something significant about orienting mechanisms for coitus. Whalen reports on adult rat mating behavior correlated with a single neonatal steroid injection. Phoenix, Goy, and Resko record chases

and fights among monkeys and show that genetic females, if prenatally treated with androgen, will show prepubertal behavior more
like males than females. While the parameters of these test situations
might seem arbitrary, they are carefully chosen, stated, and controlled,
and interpretations made therefrom are cautiously offered. Each new
technique provides a means of asking a different and unique set of
questions and presents new perspectives for evaluating old questions.
While the results may be recorded in bizarre units, e.g., mounts, or
grams of wood shavings, for all biological disciplines, behavioral
studies are usually among the most stringent in the use of statistics.
The information finally gained is no less valuable to reproductive
studies than if garnered by more biologically "orthodox" ways. In
this regard, particular attention is called to the criteria for a 5-year
follow-up imposed by Masters and Johnson for judging treatment
efficacy. This is an exemplary caution, particularly for clinical behavior studies, and is the type of requirement which is long overdue.

Repository

Among the several suggestions of importance and applicability
to all reproductive scientists made by our authors, I would like to
single out and emphasize one. Mossman considers the wealth of
material routinely discarded by investigators themselves or at their
retirement or death and unused due to an institution's lack of storage
space and means for proper cataloging and distribution. All too often
an individual's life work and scientific collections are disposed of
while still capable of yielding valuable data and serving as fertile
source material. It would indeed seem a wise investment for an
agency, private, philanthropic, or governmental, to arrange for the
acquisitioning, accessioning, and use of such collections. There are
myriads of tissue specimens collected and preserved for one specific
analysis or question which are still good for various other types of
studies. Perhaps a repository for such material could be established
by the Public Health Service under the auspices of the National
Institute of Child Health and Human Development. There may even
be sufficient interest for a private institute to accept such collections.
Raw data of all sorts if properly identified may also be included with
the tissue collections, but if primarily of behavioral interest may be
collated at a separate institute. If drawn from and used, it is anticipated many dollars would be saved in nonduplication of these preparations or collection efforts and the service cannot help but provide
an inestimable saving in time. Particularly for those on low budgets

or with specific needs, original source material of an immense variety would thus be made available for study. With proper attention to credits where due, an individual may thus continue to reap scientific kudos even after death or retirement. This is indeed an idea worthy of consideration as donors to, users of, or custodians for such collections.

Philosophy and Prophesy

All contributors were encouraged to present crucial problems and questions in need of solution and express their impressions as to the significance, implications, and future for the findings they reviewed. The authors presented questions rather freely and repeatedly provided intriguing scientific challenges. I consider this one of the features of the book. On the other hand, not all the authors took the opportunity to prophesize or philosophize and few chose to openly speculate. This may be because it is naturally quite difficult to meaningfully forecast the future, but more likely it is because by training researchers are taught to be cautious; they know all too well that today's truths and theories often become tomorrow's fables, and they are conditioned by journal editors who tend to discourage philosophy and speculation in scientific reports. This conservatism is a necessity for accumulating reliable and consistent data and ensuring that hypotheses and constructs are not taken for fact. This same conservatism, however, becomes a liability for instigating original or new lines of research. Biology, as one of the oldest experimental sciences, rooted in the tradition of the laboratory and correctly eschewing theory without data, to my mind, suffers from this concomitant dirth of cogent speculation and freely offered hypothesis. Assuming that within any discipline those of its members best familiar with the field are most able to point the way for future directions and present lifetime challenges, it is imperative we not only give license to speculate with greater freedom but we encourage it. This increased freedom and responsibility must include the right to be wrong in presenting problems as significant, suggesting courses of action, or making predictions. The resulting occasionally misplaced efforts notwithstanding, it is anticipated that many years and tears of needlessly waiting for the proper zeitgeist would be thus bypassed. Taking this as a personal mandate, I here offer the following forecasts extrapolated from the writings and questions posed within the previous chapters and colored with my own perspective.

Direction, Scope, and Techniques

Reproduction studies, as all biology in general, will become increasingly dependent upon interdisciplinary behavioral, physiological, structural, and biochemical—and multilevel—molar and molecular—techniques for its significant developments. From the present emphasis on the role of the brain and its generalized control functions, effort will expand in three main directions. First, peripheral tissues and sensory mechanisms, spinal level processes, and the environment itself will be investigated to account for many of the individual variations seen. Simultaneously, evaluation of all processes will increase in scope longitudinally to consider differences throughout the individual's life and cross sectionally to consider changes during courtship, copulation, pregnancy, etc. Second, the organization of biochemical, physiological, and behavioral patterns from stimuli of any type, e.g., genetic, endocrine, or environmental, will be further explored. An ideal experiment soon will show how a crucial set of cells is altered (genetically?) to effect responses different from those seen without the stimuli. Not only prolonged exposures but even transient events, if severe enough, will prove able to serve as inducers or organizers for subsequent phenomena. Third, simple universal mechanisms of steroid and enzyme action as now conceived will continue to be sought but will not be found. Rather the various hormones and enzymes will be seen doing different things in different tissues, and these tissue-substance reactions might, as indicated above, vary with time, age and condition. Particular responses of particular tissues, even in mosaic patterns, will be recognized as controlling factors in hormone effiicacy. Significant advances in this particular area will come when either a new investigatory technique becomes available and perfected (X-ray diffraction analysis of molecular surfaces?) or a new type of mental synthesis is made of the already available data. It seems most likely that gene activity will be involved.

Attitudes

All parameters of human and animal sexual behavior and reproduction will get closer and more detailed scrutiny and all types of sexual practices will seem fit for study. Practices now publicly considered deviant or undesirable will be acceptable and some may even be advocated. Government will feel increasingly obligated rather than reluctant to probe these areas particularly in regard to the formulation of meaningful social and criminal legislation and the providing of optimum medical care.

With world conditions of war, poverty, slums, pollution, and other innumerable ills, the control of population growth will be of pivotal concern. This concern will ensure that funds for research at all levels will continue to proportionately increase. Sexual behavior, contraception, and family-planning methods will become amenable to both personal and social regulation. While the philosophers will ponder the appropriate values to accompany particular techniques, the public will demand access to them and society will encourage that some be used. Family planning will not always be left to individual families to plan and the state will increasingly be called upon to influence this now private matter.

Technical and scientific problems aside, the future is already upon us with enormous ethical and social problems with which we all will be involved by virtue of professional interests if not by personal concern. The resolutely accelerating glacial movement of population is fast becoming a torrential river, and individuals are more and more concerned with controlling, increasing or decreasing, the size of their families, herds, or pests. And while limiting production of some species, on the one hand, we may, on the other hand, find greater need for forestalling the extinction of other species (including our own) and increasing reproductive efficiency despite enormous changes in the micro and macroenvironment. Knowledge of every phase of the reproductive process will help in augmenting whatever control methods are sought and the magic nostrums may be on molecular and molar levels, with physiological and behavioral processes.

From a heritage of reproduction and sex as taboo and publicly ignored the future demands exposure and familiarity, knowledge and education. Even eugenic control is no longer an Orwellian radical myth and must be contemplated as a conservative fact. Against the urgency of problems so large some of the questions here discussed and presented will be called to do service. The prospects for the field of reproduction and sexual behavior are awesome.

Author and Name Index

The numbers listed indicate the page on which the individual author's work or the individual is cited. An asterisk (*) indicates that his name will be found as a junior author among the "et al." listings. A dagger (†) indicates a citation without an available bibliographic reference.

Subject Index